J. K. McKay

B.A., B.Sc.Tech., C.Eng.,

A.R.I.B.A., M.I.Struct.E.

Registered architect and chartered structural engineer and Lecturer in Building Construction at the Manchester University Institute of Science and Technology

BUILDING CONSTRUCTION

VOLUME FOUR

FOURTH EDITION

With drawings by the author

Longman Scientific & Technical,
Longman Group UK Limited,
Longman House, Burnt Mill, Harlow,
Essex CM20 2JE, England
and Associated Companies throughout the world.

First published 1961
Second edition 1967
Third edition (Metric) 1975
Fourth edition 1988
Reprinted 1989

British Library Cataloguing in Publication Data

McKay, J. K. (John Kenneth)
Building construction. Vol. 4 4th ed.
1. Buildings. Construction
I. Title
Building construction
690

ISBN 0-582-03537-6

Produced by Longman Group (FE) Ltd
Printed in Hong Kong

By J. K. McKay and W. B. McKay

BUILDING CONSTRUCTION

Volumes One, Two and Three

BRICKWORK

CARPENTRY

JOINERY

By J. K. McKAY

BUILDING CONSTRUCTION

Volume Four

PREFACE TO THE FOURTH EDITION

The first edition of this book was welcomed by leaders in the building industry, teachers and students as being the first of its kind to adequately cover the important subject of fire precautions.

In this new edition the opportunity has been taken to extensively revise Chapter III on Fire Protection and Chapter XII on Thermal Insulation and Heating Systems. These chapters incorporate the latest legislation in the Building Regulations for the two subjects.

1988 J. K. McK

PREFACE TO THIRD EDITION

The production of this metric edition completes the metrication and updating of the four Building Construction volumes.

Revisions have been made to all chapters and have been particularly extensive in the following: In the section on steel-framed construction because welding has almost entirely replaced riveting, the details in the Figures show the increasing use of welded joints. The reinforced concrete section has been re-written to take account of the design theory of limit state which has replaced the elastic theory. Chapter 3 on fire protection has been recomposed in the light of new legislation. Details of an industrialised building system are given in Chapter 4. Chapter 10, which includes particulars of soil and waste installations, has been extended.

In this book, which is concerned with the more advanced building techniques, it is important that up-to-date systems are illustrated whilst at the same time giving adequate coverage of older, well-proved systems which must form part of the vocabulary of those engaged in the building industry so long as thirty per cent of expenditure is devoted to repair, maintenance and reconstruction.

One reason for the success enjoyed by this book and the companion volumes is the large size of most of the Figures enabling full delineation of the units of construction; here several of them are new and the remainder have been fully revised.

1975 J. K. McK.

PREFACE TO FIRST EDITION

Many inquiries have been made regarding the date of publication of this book. It was originally intended, after Volume III, to complete the subsequent volumes within a reasonable period, but for several reasons this was not possible. Their preparation was delayed by the war, and when it became possible to make a fresh start, it was found that a number of completed full-page drawings illustrated details of construction that had become obsolete during the intervening years. These drawings and the relevant descriptive matter were rejected. Again, it was difficult to assess which of the newly introduced building techniques and materials would be able to withstand the test of time; some of them have not survived beyond a short emergency period. It was decided therefore to defer the preparation of Volume IV until a clearer picture could be obtained.

Further, when this series of textbooks was first planned, it was anticipated that each of the later volumes would be devoted to one of the years of an approved advanced course. This is now thought undesirable as it would entail a certain amount of duplication, would break continuity and would not be the best arrangement for easy reference. In this connection, in view of the use of the previous volumes in other European countries, and also in Africa and Asia, the present one has not been limited to building practice at home. For example when an open timber framed roof is required, a glued laminated one (Fig. 60) is likely to be preferred in the United Kingdom instead of the older type (Fig. 59), which is more usual where there is a plentiful supply of large baulk timber.

Following the treatment in earlier volumes, alternatives, as many as space permitted, have been given of certain pieces of construction; thus, for example, in the sections dealing with walls and wood panelling there is a fairly wide range of details of both traditional and contemporary design. These and variations elsewhere will enable the student to select or modify features best suited to any particular project he may have in hand.

This book, a first advanced stage, is suitable for architectural, building and structural engineering students and for consultation in offices; it is concerned mainly with newer more advanced methods of construction, and servicing of buildings, but allusion has necessarily been made to older types even though they are unlikely to be repeated. One reason for this is that, of the total annual expenditure on building work, a significant proportion, exceeding one-third in some years, is devoted to the maintenance of old buildings; knowledge of this aspect is therefore important. Lecturers will recognize the drawings in this category, and will advise students that construction of the kind shown in Fig. 45, for instance, is included for reference as well as for the reasons given in the text.

Whilst the ground covered by the comprehensive courses in Building Construction provided by the various Departments of Building and Schools of Architecture may be largely the same, the syllabuses in the intermediate and final years must differ to some extent, depending perhaps on special local requirements or upon individual preferences of the teaching staff. Accordingly, a Homework Programme such as appeared in the earlier volumes, has not been included in this one.

The preparation of a substantial up-to-date textbook of this kind, would not be possible without the assistance of manufacturers and patentees; co-operation has been readily forthcoming and due acknowledgement has been made in the appropriate places. The author is also indebted to Her Majesty's Stationery Office and the British Standards Institution for permission to include extracts from several official publications. Occasional reference has been made to the Building Research Station and to other organizations, including the Fire Protection Association, and the author is grateful for the information provided by these. He thanks the following gentlemen: V. C. Barnes, C. T. G. Boucher, R. E. Bowles, F. Bowman, P. Coackley, T. G. Francis, J. R. A. McDonald, W. I. Tarn, and E. E. Wild, for their help.

The loss of the author's father, W. B. McKay, before completion of the work is deeply regretted; as initiator of the series his contribution is especially recorded, it was based on a wide teaching experience and knowledge of the industry.

1960

J. K. McK.

CONTENTS

CONTENTS

LIST OF ILLUSTRATIONS

LIST OF ILLUSTRATIONS

Note: UNLESS OTHERWISE STATED ALL DIMENSIONS ON THE FIGURES ARE GIVEN IN MILLIMETRES

LIST OF TABLES

CHAPTER ONE

SITE PREPARATION AND FOUNDATIONS

Syllabus. Earth-moving equipment, shovel, dragline, dragshovel, skimmer, trencher, angledozer, scraper and ripper. The application of dewatering, electro-osmosis, and freezing processes on waterlogged sites. Site investigations. Classification and bearing capacity of rocks and soils. Types of foundations including strip, pad, pile and beam, and raft. Damage due to brine pumping operations. Building on sites liable to mining subsidence. Bearing and sheet piles, pile-driving.

SITE PREPARATION

EARTH-MOVING EQUIPMENT

For many years after the first employment in this country, in 1880, of excavating machinery, its use was restricted to large public works projects, such as the construction of railways, canals, and docks. It was not until after the First World War that mechanical excavators were employed on an ever-increasing scale in the building industry and now, except for relatively small jobs or very restricted sites, the machine has almost entirely displaced hand-labour for forming excavations.

The motive power is that provided by either the internal combustion engine or the electric motor; probably ninety per cent of excavators are Diesel-engined.

Some of the uses for which excavating equipment is employed on building operations include digging foundation trenches, excavating and refilling drain and sewer trenches, levelling sites, road construction and excavating for basements. It is used for excavations on waterworks and sewerage schemes; in sand, gravel and clay pits it is used for stripping the cover and digging the sand, gravel or clay; in limestone, etc., quarries it is employed for removing the stone from the face (generally after being loosened by blasting); it is used for dredging and, in recent years, for excavating and cleaning up in connection with open-cast mining; it can be used also as a grabbing crane (for loading material from sand, gravel, etc., dumps into wagons) and for pile-driving.

The principal types of power-driven excavators used in building and civil engineering operations include the shovel, dragline, dragshovel, skimmer, and trencher. These machines are, in the main, of welded steel construction, built to withstand severe wear. They are illustrated in Fig. 1.

Shovel. See A. The revolving frame, with its superstructure consisting of the engine, gears, operator's desk, enclosed cab, etc., is caterpillar mounted. The machine can thus operate over rough ground and can climb steep gradients (maximum 1 in 4). It can be rotated full circle. The bucket equipment consists of a boom or jib, a dipper handle or bucket arm, the bucket shovel or dipper, together with pulleys, drums and wire ropes. The boom is pivoted at its lower end to the revolving superstructure at floor level; its length varies from approximately 4 to 12 m; it can be fixed at any angle, the working range being between 40 to 60° and a useful pitch for average digging being 45°. The dipper handle is mounted mid-way along the boom; it can be racked backwards and forwards and rotated to alter the pitch as desired. The bucket fixed at the lower end of the dipper handle has four or five teeth (of high carbon forged steel) inserted at its front lower cutting edge (or steel lip); its back consists of a hinged door which is opened to deposit its contents; the capacity varies considerably, from 0.2 to 28 m^3 but for normal contracting work a bucket rarely exceeds 1.5 m^3 and 0.3 and 0.5 m^3 shovels are common.

The shovel is used for digging where it can work on the *floor of the excavation*. The dipper arm is lowered with the bucket at the bottom of the face – see B, position "1". The bucket is then dragged up the face with a radial motion and with the teeth penetrating the soil, etc. During this operation the material passes into the bucket and, for economic working, the aim should be to form a cut of sufficient thickness to ensure a full bucket by the time it reaches the top of the excavation (position "2"). Finally, the dipper handle is racked in to clear the face (position "3"), the machine is slewed round over the lorry or dump, the contents are discharged on the bucket door being opened, the machine is then swung round and the bucket lowered to repeat the movements. The whole of these actions is performed by the operator seated at the controls in the cab who has an unobstructed view of the bucket.

The shovel is the most powerful of the excavators, as the "cutting power" is concentrated on the firmly held bucket. It is therefore very suitable for excavating heavy material such as clay and loose rocks. The length of boom varies with the height of face of the excavation and dumping height or distance; thus, for an 5.5 m long boom and a 4.5 m long dipper handle, the maximum depth of face or "cutting height" is 7 m when the boom is fixed at 45° and 8 m when

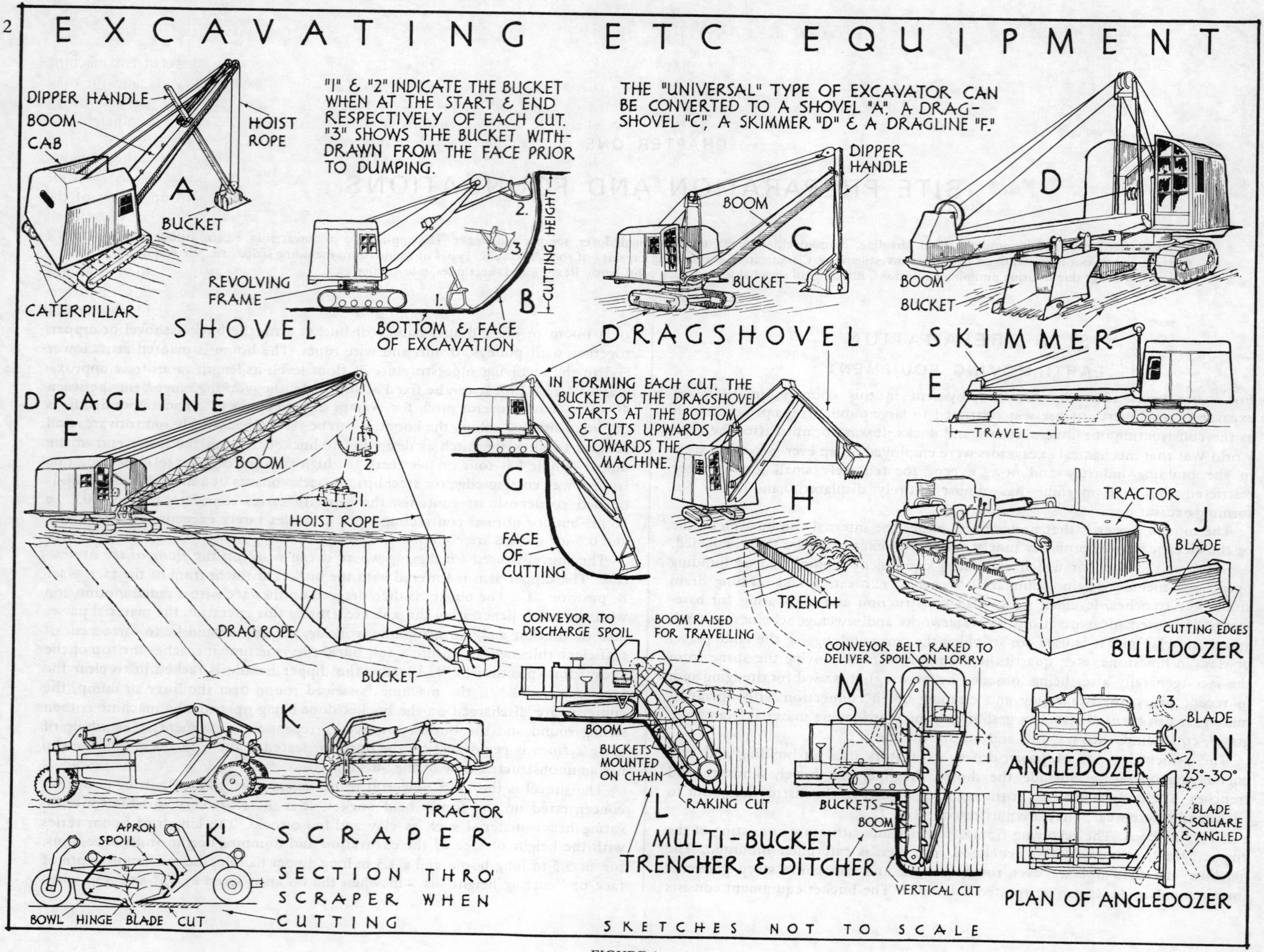

EXCAVATING ETC EQUIPMENT

"1" & "2" INDICATE THE BUCKET WHEN AT THE START & END RESPECTIVELY OF EACH CUT. "3" SHOWS THE BUCKET WITHDRAWN FROM THE FACE PRIOR TO DUMPING.

THE "UNIVERSAL" TYPE OF EXCAVATOR CAN BE CONVERTED TO A SHOVEL "A", A DRAGSHOVEL "C", A SKIMMER "D" & A DRAGLINE "F."

DIPPER HANDLE
BOOM
CAB
HOIST ROPE
A
BUCKET
CATERPILLAR
SHOVEL

REVOLVING FRAME
1.
2.
3.
CUTTING HEIGHT
B
BOTTOM & FACE OF EXCAVATION

DIPPER HANDLE
BOOM
C
BUCKET
DRAGSHOVEL

D
BOOM
BUCKET
SKIMMER

E
TRAVEL

DRAGLINE
F
BOOM
1.
2.
HOIST ROPE
DRAG ROPE
BUCKET

IN FORMING EACH CUT, THE BUCKET OF THE DRAGSHOVEL STARTS AT THE BOTTOM & CUTS UPWARDS TOWARDS THE MACHINE.
G
FACE OF CUTTING

H
TRENCH

TRACTOR
J
BLADE
CUTTING EDGES
BULLDOZER

CONVEYOR TO DISCHARGE SPOIL
BOOM RAISED FOR TRAVELLING
BOOM
BUCKETS MOUNTED ON CHAIN
RAKING CUT
L
MULTI-BUCKET TRENCHER & DITCHER

CONVEYOR BELT RAKED TO DELIVER SPOIL ON LORRY
M
BUCKETS
BOOM
VERTICAL CUT

3.
BLADE
1.
2.
N
ANGLEDOZER
25°-30°
BLADE SQUARE & ANGLED
O
PLAN OF ANGLEDOZER

K
TRACTOR
K1
APRON
SPOIL
BOWL
HINGE
BLADE
CUT
SCRAPER
SECTION THRO' SCRAPER WHEN CUTTING

SKETCHES NOT TO SCALE

FIGURE 1

fixed at 60°. Although essentially used for forward and upward cutting, the shovel can excavate to a limited extent below floor level.

Dragline. See F. This machine stands at the top of the excavation and *excavates below its own level.* It is therefore especially suitable for use on waterlogged sites; its applications include digging large general excavations for buildings, cutting agricultural drainage channels and cleaning, widening, and deepening existing ones, trimming river banks, excavating in wet sand and gravel pits, stripping overburden in quarries, etc.

As implied by its name, the bucket after being lowered and "thrown" to the position required on or in the excavation is dragged forward towards the machine by means of the drag rope; during the dragging operation the material, cut by the teeth, passes into the bucket; when full, the bucket is raised by the hoist rope, the machine is swung round and the spoil is dumped into the wagon or required position on the site.

The longer booms especially are of light lattice construction; they vary in length from 9 to 80 m. The buckets range from 0.2 to 20 m^3 capacity, those up to 0.75 m^3 being common on building sites. The digging depth below the ground level depends upon the nature of the excavated material, an average depth being approximately half the dumping radius; this depth may be doubled if the material "will stand up", *i.e.*, firm soil. The "throw" of the bucket depends a good deal upon the skill of the operator, the hoist rope being pulled smartly when the rapidly descending bucket is at its maximum swing.

Dragshovel. See C, G and H. The dipper handle of this excavator pivots at the end of the boom, which is of robust construction. It has certain advantages of both dragline and shovel: for example, it resembles the dragline in that it digs below its own level, but as the bucket can be firmly held whilst excavating (like the shovel) the dragshovel will dig heavier soils than will a dragline of the same size.

It is chiefly employed for digging trenches for drains, sewers, water pipes, etc. It is used also for excavating basements, especially on confined sites which preclude the use of the shovel at the required level.

This machine is also called a *back-acter* for, like the dragline, the bucket at the end of the dipper handle of the dragshovel has a backward cutting action towards the machine – see G and H. The maximum capacity of the bucket is 2 m^3. The width of trench can be increased if side cutters are fitted to the bucket; the width can be increased still further if side wings and teeth are fixed to the bucket. Thus, an 0.7 m^3 capacity bucket without side cutters can dig a 0.6 m wide trench, 0.76 m with side cutters and 0.9 to 1.2 m with side wings and teeth; a 0.5 m^3 bucket with side wings and teeth can dig a trench up to 1.7 m in width (or 1 m with side cutters and 0.9 m without). Wider trenches are excavated by taking two or more cuts as required. The larger machines can excavate to a maximum depth of 5.5 to 6 m. The trench output is dependent upon the pace of the men following up with the necessary timbering. Multi-bucket trenchers are described below.

Skimmer or Skimmer Scoop. See D and E. This is a most efficient machine for shallow work, as for levelling building sites and playing fields, and for road construction; a clear level surface results. It is useful also for "muck shifting" where the dumps of excavated material do not exceed 1.2 or 1.5 m in height and for stripping thin layers of overburden.

The boom is lowered to a horizontal position (or tilted as required when a sloped finish is needed) and the skimmer bucket or dipper is caused to slide along it. The length of travel of the bucket (see E) depends upon that of the boom; for a 4.6 m long boom, the travel is approximately 3.7 m. The capacity of the bucket varies from 0.3 to 0.8 m^3. When the bucket is full the boom is raised and the material is dumped into the lorry or wagon.

Universal or General Purposes Excavator. This machine, which is in big demand by building and public works contractors, can be adapted for performing all the excavating operations described above. It is thus available as a shovel, dragline, dragshovel and skimmer. By using the equipment (such as boom and bucket) most suitable for the particular excavating job required, the machine can be quickly converted on the site from one type to another. In addition, this excavator can be employed as a lifting or grabbing crane (the latter being used to remove loose material, such as sand and chalk from piles to lorries or wagons, or for unloading materials from vehicles to heaps) and for light pile-driving. As a dragline boom is the same as that for the grabbing crane, conversion from the former to the latter is readily made by provision of the grab bucket. As a pile-driver, the machine is provided with guides fixed at the end of the boom, and a drop hammer; it can be used also for withdrawing piles.

All the above machines are known as single-bucket excavators.

Trencher. Another type of machine, known as a *multi-bucket continuous chain trencher or ditcher*, is now extensively employed on housing sites for cutting narrow and shallow trenches such as are required for drains, electric cables and gas and water pipes. It is used also for shallow house foundation trenches.

The multi-bucket trencher shown at L is capable of excavating trenches 350 to 550 mm wide to a depth not exceeding 2 m; larger models will dig trenches up to 1.5 m wide, and 5 m deep. The boom is raised and lowered as required by the driver moving a lever and can be locked in any position. The spoil is carried up from the trench by buckets (having cutting teeth) attached to a continuous steel chain and tipped on to a belt conveyor at the top of the rise, whence it is deposited to either the left or right-hand side of the trench. This machine produces a raking cut and therefore it leaves a ramp at the end of the trench which must be dug by hand if a vertical face is required.

The multi-bucket ditcher illustrated at M excavates trenches 330 to 610 mm wide to a maximum depth of about 2.5 m. It cuts vertically and the excavated material is delivered by the buckets to the conveyor belt which discharges it into a lorry or alongside the trench. Another model, suitable for cable-laying, etc., is capable of digging trenches 140 to 300 mm wide and up to 1.2 m deep.

TRACTOR EQUIPMENT

This is used extensively on the larger excavating jobs. It includes the bulldozer, angledozer, scraper, and ripper. When the tractor is not required for hauling the scraper or other duties, it can quickly be converted for use as a bulldozer or angledozer.

Bulldozer. See J. This has a large rectangular plate or blade (curved in cross section) on front of the tractor and attached to the side frames of the caterpillar tracks. This plate, of manganese steel, varies in width from 2 to 3 m and is from 0.7 to 1.2 m high; it has cutting edges at the bottom and sides; it can be lifted 600 to 900 mm above and dropped 200 to 305 mm below the ground.

This equipment acts on a site as a leveller, the blade pushes or rolls loose earth, debris, etc., ahead of the tractor to fill up low-lying parts. The depth of cut below the ground level or heap can be regulated by lowering the blade, and the latter can be raised to the desired height to give the necessary spread as the tractor passes over the material. When operating on sloping ground the bulldozer should push the material downhill in order to obtain maximum efficiency and reduce fuel consumption. It is considered that this is the cheapest form of excavating equipment for moving earth over distances up to 60 m. It is frequently used on road construction and as a trench filler ("backfilling"), and for site stripping.

Angledozer, or Bullgrader, or Trailbuilder. See N and O. This resembles the bulldozer, except that the blade or mouldboard can be set at an angle of 25 to 30 degrees, as shown at O, and in addition, the blade can be tilted or "cambered" so that the difference in height of the blade ends is from 200 to 360 mm. Hence, the excavated earth or debris can be pushed to either side as the tractor moves forward. The blade at N is shown in alternative positions, *i.e.*, ground line ("1"), below ground line ("2") and above ground line ("3").

Like the bulldozer, the angledozer is especially suited for jobs connected with the making of roads and particularly those on hillsides where the excavated material can be readily deflected to the downward slopes. It is also used for backfilling trenches after drains, etc., have been laid.

Scraper or Wagon Scraper. See K and K′. This equipment consists of a relatively large receptacle, called the scraper or bucket, and a tractor. The type of scraper shown has a capacity ranging from 3 to 8 m^3; larger scrapers have a capacity up to 20 m^3. It is mounted on four (or two) wheels and has a 1.8 to 2.5 m long cutting edge or blade at the bottom which can dig to a depth of about 250 mm. The scraper is connected *behind* the trailer and during its forward movement the blade cuts the ground, the excavated material passing into the body of the scraper. Normally, the scraper should be loaded within one minute; when full, the scraper is raised (330 to 400 mm) clear of the ground, as shown at K, and hauled to the dumping site where the material is ejected at the bottom and spread in a layer of required thickness as the trailer continues to travel forward. The scraper thus combines the three operations of digging, transporting and dumping.

In the section at K′ the blade is shown in the cutting position; the curved plate at the back called the *tilting bowl* swings on a hinge behind the blade; the front portion of the bowl is called the *apron*. As indicated by arrows, the excavated material passes into the bowl between the cutting edge of the blade and the lower edge of the apron. The space between the blade and apron is regulated as required. During ejection (spreading of the spoil) the tilting bowl is rotated forward and the apron is lifted to give the desired depth of spread. Another type of scraper has a back plate in lieu of the tilting bowl, which is pushed forward to empty the scraper; the ejected material passing between the blade and the raised apron.

The two-wheeled type of scraper, towed behind the tractor, is emptied by lifting the front of the machine to permit the spoil to be ejected at the back.

The scraper is suitable for work similar to that described for the single bucket skimmer on p. 3, *i.e.*, for shallow excavations, such as for levelling sites, and especially large sites on which the excavated material can be dumped.

Ripper or Scarifier. This is provided with two to four teeth, usually three, and it is used to break up heavy ground, which loosened material is then removed by the scraper.

EXCAVATION OF WATERLOGGED SITES

Where shallow excavations are required in waterlogged sites, the use of close boarded sheeting or piling (see p. 22) and pumps generally suffices to enable construction work to proceed. For larger works, those adjacent to rivers or the coast and in other instances given below, these simple methods become costly and often impracticable. Under such circumstances, one or other of the following methods can be adopted in appropriate situations: dewatering, electro-osmosis and the freezing process.

Site Dewatering. This consists of lowering the water table over the area of the site and is satisfactory for depths up to 16 m. It is particularly suitable where running sand is encountered, for once the water has been removed in this ground, the sand becomes relatively stable and only a small amount of timbering to the sides of the excavation is needed. On such a site, prior to the adoption of dewatering, it was necessary to enclose the area with sheet piling and pump water away from the bottom. This caused the site to act as a sump, increasing the water flow and may only be practicable where the piling is taken down to impervious strata such as clay. Clay strata itself cannot be dewatered, although beds of sand above and below the clay can be treated. Nor is it possible to dewater rock, or ground with large boulders and an absence of sand; sand below such media can be dewatered by boring through these upper layers.

The basic principles of site dewatering are shown in Fig. 2, and at D, the comparative effects in the most suitable sandy subsoils for treatment are shown, different horizontal and vertical scales have been used in plotting the "drawdown" curves to illustrate the effect.

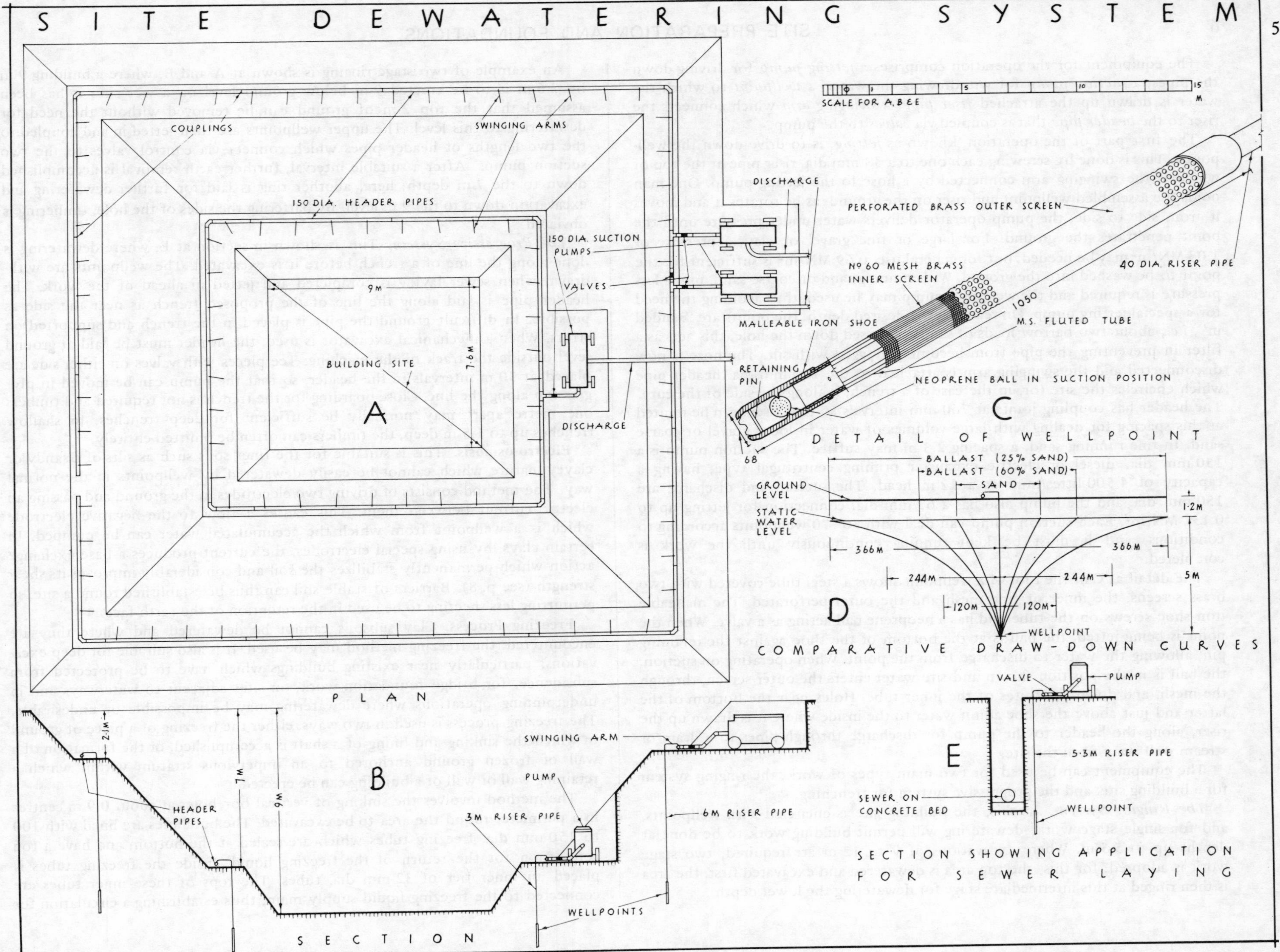
SITE DEWATERING SYSTEM
COUPLINGS
SWINGING ARMS
150 DIA. HEADER PIPES
150 DIA. SUCTION
PUMPS
VALVES
9m
16m
BUILDING SITE
DISCHARGE
A
PLAN
SWINGING ARM
2·1m
HEADER PIPES
PUMP
3m RISER PIPE
1m
9m
B
WELLPOINTS
SECTION
SCALE FOR A, B & E
5
10
15
m
DISCHARGE
PERFORATED BRASS OUTER SCREEN
40 DIA. RISER PIPE
Nº 60 MESH BRASS INNER SCREEN
105
M.S. FLUTED TUBE
MALLEABLE IRON SHOE
RETAINING PIN
NEOPRENE BALL IN SUCTION POSITION
C
DETAIL OF WELLPOINT
68
BALLAST (25% SAND)
BALLAST (60% SAND)
SAND
GROUND LEVEL
STATIC WATER LEVEL
1·2m
366m
366m
244m
244m
5m
120m
120m
WELLPOINT
D
COMPARATIVE DRAW-DOWN CURVES
VALVE
PUMP
E
5·3m RISER PIPE
SEWER ON CONCRETE BED
6m RISER PIPE
WELLPOINT
SECTION SHOWING APPLICATION FOR SEWER LAYING

FIGURE 2

The equipment for the operation comprises a *jetting pump* for driving down the pipes, a *suction pump* for withdrawing the water, a *wellpoint* to which the water is drawn up the attached *riser pipe*, a *swinging arm* which connects the riser to the *header pipe* that is coupled via *valves* to the pump.

The first part of the operation, known as *jetting*, is to drive down the wellpoints. This is done by screwing each one to a 38 mm dia. riser pipe at the top of which is the swinging arm connected by a hose to the jetting pump. One man holds the assembled wellpoint and riser on the ground; as he rotates it and moves it from side to side, the pump operator delivers water under pressure until the point penetrates the ground. For large or fine gravel or clay, a pressure of 1.03 MN/m^2 may be needed, but for general use, 0.69 MN/m^2 is sufficient for the point to be washed into the ground. With running sand or coarse sand, much less pressure is required and the wellpoint pump may be used, thus avoiding the need for a special jetting pump. On reaching the desired depth, the points are "sanded in", *i.e.*, about two barrow loads of sand are passed down the hole, this acts as a filter in preventing the pipe from becoming clogged with silt. The hose is now disconnected and the swinging arm is attached to the 150 mm dia. header pipe which encircles the site (or, in the case of a trench, is along the side of the cut). The header has coupling joints at 760 mm intervals so that risers can be jointed at this spacing for dealing with large volumes of water in loose gravel or coarse sand. In fine running sand, a spacing 2.3 m may suffice. The suction pump is a 150 mm dia. diesel or electric exhauster priming centrifugal type, having a capacity of 4 500 litres/min. at a 12 m head. The suction and discharge are 150 mm dia. and the pump also has a 63 mm dia. connection for jetting up to 0.137 MN/m^2. Each suction pump can deal with 50–70 wellpoints according to conditions, and it must be kept running continuously until the work is completed.

The detail at C of the foot of a wellpoint shows a steel tube covered with two brass screens, the inner of fine mesh and the outer perforated. The malleable iron shoe screws on the tube and has a neoprene ball acting as a valve. When the point is being jetted, the ball is at the bottom of the shoe against the retaining pin, allowing the water to discharge from the point. When operating on suction, the ball is in the position shown and site water enters the outer screen, through the mesh, and down the flutes of the inner tube. Holes near the bottom of the latter and just above the shoe admit water to the inside where it is drawn up the riser, along the header to the pump for discharge through pipes to a drain or stream well away from the site.

The equipment can be used for two main types of work; the ringing system for a building site, and the progressive system for trenching.

The Ringing System. In this, the building site is encircled with wellpoints, and for single stage work, dewatering will permit building work to be done at depths up to 5.5 m. Where excavations of 9 to 12 m are required, two stage work is adopted; for this, the top area is dewatered and excavated first, the area is then ringed at this intermediate stage for dewatering the lower depth.

An example of two stage ringing is shown at A and B, where a building 9 m by 7.6 m is to be erected 9 m below ground level on a wet site; it has been assumed that the top 2 m of ground can be removed without the need for dewatering to this level. The upper wellpoints are then jetted in and coupled to the two lengths of header pipes which connect via control valves to the two suction pumps. After a suitable interval, further earth removal is accomplished down to the 7 m depth; here, another ring is laid for further dewatering and excavation down to the 9 m level. By battering the sides of the hole, timbering is obviated.

The Progressive System. This is shown in section at E, where dewatering is done along the line of a trench before it is excavated. The wellpoints are withdrawn when sewer laying is completed and jetted in ahead of the work. The header pipe is laid along the line of the proposed trench as near the side as possible. In difficult ground the pipe is placed in the trench and supported on struts. When a mechanical excavator is used, the header must be laid at ground level outside the track of the machine. Tee pieces with valves on either side are placed at 30 m intervals in the header, so that the pump can be moved in progression along the line. Close boarding for the trench is not required and timbers one metre apart may normally be sufficient for deep trenches. In shallow trenches up to 1.5 m deep, the timbers can often be omitted entirely.

Electro-osmosis. This is suitable for the finer soils such as silts of a sandy or clayey nature which cannot be easily dewatered by wellpoints in the normal way. The method consists of driving two electrodes in the ground and passing an electric current between them. This causes a flow to the negative electrode which is a wellpoint from which the accumulated water can be pumped. In certain clays, by using special electrodes, the current produces a base exchange action which permanently stabilizes the soil and considerably improves its shear strength (see p. 8). Barriers of stable soil can thus be established round a site, so permitting less sheeting to be used in the retention of the earth face.

Freezing Process. Clay subsoils cannot be dewatered and where they are encountered, the freezing method may be used. It is also suitable for deep excavations, particularly near existing buildings which have to be protected from subsidence, for bridge foundation work, on sites adjacent to waterways and in underpinning operations where dewatering may be impossible or undesirable. The freezing process is used in two ways, either the freezing of a piece of ground in which the sinking and lining of a shaft is accomplished, or the formation of a wall of frozen ground anchored to an impervious stratum within which a retaining wall or wall of a building can be erected.

The method involves the sinking of vertical boreholes at about 0.9 m centres in a perimeter round the area to be excavated. The boreholes are lined with 100 to 150 mm dia. freezing tubes which are sealed at the bottom and have a top connection for the return of the freezing liquid. Inside the freezing tubes is placed an inner tier of 32 mm dia. tubes. The tops of these inner tubes are connected to the freezing liquid supply main, thus establishing a circulation for the liquid which enters the top of the inner tubes, leaves them at the bottom and rises up the outer freezing tubes, whence it returns to the cooling plant. The cooling liquid is brine which is reduced to a temperature below freezing point. The refrigerator producing the cold brine has a coil of pipes containing ammonia or carbon dioxide in a cylinder of brine. The gas is vaporized, the latent heat of evaporation being taken from the brine causing its temperature to be reduced below freezing point.

Cylinders of frozen ground are thus obtained and the action is continued until these are welded together so as to form an ice wall. Excavations 30 m deep can be made in this way, being self-supporting to this depth; the wall has a strength similar to that of lean concrete. In fact, frozen walls up to 90 m deep can be made by the method and this may take up to four months for the process to be completed; the action must be continued without a break until the excavations are completed and the building work finished behind the frozen wall. These greater depths are usually only encountered in the sinking of shafts which must be lined with steel or cast iron casings as the excavation proceeds.

FOUNDATIONS

Foundation is defined as that part of a structure which is in direct contact with the ground to which the loads are transmitted. During the construction of a building the load on the foundations gradually increases and eventually this will produce settlement. Provided this movement is slight and uniform throughout no damage will be caused to the building. If, however, the *settlement is extensive or unequal* serious damage may result in the form of cracked walls, distorted door and window openings, walls thrown out of plumb, etc.; failure may be complete by the collapse of a building. A foundation should therefore be sufficiently strong to prevent marked and unequal settlement. Such settlement may be caused by weak subsoils (such as made-up ground – p. 10), shrinkable subsoils (*e.g.*, soft clay – p. 9), frost action (p. 10), movement of ground water (p. 10), excessive vibration (due to vehicular traffic, machinery, pile-driving, etc.), slipping of strata on sloping sites (p. 10), brine pumping (p. 15), coal mining (p. 15) and subsequent building operations involving deep excavations on an adjacent site.

SITE INVESTIGATIONS

B.S. 5930 *Site Investigations* is relevant.

Normally, the type of foundation to be adopted for a building depends upon the load to be transmitted and the bearing capacity of the soil. When a suitable site can be selected having a satisfactory subsoil (*e.g.*, one with a good bearing capacity of reasonable depth) it is not difficult to decide upon the type of foundation. On the other hand, the character of the soil may be such as to necessitate a close investigation, involving tests, before the foundations can be designed; soils of low-bearing capacity of varying depths, are of this order. Also, in certain localities there are exceptional conditions which influence foundation design; thus, in coal-mining districts extensive cracks may develop in walls of buildings due to unequal settlement; in coastal areas, especially when the upper stratum is sand and the subsoil water is near the surface, buildings may develop a tilt; and in localities where brine pumping operates buildings may be subjected to complete collapse owing to subsidence.

When the nature of the soil is not known to the designer it is necessary for investigations to be made on and about the site before the type of foundation can be decided upon. As a preliminary, useful information can be obtained by reference to geological survey maps and to the surveyor's department of the local authority, and an examination of adjacent property may reveal defects due to foundation failure, such as cracked walls, gable walls out of alignment, etc. Three or four holes dug with the spade at, say three spits deep, at different parts of the site will expose the top soil to good purpose, as will holes bored with a small post-hole auger (p. 8 and P, Fig. 6). If the proposed building is small and loads to be transmitted light, serviceable data can be readily obtained by driving with a sledge hammer a pointed metal rod (say, 20 mm dia. and about 1.8 m long) into the ground and noting the penetration; a soil of uniform character is indicated if the penetration gradually decreases with the depth; if there is an appreciable decrease in the penetration a denser soil may be implied but, conversely, if the penetration per blow suddenly increases the indication is that the lower stratum is less dense; the depth of this bed of weaker soil may be determined approximately by withdrawing the rod and replacing it by a longer one which is driven down until a soil offering greater resistance is encountered.

For a proposed large building project, such as a multi-storeyed structure, the site exploration may possibly be both extensive and costly and may include one or more of the following: (1) trial pits, (2) boreholes, and (3) load tests.

B.S. 1377. *Methods of Testing Soils* is relevant.

(1) A Trial Pit, large enough to accommodate a man (say 1.2 m by 1 m or larger if timbering is required), is excavated to a depth which varies according to that of the proposed foundations; it rarely exceeds 6 m and is usually not more than half that depth. A section through the ground is thus exposed, revealing for examination the character and depth of the strata, including that stratum upon which the foundation is to rest and which requires to be of adequate thickness and having a satisfactory bearing capacity. Samples of the soil for laboratory testing can be readily obtained (p. 8). A pit also gives to the contractor valuable information affecting labour costs, such as the relative ease with which the material can be excavated, the type and amount of timbering needed and if underground water (which would necessitate pumping, dewatering or use of other methods previously described) is present. For a building covering a large area four trial pits may be required, one near each corner; if these show a marked difference in the nature and thickness of the strata it may be advisable to have intermediate pits dug. Care should be taken to ensure that these excavations are not too close to the proposed foundations, otherwise they would be a source of weakness, and they should be filled in (preferably with concrete) and consolidated.

(2) Boreholes. These are formed as required on the site for the purpose of raising samples of soil for examination. One of the simplest tools for sinking holes is the auger of which there are several types. The post-hole auger (similar in principle to the joiner's boring tools – described in Chap. IV, Vol. I, and so-called as it is used for boring holes for fence posts, etc.), having a rod with cross-head, is capable of forming holes in clay or soft soils up to about 6 m deep and 150 mm or more in dia. – see P, Fig. 6; it is rotated by hand (two men) or by power.

For deeper borings and where rock is likely to be encountered either the percussion or the rotary method is employed. A hole is formed by the percussion method with a chisel-shaped steel bit, screwed to a rod; this is driven vertically into the ground, lifted, partially rotated and again driven; this is repeated rapidly until the desired depth is obtained, extension rods being screwed on when required; samples of the soil are obtained during the process – see below. By the rotary method, usually applied to rock formations, a small (up to 50 mm dia.) hole is drilled with a rotating bit (having diamonds set round the cutting edge) jointed to a hollow rod; the cylindrical core of rock thus formed within the tool is broken off at intervals and removed for inspection and testing.

Sampling. Valuable data is obtained by the expert from a visual inspection of and subsequent laboratory tests on samples obtained from trial pits and borings. The form of sample depends upon the nature of the soil and whether it was disturbed or undisturbed. Thus, for example, an undisturbed sample of rock can be obtained if such stratum has been exposed in a trial pit; this is then dressed to a cube of at least 75 mm side when it can be tested for compression, permeability, etc., and slides prepared from it can be examined (see Chap. III, Vol. II). An undisturbed sample of clay from a trial pit is cut by a knife in the form of a cube, coated with paraffin wax to prevent loss of moisture, placed in an airtight container and labelled ready for testing. Such a sample can also be obtained from an exposed clay stratum by using a tool called a *sampler* or *spoon*. There are several types of samplers, one being a metal tube, 100 to 150 mm internal diameter and 1 to 1.5 m long, having an open end with a cutting edge and at the opposite closed end there is an air valve; as the sampler is driven down it gradually fills with clay (air escaping through the valve); it is withdrawn when full and the sample is removed.

Disturbed samples of soils are obtained during the actual boring operation. The sampler is attached to the boring rod in place of the bit, forced down into the loosened soil and withdrawn when full. The soil cores are carefully removed from the sampler and placed in a box (which is about 1.5 m long, divided into compartments) in correct sequence and numbered in their proper order. Thus, when laid end-to-end according to depth they reproduce a section showing the nature and thickness of each stratum. Small specimens for laboratory tests are taken from the cores as required; these should be placed in airtight containers until needed.

Undisturbed samples of certain soils, such as clays and moist sand, can also be obtained from boreholes. Thus, when reaching such a bed of soil the sampler is substituted for the bit, lowered to the bottom of the borehole, driven into the soil and carefully withdrawn after becoming filled and the core has been broken off by rotation of the sampler.

Tests. These are carried out after the samples have been carefully examined and the characteristics of the various soils noted and classified – see p. 9. A complete record is made, including a dimensioned sketch of the section showing the thickness of the various strata. Two tests of most importance to the foundation designer are those for (1) consolidation and (2) shear.

(1) The consolidation test is usually applied to clay (or cohesive) soils. The weight of a building on a clay soil tends to consolidate the soil by squeezing out the water between the particles, rendering it more compact and so producing settlement of the building. The testing device consists of a metal cylinder in which the soil specimen is placed between two porous stone discs; top pressure is applied and increased by stages, the amount (registered on a dial) and rate of compression are noted at each stage and a time-settlement curve is plotted which gives some indication of the probable amount of settlement that may result.

(2) The load from a building sets up compression and shear stresses in the soil. The soil tends to squeeze out from under the load. The shear stresses are the forces tending to produce this sliding movement between adjacent portions of soil, such as clay. Gravel is not normally subject to shear failure. *The safe load which can be supported by a soil depends to a large extent upon its shear resistance.* One piece of apparatus for measuring the shear strength of clay or plastic soil consists of a metal box, 100 mm square by about 75 mm deep, in two portions (upper and lower halves); welded to one side of the top half is a projecting arm to which is fastened a length of wire fixed to a scale pan. The bottom half is clamped to the bench top and the wire is passed over a pulley, clamped at the edge of the bench, suspending the pan. The box is filled completely with the clay specimen and weights are placed on the pan until the upper half begins to slide over the lower as the clay shears through at this level. The total weight producing this, divided by the internal area of the box gives the shear strength of the soil.

If there is subsoil-water it may be necessary to have this analysed.

(3) Load or Bearing Test. This is applied at the proposed level of the foundations (not at ground level). There are several forms of equipment used for this test. One simply consists of a level reinforced concrete raft, say 1.5 m square by 0.3 m thick, formed at foundation level and which serves as the loading table; this is loaded as described below.

In another form of apparatus a small hole is dug at foundation level to receive a square or circular steel sole plate of known area (say 1 m^2) bedded level on a cushion of sand; this supports centrally a steel tube or spindle (about 1.2 m high) having a cross-head forming the base of the loading platform, some 2 m^2 in area. The whole is prevented from tilting by guys or other means which must be arranged not to restrict the downward movement of the platform. The weight of the apparatus must be known. The table is loaded carefully and uniformly; bars of pig iron (each of equal weight) or bricks (the average weight of twelve being taken as the unit) are often used for this purpose. The load is applied in increments (say 204 bricks at a time) and at least two hours must elapse between the time one increment has been completed and the next started. Fine readings are taken by means of a dumpy level (with the staff at the centre and at each corner of the table top) immediately before and after each loading, and the mean settlement obtained. A record is kept of the readings and a load/mean settlement curve is plotted. The amount of settlement after each increment-loading will depend upon the character of the soil, but if the bearing capacity is satisfactory it will only amount to a few millimetres. When the "yield point" of the soil has been reached, as indicated when there is an appreciable increase in settlement after the last increment has been applied, this increment is removed from the table and the readings again taken after an interval of three or four days. If no further settlement has taken place *half* the total load on the table (together with the weight of the apparatus) divided by the area of the sole plate is taken as the safe bearing value of the soil.

Ground Water or Subsoil Water can cause much damage to foundations. This is water which enters the soil during rains and thaws. Up to a certain level, called the *ground water level* or *water table*, the soil is saturated, the water completely filling the pores. This ground water level is subjected to seasonal variations and in some localities this level may be only a few centimetres below the ground level; in such cases the ground water level is readily disclosed by a spade, otherwise it may be observed when a test pit is being dug or by lowering into a borehole an open-ended tube down which a plumb-line is passed. Ground water reduces the bearing capacity of some soils, such as sand and gravel. Building on a subsoil of wet sand should be avoided; the lowering of the ground water level due to pumping operations, even at a distance, may cause settlement and fractures in a building. Running sand especially has been the cause of many foundation failures, due to the removal of soil by the water flow. If a building must be erected on a subsoil of wet sand it may be essential to lower the water level by drainage; if such a subsoil overlies a bed of clay the sand may be confined by enclosing the site by sheet piling (p. 22) down to the clay and removing the ground water by pumping. Determining the moisture content (*e.g.*, water in the pore space) of a soil may give useful information as to the characteristics of the soil. The percentage moisture is found by drying the specimen of soil in an oven (at 105° C) and weighing it; it equals

$$\frac{\text{original weight} - \text{dry weight}}{\text{dry weight}} \times 100.$$

Certain subsoils (those containing naturally occurring sulphates from gypsum or those consisting of made ground containing industrial waste products) and ground water may contain injurious chemicals, such as sulphates (of calcium, sodium, potassium and magnesium) and acids (*e.g.*, sulphuric acid and peat waters) and may cause serious damage to foundations and retaining walls of normal Portland cement concrete. Chemical analyses of such soils and waters are necessary. Lean concretes especially are liable to chemical attack and dense concretes are less vulnerable. The concrete should be composed of special cement, such as sulphate-resisting Portland cement if the concentration of sulphates is very high; cement mixes of Portland blast-furnace cement and high alumina cement concretes are more resistant to chemical attack than normal Portland cement concrete; super-sulphate cement is used also for concreting in contaminated ground. In some cases it may be necessary to protect the concrete with asphalt or asphalt-felt; a concrete bed of this description should have the damp-proof lining applied to the inner face of an outer protecting thin casing of concrete when dry; the main mass of concrete is then deposited.

It should be borne in mind that the strata formation of a site may not be uniform. When this is revealed as the excavation proceeds the normal foundation should be strengthened at the weak spots; this may entail additional and deeper excavation until a more resistant stratum is reached and an increase in the size of the concrete bed with, possibly, additional reinforcement.

ROCKS AND SOILS

A broad classification, comprising five groups, is: (1) rocks, (2) cohesive soils, (3) non-cohesive soils, (4) peat, and (5) made ground. Table 2 shows how these are classified and distinguished.

(1) Rocks. These embrace igneous rocks (which include granites – see Chap. III, Vol. II), massively bedded (at least 900 mm thick) limestones and hard sandstones, slates, hard shales and soft sandstones, clay shales, chalk, thin-bedded (a few centimetres thick) limestones and sandstones, and heavily-shattered rocks.

(2) Cohesive Soils. These are soils, the particles of which stick together, such as clays. The degree of cohesion depends upon the size and shape of the particles and the water content. The clays are classified as (i) very stiff boulder clays and hard clays with a shaly structure (boulder clay contains stones of various sizes), (ii) stiff and sandy clays, (iii) firm clays and sandy clays, (iv) soft clays and silts (silt is a natural sediment composed chiefly of very fine grains of rock), and (v) very soft clays and silts.

Clay soils are subject to shrinkage and cracking in hot dry weather, followed by expansion in wet weather; they change in volume according to their water content. Unless adequate precautions are taken, such movement may cause considerable damage to buildings erected on subsoils of very soft clay especially. As the movement decreases with the depth below ground level it is important that the foundations should be relatively deep. Hence, on shrinkable soils it is recommended that the foundations of external walls should be at least 850 mm deep (as shown at C and E, Fig. 3), or be of the pile and beam type (see H, Fig. 3), or of raft construction, as shown at G, Fig. 4, but with a projection beyond the outer face of the wall of some 900 or 1 200 mm – see p. 14. In the U.K. the main area where shrinkable clays are found lies to the east of a line stretching approximately from Hull to Exeter.

In addition to having this undesirable property of expanding and contracting, clay soils have a relatively low shear strength and a correspondingly small safe load bearing capacity – see Table 1.

(3) Non-cohesive Soils include gravels and sands. The strength or bearing capacity of such soils depends upon the grading, packing and average size of the particles. In general, the better the grading (as distinct from uniformity) the tighter the packing and the larger the grains, the higher will be the capacity for load carrying. These soils are divided into: (i) compact well-graded sands and gravel-sands, (ii) loose well-graded sands and gravel-sands, (iii) compact uniform sands, and (iv) loose uniform sands.

TABLE 1 PERMISSIBLE BEARING PRESSURES

Group	Types of Rocks and Soils	Maximum Safe-Bearing Capacity (MN/m^2)
I Rocks	Igneous rocks in sound condition	10
	Massively-bedded limestones and hard sandstones	4
	Slates	3
	Hard shales, soft sandstones	2
	Hard clay shales	1
	Hard solid rock	0.64
	Thinly-bedded limestones and sandstones Heavily-shattered rocks	To be determined after inspection
II Cohesive soils	Very stiff boulder clays and hard clays with a shaly structure	0.4–0.6
	Stiff clays and sandy clays	0.2–0.4
	Firm clays and sandy clays	0.1–0.2
	Soft clays and silts	0.05–0.1
	Very soft clays and silts	0.05–nil
III Non-cohesive soils	Compact well-graded sands and gravel-sands	0.4–0.6
	Loose well-graded sands and gravel-sands	0.2–0.4
	Compact uniform sands	0.2–0.4
	Loose uniform sands	0.1–0.2
IV	Peat	To be determined after investigation
V	Made ground	To be determined after investigation

The above values have a factor of safety of 2. They serve as a useful guide for normal conditions. In the absence of sufficient information, load tests, etc., on the site should be made to determine the bearing capacity. As the presence of water reduces the bearing capacity of sands and gravels especially, the values for Group III should be halved if the non-cohesive soils are waterlogged.

Non-cohesive soils vary considerably in their value as building sites. For example, a deep bed of dry compact gravel provides an excellent support, but a subsoil of loose uniform sand, if not confined (by sheet piling) may develop considerable settlement when loaded. A building to be erected on a loose sand must be provided with either wide strip foundations (Fig. 3) or a raft foundation (Fig. 4) to ensure that any settlement is uniform.

The presence of ground water adversely affects the bearing capacity of soils. Thus, pumping operations may loosen a compact bed of gravel and thereby considerably reduce the capacity for load bearing. Serious damage may be caused to a building on a sand subsoil by the removal of water and sand resulting from pumping on an adjacent site; indeed, damage to an existing building may result, even if the soil is dry, by the escape of sand under its foundations when, for example, an excavation is made for a basement for an adjoining building.

Frost may damage foundations. Fine sand, some clays and chalk are soils liable to expand when frozen, and especially if the subsoil water is just below the ground level. The expansion due to the formation of ice may cause local lifting (called *frost heave*) of the foundations and settlement due to the subsequent disintegration of the soil. It is necessary, therefore, for the bottoms of the foundations to be below the frost line. Normally, it is regarded that a depth of 600 mm provides an adequate protection in this country.

(4) **Peat** is decayed vegetable matter, black or dark brown in colour. It is highly compressible and *quite unsuited to receive foundations*, even those of light structures. If such a site must be used for a building project it is necessary to support the foundations on piles which are driven down to an underlying firm stratum.

(5) **Made Ground or Fill.** This is excavated soil or house refuse which has been deposited in a depression. Such sites should be avoided. If the made ground is house refuse, it will be insanitary; injurious chemicals may be present if it is industrial waste. Even if the fill consists of excavated soil, such as quarry waste, and well compacted in thin layers as the material is tipped there is a risk of unequal settlement occurring. If such a site must be used for building purposes the foundations should be carried down to the original stratum or be supported on piles (pp. 16–22).

Sloping Sites. Provided the subsoil is satisfactory, compact and not liable to shrinkage, no difficulty is presented when designing the foundations of a building on a sloping site; the foundations are stepped, as described in Chap. I, Vol. II. If, however, the stratum supporting the foundations is a yielding one, such as clay, and this dips steeply (the angle of dip being that between the slope and the horizontal) there is a tendency for such stratum to slide over an underlying firm stratum with the result that serious damage, such as tilting, may be caused to the building. Such movement may result if the inclination is no greater than 6° (approximately 1 in 10). Normally, such unstable sites should be avoided, otherwise they should be properly drained before building operations are commenced and the foundations should preferably be of the pile and beam type described on p. 13.

Trees. The near proximity of trees, especially elms and poplars, may cause serious damage to a building on a clay subsoil. The roots of a fast growing tree extract a good deal of moisture from the soil, and clay soil shrinks as its water content decreases. During a prolonged dry period the clay soil under a foundation near a tree will be drier than the rest and be liable to greater shrinkage, with the result that unequal settlement may occur which may cause cracking of the walls. It is considered advisable that buildings should not be nearer to single trees than the height of a tree at maturity and this distance should be increased by 50 per cent for *rows* of trees. Trees can be the cause of considerable structural failure, apart from that referred to above. For example, a tall tree with its roots below a boundary wall may completely overturn the wall by the root leverage produced in a high wind. Roots may also penetrate drains through their joints, causing chokage.

Bearing Capacity of Rocks and Soils. The safe-bearing capacity is the safe load per unit area which the ground will support. Recognized values are listed in Table 1.

According to the Building Regulations, the concrete foundations of a load bearing wall (p. 121) consisting of a strip foundation shall be composed of a mix of 50 kg cement to not more than 0.1 m^3 of fine aggregate and 0.2 m^3 of coarse aggregate, its thickness shall be at least 150 mm and not less than its projection beyond the face of the wall, and its width must not be less than that stated in column 3 of Table 2.

TYPES OF FOUNDATION

So-called spread foundations may be divided into (1) strip foundations, (2) pad foundations, (3) pile and beam foundations, and (4) raft foundations.

(1) Strip Foundations. A strip foundation is one which provides a continuous longitudinal bearing, namely, the type illustrated in Fig. 10, Vol. I. Five sections through typical strip foundations are shown in this volume at A, B, C, D, and E, Fig. 3.

That at A is commonly adopted for one or two-storeyed domestic buildings on good firm non-shrinkable subsoils, such as gravels. At 600 mm depth, as shown, the foundation is not likely to be affected by frost. The 150 mm projection of the concrete bed at each side of the wall provides the necessary "working space" for the bricklayers, although for shallow trenches, especially if a 150 mm depth of vegetable or virgin soil has been previously removed, this is hardly necessary. For deeper trenches a minimum width of 610 mm is needed to enable labourers to dig by hand; this does not apply if a mechanical excavator, such as a trencher, is employed. The depth of trench for an external wall should be increased to 850 mm if the subsoil is shrinkable, *e.g.*, a soft clay.

The section at B complies with the provisions of the Building Regulations in respect to dwelling houses of two storeys – see Table 2 – on compact and stiff subsoils. For shrinkable subsoils the depth should be 915 mm minimum, but such narrow trenches can only be excavated to this depth by mechanical means. This depth applies to external walls only; for internal walls, where the subsoil is not so liable to volume changes, the depth need only be 600 mm.

Section C conforms to the Building Regulations for foundations of external walls of two-storeyed houses on very soft clay sites – see Table 2, the thickness

TABLE 2 MINIMUM WIDTH OF STRIP FOUNDATIONS

(1)	(2)	(3)	(4)					
Type of subsoil	Condition of subsoil	Field test applicable	Minimum width in millimetres for total load in kilonewtons per lineal metre of loadbearing walling of not more than					
			20 kN/m	30 kN/m	40 kN/m	50 kN/m	60 kN/m	70 kN/m
I Rock	Not inferior to sandstone, limestone, or firm chalk	Requires at least a pneumatic or similar pick for removal	In each case equal to the width of wall					
II Gravel Sand	Compact Compact	Requires pick for removal. Wooden peg 50 mm square hard to drive beyond 150 mm	250	300	400	500	600	650
III Clay Sandy clay	Stiff Stiff	Cannot be moulded with the fingers and needs pick or mechanical spade for removal	250	300	400	500	600	650
IV Clay Sandy clay	Firm Firm	Can be moulded by substantial pressure with the fingers and can be excavated with spade	300	350	450	600	750	850
V Sand Silty sand Clayey sand	Loose Loose Loose	Can be excavated with a spade. Wooden peg 50 mm square can be easily driven	400	600				
VI Silt Clay Sandy clay Silty clay	Soft Soft Soft Soft	Fairly easily moulded in the fingers and readily excavated	450	650				
VII Silt Clay Sandy clay Silty clay	Very soft Very soft Very soft Very soft	Natural sample in winter conditions exudes between fingers when squeezed in fist	600	850				

Notes:
1. Loads on walls of two-storey domestic buildings are not likely to exceed 30 kN/m.
2. If the load exceeds 30 kN/m on soil types V, VI and VII the foundations need special consideration; *e.g.*, increased width or reinforcement or both.

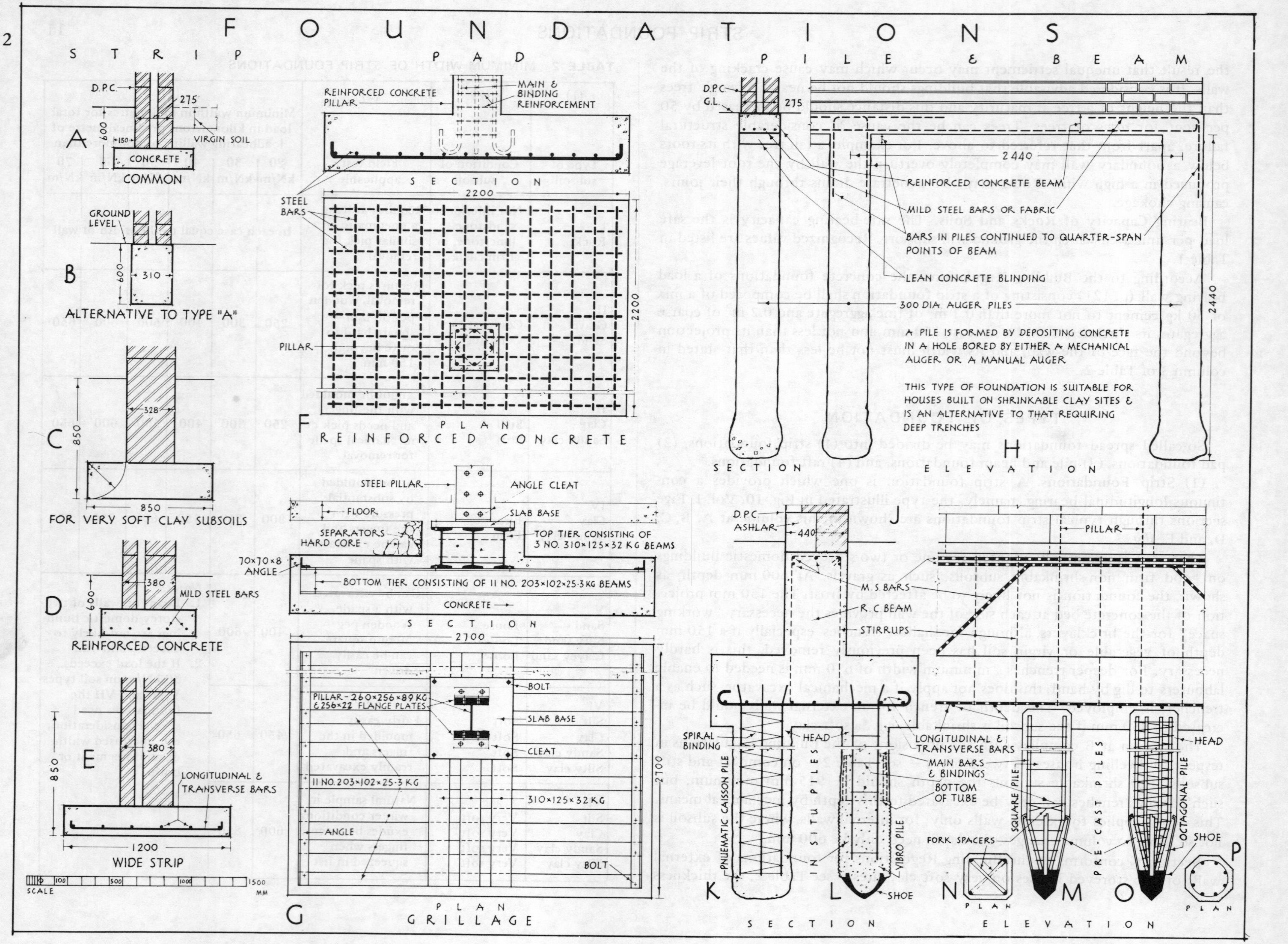

FOUNDATIONS

STRIP

D.P.C.
275
600
150
VIRGIN SOIL
CONCRETE
A
COMMON

GROUND LEVEL
600
310
B
ALTERNATIVE TO TYPE "A"

328
850
C
850
FOR VERY SOFT CLAY SUBSOILS

380
600
MILD STEEL BARS
D
REINFORCED CONCRETE

380
850
E
LONGITUDINAL & TRANSVERSE BARS
1200
WIDE STRIP

SCALE 100 500 1000 1500 MM

PAD

REINFORCED CONCRETE PILLAR
MAIN & BINDING REINFORCEMENT
SECTION
STEEL BARS
2200
PILLAR
2200
PLAN
F
REINFORCED CONCRETE

STEEL PILLAR
ANGLE CLEAT
FLOOR
SLAB BASE
SEPARATORS
HARD CORE
TOP TIER CONSISTING OF 3 NO. 310×125×32 KG BEAMS
70×70×8 ANGLE
BOTTOM TIER CONSISTING OF 11 NO. 203×102×25·3 KG BEAMS
CONCRETE
SECTION
2700
BOLT
PILLAR - 260×256×89 KG & 256×22 FLANGE PLATES
SLAB BASE
CLEAT
11 NO. 203×102×25·3 KG
310×125×32 KG
2700
ANGLE
BOLT
G
PLAN
GRILLAGE

PILE & BEAM

D.P.C.
G.L.
275
2440
REINFORCED CONCRETE BEAM
MILD STEEL BARS OR FABRIC
BARS IN PILES CONTINUED TO QUARTER-SPAN POINTS OF BEAM
LEAN CONCRETE BLINDING
300 DIA AUGER PILES
2440
A PILE IS FORMED BY DEPOSITING CONCRETE IN A HOLE BORED BY EITHER A MECHANICAL AUGER OR A MANUAL AUGER

THIS TYPE OF FOUNDATION IS SUITABLE FOR HOUSES BUILT ON SHRINKABLE CLAY SITES & IS AN ALTERNATIVE TO THAT REQUIRING DEEP TRENCHES

SECTION
H
ELEVATION

D.P.C.
ASHLAR
440
J
PILLAR
M.S. BARS
R. BEAM
STIRRUPS
SPIRAL BINDING
HEAD
LONGITUDINAL & TRANSVERSE BARS
MAIN BARS & BINDINGS
BOTTOM OF TUBE
FORK SPACERS
PNEUMATIC CAISSON PILE
IN SITU PILES
VIBRO PILE
SHOE
SQUARE PILE
PRE-CAST PILES
OCTAGONAL PILE
HEAD
SHOE
K L N M O P
PLAN
PLAN
SECTION
ELEVATION

FIGURE 3

shall be at least equal to the projection beyond the face of the wall, characteristics of this class of soil to shrink and expand are mentioned on p. 9.

On some sites, such as those which may be subject to unequal settlement – as in mining districts or where the subsoil is not uniform in character – it may be necessary to reinforce the concrete with longitudinal mild steel bars or light mild steel fabric (p. 48). This type of foundation is shown at D.

A *wide strip* foundation is one which provides a continuous bearing of such width that transverse reinforcement may be necessary. This type is illustrated at E and shows a 380 mm cavity wall supported on a concrete bed having both transverse and longitudinal mild steel bars. Such may be needed for external walls on shrinkable soils which may be liable to unequal settlement.

It should be noted that very rarely is the type of foundation having *brick footings* and a concrete bed (as shown at C, Fig. 10, Vol. I) now adopted. Such were required by local authorities when the loads from floors and roofs were carried by the walls and when cement was inferior to that now produced. The introduction of steel-framed and reinforced concrete structures (Chap. II) with their relatively thin non-load bearing walls, has rendered brick footings obsolete. If a wall is required to carry a heavy load and if the concrete foundation is not suitably reinforced, brick footings are effective in spreading the load and preventing shear failure of the concrete.

(2) Pad Foundations. These are isolated foundations and are required to support reinforced concrete or steel pillars, or detached brick or masonry piers. Reinforced concrete pads and grillages are examples.

A section and part plan of a typical *reinforced concrete pad* foundation is shown at F, Fig. 3 and E′, Fig. 23. The area of the square foundation equals the total load divided by the safe bearing capacity of the soil. The reinforcement consists of small round bars, equally spaced, in both directions. The depth of the foundation and the amount of reinforcement are determined by calculation. The concrete cover to the bars should be at least 50 mm and, in order to ensure a clean bed for the main concrete it may be advisable to "blind" the bottom of the excavation with a 50 or 75 mm layer of lean concrete (say, 1 : 4 : 8 mix) before the main concrete (usually a 1 : 2 : 4 mix) is deposited. If two or more pillars are to be supported on one pad, the latter may be rectangular or trapezoidal on plan. Typical details of reinforced concrete pillars, etc., are shown in Figs. 22 and 23.

Another form of pad is the *steel grillage*. The section and plan at G, Fig. 3, is a typical example of a two-tier grillage. The top tier consists of three steel beams and the bottom tier comprises eleven smaller B.S. beams. The load from the steel pillar is distributed by the top tier in one direction and spread by the bottom tier in the opposite direction; the load is thus uniformly distributed over a relatively wide area (equal to the load divided by the bearing capacity of the soil). The beams in the bottom layer are evenly spaced and are connected together at their ends by the two steel angles. The three beams in the top tier are maintained at the correct distance apart by cast iron separators (of length equal to the distance between the webs of adjacent beams) through the holes of which and those drilled through the beam webs are passed two long bolts; three pairs of separators are provided, one at the centre and one near each end. When the nuts of the bolts are tightened the beams act as one unit and are bolted to the bottom tier – see section. The square steel slab to which the pillar is fixed is secured to the top tier by means of the four bolts shown at the corners. Additional stiffness is afforded by the concrete which thoroughly encases the beams and protects the steel from corrosion; the distance between the flanges of the beams should be at least 75 mm to permit of the placing and consolidation of the concrete. This grillage is designed to support a load of 2 MN. It is not economical to adopt steel grillages for forces less than this. An alternative form of grillage consists of a top tier of beams, as shown, resting on a reinforced concrete raft, the round bars serving the purpose of distributing the load in lieu of the bottom tier of beams.

(3) Pile and Beam Foundations. This type of foundation is an alternative to the deep strip foundation required for a building to be erected on a heavy clay site. As stated on p. 9, clay soils shrink and swell and this movement decreases with the depth; hence strip foundations on shrinkable clays should be of types C or E, Fig. 3 (p. 12). Alternatively, the pile and beam foundation shown at H may be adopted. This consists of a foundation at ground level in the form of a thin reinforced concrete beam supported at intervals by columns in the shape of concrete *piles* (see p. 16). The size and reinforcement of the beam depend upon the load to be supported and the distance apart of the piles. That shown is 305 mm wide by 150 mm thick with four 10 or 12 mm dia. mild steel bars (or steel fabric, such as Expamet or B.R.C. fabric) having 25 mm cover of concrete. This is regarded as adequate for 280 mm cavity walls of two-storeyed houses with the piles situated between door and window openings and not exceeding 3.7 m centres. The beam concrete should be composed of 1 : 2 : 4 and, as shown, it is formed on a 50 or 75 mm thick blinding layer of lean concrete (1 : 4 : 8) or gravel to ensure a reasonably clean level bed for the structural concrete which must provide an adequate cover to the reinforcement. The piles vary from 250 to 360 mm dia. and 2 to 3.7 m in length; holes are formed by a suitable manual post-hole auger, similar to that shown at P, Fig. 6 (which is operated by two men), or mechanical earth auger, and these are filled with concrete. As shown, bent bars are embedded in the heads of the piles and extend 50 mm below the top of the beam to the points of contra-flexure (approx. one-quarter of the span).

Another example of a pile and beam foundation is shown at J, Fig. 3. The 440 mm thick ashlar-faced wall is supported on an inverted reinforced concrete tee-beam foundation with four reinforced concrete piles under each pillar (the latter is indicated by broken lines in the elevation). Four different piles have been shown to illustrate the description on pp. 16, 19 and 21 (in actual practice, of course, only one type would be used. If the piles are of the in-situ type, the upper ends of the vertical bars of the piles are bent and embedded in the beam concrete, as shown at K and L. If precast, as at M and O, the heads of the piles

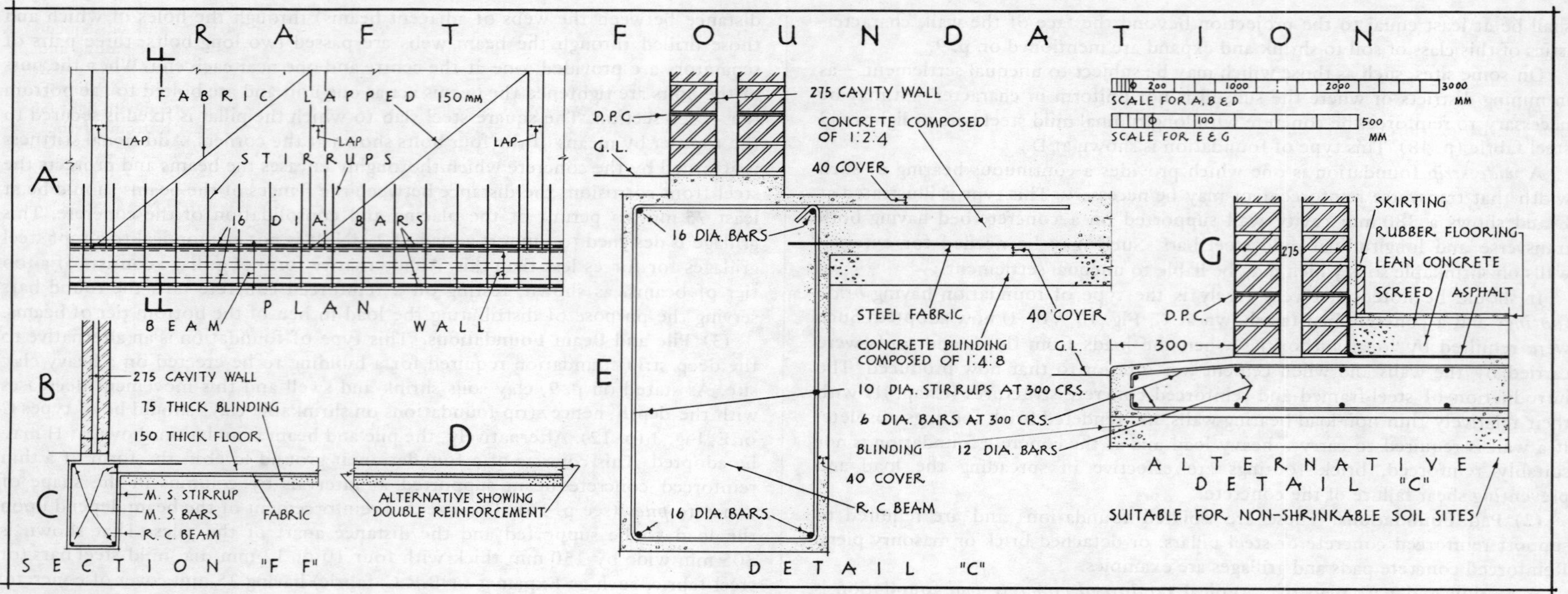

FIGURE 4

should project at least 150 mm into the beam; the pile heads should have been stripped of concrete to expose the vertical reinforcement and thus ensure that the piles are bonded to the beam when the foundation concrete is deposited.

Pad foundations, such as F, Fig. 3, may be supported on piles, the number of these varying in accordance with their size and the load to be transmitted. If, for example, it is a four-piled group, the centre of each pile would be about 460 mm from a corner. They should not be placed closer than 760 mm centres for precast piles and 1 m centres for in-situ piles.

For the main description of piling, see pp. 16–22.

(4) **Raft Foundations.** A raft foundation is one which at least covers, and may extend beyond, the area of a building and consists of concrete suitably reinforced; the reinforcement may take the form of mild steel circular bars laid in both directions or fabric. Such foundations may be adopted on sites where the subsoil is a yielding one (*e.g.*, soft clay or made-up ground) or where unequal settlement may occur as a result of, for example, mining subsidence, and for which the relatively narrow strip type of foundation would provide an inadequate spread.

One type of raft is shown in the part plan A and section B, Fig. 4. The whole of the ground floor is covered with concrete reinforced with a layer of steel fabric, lapped 150 mm at the joints, near the bottom surface; an alternative and better arrangement is shown at D, where two layers of fabric having 40 mm cover of concrete top and bottom are provided. As shown, the reinforced concrete beam foundation under the wall is incorporated with the floor by extending the mild steel stirrups – see enlarged detail at E. The lean concrete blinding shown provides a clean bed for the structural concrete; alternatively, a layer of gravel may be used for this purpose.

Another form of raft, alternative to the type at C and suitable for gravel or similar non-shrinkable soil sites, is shown at G. Only light reinforcement is necessary, in the form of 6 mm dia. bars, top and bottom as indicated, or layers of fabric. Instead of the beam below the wall shown at C, 12 mm longitudinal top and bottom bars are placed at this point; the concrete below internal walls should be similarly reinforced. On clean sites the blinding may be omitted. This construction is economical when the floors are solid and especially if they are finished with mastic or coloured asphalt (in lieu of rubber flooring with asphalt damp proofing). A necessary precaution against frost-heave (p. 10) is taken by projecting the raft 300 mm beyond the face of the wall. This 150 mm thick reinforced concrete slab projection should be increased to at least 1 m if the soil is shrinkable (such as clay – see p. 9), although a suitable path would serve the same purpose of preventing soil shrinkage and swelling.

Damage due to Brine Pumping. As stated on p. 7 buildings are very liable to be damaged by subsidence resulting from the pumping and raising of brine, and in such districts, special forms of construction, enabling the building to be lifted, have to be adopted. Near Northwich, Cheshire, brine pumping occurs on a large scale and in certain defined areas subsidence is troublesome. The Cheshire Brine Subsidence Compensation Board has therefore been formed, it administers a fund created by contributions from the salt and chemical companies who subscribe to it in proportion to the amount of brine pumped. The fund is used to compensate property owners for the damage caused by brine pumping, and the Board has powers to recommend the type of framing and construction to be adopted, and would probably disclaim responsibility in the event of non-compliance. Under the Cheshire Brine (Compensation for Subsidence) Act 1952, regulations concerning compensation and recommendations on the construction of buildings are made. Hence building in this area must conform to the requirements of the local and planning authorities and the recommendations of the Compensation Board, if the owner wishes to claim for future damage.

Buildings should be constructed in units capable of being lifted independently, each unit having a ground floor area not exceeding 130 m^2. The maximum height of a building from ground level is 9 m to the eaves and 13.7 m to the ridge. Framed construction of steel or reinforced concrete should be used and be designed as a rigid structure so that it can be lifted or lowered by jacks, pockets not less than 440 mm high being formed in the foundations for lifting operations, also sufficient working space being left below the ground floor. The load per stanchion is not to exceed 500 kN and the framework is to be constructed so that its parts can sustain the in-situ stresses as well as those caused by lifting or lowering. The foundations shall be made so that the pressure on the ground is not greater than 107.25 kN/m^2, brickwork to foundations should be in engineering brick with hydraulic lime and/or cement mortar.

As shown in Fig. 5 steel frames shall include cill beams beneath and connected to all the stanchions by a rigid joint. The cladding of the frame is frequently in brickwork, although many of the sheeting materials are suitable.

Building on Sites liable to Mining Subsidence. Reference has already been made to the damage caused to buildings in coal-mining areas due to underground workings. Whilst the majority of existing buildings in such districts are not affected and show no damage after a long period of years, cases occur from time to time of buildings becoming defective as a result of subsidence. In mild cases the defects take the form of cracked plaster ceilings and walls; more extensive damage may include wide cracks in walls, distorted door and window openings (which, besides being unsightly, may prevent the opening of doors and windows); cracked and uneven solid ground floors, etc.; where settlement has become serious, walls may collapse. The National Coal Board usually compensates owners for this damage. For new buildings, precautions should be taken to prevent damage occurring from proposed new workings.

Subsidence moves as a wave across the site and has three effects: lowering of ground level, changes in length of ground surface, and tilting of buildings. Two types of foundation are used, firstly one that is deep and very strong and secondly, one that is light and capable of moving over the ground. With the first type, reinforced concrete foundations perhaps up to 1.5 m deep made into an egg-crate formation are used (see O, Fig. 17), they are sufficiently strong to cantilever over depressions formed by the subsidence wave. Generally, the building assumes a level position after the passing of the wave, but pockets can be left in the foundation for the insertion of jacks and subsequent re-levelling. Such deep foundations are costly, they tie the building to the ground and are normally only appropriate for small heavy square buildings when the normal construction of the superstructure (plus a few precautionary measures given below) applies. For a house, the best arrangement is to have a 150 mm thick slab reinforced with light fabric near the top and bottom, additional bars will be required at the bottom of the slab beneath the chimney breast and stack.

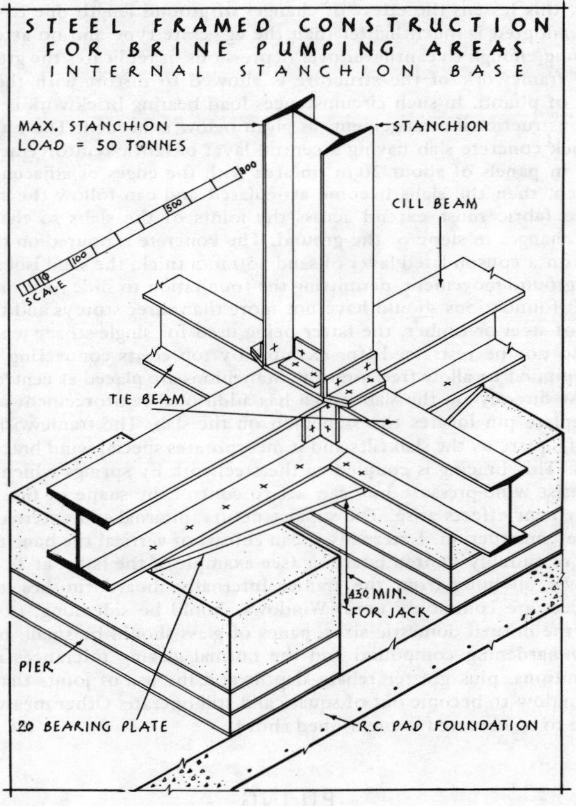

FIGURE 5

When the egg-crate system is adopted, the length of the building must be controlled, and if it is particularly long then it must be sub-divided into independent units of maximum dimensions 24 m by 9 m wide; the units being separated by a gap known as a subsidence joint which is not less than 50 mm wide. One method of keeping out the weather at such a gap is shown at O, Fig. 25 for a wall, and at N, Fig. 25, and D, Fig. 65, for a roof. Brick walls must be horizontally reinforced by steel bands or fabric reinforcement built into the top and bottom of walls, vertical reinforcing bars can be included at the corners, both these applications being detailed in Vol. II. Joints in pipework must allow for movement and drains should be made of a flexible material such as pitch fibre laid to twice the normal fall. There should be a flexible coupling (a P.V.C. sleeve is suitable) between the W.C. and drain, the coupling passing through the ground slab with a 50 mm space all round that is filled with a non-hardening sealer. Normal open gullies with swivel rainwater shoes should be used in preference to the back inlet type with its rigid pipe joint.

With the second type* of foundation mentioned, the building is allowed to slide over the ground, this lessens the effect of changes of ground length due to subsidence. The foundation adopted is much lighter than the egg-crate type and no attempt is made to make it strong enough to cantilever over depressions, it replicates the ground movement. Hence, the framework of the structure is allowed to distort with the stanchions becoming out of plumb. In such circumstances load bearing brickwork is unsuitable and a different constructional arrangement, as given below is needed. The building rests on a 150 mm thick concrete slab having a central layer of fabric reinforcement. Provided the slab is cast in panels of about 20 m^2 in area with the edges of adjacent panels painted with bitumen, then the slabs become articulated and can follow the subsiding ground surface. The fabric must extend across the joints of the slabs so that these are tied together at changes in slope of the ground. The concrete is poured on to building paper which rests on a consolidated layer of sand 150 mm thick, the sand isolates the effect of differential ground movement, permitting the foundation to slide over the ground. Buildings on such foundations should have not more than three storeys and they must have a framework of steel or timber, the latter being used for single-storey work. Joints of the frame should not be restrained (for example by top cleats connecting steel beams and pillars) but pinned to allow free rotation. Stanchions are placed at centres not exceeding 3 m and rest directly on the slab which has additional reinforcement at the bottom, a central baseplate pin locates the stanchion on the slab. The framework is thus free to move out of square as the slab tilts and it incorporates special wind bracing to overcome wind forces. This bracing is coupled to the steelwork by springs which are sufficiently strong to resist wind-pressure but can act to control the shape of the frame when the greater settlement effects arise. The superstructure, internal and external cladding are of light flexible construction. Externally it can consist of vertical tile hanging (see Vol. III), overlapping or suitably jointed boarding (see example of the latter at T, Fig. 18), or thin concrete slabs all hung from the frame. Internally, board finishes are suitable and asbestos sheets are commonly used. Windows should be side-hung, of timber and not larger than the normal domestic sizes; panes of glass should be small, bedded in a proprietary non-hardening compound and the normal glazing tolerances need increasing. These precautions, plus greater rebate depths and the use of joints that are not glued, allow the window to become out of square and still operate. Other measures in regard to services have to be observed as mentioned above.

PILING

There are two main groups of piles, bearing piles, and sheet piles.

BEARING PILES

These carry loads and transmit them either (i) through one or more weak yielding soils, such as soft clay, to a lower and firmer stratum, such as rock or gravel, and so act as pillars having a direct or *end-bearing* on a natural sound foundation, or (ii) through relatively weak strata for their entire length without having a reasonably high end-bearing capacity; the latter are referred to as *friction piles*, as the support which they give depends chiefly on the friction between their surfaces and the adjacent soil.

Formerly, bearing piles were of timber, such as oak, teak, jarrah, elm and northern pine. Wood piles are now rarely used except for temporary work and in countries where suitable timber is cheap and plentiful.

Reinforced concrete is now mainly employed for bearing piles. They are either precast or cast in-situ of square (with chamfered corners), octagonal and circular cross-section.

Bearing piles can be distinguished as either *displacement* piles which are driven into the ground and so displace the soil or *non-displacement* (or *replacement*) piles for which the soil is bored or excavated. A precast R.C. pile is an obvious example of a displacement pile; an in-situ R.C. pile may be of the displacement or non-displacement type (see p. 19).

PRECAST PILES

A typical square precast reinforced concrete bearing pile is shown at M and N, Fig. 3, and one of octagonal cross-section is illustrated at O and P. Normally, sizes vary from 300 to 450 mm length of side (or between flats or diameter) and up to 18 m or more in length; piles up to 1.5 m dia. are also made. They are reinforced with mild steel bars, the main or vertical bars varying from 20 to 38 mm dia. and the subsidiary bars or lateral reinforcement (called bindings or links or stirrups) are usually 6 mm or 8 mm dia.; for piles square in cross-section the bindings (known as square bindings or links) are pitched at 125 or 150 mm centres except at the toe and head when the pitch is halved — see *M*; this increase in lateral reinforcement at the ends assists in withstanding the high stresses which occur during driving (see below). For octagonal and circular piles the binding is spiral or helical — see O. The bindings are wired to the vertical bars.

The concrete is usually composed of 1 part Portland cement, 2 parts sand and 4 parts coarse aggregate graded from 19 mm down. If high driving conditions (see below) are likely to be encountered a richer mix, $1:1\frac{1}{2}:3$, may be used. When a pile is driven it is subjected to greatest impact stresses at its head, and it is therefore sometimes strengthened at the upper 600 or 900 mm of its length by the use of a stronger grade of concrete (1:1:2). Piles of normal Portland cement concrete must be allowed to mature for at least one month before being driven. This period can be reduced to one week if, instead of normal Portland cement, rapid-hardening cement is used.

A pile is normally provided at its toe with a cast-steel shoe, secured by mild steel straps, as shown at M and O, cast into the concrete. This protects the toe and increases the penetration during the driving operation.

* As first used by Nottinghamshire C.C.

Care must be taken to prevent damage to piles when being handled, transported and stacked. To facilitate handling, slinging and pitching (see below), it is usual to cast two or more cardboard tubes to receive short metal 30 mm dia. rods to the projecting ends of which the sling is attached. A short pile is slung from two points at about one-fifth length from each end; long piles are lifted at four points. A pair of *fork spacers* or *spreaders* (pressed steel bars, placed diagonally with their forked ends engaging the main bars) is placed at every 1.5 m along the length of the pile to keep the main reinforcement in place whilst the lateral reinforcement is being wired to it – see M and N; they also prevent the bars from inward buckling during the placing of the concrete.

Specialist firms usually have a stock of mature piles, although long piles especially are often made on the site. They are cast horizontally in moulds and, in order to ensure maximum density of the concrete, which should be a dry mix, it is well compacted by the application of external vibrators (see Chap. I, Vol. II).

Precast piles of prestressed concrete (p. 50) have now been developed. These are claimed to be stronger than normal reinforced concrete piles and, therefore, because of the reduction in cross-sectional area, they are lighter and can be more easily handled.

Pile Driving. The plant used for driving piles into the ground consists of a frame and winch.* Nowadays, the frame is of steel of stock height varying from 6 to 24 m mounted on wheels (for running on a rail track on the site) or rollers, and having at its head a pulley block through which wire ropes run from the winch for lifting the pile and monkey or hammer (see below). The winch, with two or more drums round which ropes are coiled, is operated by a petrol, diesel or electric motor; its function is to lift the piles into position and provide the driving power. The equipment includes a hammer which may be of the single-acting or double-acting type. At A and B, Fig. 6 is shown a pile frame together with a single-acting hammer and a precast pile. The frame is stayed by four guy ropes secured at the head and anchored at ground level; as an additional safety precaution against lateral movement, steel beam stops are provided within the wheelbase (see A).

The heads of the piles must be protected against damage, such as spalling of concrete, during the driving operation. One form of protection, called a *driving helmet* or *cap*, consists of a steel casing which is fitted over the head of the pile. The helmet has a shallow recess at the top which receives a thick pad of hardwood such as elm, known as a *dolley*, circular shaped at the top and strengthened by a forged steel ring. The dolley, which is renewable, cushions the blow and distributes it evenly over the pile. Another form of dolley, more expensive but one which lasts considerably longer, is of plastic material bedded on a layer of hardwood and having a steel top.

The piles are lifted and driven by an operator at the winch. When the frame has been moved to the required position the pile is *pitched*, *i.e.*, it is carefully lifted and placed in correct position on the site, vertically in front of a pair of guides or *frame leaders* (steel channels – see A, B and Q – which extend to the full height of the frame). The pile is secured temporarily by means of a *toggle bolt* which is passed through a hole formed near the head of the pile during casting. At this point a wood packing of correct thickness to ensure that the pile is centrally under the hammer, is placed between the pile and the leaders. The toggle bolt passes through the pile, packing piece and a metal plate at the back of the leaders – see B. A second bolt and packing are fixed lower down the pile, and these are removed in due course as the pile is driven down.

One type of *single-acting hammer* (A and B, Fig. 6) has an outer mobile ram or cylinder of cast steel (weighing from 500 to 10 000 kg, 1.8 to 2.7 m high and 400 to 500 mm dia.) which rests on the dolley of the pile helmet, and a hollow vertical piston rod which passes centrally down the cylinder and at its upper end is fixed to a hammer rod (about twice the height of the ram) which is secured to the pile frame. The hammer is operated by steam or compressed air, usually the former. When it is in operation the ram slides up and down the stationary piston and hammer rods. Steam passing down the hollow piston rod enters the cylinder through a valve when at the bottom of its stroke and raises the ram to the top of its stroke, followed by the down stroke – the hammer falling by its own weight on to the pile as the steam escapes. The driving operation is in control of the operator; when he pulls on a rope attached to the valve lever, the valve is opened admitting the steam to the cylinder; the valve closes when he releases the rope. Thus the pile is driven by a succession of powerful blows, a minimum of about 45 per minute, the length of the stroke varying from 1.4 to 1.8 m. At the back of the cylinder there are two projecting lugs or *cods* (see B) which pass between the leaders. A pair of rollers, pinned to each cod, traverses the back flanges of the leaders (see Q) as the hammer descends.

The ram of the *double-acting hammer* is also lifted by steam (or compressed air) but, in addition, steam is admitted above the piston and thus the ram falls by its own weight and this additional pressure, to deliver a powerful blow on the pile. During the driving operation the blows are delivered in rapid succession, 95 (weight of hammer, 6 350 kg) to 145 (a 3 175 kg hammer) blows per minute, so keeping the pile in constant motion.

The distance that a pile penetrates after each blow is called the *set*. Throughout the driving operation the set produced by a given number (6, 8 or 10) of blows is recorded, from which some idea can be obtained of any variation in the resistance offered by the strata, checks caused by local obstructions, etc. The final set necessary to develop the desired driving resistance of a pile varies, but it is considered that this should not be more than 2.5 mm per blow (or "a final set of 25 mm per 10 blows"). Many formulae have been derived to determine the theoretical bearing capacity of piles. A satisfactory but costly method for finding the carrying capacity is to apply a test load (see p. 8) on a driven pile and record any settlement which may occur. A lengthy and wide experience of piling under varying conditions is a necessary qualification for estimating the behaviour

* The universal or general purposes mechanical excavator is also used for light pile-driving.

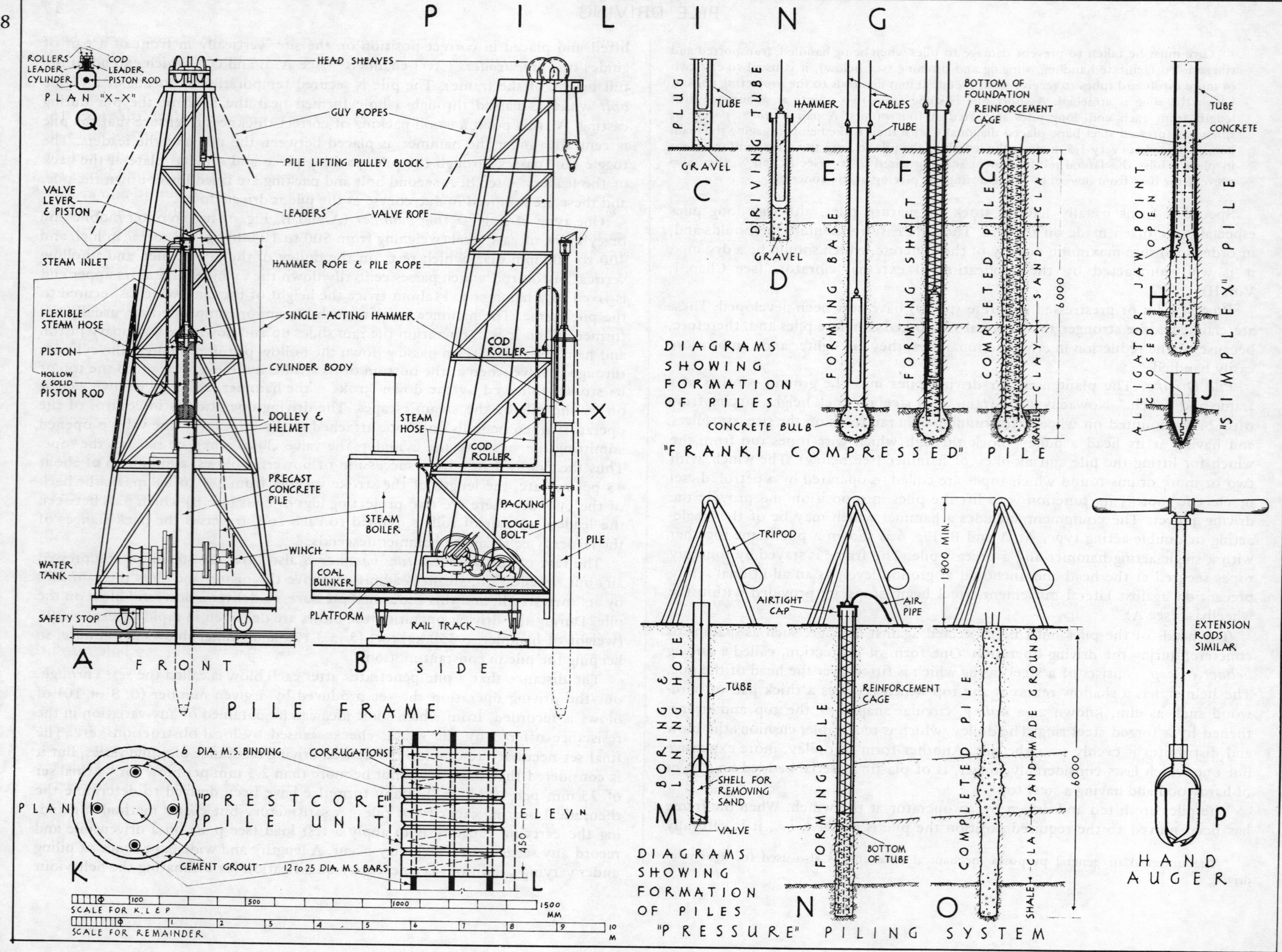
PILING
ROLLERS
LEADER
CYLINDER
COD
LEADER
PISTON ROD
PLAN "X-X"
Q
HEAD SHEAVES
GUY ROPES
PILE LIFTING PULLEY BLOCK
VALVE
LEVER
& PISTON
LEADERS
VALVE ROPE
STEAM INLET
HAMMER ROPE & PILE ROPE
FLEXIBLE
STEAM HOSE
SINGLE-ACTING HAMMER
PISTON
CYLINDER BODY
HOLLOW
& SOLID
PISTON ROD
DOLLEY &
HELMET
COD
ROLLER
X
X
STEAM
HOSE
COD
ROLLER
PRECAST
CONCRETE
PILE
PACKING
TOGGLE
BOLT
STEAM
BOILER
PILE
WINCH
WATER
TANK
COAL
BUNKER
PLATFORM
SAFETY STOP
RAIL TRACK
A FRONT
B SIDE
PILE FRAME
PLUG
TUBE
GRAVEL
C
HAMMER
DRIVING TUBE
GRAVEL
D
CABLES
TUBE
FORMING BASE
E
BOTTOM OF
FOUNDATION
REINFORCEMENT
CAGE
FORMING SHAFT
F
CONCRETE BULB
COMPLETED PILE
G
CLAY
SAND
CLAY
GRAVEL
6000
"FRANK COMPRESSED" PILE
DIAGRAMS
SHOWING
FORMATION
OF PILES
TUBE
CONCRETE
H
ALLIGATOR JAW POINT
CLOSED
OPEN
"SIMPLEX" PILE
J
6 DIA. M.S. BINDING
CORRUGATIONS
PLAN
"PRESTCORE"
PILE UNIT
ELEV
450
K
CEMENT GROUT
12 to 25 DIA. M.S. BARS
L
SCALE FOR K, L & P
100
500
1000
1500
MM
SCALE FOR REMAINDER
1
2
3
4
5
6
7
8
9
10
M
TRIPOD
1800 MIN.
AIRTIGHT
CAP
AIR
PIPE
TUBE
REINFORCEMENT
CAGE
BORING & LINING SHOE
SHELL FOR
REMOVING
SAND
VALVE
M
FORMING PILE
BOTTOM
OF TUBE
N
COMPLETED PILE
O
SHALE
CLAY
SAND
MADE GROUND
6000
DIAGRAMS
SHOWING
FORMATION
OF PILES
"PRESSURE" PILING SYSTEM
EXTENSION
RODS
SIMILAR
P
HAND
AUGER

FIGURE 6

of piles during the driving operation and for interpreting test results; formulae serve as a useful check.

The above-mentioned pile driving methods are very noisy and may damage adjacent buildings by vibration. An alternative method which excludes these undesirable features has been developed by GKN Foundations Ltd. This uses a powerful *high-frequency* vibrator wherein resonance is achieved by matching the frequency of the vibrations of the machine and the frequency of the pile. Skin friction between the pile and the soil is temporarily destroyed by the energy transmitted from the resonating pile so that it sinks quickly into the ground. Shock waves in the ground and hammer noise are eliminated.

Normally, precast piles are driven vertically. Occasionally, however, they are required to be driven at an inclination; the foundations of retaining walls, for example, are sometimes supported by these so-called *batter piles* or *raking piles* because of their efficiency in resisting the forces tending to overturn the walls. The piling frame is raked back to the required slope (which should not exceed 1 in 3 for convenient driving) and the hammer usually employed is of the single-acting type.

Precast piles afford a very satisfactory support, both as columns having end-bearing and as friction piles; they are particularly suitable for waterlogged sites and, as they can be loaded immediately after driving, work on the foundations and the superstructure can be proceeded with at once. They have, however, certain demerits, including: the larger ones especially are not very easy to handle; transporting them from a distance may be costly or, if formed on the site, the space required for casting and curing may be ill-afforded; if proved to be too long or too short after being driven, the cutting down or splicing (for lengthening) cause additional expense and delay; because of the height of the pile-driving frame (15 m is a common height) the piles cannot be used when the height available is restricted; because of the vibration produced when driving they cannot be used on sites closely adjacent to existing buildings, and the noise created during this operation can be very annoying to those living or working in the vicinity – unless the GKN driving method (above) is used.

IN-SITU OR CAST-IN-PLACE PILES

As implied, these are cast in position on the site in a hole made either by driving (displacing the soil) or by boring (removing the soil). The (1) Vibro, (2) Frankipile, and (3) Simplex concrete piles are of this order.

(1) Vibro Piles.* Both "Standard" and "Expanded" piles are formed by the Vibro process.

The *standard pile* (L, Fig. 3) is made in sizes of 350, 450 and 500 mm dia., the larger sizes for loads of 600 and 750 kN respectively, they can be formed in lengths of 25 m and over. A pile is produced as follows: A steel tube, fitted with (but not fixed to) a cast iron shoe, is driven until the desired set has been obtained by a 2 000 or 2 500 kg hammer, operated by steam or compressed air delivering up to 40 blows per minute with a stroke of up to 1.4 m. If required, a cage of reinforcement (consisting of four or six 12 or 24 mm dia. main bars with 4 or 6 mm bindings at 150 to 225 mm pitch) is lowered down the tube. The tube is now filled with concrete (usually a 1 : 2 : 4 mix) and extracting links are fitted to the hammer and top of the tube. The withdrawal of the tube and the ramming of the concrete are effected by the hammer operating at 80 blows per minute. The tube is withdrawn (leaving the shoe behind) about 40 mm at each upstroke and the concrete is consolidated at each downward blow, the concrete being forced downwards and outwards, filling the space left by the tube and forming corrugations on the face of the pile (see L) which increase the frictional resistance and consequently the bearing capacity. The concrete pile can be formed at a rate up to 1.2 m per minute.

* The British Steel Piling Co. Ltd.

The *expanded pile*, which is not so frequently used as the standard type, is employed on sites where the desired driving resistance cannot be obtained at reasonable depths owing to the low bearing capacity of the ground. The expanded base of the pile is shaped in the following manner: The tube with its cast iron conical shoe is driven into the ground, as described above, after being partially filled with concrete, the tube is completely withdrawn and a flat shoe is fitted to it; the tube is again lowered into the hole until it reaches the deposited concrete, when it is driven down to produce the bulged end. If the base is required to be expanded still further, more concrete is deposited and expanded. During this operation the tube (with its flat shoe) has penetrated into the concrete, forming a cylindrical hole. The reinforcement cage is now lowered to the bottom of the tube until it rests on the flat shoe (which is left in the concrete and is a metre or two above the conical shoe), the tube is filled with concrete and the pile is completed by a succession of upward extracting and downward consolidating blows as explained above.

Batter piles can be formed also by this plant.

(2) Frankipiles* are formed in-situ. Four stages in the formation of this pile and a finished one are shown at C, D, E, F and G, Fig. 6. A steel tube is pitched vertically with its lower end resting on the ground at the spot the hole is to be formed and the bottom 0.6 or 0.9 m is filled with gravel (C). A diesel-operated drop hammer, weighing 2 000 or 3 000 kg (depending on the soil conditions and the size of the tube which is 370 or 470 mm internal diameter), delivers blows on the gravel as it falls freely within the tube. When the gravel plug is consolidated, the friction between it and the sides of the tube allows subsequent hammer blows to pull the tube down into the ground (D). When the tube has been driven to the required depth it is held in position by cables, and hammering on the gravel is continued to free the plug and force it downwards below the bottom of the tube. Whilst some gravel still remains in the tube (to prevent the

* Frankipile Ltd.

entrance of any water and soil) hammering is stopped and a charge of semi-dry concrete is passed down the tube and rammed. This is repeated until a much enlarged bulb has been formed at firm stratum level (E), this is a feature of the system which makes an effective contribution to the load-carrying capacity of the pile. The shaft of the pile is now formed by pouring successive charges of concrete down the tube and as each is rammed the tube is partially extracted, about 300 mm at a time (F). The reinforcement cage consisting of four or more 16 to 20 mm dia. vertical bars with 6 mm dia. spiral binding is lowered into the tube before the shaft is commenced and the shaft is built up with successive batches of concrete as described above, the hammer being operated within the cage. This pile has a corrugated surfaced shaft varying from 400 to 600 mm dia. and capable of supporting from 600 to 900 kN (G).

(3) Simplex Cast-in-Situ Piles. It is claimed that the "Simplex" was the first in-situ system to be introduced into Great Britain. The proprietors† produce four types, *viz.*, Standard, Tamped, Bulb and Alligator Jaw.

Simplex Standard Piles. These are formed by driving a 400 or 450 mm dia. steel tube, with fitted cast iron shoe, into the ground until the required set is reached. The reinforcement cage is inserted, and after the concrete (a wet mix) has been charged into the tube, extracting gear is attached to it and the tube is slowly withdrawn, leaving the shoe behind. The concrete is not tamped.

Simplex Tamped Piles. The tube is driven, the reinforcement is lowered into position and the tube is filled to the level required for the top of the completed pile, as described above. The extracting gear is now fixed and the tube is withdrawn; at every few centimetres of withdrawal, the tube is given a downward blow by the drop hammer to ram the concrete against the surrounding ground. The operation of partial withdrawal of the tube followed at intervals by tamping the concrete is repeated until completion.

Simplex Bulb or Extended Piles. The tube, with its fitted conical shoe, is driven down to a satisfactory set. After being partially filled with one or more batches of semi-dry concrete, the remainder of the tube is filled with a mixture of coarse aggregate (2 parts) and sand (1 part). The tube is withdrawn, a second shoe is fitted, followed by a re-drive which consolidates the adjacent strata as the aggregate is displaced around the outside of the tube, and as the tube penetrates the concrete an enlarged base or bulb is formed. The reinforcement is lowered into position and the tube, after being filled with concrete, is withdrawn. Two shoes are thus left behind. An alligator jaw tube (see below) in lieu of one fitted with shoes can be used to form bulbs of short piles.

Simplex Alligator Jaw Piles (see H and J, Fig. 6). A mild steel tube with a cast iron alligator jaw point (so-called because of its shape) attached by hinges to its lower end is used for forming piles up to 6 m long. The jaws are closed before driving is commenced (J). After being driven down to the depth required the tube is filled with concrete (after any reinforcement needed is placed in position) and is then withdrawn. The weight of the concrete causes the jaws to open automatically when withdrawal commences, permitting the concrete to flow freely from the tube (H). These piles are therefore similar to the "Standard" piles except that as a stronger shoe is used (which does not remain in the pile), they can be driven through harder ground.

The above in-situ piles have not the demerits of precast piles in respect to handling, transporting and casting. Also, as cast-in-place piles are formed to the required length, they have the advantage over precast piles which may have to be shortened or lengthened (p. 19). Like precast piles, however, the above in-situ piles cannot be employed in situations where headroom is restricted, and where vibration and noise must be avoided. Also, cast-in-place piles must not be heavily loaded until they have matured and this waiting period may delay subsequent building operations, a demerit which does not apply to precast piles, unless the casting of the latter has been delayed.

An alternative to the above driven piles, both precast and cast-in-place, must therefore be resorted to in situations where vibration would endanger the stability of adjacent buildings, where noise would create a nuisance, and where headroom is restricted. Further, a cheaper form of equipment is necessary if only a small number of piles is needed and for which the cost of transporting and erecting the piling plant required for precast piles and those in-situ piles described above would be prohibitive. The following: Pressure pile, Pneumatic Caisson pile and Prestcore pile are a few systems of this alternative class.

Pressure Piles.* See M, N and O, Fig. 6. This system, the first to be introduced into this country, practically eliminates vibration. They are in-situ reinforced concrete bearing piles formed in the predetermined positions, the concrete being deposited in steel-lined boreholes and consolidated by air pressure. A tripod frame (or shear legs) is used for the boring tackle and for lifting sections of the steel tube; when space is restricted the minimum headroom for the frame is only 1.83 m. The holes are bored by a clay auger (which also extracts the clay) or a shell (which withdraws sand, gravel, etc., see M).

As the boring proceeds the hole is lined with a steel tube in 1.2 to 1.8 m long sections having screwed joints, the tube sinking by its own weight or by a light tapping and additional sections being screwed on at the top as the depth increases. When the tube has reached a firm stratum, the boring tool is withdrawn, the reinforcement cage (normally of four or five 12 to 16 mm vertical bars with 6 m helical binding at 230 mm pitch) in suitable lengths is lowered down the tube and the concrete (which is usually of a $1:1\frac{1}{2}:3$ mix) is then deposited in batches. After each batch has been introduced a pressure cap is screwed on top of the tube and compressed air is admitted through a nozzle (N). The pressure of the air on the cap, assisted by the winch, causes the tube to lift slightly; at the same time the pressure consolidates the concrete and forces it out against the adjacent ground. Thus, the diameter of the pile exceeds that of the tube owing

† The Simplex Concrete Piles Ltd.

* The Pressure Piling Co. (Parent) Ltd.

to the compression of the soil, and a rough irregular surface is formed which increases the frictional resistance of the pile. As the bottom of the tube is not allowed to rise above the top of the concrete there is no possibility of water or soil gaining entrance (see N). This operation is repeated until the pile is completed; as each section of the tube is raised above the ground it is unscrewed, a further batch of concrete is added, the pressure cap is replaced and the compressed air is turned on. To prevent an excess formation of concrete near the surface the air pressure is gradually reduced as the bottom of the tube approaches foundation level. If a bulbed base is required, after the lined borehole has been formed, cement grout is admitted and forced down into the soil below the bottom of the tube.

In waterlogged ground an air-lock in the form of a cylindrical container (having a bottom valve and two air inlets) is fixed to the top of the tube after the latter has been sunk to the required depth. The concrete is fed through the air-lock, any water present in the tube is forced out by the compressed air and concrete is fed through the air-lock into the tube. The pile is then gradually built up with concrete as described above.

Pressure piles, besides being used to support new structures – especially those adjacent to existing buildings – are particularly suited for underpinning. Due to the small space and headroom which the plant occupies and the absence of vibration, the piles can be formed close to existing walls, both inside and outside buildings that are occupied. They are formed in three sizes, 340 mm dia. (by using 300 mm tubes), 440 mm dia. (400 mm tubes), and 500 mm dia. (460 mm tubes); the minimum spacing is 0.9 m, 1 m, and 1.4 m respectively; 25 m vertical lengths have been made; batter piles can also be formed.

Pneumatic Caisson Piles* (see K, Fig. 3). These are especially suitable for congested sites where vibration and noise must be reduced to a minimum, where the moving of heavy pile frames would be impracticable, where headroom is limited (the light shear leg plant can operate in a restricted headroom of 1.8 m) and where, inside existing buildings, piling work (as required for underpinning, heavy engine beds, etc.) has to be done without interfering with business and production. The mean diameter of the pile is approximately 430 mm.

A 400 mm dia. steel tube, consisting of 1.5 m long sections screwed together is sunk in the ground, whilst a boring tool, working inside it, excavates the soil which emerges as a complete core of the penetrated strata. The boring tools employed depend upon the nature of the strata, thus, for clays and silts a tubular clay cutter is used; for sands and gravels a shell or bailer fitted with a clack valve at the bottom (which opens and shuts to pick up the spoil) is suitable.

When the tube has reached the necessary depth, which varies in accordance with the strata and the load to be supported, the bottom of the hole is cleaned, the reinforcement cage is lowered into position and the concrete is introduced in batches. After each batch has been deposited, a pressure cap is fixed to the top of the tube and compressed air introduced to force the concrete down and out against the surrounding soil below the bottom of the tube whilst the latter is slowly extracted.

The bearing value of a pile can be increased by providing it with an enlarged base. The bulb is formed before normal concreting is started by introducing cement grout and forcing it by air pressure into the adjacent soil.

If ground water is encountered, an air-lock is fixed at the top of the tube, this is a hopper with a valve at the bottom; compressed air forces the water out of the tube and the internal pressure, being equal to the hydrostatic pressure, keeps the tube free from water whilst concrete is introduced from the hopper through the valve.

Prestcore Piles.† These are cast in-situ bored piles and have all the advantages, stated above, over driven piles. There are three nominal sizes, *viz.*, 350, 450 and 750 mm, reinforced with four, five and six 12 to 24 mm vertical bars respectively and 6 mm spiral binding at 100 mm pitch. The minimum height required for the tripod used in the formation of the piles is 2.6 m, though in exceptional circumstances a 1.8 m tripod can be substituted. The main reinforcing bars are continuous; when piles are formed in very limited headroom it is often necessary to splice the bars by screwed couplings, although it is frequently possible to work the bars in by making use of their flexibility.

A borehole is formed, and lined with steel tube or casing. The upper section of the casing is fitted with a special head provided with lugs and the lower end of the bottom section has an enlarged cutting edge. A pile consists of a central core of *precast* concrete cylindrical units, each 450 mm high, surrounded by a solidified skin of cement grout approximately 40 mm thick. Each core unit has a central hole, about 115 mm dia., and smaller holes through which the vertical bars are threaded; the surface is corrugated, the vee-shaped grooves being about 12 mm deep; the spiral binding is incorporated in the unit. A cross-section through a pile is shown at K, Fig. 6, and an elevation of a core unit at L.

After the steel-cased borehole is formed a 100 mm dia. steel tube (in short lengths screwed together, and with a flange or special release gear at its lower end) is placed in the casing and the core units are threaded on it. The core pile is built up as it is lowered (pilot rods being inserted in the smaller holes to ensure that they are in alignment to receive the vertical bars) until it reaches the bottom of the borehole, when the vertical bars are lowered in the holes to receive them. The core pile is then raised and dropped several times in order to consolidate the bearing stratum.

Assisted by the use of a hydraulic jack operating between the head of the core and the underside of the cross-head (connected by tension links to the lugs at the top of the casing), the casing is slightly withdrawn. Cement grout from a portable tank is then forced down the central tube by means of compressed air;

* Piling and Construction Co. Ltd.

† The British Steel Piling Co. Ltd.

the pressure forces the grout through holes at the base of the core, filling the space between the core and the casing in addition to the voids within the body of the pile. During the grouting process the casing is gradually withdrawn (by the winch attached to a leg of the tripod) and the space so left is filled with the grout. The precast concrete units are thus grouted together and encased in cement grout to form a solid pile. Piles up to 27 m long have been formed in this manner.

If an enlarged base is required, a semi-dry mixture of sand and cement (or a bag of cement if water is present) is passed down the casing before the core units are assembled; the core pile is then formed as described above and, by means of the winch, is dropped several times, forcing the concrete downwards and outwards and thus producing the bulb.

During the piling operation, any water present collects on top of the grout and as the level of the latter rises, the water is expelled through a pipe provided at the airtight capped head, closed by a valve when grout appears.

Short concrete piles are referred to on p. 13.

Large Diameter Bored Piles. To carry the high loads which are a feature of some multi-storey buildings, Frankipile Ltd. can construct in-situ piles in a 1.27 m dia. steel casing which have a bearing capacity from 3 500 to 12 000 kN each, in lengths up to 30 m. The equipment comprises a caterpillar mounted crane 26.5 m high and a separate hydraulic unit. The hole is bored by a *turn grab* (mounted on the crane) which has three rotating blades operating inside the casing. The latter, in 3 m lengths, is recoverable and the first one has a cutting edge; it is jacked into the ground by the hydraulic unit which uses the weight of the crane for leverage. The subsoil content of each length of casing is removed by the grab before the next section is jacked down. After the required depth has been reached the reinforcement cage is positioned and the concrete is added in the usual way as the lining is withdrawn. No vibration* is caused and the grab can be used for under-reaming to give an enlarged base.

SHEET PILES

These are used for many purposes, including (1) enclosing a site or part thereof to prevent the escape of a loose subsoil, such as sand, and so safeguard against settlement any structure which is to be erected on it, (2) retaining the sides of trenches and general excavations, (3) forming cofferdams (watertight enclosures necessary in the construction of foundations in water – as for foundations of piers of river bridges, etc.), (4) construction of retaining walls in docks and similar marine works, (5) coastal defence works (as a protection against sea erosion), and (6) river bank protection. To be effective, the sheets must be in close contact with each other and various types of joints are used to achieve this purpose.

Sheet piles are either of (i) steel, (ii) reinforced concrete, or (iii) timber.

(i) **Steel sheet piles** are now generally employed. They are trough-shaped and, when driven, the piles are interlocked with alternate ones reversed. One of this earliest type, the Larssen† pile, is obtainable in several sizes, as indicated at C, Fig. 7; two sections in this range have a uniform thickness throughout, as shown, and the webs of the others (six in number) are slightly thicker than the tapering flanges. The maximum length of the piles depends upon the depth of penetration, nature of the soils through which they are to be driven, etc., but normally the length is restricted to 5.5 m for the smaller sections and 18 m for the larger. They are made of three grades of steel, *e.g.*, mild steel, copper steel and high-tensile rust-resisting steel. They are strong and durable, and they can be easily driven without distortion. When used for permanent work the piles should be coated with acid-free tar or similar preservative before driving.

Driving Steel Sheet Piles. The frame equipment may be similar to that illustrated at A and B, Fig. 6, but of lighter construction specially designed to deal with the relatively light sheet piles; the hammers employed may be of the single-acting type (for clay soils), or the double-acting type (for sand or gravel soils) or a petrol hammer (for small piles). Alternatively, in the absence of a frame, a double-acting hammer suspended from the jib of a crane may be used, or for soft ground a small pneumatic hammer fitted on top of the pile. A driving cap or anvil block is used as a protection against damage. In order to maintain a straight line of vertical piles it is necessary to provide one or two pairs of horizontal timbers, called walings, which are bolted to temporary wood square-sectioned piles. This temporary construction is illustrated at A and B, Fig. 7. The wood piles are driven in at from 3 to 4.5 m apart. If a frame is employed, only one pair of walings is necessary at ground level, otherwise, a second pair of walings is required, as shown. The distance between a pair of walings is 6 mm more than the depth between the webs of adjacent piles. There is a tendency for the piles to wander or lean forward in the direction of driving. This is avoided or minimised if the work is carried out in the following manner: A series or panel of, say, twelve piles are interlocked, pitched and held in position between the walings. A pair of piles, numbered 1 at A, is carefully driven to part penetration. The pair at the opposite end, numbered 2, is then partially driven, followed in turn by pairs 3, 4, 5 and 6. If the top pair of walings is not provided, these intermediate pairs of piles are driven at once to their final level, otherwise the upper walings must, of course, be removed to enable the piles to be driven to their required depth.

Box Piles. These interlocking steel sheet piles can be formed into box piles for permanent work and where a large carrying capacity is required. Thus, Larssen box piles consist of two ordinary Larssen sheet piles of any of the larger

* Another pile, only occasionally used when vibration is to be avoided, is the *screw pile*. This is made of tubular cast or wrought iron and has a screw blade at the bottom end. It is driven into the ground by rotation.

† The British Steel Piling Co. Ltd.

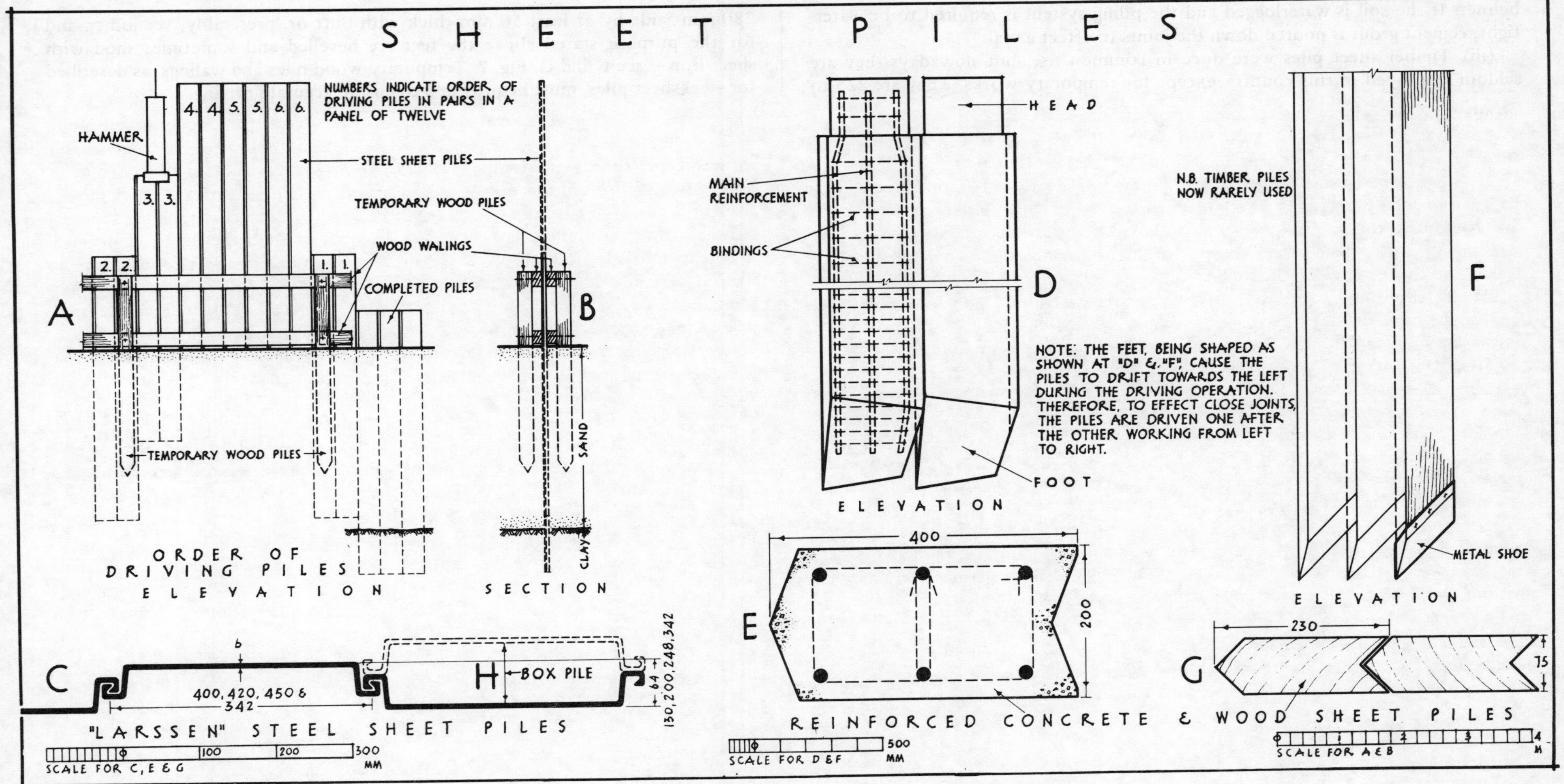

FIGURE 7

sections which are welded together at intervals along the interlocks – see H, Fig. 7.

Steel sheet piling is often used for temporary work and after the piles have served their purpose they are withdrawn. The simplest method of withdrawal, when the piles are relatively short and the extraction easy, is to apply a pair of metal grips or tongs at the top end of the pile which is then lifted by a rope from the winch or crane. Otherwise, the best method is to employ a double-acting pile hammer (used for normal driving), this is inverted and fitted with extractor grips at the lower end which are applied at the top end of the pile. The piles so salvaged can be re-used, reconditioning may be required after frequent re-use.

(ii) **Reinforced concrete sheet piles** are sometimes used for permanent work. In cross-section they are usually rectangular and either tongued and grooved or vee-jointed, as shown at E, Fig. 7. The feet are shaped obliquely or bevelled and feather-edged, as indicated at D, to assist penetration and give a lead in the direction of driving. If the piles are required to be driven through resistant strata the feet are protected by metal shoes; the heads are shaped to receive the driving helmet. If the soil is waterlogged and the piling system is required to be water-tight, cement grout is poured down the joints to effect a seal.

(iii) **Timber sheet piles** were once in common use, but nowadays they are seldom employed in this country except for temporary works. They are 225 to 280 mm wide by at least 50 mm thick with butt or, preferably, vee-joints, and for the purpose stated above the feet are bevelled and sometimes shod with sheet-iron – see F and G, Fig. 7. Temporary wood piles and walings, as described for steel sheet piles, must be provided to ensure accurate driving.

CHAPTER TWO

STEEL AND REINFORCED CONCRETE CONSTRUCTION

Syllabus. Manufacture of pig iron, cast iron, and wrought iron. Bessemer, open hearth, and electric arc processes for the manufacture of steel, comparison. The rolling and working of steel, chemical composition. Structural and alloy steels. Heat treatment and prevention of corrosion of steel. Structural steel frames with riveted and bolted, and welded joints. Typical steelwork joints, including beam to beam, beam and truss to column, gusseted and slab bases, column splices. Portal frame construction. 15 m span tubular steel truss. Methods of roofing large floor areas, lattice girder and North light roof, monitor roof in tubular steel. Light-gauge steelwork.

Reinforced concrete construction. Types of reinforcement. Prestressed reinforced concrete. Design of slabs and lintels. Details of reinforced concrete framed building. Shell roofs with North light and barrel vaults. Reinforced concrete retaining walls. Reinforced concrete staircases. Patent reinforced concrete floors and roofs. Formwork for columns, beams and slabs including patent types and design. Striking of forms.

STEELWORK

IRON AND STEEL

Before considering the various structural steels it is desirable to review briefly the following related metals: pig iron, cast iron, and wrought iron.

Steel, and the above three types of iron are composed as shown in Table 3 and are derived from iron ore — deposits of which are to be found in many parts of the world.

TABLE 3 AVERAGE CHEMICAL COMPOSITION OF PIG, CAST AND WROUGHT IRON AND STEEL

Element	Average Percentage Chemical Composition of:			
	Basic Pig Iron	Cast Iron	Wrought Iron	Plain Carbon Steel
Carbon	1.8–4.0	1.8–4.0	0.05	0.05–1.8
Silicon	1.0	2.0	0.2	0.05–0.35
Manganese	1.4	0.5	0.02	0.3–1.0
Sulphur	0.07	0.07	0.03	0.05–1.0
Phosphorus	1.02	0.07	0.07	0.03–1.0
Iron	Remainder			

Iron Ores. These are mostly the oxides or carbonates of iron according to their origin. They are obtained by open cast or underground mining and the most important are:

Ferrous Ore in the form of ferrous carbonate (containing about thirty-five per cent iron) is of two types, blackband and clayband ironstone; the former has coal and the latter clay incorporated with it. Both contain varying amounts of these impurities, and they are to be found in Yorkshire, Derbyshire and Scotland.

Ferric Ores. Also known as haematite (containing about fifty per cent iron) is one of the purer types of ore to be found in North Lancashire, South Wales, and the Midlands. Other constituents of this ore are ferric oxide, and the oxides of manganese, aluminium, silicon, sulphur, phosphorus, and carbon dioxide which are classed as impurities.

Ferrous-ferric Ore exists only in small deposits in this country, but is found in large deposits in Sweden, and considerable quantities of it (in form of magnetite) are shipped to Tees-side* for refining to steel. It can contain up to 60 per cent iron.

Chemical Changes Involved in the Refining Processes. In the purification of the ore the chemical changes may be either *acidic* or *basic* depending on the type of impurity present. The oxide of a non-metal (such as silica or sand) is classed as an *acid* whilst the oxide of a metal [*i.e.*, iron oxide, calcium oxide (lime)] is known as a *base*.

The refining process involves both *oxidation* (*i.e.*, the combination between impurities such as silica with oxygen to form a *slag* or waste product); and *reduction* (or deoxidation) which is the reverse process, where the iron oxide loses its oxygen content and becomes a metal, and this reaction is accompanied by the secondary chemical change which forms the slag.

* This and other districts mentioned have easy access to ample supplies of coal and coke necessary for production purposes.

Pig Iron. This is obtained from a blast furnace which is a vertical steel cylinder lined with firebrick. Briefly, the process of *smelting* consists of loading the ore, coke and limestone (which acts as a flux) into the top of the furnace, whilst a continuous upward blast of preheated air enters near the bottom. The chemical changes previously outlined occur gradually as the ore descends. Thus near the top of the chamber the air (at about 204° C) causes combustion of the coke to form the reducing agent carbon monoxide, which combines with oxygen in the ore to give iron, carbon (soot) and carbon dioxide. Lower down further reduction occurs by some of the free carbon combining with oxygen in any of the unchanged ore to give more carbon monoxide and iron. Any unused carbon is dissolved in the iron which also absorbs more carbon from contact with the coke.

Near the bottom of the furnace, limestone is converted to lime (calcium oxide) and carbon dioxide. The former combines with aluminium oxide and silica (which are the bulk of the impurities) to give eventually aluminium silicate which floats on the molten metal and is run off as a slag. The lime also reacts with sulphur and coke ash which runs into the slag. The slag, although a waste product,* serves many useful purposes in the smelting process: (1) by acting as an oxidizing agent in the conversion, (2) it dissolves several of the impurities contained in the ore, (3) it protects the molten metal, preventing overheating; the slag is run off at intervals during refining.

The gases piped off from the top of the furnace are used to pre-heat the air forming the blast.

After adequate smelting in the furnace the molten metal is tapped off to (*a*) a pig casting machine, (*b*) via insulated troughs into heavy cast iron troughs, or (*c*) direct to certain steel producing ovens. The average pig (915 mm long by 150 mm square) has the composition given in Table 3. It is a hard, brittle and impure form of iron, hard on account of its relatively high carbon content, and brittle as a result of the presence of phosphorus and sulphur.

Cast Iron. This is obtained by re-melting the pig iron in a furnace similar to that already described. The pigs, coke and very often, scrap iron are loaded into the furnace, and a blast of heated air is used to melt the metal. A limited refinement takes place and all the impurities, except sulphur, are reduced in volume. The slag is run off and the metal discharged into a ladle which is used to pour the metal into moulds. The moulds are made from a type of sand which is formed into the shape of the finished product by the use of patterns. Because it expands slightly while cooling, cast iron is an ideal material for the making of castings.

Cast iron is crystalline, strong in compression, but comparatively weak in tension and bending, it has a good resistance to corrosion. It is possible, by suitable heat treatment of the cast iron, to reduce its brittle nature, and thus produce a malleable cast iron. Keys, hooks, etc., are made from this material. Before the days of modern structural steel cast iron beams and columns were frequently used.

Wrought Iron. This is a more refined type of iron and is obtained by (1) the puddling process, or the more recent method (2) the Aston process.

(1) *Puddling Furnace*. This is an oven lined with fire bricks, consisting of a coal fired furnace at one end and the bed on which the melting takes place at the other.

Pig iron is loaded on to the bed, and heated gases are forced through the oven. The iron melts and owing to the ferrous oxide lining, the silicon, manganese and sulphur are oxidized forming a slag. Continual stirring (puddling) with an iron tool encourages this reaction, and eventually causes removal of much of the carbon. The temperature is such that the mass forms into a spongy condition and allows the operator to shape it into balls up to 45 kg in weight, which are removed from the furnace. The ball of iron, which contains some slag, is squeezed or beaten into a rough rectangular block thus forcing out more slag. Depending on the use for which the metal is required, the block is either taken to forge mills, or is rolled into smaller bars. Alternatively, it can be stocked for future use which entails reheating and rolling into various shapes (*i.e.*, flat, square, or circular bars).

(2) *The Aston Process*. This is a speedier process consisting of: (*a*) Melting the iron in a cupola† and purifying it in a Bessemer converter. (*b*) Simultaneously an iron silicate slag is heated in an open furnace and poured into a ladle. (*c*) The purified metal is tipped into the ladle containing the slag forming a spongy mass. Excess slag is removed and the 3 175 kg block of metal is transferred to a press, which shapes it, and removes more slag. (*d*) Rolling processes are carried out as before.

Wrought iron contains up to three per cent slag, and has a fibrous nature. This fibrous structure is an important characteristic of wrought iron, giving it good tensile strength parallel to the grain (but much weaker at right angles to the grain). The presence of slag renders it less liable to corrosion, and enables it to resist the effects of shock, as well as making it readily weldable (the slag being self-fluxing). It is used in decorative iron work, or chains, bolts, water pipes, and bars.

Properties of Metals. The following characteristics are present in varying degrees in many metals, including steel.

Ductility. A ductile metal is one capable of being drawn or stretched into wires without breaking.

Elasticity. An elastic metal is one which will return to its original shape after removal of a force tending to change that shape. This property is only applicable within a certain limit; thus if the force is too great, and the elastic limit is exceeded, the metal will not resume its original form and "permanent set" occurs.

Malleability. This property enables a metal to be rolled or beaten (hot or cold) without cracking.

Toughness. This implies that the metal can offer strong resistance to repeated bending, compression, and other stresses without fracture. Its presence ensures that the metal does not suffer "fatigue" (which causes eventual fracture when loads are repeatedly added and removed).

Weldability. A weldable metal is one which is easily jointed by welding.

STEEL

Steel is an alloy mainly of carbon and iron together with small amounts of impurities, previously noted, and is of a finely crystalline nature. It is a more refined type of iron than wrought or cast iron, being hard, tough, elastic, malleable, and capable of resisting various stresses.

Methods of Steel Production. Of the several methods of manufacturing steel the following are accepted for structural steels; ninety-five per cent of production is by the

* This is converted to useful purposes like making ballast for building blocks, insulating fillers and fertilizers.

† A cupola is a simple type of blast furnace, but lower temperatures are used and slight oxidation, rather than reduction takes place.

open hearth furnace, although as electricity becomes comparatively cheaper, the electric furnace is being increasingly used:

(1) The open-hearth (Siemens-Martin) acid or basic processes.
(2) The acid Bessemer process.
(3) The electric furnace processes.

(1) *Acid Open Hearth Process.** The furnace used in this method is a rectangular brick and concrete structure having a silica brick lining, and a shallow bottom or hearth.

Silica sand is first fired alone in the furnace, thus imparting to it a silica lining (the acid nature of the process). Connected to the furnace are two regenerative chambers,† which are brick structures containing firebricks stacked in an open honeycomb pattern, they are used in turn to heat the air required for combustion. The fuel for the furnace can be natural gas, producer gas, or fuel oil.

As soon as the furnace is heated and the acid lining has formed, the charge of molten metal from the blast furnace (or cold pigs) and scrap steel is loaded through electrically operated doors at the front. The chemical reaction is one of oxidation effected by the air, and also by small amounts of ore which are added towards the end of the process. Oxidation products are silica and magnesium oxide which enter the slag. The carbon content of the pig iron is also lessened by the formation of carbon monoxide which burns and thereby assists in the melting.

Before tapping the metal, samples are taken of it and the slag to check their composition. The principal test is performed on the metal by fracturing a small piece of it when cold and rapidly ascertaining the carbon content. The latter can be adjusted as required (for mild steel it is about 0.2 per cent) it being lessened by adding more pig iron or increased by adding more ore. After several hours, the tap hole opposite the doors is opened and the molten steel runs out into a ladle. Small additions are made in the ladle, of ferro-manganese and other substances to improve the quality. Aluminium is also added to refine the grain of the molten metal and deoxidize it. Slag is discharged along with the metal and rises to the top of the ladle, overflowing down to a container below.

From the ladle the steel is poured into ingot moulds, of various sizes depending on the use to which the ingot is placed. Rapid cooling occurs and the ingot shrinks away from the cast iron mould which is then removed. A small portion at the top of the ingot contains the impurities and blow-holes caused by rising gases and is subsequently removed.

Further treatment of the ingot is described below.

(2) *Basic Open Hearth Process*. This method (once the most popular one in use in this country) is a development of the acidic process, and enables cheaper ores containing phosphorus to be used. The equipment for refining is similar to that for the acid method, the main difference being that the furnace is lined with basic material such as magnesite (calcined magnesium carbonate). This basic lining causes removal of phosphorus impurities (which create brittleness) and sulphur (which gives rise to cracking during subsequent rolling).

After the lining has been formed a small amount of scrap is first added and allowed to melt. Then limestone, a little ore and pig iron are charged, in that order. Refinement of the iron and oxidation of phosphorus, manganese, silicon and carbon proceeds, and the oxides of these elements enter the slag. The lime which is produced reacts with phosphorus and sulphur to form calcium phosphate and sulphide which also combine with the slag. After adequate boiling the impurities are largely eliminated and some slag is then removed. The carbon content can then be adjusted as previously described, and tapping proceeds. Treatment of the ingot is described below.

(3) *The Acid Bessemer Process.*† This is a suitable process only when the ores are low in phosphorus and sulphur, and is popular in the United States.

Molten pig iron from the blast furnace is run into a mixer (a heated storage vessel), and thence into a Bessemer Converter where the steel is produced. The converter is a pear shaped steel plated container having a refractory brick lining, it is mounted on trunnions enabling it to be rotated for charging and unloading at the narrow end. At the other end, small openings permit air, at ordinary temperatures and at 172 kN/m^2 pressure, to be blown through. After charging in the horizontal position, the blast of air is turned on, and the converter moved to an upright position when the "blow" commences.

The passage of air causes efficient mixing and oxidation of part of the iron to ferrous oxide which reacts in three ways: (1) Ferrous oxide and carbon form iron and carbon monoxide, the latter burns providing a natural evolution of heat. (2) Ferrous oxide oxidizes manganese and silicon, and is itself thereby reduced to iron. (3) The silicon oxide produced reacts (*a*) with ferrous oxide to give iron silicate and (*b*) with manganese oxide to give manganese silicate. These silicates run into the slag.

At the end of the "blow", any remaining ferrous oxide is deoxidized* by the addition of ferro-manganese which changes it to iron, and also removes sulphur. Carbon content is adjusted, and if necessary this is increased by adding coke or more pig iron. The process is all over in about half an hour, and the steel is poured into ingot moulds.

(4) *The Electric Furnace Process*. This is especially suitable for making the high grade alloy steels but is being used increasingly for the other steels and eventually will replace the other production methods. The furnace is a circular bath (which may be acid or basic lined) and has electrodes in the roof, the raw materials consist of selected scrap. The lime and charge are added and current passed to the electrodes, the latter are then withdrawn slightly so that an electric arc (which generates a temperature of 3 400° C) is formed across the gap.‡ The oxidizing slag removes most of the silicon, manganese and phosphorus and is raked off and replaced by a reducing slag of lime, carbon and fluorspar. This second slag deoxidizes and desulphurizes the steel and the non-metallic impurities are removed. The alloying metals are then added and the composition of the steel is checked prior to pouring into ingots.

Comparison between Bessemer and Open Hearth Steels. Sound acid steels by either method require the use of pig iron, low in phosphorus content, such pigs are obtained only from the more pure and expensive ores. Good basic steel can be made from the cheaper ores (which usually contain phosphorus), and basic practice eliminates almost entirely this undesirable element.

The open hearth method is the more lengthy (and therefore costly) process, but it produces a better quality steel (having fewer inclusions of sulphides and oxides), due to the fact that the reactions can be carefully controlled. Less waste results from this method and fewer blow-holes are produced.

Bessemer steel is more suitable for machining and welding.

* Metals must be low in sulphur and phosphorus content for this method.

† Regenerative, because whilst one furnace is heating air, the other is being heated by waste combustion gases. When one has been cooled the air current is reversed so that cold air enters the newly heated chambers on its way to the furnace and hot gases enter the cooled chamber.

† There is also a basic Bessemer process, where the converter is lined with crushed dolomite and tar to refine the high phosphorous ores.

* Deoxidation is very important as otherwise oxygen bubbles in the mass would combine with carbon to give carbon monoxide during solidification, this would burn and leave blow-holes.

‡ In another type of electric furnace, used mainly for melting steel, the furnace (an induction type) is enclosed in an insulated copper coil through which the current is passed.

The Rolling and Working of Steel. When the ingot has completely solidified, the mould is removed and the ingot is either stored for future use, or placed in a soaking pit for more immediate treatment. The pit is an underground chamber which maintains the block of steel at about 1 200° C throughout its mass – a temperature suitable for rolling. Cold ingots must be brought to this heat gradually so as to avoid cracking which may be caused by the outside expanding more quickly than the inside.

Ingots vary in size, an average being 1.8 m long by 0.4 to 0.6 m square with rounded angles, each ingot is stamped with the cast number.

Hot Rolling. From the soaking pit, the ingots pass to the rolling mills where their cross sectional area is reduced to form progressively, blooms, billets and slabs according to the finished product required. Conveyor rollers move the bloom to and fro‡ between a set of rollers§ which gradually impart the desired shape. During the manufacture, water is sprayed on the rollers to keep them cool and the resulting steam removes the mill scale of iron oxide which forms on the surface of the metal. After rolling, the ends (particularly the top ends of the ingots) are cropped off where segregation has occurred – about twenty-five per cent is lost in this way and returns to the furnace. Most structural sections are obtained by this method.

Sheet steel thicker than 1.2 mm is also produced by hot rolling of slabs. Billets are rolled into the smaller sections including bolt and rivet bars.

Cold Rolling. This is used for thin plates. Hot rolled plate steel is pickled by immersion in dilute acid and water baths to remove mill scale. After drying, it is coated with oil and rolled to the required thickness. This causes hardening and increased strength, hardening can be reduced by annealing (see p. 29).

Forging. This is the shaping of the heated, plastic steel by a press or drop hammer which are developments of the blacksmith's art. Engine parts such as crankshafts are made in this way. Similar products can also be made by casting the steel, after being heated in an electric furnace. Plastic welding* is a type of forging, and the parts to be joined are heated to the right temperature and beaten together.

Rods, Tubes and Wires. Bars, rods, squares and flats are obtained by hot rolling in the mill, thus giving a somewhat rough finish. A smoother finish is imparted if they are then drawn, cold, through a die (being about 3 mm less in size). Tubular products (see also p. 39) are made by passing hot strip steel (having a width equal to the pipe circumference) through a series of rollers which are so placed to give a butt welded joint in the finished pipe. Seamless tubes are obtained by drawing cold rods through a die (forming the external surface) at the same time as the rod is being hollowed out by passing along a pointed mandrel.

Rods below 25 mm in diameter can be converted, and drawn out cold into wire by drawing them through successively smaller dies. The drawing increases hardness and thus the wire must be annealed (softened to restore ductility) before each diminishing process.

Chemical Composition of Steel

Carbon. The percentage of this element in the steel has a very marked influence on the properties. Increased carbon causes increased hardness and resistance to wear, but decreases ductility, malleability, toughness and corrosion resistance, it also makes welding more difficult. Carbon is present in combination with iron and also with some of the other elements mentioned below. The average range of carbon content for various steel products is: 0.06–0.15% – rivets, chains, pipes, screws, nails; 0.06–0.25% – structural steels (these are classed as low carbon steels); 0.3–0.5% – gears, axles, etc.; 0.5–0.6% – scraper blades; 0.9–1.0% – knives, springs; 1.0–1.5% – tool steels, drills, steel saw cutters.

Silicon. This varies from 0.05–0.35 per cent and is dissolved in the iron. It has the virtue of improving the tensile qualities of the steel and is important as a deoxidizer in the production methods.

Manganese. This occurs in the range 0.5–1.8 per cent in solution with carbon and iron. By its inclusion, tensile strengths are improved and it is also important as a deoxidizer, and desulphurizer.

Nickel. Increase in this content from 0.3–0.5 per cent results in higher strength without loss of ductility.

Chromium. The addition of chromium, like carbon, hardens the steel, but unlike carbon, does not cause brittleness. An amount up to 0.8 per cent for certain structural steels results in greater tensile strength.

Copper. This may be added in structural steel up to 0.6 per cent thereby improving corrosion resistance.

Sulphur and Phosphorus. These must be kept below 0.06 per cent. If this amount is exceeded, then the steel cracks during rolling, it also produces a coarse grained steel which is therefore more brittle.

Structural Steel. Steel structures are made with mild steel conforming to B.S. 4360: *Weldable Structural Steels* which defines the properties of the metal and divides it into four main grades and various subgrades according to the strength. The grades are defined by numbers which describe the range of the tensile strengths. Thus grade 43 has a tensile strength of 43 to 51 $\times 10^7$ N/m^2 and grade 50 a tensile strength of 50 to 62 $\times 10^7$ N/m^2; these two grades are the most widely used, grades 40 and 55 are also available for special purposes. (Note in the above values the grades can be expressed in hectobars, *i.e.*, 1 hectobar (1 h bar) = 100 bars = 10 MN/m^2 = 10 N/mm^2 = 1.019 72 kgf/mm^2 = 0.647 49 tonf/in^2 = 1 450.38 lbf/in^2; so grade 43 has a tensile strength of 43 h bars.)

Alloy Steels. These steels, though not necessarily used for structural purposes, form important components in general building construction, and a degree of familiarity with them is valuable.

An alloy steel is one containing carbon and small percentages of the other elements given previously, certain amounts of other elements are also added which change the characteristics of the ordinary steel. Alloying elements are numerous, the following are in common usage: manganese, silicon, chromium, tungsten, molybdenum, and nickel (the percentages given are average ones).

Manganese Steel. This contains over 1.5 per cent of manganese; if this element is increased to between 10 and 15 per cent and providing the alloy is suitably treated it becomes very hard and tough, in this form it is used for the blades of earth moving equipment.

‡ Even rolling is ensured by turning the bloom at right angles after each pass.

§ Alternatively several sets of rollers can be used and the metal is passed continuously along from one roller to the next, and its section reduced by successive amounts.

* See p. 30 for other types of welding.

Nickel Steel. This alloy, being one of the first produced, has increased strength without loss of ductility when up to 5 per cent nickel is added. When containing 25 to 35 per cent, the alloy has a good resistance to shock and corrosion and a small coefficient of expansion. It is used in scientific instruments and measuring tapes.

Chromium Steel. This is steel having 1 per cent carbon and 1.25 per cent chromium, and is hard without being brittle. It is used for ball bearings and machinery parts.

Tungsten Steel and Molybdenum Steel. The introduction of these elements in steel improves its toughness and hardness without making it brittle. Both are added in conjunction with chromium and the alloy is used for axle shafts, gears and special tough bolts.

Stainless Steel. As well as having the normal constituents present in mild steel, stainless steel contains 2 per cent nickel, 1 per cent silicon and when used for kitchen equipment and the like, in sheet form, it also has 17 to 19 per cent chromium and 8 to 10 per cent nickel and is therefore rustproof.

Tool Steels. *Plain Carbon Steels*. In this category the carbon content is between 0.6 and 1.25 per cent. Steels of this type make a satisfactory tool cutting material providing the operation is slow, and excessive temperatures are not produced.

High Speed Steels. Many types of these exist which contain varying amounts of the above alloying elements. They are an invaluable adjunct to modern rapid industrial techniques, and are used for drills, shears, punches and the like, where shock and abrasion resistance are important.

Heat Treatment of Steels. This aspect of engineering may only be of general interest to the structural designer, nevertheless it is considered that he should have some knowledge of the hardening, tempering, and annealing of steel.

Suitable heat treatment of the steel or alloy changes its grain structure and can produce either softening (annealing) or hardening.

Annealing. This entails heating the steel to between 760° to 815° C and maintaining it at this temperature for several hours, depending on the thickness; it is then allowed to cool slowly in the furnace. A softer more ductile metal is produced which can be drawn into wires and machined more easily.

Normalizing. The steel is heated to the same temperature as for annealing when it is then removed from the oven and allowed to cool in air at normal room temperature. It is a milder form of annealing and the resulting product is not quite so hard or ductile as fully annealed steel. The process removes internal stresses set up by welding (see p. 30) or forging.

Hardening. From the above, it is apparent that hardness depends, to a certain extent, on the rate of cooling (the quicker this is, the harder the steel). Steel is hardened by first heating it to just above 704° C and cooling it rapidly by plunging it quickly into water, brine or oil (quenching process). Increased hardness is thus accompanied by brittleness and loss of ductility of the metal in which quenching stresses are also present.

Tempering. This removes brittleness and internal stresses caused by hardening, and consists of reheating the hardened steel (before it has finally cooled) to temperatures in the region 150° to 482° C (depending on its composition) and allowing it to cool once more.

Methods of Preventing the Corrosion of Steel. Corrosion occurs because the combined action of air and moisture forms a film of iron oxide (rust) on the steel surfaces. In steel framed buildings this reaction is avoided, and fire resistance greatly improved, when members are encased in concrete or other materials (see Chap. III). Alternative rust protection is afforded by using a lead or bitumastic paint which is applied after first thoroughly cleaning the surfaces, or by galvanizing (light cold rolled sections and hot rolled angles only).

Rust protection for non-structural steels takes many forms including: enamelling, japanning, electro-plating, galvanizing, sheradizing, zinc spraying, chromizing, phosphating, and bonding bituminous felt to the surface. Before any of these methods are used the metal surfaces must be properly cleaned.

Vitreous Enamelling. Silica and borax compounds are sprayed on to the surface, and the article transferred to an oven at a temperature of about 815° C. The compounds form a hard, smooth, glossy surface. Domestic ovens, cast iron baths, and rain water goods, and cladding panels are among those articles treated in this fashion.

Japanning. This comparatively cheaper, and less effective finish is used for fire grates, etc. Surfaces are coated with a lacquer paint, and then the whole placed in an oven at about 260° C when a hard baked skin is formed.

Electroplating. This more costly method requires an electric current carried in a suitable solution between the positive electrode (of chromium or zinc, or nickel forming the coating substance), and the negative electrode which is the metal to be plated. It is used to give a decorative and utilitarian finish to many products.

Galvanizing. A comparatively cheap and very effective type of metallic coating is obtained by the "hot dip" process. The article to be protected is washed in caustic soda to cleanse it and remove grease, it is then rinsed and pickled in hot, dilute sulphuric acid, to remove scale and rust, and washed in clean water. After immersion in a fluxing bath of zinc ammonium chloride solution, the actual galvanizing is done in a bath of molten zinc to give a coating of between 0.6 and 0.3 kg/m^2. Finally a dipping in a tank of dilute sodium dichromate is given to retard oxidation of the surface.

Sheradizing. This provides a similar result to the last mentioned method. The part to be covered is cleaned and then placed in a rotating drum containing powdered zinc, and subjected to a temperature of 400° C for 2–3 hours. It is more applicable to the treatment of small parts such as nuts, screws, and bolts.

Zinc Spraying and Stoving. After cleansing, as described above, or by shot blasting (which leaves an ideal surface that is slightly pitted to give a good bond to the finishing coats), a special gun is used to spray a stream of molten zinc on to the article. It is then taken to a paint dipper where it is immersed in a red oxide primer, which is stoved on in an oven. Additional coats of paint can be given if desired.

Chromizing. A similar method to sheradizing, chromium and aluminium powder being used instead of zinc, and a temperature of about 815° C is required for the drum.

Phosphating. This comprises an alkali degrease, rinse and immersion in a phosphating solution. After another water rinse and one in chromic acid, the article is dried and painted.

STRUCTURAL STEELWORK*

Structural steelwork is introduced in Vol. I where the different steel sections in hot-rolled and cold-rolled steel are described together with methods for building these up to form larger beams and columns. Vol. II contains examples of steel roof trusses up to 12 m span.

The text which follows here deals with the different kinds of steel framed structures which are in regular use. Construction with hot-rolled sections is described first, followed by examples of light-gauge steelwork using cold-rolled sections.

Steel framework (see also pp. 123 and 134) may be composed of beams, channels, angles, etc. The fastenings between the different parts of a frame is by means of bolts, rivets and welding used in four ways. In any one joint bolts alone may be used; or bolts and rivets used together; or bolts and welding used together; in a few cases the whole of the joint may be welded (see p. 43).

Apart from the infrequent times when welding is used for the on-site fastenings, bolts are always used for fixings which are made on the site with as much of the rest of the joint being made in the steel workshop by welding (or less seldom with riveting).

Riveting was once the universal workshop fixing. Nowadays it has disappeared almost entirely in building work, except in the case of very heavily loaded pieces like large plate girders for which some designers still prefer the traditional riveting technique, to be replaced by welding. Because riveting has been used for so many years and since it is encountered in alteration work a few examples of it are included here.

Bolts. These are of two types: ordinary mild steel bolts (also called black bolts) and high-strength friction grip bolts (h.s.f.g.). Much work is done with the former particularly to take the shear forces in a joint. By using h.s.f.g. bolts and nuts the joint can be made as rigid as if the whole of the joint were made with welding.

H.s.f.g. bolts are distinguished from ordinary black bolts by being marked on the head by three radial lines, the manufacturers identification mark and the letters ISOM. Nuts for use with the bolts are marked with three semi-circular arcs and washers have three ribs on the perimeter with the indented letter M on the face. In using these bolts the hardened steel washer must be placed under the nut or bolt head, whichever is tightened. In assembling the joint the bolt is subject to a preliminary tightening to bring the parts into close contact. Marks are placed on the nut and protruding head of the bolts to record their relative positions. Each nut is then finally tightened with a power-operated wrench so that it turns by a predetermined amount as laid down in BS 4604, Part 1: *The Use of High Strength Friction Grip Bolts in Structural Steelwork*. Alternatively a calibrated torque wrench is used to apply a predetermined tension in the bolt.

Welding. The use of welding was given an impetus by the 1939 War when speed was important. It has now replaced riveting, the site connections still being effected with bolts. Welding is not often adopted on site; supervision and inspection are difficult and the ideal "down-hand" welding position (see below) cannot always be used.

In comparison with riveting, it is known that in a welded structure: (*a*) less steel is usually used, reducing dead weight, (*b*) a welded structure has a better aesthetic appeal, (*c*) the elimination or reduced use of bolts and rivets simplifies maintenance because these are always the first to be attacked by corrosion, (*d*) fabrication time in the workshop is generally reduced, and (*e*) there is less wastage of metal (*e.g.*, by the drilling of holes). The welding of large components requires special care in devising a suitable welding technique which will overcome the inclination of members to become distorted due to temperature changes. Welding is certainly ideal for tubular work and the tube is an efficient load-carrying member (see p. 39 and Figs. 14 and 16).

Briefly, the craft of welding consists of melting the interfaces of the steel parts to be joined, accompanied by the simultaneous deposition of weld metal, so that a complete mixing and fusion of parent and deposited metal occurs. In the action, a slag forms on top of the weld metal which must be chipped off after the joint has cooled.

Electric arc welding† is the most usual kind for structural work, the equipment comprises a set giving a pressure from 60 to 110 volts with a current variable from 150 to 500 amps. The set is securely earthed and has two cables, one being clamped to the work to be welded and the other connected to the electrode holder. Various types of electrode are available, up to 450 mm long (for hand operation) and perhaps of 4 mm thick wire coated with a skin of flux which melts during welding, excluding air and finally forming a slag. The electrode may be fixed to a machine for automatic welding (when it would be in the form of a long reel) or it may be clamped to a hand-operated electrode holder. The operative is provided with protective gloves and a helmet having a vizor of dark glass for observation of the work. When the set is switched on, and the electrode brought into contact with the steel, the circuit is completed and current flows. By now withdrawing the electrode slightly, the power continues to flow and an arc is created in the small gap which provides the heat for the process. For the best results, and ease of operation, welding is done in the *down-hand* position where the electrode points obliquely down to the joint. The parts being welded are clamped into a jig which may be capable of rotation and movement to suit the welder, stops are provided in the jig which automatically position the pieces to be joined.

* B.S. 5950: Structural Use of Steelwork in Building.

† Oxy-acetylene welding is sometimes used on small scale work, where a gas flame provides the heat. Spot welding is also used for light-gauge sections that are lightly loaded, it consists of fusing the parts together at spots about 3 mm in dia.

There are two main types of weld, the fillet weld and the butt weld, the former being the most common and easily accomplished. The section of a 10 mm fillet weld approximates to the quadrant of a circle as at T, Fig. 13, examples of butt welds are also given at F, R, O and S, Fig. 13.

Structural Design Methods. There are two main design methods: *simple design* and *fully-rigid design*. In simple design the structure is assumed to be pin-jointed and beams are described as being "simply supported"; *e.g.*, in the connections between beams and a column at L, Fig. 8, ordinary black bolts are used which cannot develop the high tension which h.s.f.g. bolts can carry; when a beam is loaded the top end of the beam next to the column tends to be pulled away from the column as the beam bends. In the more complicated fully-rigid design method illustrated in the beams to column connection at M, Fig. 8, h.s.f.g. bolts are used at the top of the beams which prevent the ends of the beam being pulled away from the column when the beam is subjected to bending. A stiff or rigid joint is thus obtained wherein a bending moment is induced in the top of the beam which is transferred to the column. The creation of this "end moment" at the end of the beam causes a reduction in the bending moment at the mid-span of the beam and so leads to economy in design (see also p. 54).

In Fig. 8 at Q and R the part plan and section are shown of a typical steel frame and in this Figure and Figs. 9, 10 and 11 the various joints are illustrated. Some of these show simple design and some fully-rigid designed connections to give as many variations as space permits; of course in any one building the jointing methods would not be mixed.

The following connections are now described: beam to column, beam to beam, column splice, column base and roof truss to column.

Beam to Column Connections. The simple design method is shown at L, Fig. 8, and B, Fig. 9, where ordinary m.s. bolts are used throughout; top and bottom angle cleats are adopted. Bottom cleats are fixed to the stanchion either in the workshop or on site before it is hoisted into place; before the beams are raised the top cleats are attached to them – usually on site. As the steel erector has to operate without a scaffold his task is greatly simplified by having the previously fixed bottom cleat in place to serve as a resting point for the beam.

It will be clear that in making a connection of the above sort the beam which is fastened to the column flange is more easily placed than the beam which is fixed to the column web because the latter beam has either to be lowered down the column web or the column has to be tilted to allow the beam to clear the projecting column flanges before it can be put in place. In the example shown, because it is a roof level connection, the beam does not have to be lowered very far so this method can be adopted.

Connections using bolts entirely are seldom seen, thus in the above example it is more usual to have the bottom cleats welded to the column in the workshop with bolts being used for the remainder of the fixings.

As noted on p. 30 in earlier times the universal workshop fastenings were rivets; thus in the detail at L, Fig. 8, the bottom cleats were fixed to the column by four rivets instead of the four bolts shown.

The detail at M, Fig. 8, and D, Fig. 9, shows the modern method of attaching a beam to a column using the fully-rigid method of design. A plate is welded to the end of the beams by means of a fillet weld deposited all round the beam profile. In the case of the right-hand beam abutting the column flange bolts are placed through the plate into the stanchion flange; the four upper bolts must be of the h.s.f.g. type to resist the end moment, the two lower bolts could be of the ordinary m.s. type but designers usually prefer that if h.s.f.g. bolts are used on a job they should be adopted for all fastenings so that there can be no mistake in putting a black bolt where the stronger type is needed. The beam to column connection at O, Fig. 8 is of the fully rigid type where the beams are joined to the column by site fillet welds round the profile of the beams. Small angle cleats are used to permit subsequent site welding; site welding of this kind is rarely adopted.

The beam to column connection at B, Fig. 10, is typical of the case where the column does not continue to an upper floor but has a cap plate welded to it to serve as a seating for the beams resting on it.

The eccentric beam to column joint at D and E, Fig. 10, shows the case where the stanchion is on the perimeter of a building and the two beams joined to it carry the external wall. The flanges of the beams are notched out so that the beam webs fit flush against the outer face of the column flange.

The beam to column connection at A, Fig. 11, is appropriate for a single-storey building where the beam can rest directly on the column via a cap plate welded to the column, the beam has flange bolts for fixing to the cap plate. In the same Figure at C there are three beams attached to the column, the beams are bolted to the top flange of seating angle cleats which are welded to the column; this is typical of a simple designed joint between beams and a column. The column in this example is strengthened by having flange plates welded to it by intermittent fillet welds.

Beam to Beam Connections. At T, Fig. 8 and A, Fig. 9 a simple design method joint showing two minor beams joined to a major beam is shown. Web cleat angles are attached to the smaller beams by welding as indicated; in former days rivets (shown in broken line) were employed. Black bolts fix the other legs of the angles to the main beam.

The detail at B, Fig. 11, is similar except that because the main beam is deep enough it is possible to include seating angles welded to the web of the main beam in order to assist erection. Web angle cleats are welded to the webs of the minor beams and site bolts complete the fastening.

Column Splice. This is used to join an upper to a lower stanchion length. The splice is placed near a floor level where the smaller upper stanchion joins the lower one as at O, Fig. 8, and C, Fig. 9. As a result of the different sizes of the two column lengths a bearing plate and packing plates have to be used with

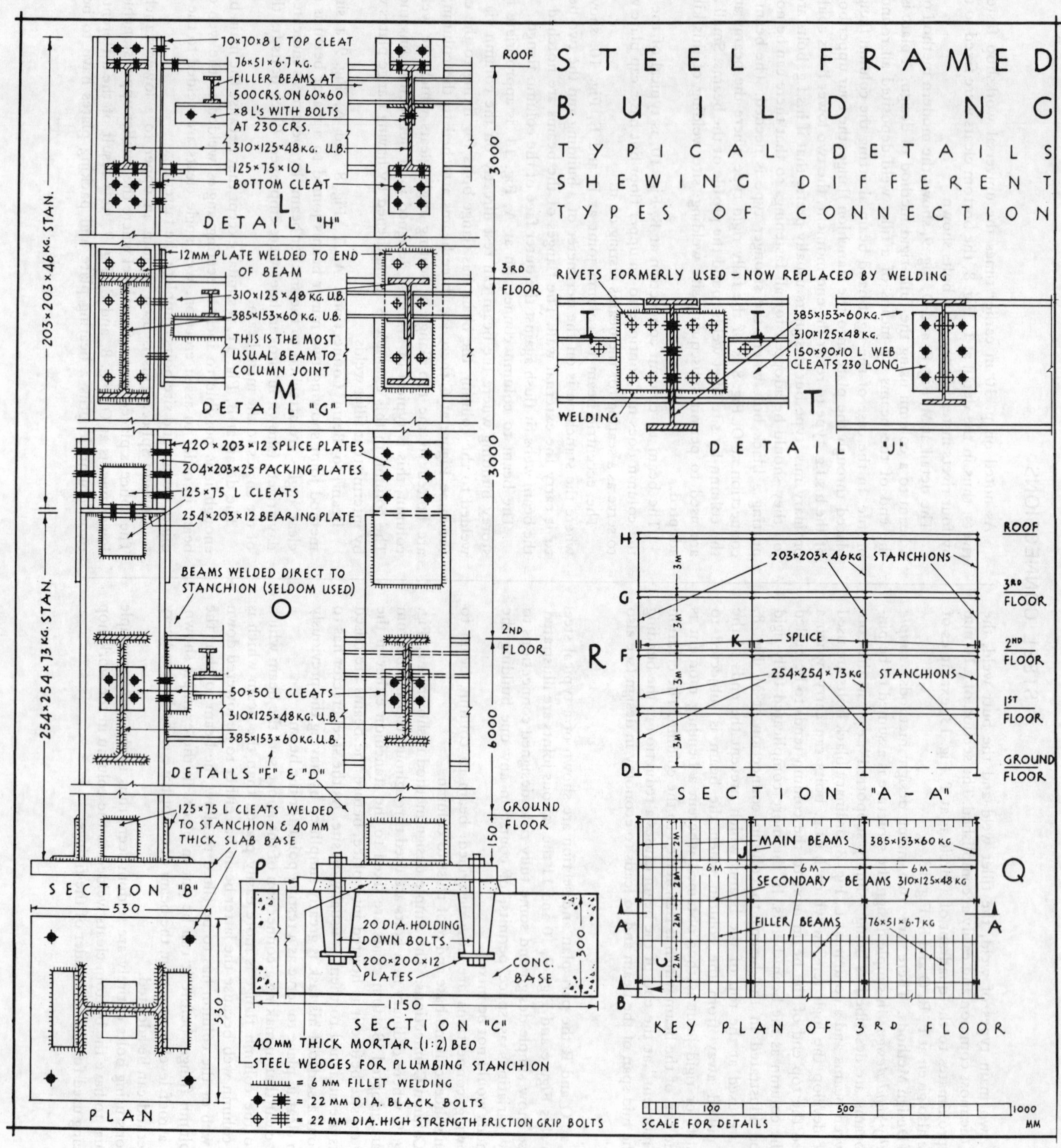
STEEL FRAMED
BUILDING
TYPICAL DETAILS
SHEWING DIFFERENT
TYPES OF CONNECTION
70×70×8 L TOP CLEAT
76×51×6·7 KG. FILLER BEAMS AT 500 CRS. ON 60×60 ×8 L'S WITH BOLTS AT 230 CRS.
310×125×48 KG. U.B.
125×75×10 L BOTTOM CLEAT
L
DETAIL "H"
12 MM PLATE WELDED TO END OF BEAM
310×125×48 KG. U.B.
385×153×60 KG. U.B.
THIS IS THE MOST USUAL BEAM TO COLUMN JOINT
M
DETAIL "G"
420×203×12 SPLICE PLATES
204×203×25 PACKING PLATES
125×75 L CLEATS
254×203×12 BEARING PLATE
BEAMS WELDED DIRECT TO STANCHION (SELDOM USED)
O
50×50 L CLEATS
310×125×48 KG. U.B.
385×153×60 KG. U.B.
DETAILS "F" & "D"
125×75 L CLEATS WELDED TO STANCHION & 40 MM THICK SLAB BASE
SECTION "B"
530
PLAN
203×203×46 KG. STAN.
254×254×73 KG. STAN.
ROOF
3RD FLOOR
2ND FLOOR
GROUND FLOOR
3000
6000
150
RIVETS FORMERLY USED – NOW REPLACED BY WELDING
385×153×60 KG.
310×125×48 KG.
150×90×10 L WEB CLEATS 230 LONG
WELDING
T
DETAIL "J"
203×203×46 KG STANCHIONS
SPLICE
254×254×73 KG STANCHIONS
R
1ST FLOOR
SECTION "A – A"
MAIN BEAMS 385×153×60 KG
SECONDARY BEAMS 310×125×48 KG
FILLER BEAMS 76×51×6·7 KG
Q
KEY PLAN OF 3RD FLOOR
P
20 DIA. HOLDING DOWN BOLTS.
200×200×12 PLATES
CONC. BASE
1150
SECTION "C"
40 MM THICK MORTAR (1:2) BED
STEEL WEDGES FOR PLUMBING STANCHION
= 6 MM FILLET WELDING
= 22 MM DIA. BLACK BOLTS
= 22 MM DIA. HIGH STRENGTH FRICTION GRIP BOLTS
SCALE FOR DETAILS
MM

FIGURE 8

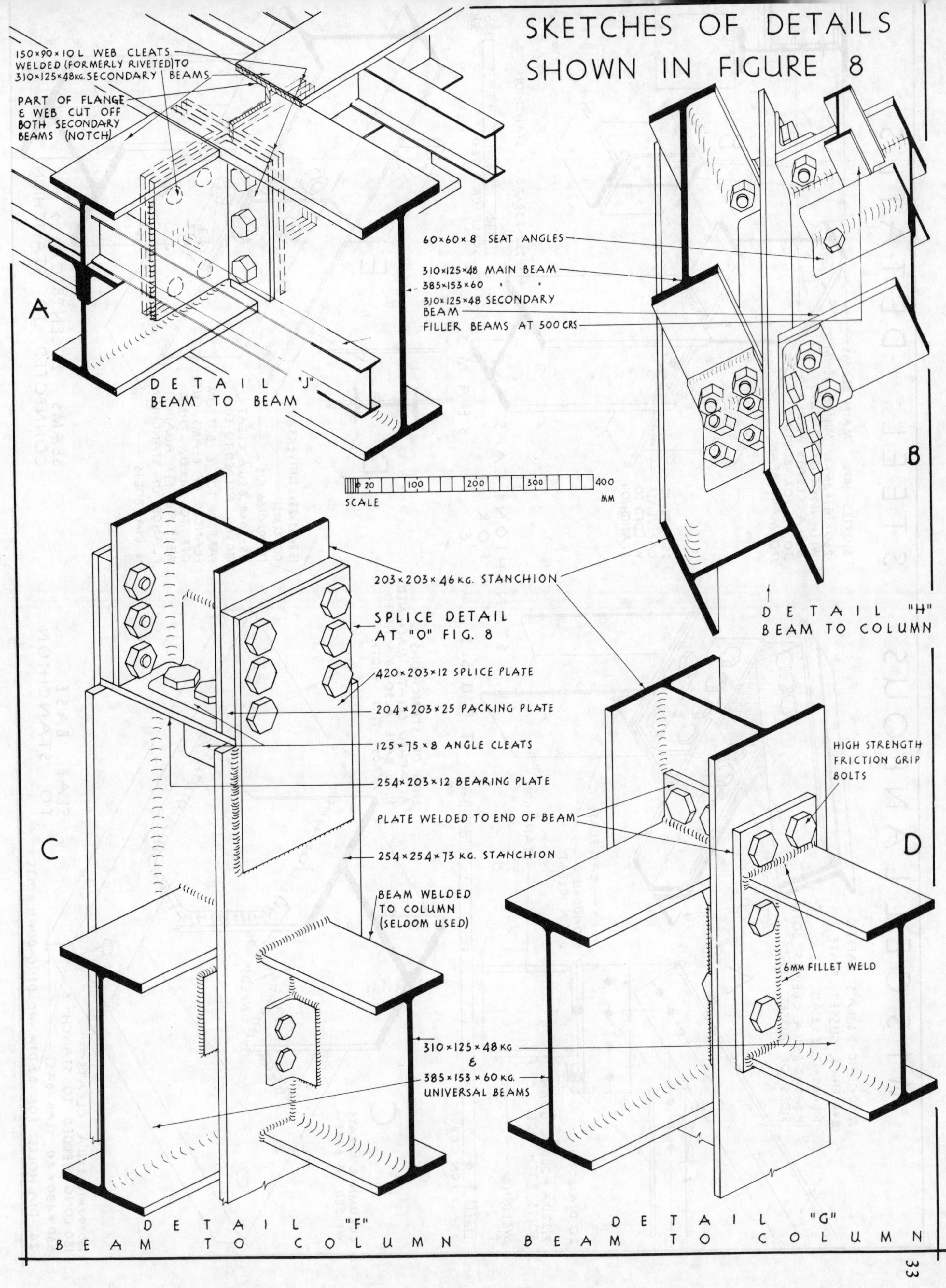
SKETCHES OF DETAILS
SHOWN IN FIGURE 8
150×90×10 L WEB CLEATS
WELDED (FORMERLY RIVETED) TO
310×125×48KG. SECONDARY BEAMS
PART OF FLANGE
& WEB CUT OFF
BOTH SECONDARY
BEAMS (NOTCH)
A
DETAIL "J"
BEAM TO BEAM
60×60×8 SEAT ANGLES
310×125×48 MAIN BEAM
385×153×60 " "
310×125×48 SECONDARY
BEAM
FILLER BEAMS AT 500 CRS
B
DETAIL "H"
BEAM TO COLUMN
20 100 200 300 400
MM
SCALE
203×203×46KG. STANCHION
SPLICE DETAIL
AT "O" FIG. 8
420×203×12 SPLICE PLATE
204×203×25 PACKING PLATE
125×75×8 ANGLE CLEATS
254×203×12 BEARING PLATE
PLATE WELDED TO END OF BEAM
254×254×73 KG. STANCHION
HIGH STRENGTH
FRICTION GRIP
BOLTS
C
D
BEAM WELDED
TO COLUMN
(SELDOM USED)
6MM FILLET WELD
310×125×48 KG
&
385×153×60 KG.
UNIVERSAL BEAMS
DETAIL "F"
BEAM TO COLUMN
DETAIL "G"
BEAM TO COLUMN

FIGURE 9

MISCELLANEOUS STEEL DETAILS

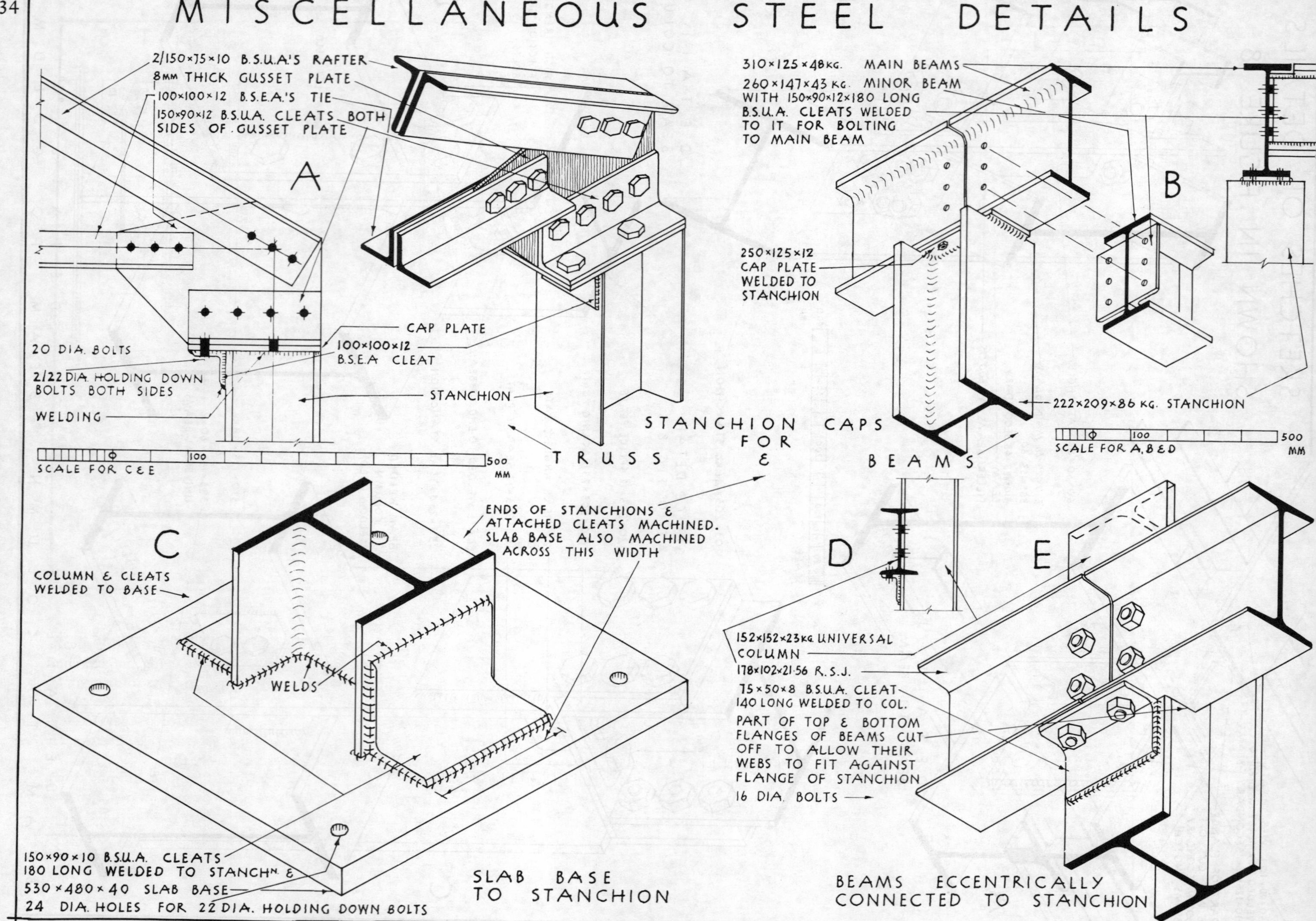

FIGURE 10

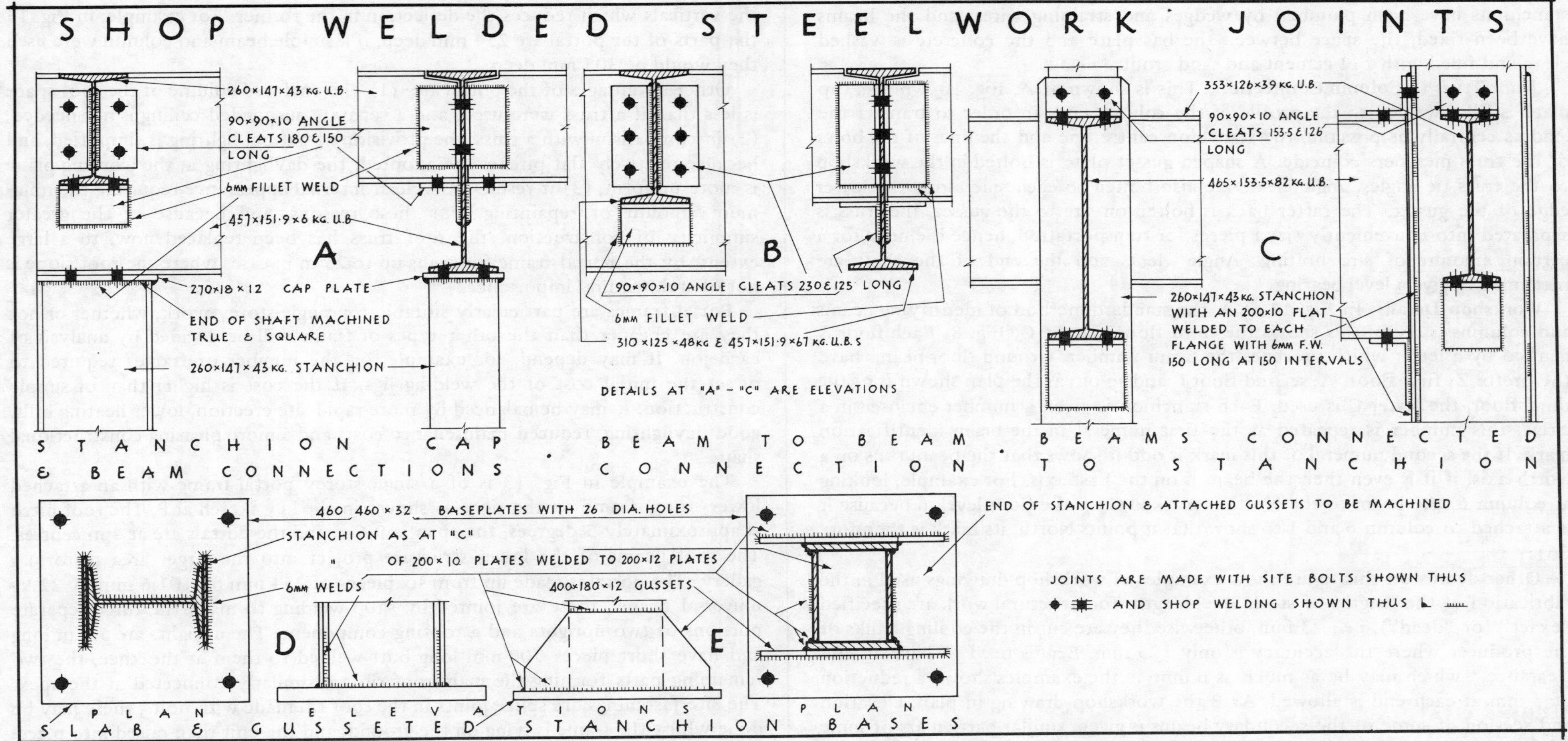

FIGURE 11

splice plates to fasten the two lengths together. The ends of the columns and the faces of the bearing plate are machined to give a true bearing surface. The bearing plate is shop welded to the top of the lower column length and the splice plates are welded to the flanges of the lower column. Site fastenings are bolts through the splices, packing plates and upper column length.

Column Base. The details at P, Fig. 8, C, Fig. 10, D, Fig. 11 and H, Fig. 13 show various constructions at the base of a column. These are described as slab bases because the baseplate is a relatively thick slab of steel. The simplest is the one in Fig. 13 where the base of the pillar is fillet welded to the slab base which has two holes for securing the baseplate to the concrete foundation. Flange cleats and web cleats welded to the column and base as at P, Fig. 8, or flange cleats alone as at C, Fig. 10, are also used. A true bearing surface must be provided for all parts in contact at the upper surface of the baseplate; this means that the top of the baseplate and the underside of the column (plus any attached cleats) are machined smooth before being fastened together. The column at D, Fig. 11, is a universal section strengthened by the addition of flange plates welded to it. The column at E, Fig. 11, is made up from four separate steel plates welded together at the corners; it shows a gusseted base, gussets are required when (unlike a slab base) the base plate is relatively thin.

The column base is attached to the concrete foundation by holding-down bolts which have plates at their lower ends set into the concrete. In order to give some tolerance in manoeuvring the stanchion into place over the bolts the latter are placed in holes formed in the concrete by expanded metal or timber boxes or by asbestos pipes which are broken away after the concrete has set. After the stanchions have been plumbed by wedges and straining wires, and the beams have been fixed, the space between the baseplate and the concrete is washed clean and filled with 1 : 2 cement and sand grout.

Roof Truss to Column Connection. This is shown at A, Fig. 10, where a cap plate is fillet welded to the profile of the column end. In order to transfer the load as centrally as possible, the stanchion centre line and the lines of the bolts of the truss members coincide. A shaped gusset plate is bolted in the workshop to the truss tie angles, angle cleats are also bolted to each side along the lower edge of the gusset. The rafter back is bolted on site to the gusset, the truss is separated into conveniently sized pieces for transportation, hence the need for a certain amount of site bolting. Angle cleats and the end of the shaft are machined to give a level bearing.

Workshop Details. In Fig. 12 at A, the standard method of identifying beams and columns is given, this shows the third floor plan at Q, Fig. 8. Each floor is marked by a letter which precedes the beam number. Ground floor beams have the prefix Z; first floor, A; second floor B and so on; as the plan shown is of the third floor, the letter C is used. Each stanchion is given a number enclosed in a circle, this number is repeated as the first numeral in the beam identification mark. If the second numeral of this mark is odd it shows that the beam runs on a North axis, if it is even then the beam is on the East axis. For example, looking at column 6, the beam to the North is marked C for the floor level, 6 because it is attached to column 6 and 1 to show that it points North, its mark is therefore C61.

Other details on this figure show examples of workshop drawings used in the fabrication of the lengths of steel. Steel lengths for structural work are specified "exact" (or "dead"), *i.e.*, ±3 mm, otherwise they are cut in the cooling banks of the producer where the accuracy is only ±25 mm. Beams need to have an end clearance,* which may be as much as 6 mm; in the examples shown a reduction of 3 mm at each end is allowed. At B the workshop drawing in plan, elevation and section of some of the secondary beams is given, similar particulars of some of the main beams are drawn at C and columns at D.

Portal Frame Construction. The difference between this construction and the ordinary pin jointed beam and column arrangement described above is that the former makes use of the principle of *continuity* by attaching the parts together by a rigid joint such as can be obtained by welding. One type of portal is given in Fig. 13; another type has the roof members horizontal and a third type extends through two storeys. In a continuous frame, the effects of a load on one part extend to all parts; this produces a sharing by the members of the moments caused by a load and leads to an economy in the size of the horizontal part of the portal, although it may increase the size of the vertical legs of the frame. Due to the continuity, a load on the horizontal member causes a bending moment in the verticals which reduces the deflection in the former. For example, in Fig. 13 the parts of the portal are 254 mm deep, if a simple beam and column were used they would be 305 mm deep.

Other advantages of the portal are: (1) The enclosed volume of the roof space is less than if a truss were used, and a separate suspended ceiling is not needed; (2) in comparison with a truss, the provision of natural lighting is simplified, and because relatively flat pitches are adopted, the daylighting at the working plane is more uniform; (3) it results in a clean internal appearance requiring the minimum amount of repainting. For these reasons, and because of the greater simplicity of construction, the roof truss has been replaced now, to a large extent, by the portal frame for spans up to 25 m in cases where the roof slope is not of architectural importance.

Portal frames are particularly suitable for single-storey work; whether or not they are cheaper than the other types of frame will be decided by analysis of each job. It may depend, for example, on the number of frames required to offset the initial cost of the welding jigs. If the cost is higher than of simple construction, it may be balanced by more rapid site erection, lower heating bills, good daylighting, reduced maintenance costs and a more pleasing constructional shape.

The example in Fig. 13 is of a single-storey portal frame with an attached lower storey frame on the right as shown in the key sketch at P. The roof pitch is approximately 5 degrees, the span is 9.6 m and the portals are at 4 m centres. The roof beams of the lower structure project into the larger area to form a gallery. The portal is made up from six pieces of 254 mm by 101.6 mm by 22 kg universal beams, these are jointed by shop welding to make the three separate portions of two uprights and a roofing component. The uprights are 5.2 m long and have short pieces 700 mm long butt welded to them at the knee, the two remaining parts forming the main roof rib are similarly connected at the apex. The site fastenings are splice joints in the roof rib made with bolts, these may be done whilst the frame is lying on the ground, and the unit then raised into place; alternatively, with larger portals, the uprights are erected on their bases and the roof ribs are bolted into position at roof level.

The knee and splice detail at F shows the welded joint, enlarged details of the knee welds are drawn at O. These show single-V butt welds where the edges of the metal are machined to allow for sufficient deposition of weld metal to resist the forces involved. A sealing run of weld is first run along the narrower side of the joint, subsequent runs being placed on the opposite side. The splice has flange plates which are welded on opposite flanges, bolts complete the joint and are also used for the web plates. There is an alternative to this sloping knee butt weld arrangement and that is to cut the top of the vertical leg of the frame at the same angle as the roof slope, sit the 700 mm long portion of the roof rib on top of it and weld roof rib and leg together by a fillet weld round the profile of the leg to the underside of the bottom flange of the rib. If this is adopted the rigidity of the knee joint is increased by having a plate welded to the end of the

* This is done to simplify fixing. The erection of steelwork is a skilled and hazardous operation, being the only trade performed at high level without a scaffold. Beams must therefore be cut sufficiently short and never too long.

WORKSHOP DETAILS OF STEELWORK

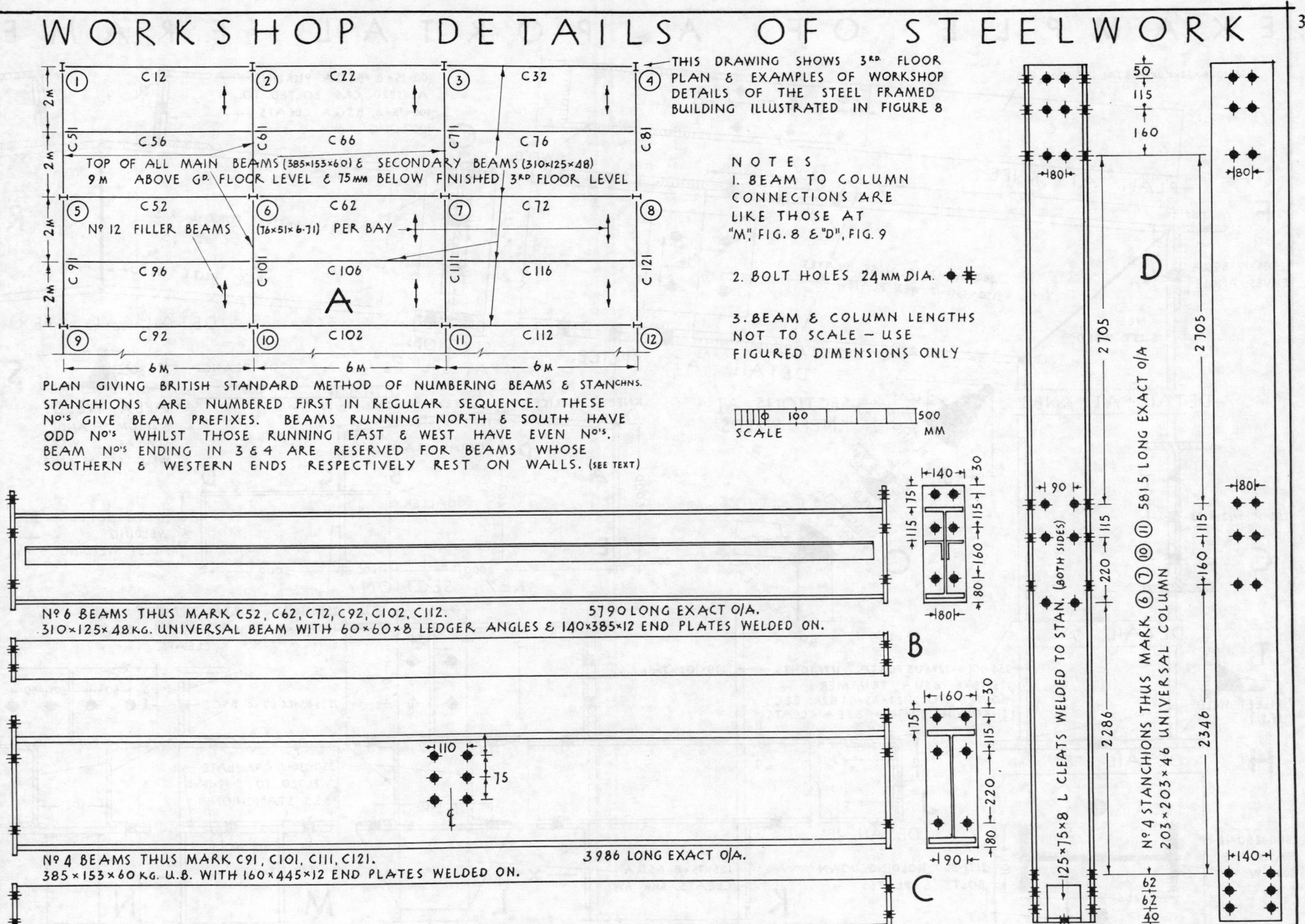

FIGURE 12

EXAMPLE OF A PORTAL FRAME

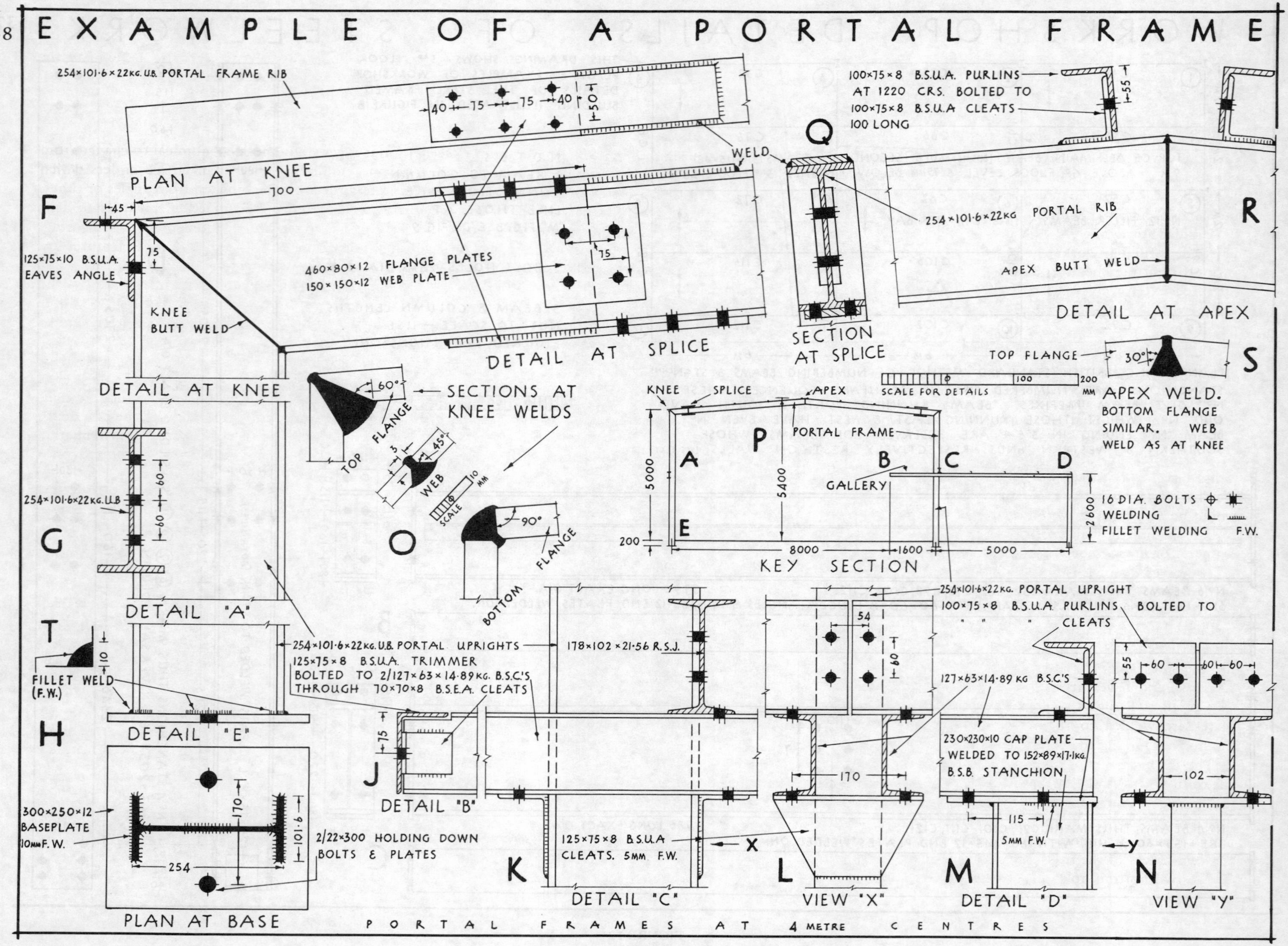

254×101·6×22KG. U.B. PORTAL FRAME RIB
40 75 75 40 50
WELD
PLAN AT KNEE
700
45
75
125×75×10 B.S.U.A. EAVES ANGLE
KNEE BUTT WELD
460×80×12 FLANGE PLATES
150×150×12 WEB PLATE
75
DETAIL AT SPLICE
DETAIL AT KNEE
SECTION AT SPLICE
254×101·6×22KG PORTAL RIB
APEX BUTT WELD
DETAIL AT APEX
100×75×8 B.S.U.A. PURLINS AT 1220 CRS. BOLTED TO 100×75×8 B.S.U.A CLEATS 100 LONG
55
TOP FLANGE 30°
APEX WELD. BOTTOM FLANGE SIMILAR. WEB WELD AS AT KNEE
SCALE FOR DETAILS 0 100 200 MM
60° TOP FLANGE
SECTIONS AT KNEE WELDS
3 45° WEB
SCALE 0 10 MM
90° BOTTOM FLANGE
254×101·6×22KG. U.B
60 60
DETAIL "A"
KNEE SPLICE APEX
PORTAL FRAME
GALLERY
5000 5400 200 2600
8000 1600 5000
KEY SECTION
16 DIA. BOLTS
WELDING
FILLET WELDING F.W.
10
FILLET WELD (F.W.)
DETAIL "E"
254×101·6×22KG. U.B. PORTAL UPRIGHTS
125×75×8 B.S.U.A. TRIMMER BOLTED TO 2/127×63×14·89KG. B.S.C'S THROUGH 70×70×8 B.S.E.A. CLEATS
178×102×21·56 R.S.J.
75
DETAIL "B"
300×250×12 BASEPLATE
10MM F.W.
170
101·6
254
2/22×300 HOLDING DOWN BOLTS & PLATES
PLAN AT BASE
125×75×8 B.S.U.A CLEATS. 5MM F.W.
DETAIL "C"
254×101·6×22KG. PORTAL UPRIGHT
100×75×8 B.S.U.A PURLINS BOLTED TO " " " CLEATS
54 60
127×63×14·89 KG B.S.C'S
170
X
VIEW "X"
230×230×10 CAP PLATE WELDED TO 152×89×17·1KG. B.S.B. STANCHION
115
5MM F.W.
DETAIL "D"
Y
55 60 60 60
102
VIEW "Y"
F G H J K L M N O P Q R S T A B C D E

PORTAL FRAMES AT 4 METRE CENTRES

FIGURE 13

roof rib which extends a short way down the outer flange of the leg to which it is also welded; in addition small plates are welded into the web of the roof rib on line with the inner flange of the leg (*i.e.*, the small plates form vertical "extensions" to the inner flange of the leg).

The apex butt welded joint at R and S is similar to that at the knee. The base detail is given at H, where the upright is fillet welded to the baseplate. The connection of the roof channels of the smaller structure to the portal is shown at K and L, and further details at M and N are of the roof channels jointed to the outer 2.6 m high stanchion.

Tubular Steelwork. As the use of welding has increased in recent years, so has that of tubular work. The two are complementary and although the tube is a very efficient member for resisting both tension and compression forces, it was not used extensively in the past due to the difficulty of making bolted joints; these are still used but confined to site connections and as many of the joints as possible are made by welding. Exposed internal tubular structures are more easily maintained than those with angles and steel beams, etc., because they do not offer the same ledge area for the settlement of dust. In external work, the absence of ledges (where water collects) means that rusting does not develop so easily. Rivet heads and bolts are always the first parts to be corroded, so that welding is an additional advantage in this respect.

Tubular Steel Truss (Fig. 14). The key elevation of a welded tubular steel truss is given at A, it is in two halves with bolted joints at P and Q, the remaining joints being 5 mm fillet welds (see p. 31) made in the workshop. The main tie member rises 130 mm from L to N to counteract any appearance of sag that would be evident if it were horizontal. A bend at N reduces the mid span height to 2 m so that the half truss is a manageable size for transportation. The overall diameter of the members is given in the table, all are of 3.2 mm thick metal.

The eaves detail L is given at G, where the rafter and main tie tubes are fillet welded to an end plate, another view of the joint is given at B. The site connection to the column is with four 16 mm dia. bolts using a backing angle cleat, a further angle bracket at the top is used for the purlin attachment. Small plates are welded to the purlin for this purpose, this purlin also acts as a sheeting rail for the side cladding. The roof covering is two thicknesses of asbestos sheeting which should have bitumen bonded glass wool insulation between the sheets. The detail at F shows a typical purlin fixing further detailed at C, small 10 mm plates are welded to the rafter and the purlin for the two site bolts. Other methods of joining adjacent lengths of purlin are given on p. 43.

The detail at H is of the joint N, showing the gradual bend (460 mm radius to the centre of the main tie) in the tie.

The ridge joint at E and D show the 150 mm by 165 mm by 10 mm plates which are welded to the rafters, these are holed for the four site bolts. The plates are also used to connect the 27 mm o/d by 3.2 mm thick vertical end tubes of the two halves of the truss. The corresponding joint Q of the tie is given at J and K, the two bottom holes in the circular plate are used to fix a longitudinal tie at right angles to the trusses, the two holes above these can also be used to fix braces against the gable walls of the building in the end bays.

ROOFING OF LARGE FLOOR AREAS*

When floor spans exceed 15 m it is generally more economical to change from a simple truss arrangement to one employing wide span lattice girders which support trusses at right angles. The girders can be built up from angles or tubes, the latter welded and the former welded and bolted together. In order to light the space satisfactorily, roof lighting has to replace, or supplement, side lighting; provision must also be made for ventilation from the roof – these features are described on pp. 178–179 and 176 respectively.

One of the oldest and economical of methods of covering large areas is the *North light and lattice girder* (or *saw tooth roof*) system shown in Fig. 15, this is sometimes objected to because the lighting is directed from one side only and so there is a tendency for shadows to be created at the working plane.

Another method will be apparent by referring to A, Fig. 14. Instead of supporting the trusses at the ends L and U, they can be connected at these ends to each other, they are all then supported by lattice girders running at right angles and placed at the truss centres. The lattice girder would thus be of a depth extending from P to Q at A, they would be about 21 m long (*i.e.*, approximately ten times their depth), the whole roof would accordingly be supported on a 21 m by 15.25 m column grid.

A further method is to produce a basically flat roof with lattice girders at right angles as at A, Fig. 16, where the grid is 18.24 by 12 m. Lighting is provided by building monitors above the flat, these admit light from both sides. Alternatively, lighting can be provided by using lantern lights similar to that sketched at D, Fig. 66.

North Light and Lattice Girder Roof (or Sawtooth) (Fig. 15). This roof consists of a series of trusses fixed to girders. The short vertical (or near vertical) side of the trusses is glazed so that when the roof is used in the northern hemisphere the glazed portion faces North for the best light; when used in the southern hemisphere the glazing would face South for the same reason. The arrangement is shown at D, where the lattice girders span 30 m; at right angles to them and connected to each vertical of the girder, a North light truss of 11 m span is fixed.

A diagram of the girder, showing the centre lines of the members is drawn at A, it is divided into 3.75 m intervals and the trusses are connected to it at these centres. A pair of the trusses is shown in diagram form at B, and a table is given to show the sizes of all the members.

Detail G at D is shown at C and illustrates the construction at the lower portion of the glazing and the connection of the truss to the bottom of the

* See also p. 178.

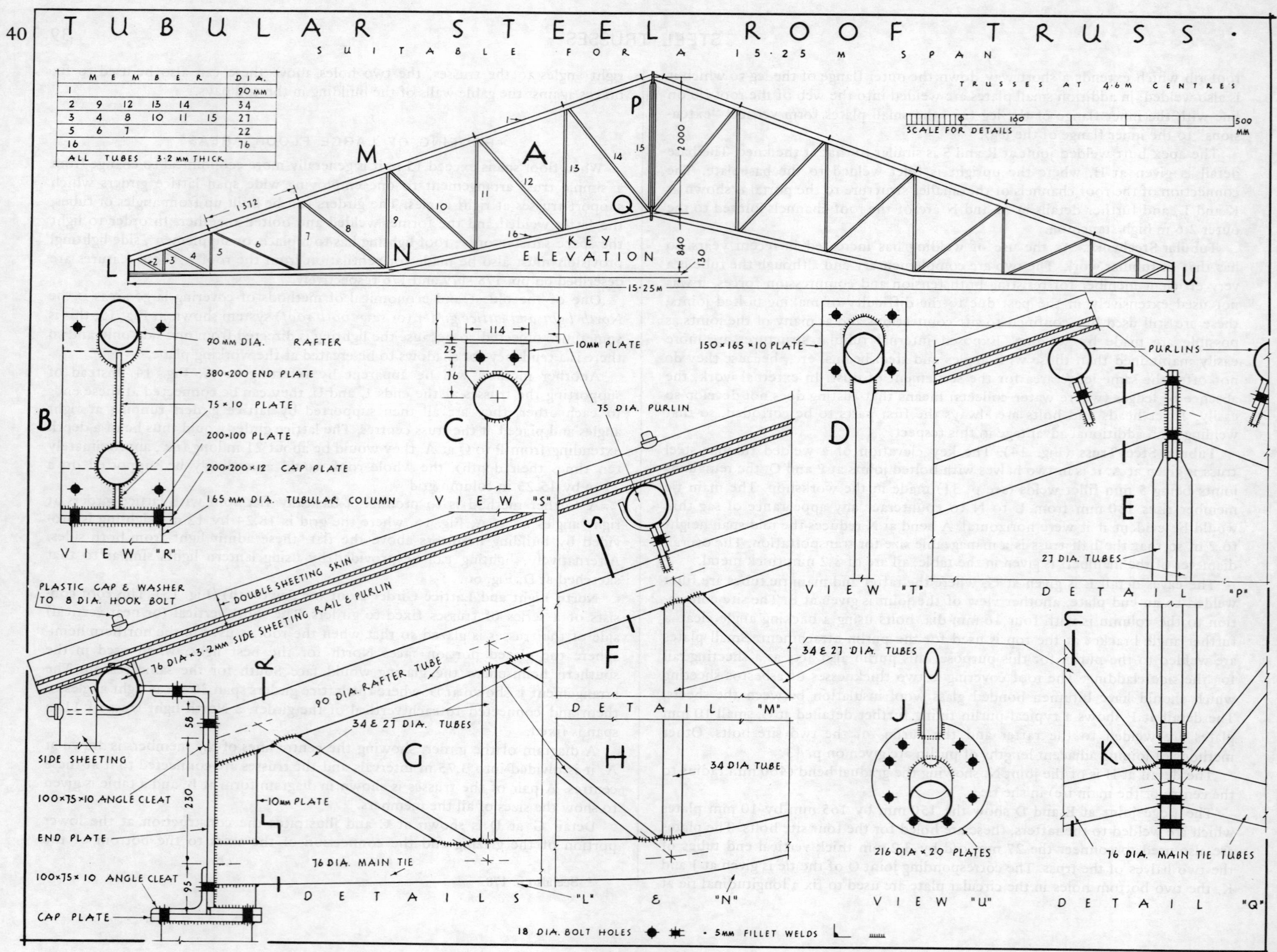
TUBULAR STEEL ROOF TRUSS.
SUITABLE FOR A 15·25 M SPAN
TRUSSES AT 4·6M CENTRES
MEMBER	DIA.
1	90 MM
2 9 12 13 14	34
3 4 8 10 11 15	27
5 6 7	22
16	76
ALL TUBES 3·2 MM THICK	
SCALE FOR DETAILS
100
500 MM
KEY ELEVATION
15·25M
2000
1372
840
30
VIEW "R"
90 MM DIA. RAFTER
380×200 END PLATE
75×10 PLATE
200×100 PLATE
200×200×12 CAP PLATE
165 MM DIA. TUBULAR COLUMN
114
25
16
10MM PLATE
75 DIA. PURLIN
VIEW "S"
150×165×10 PLATE
PURLINS
VIEW "T"
27 DIA. TUBES
DETAIL "P"
PLASTIC CAP & WASHER TO 8 DIA. HOOK BOLT
DOUBLE SHEETING SKIN
3·2MM SIDE SHEETING RAIL & PURLIN
76 DIA×3·2MM
90 DIA RAFTER TUBE
34 & 27 DIA. TUBES
DETAIL "M"
34 DIA TUBE
SIDE SHEETING
100×75×10 ANGLE CLEAT
230
58
10MM PLATE
END PLATE
76 DIA. MAIN TIE
100×75×10 ANGLE CLEAT
95
CAP PLATE
DETAILS "L" & "N"
216 DIA×20 PLATES
VIEW "U"
76 DIA. MAIN TIE TUBES
DETAIL "Q"
18 DIA. BOLT HOLES
5MM FILLET WELDS

FIGURE 14

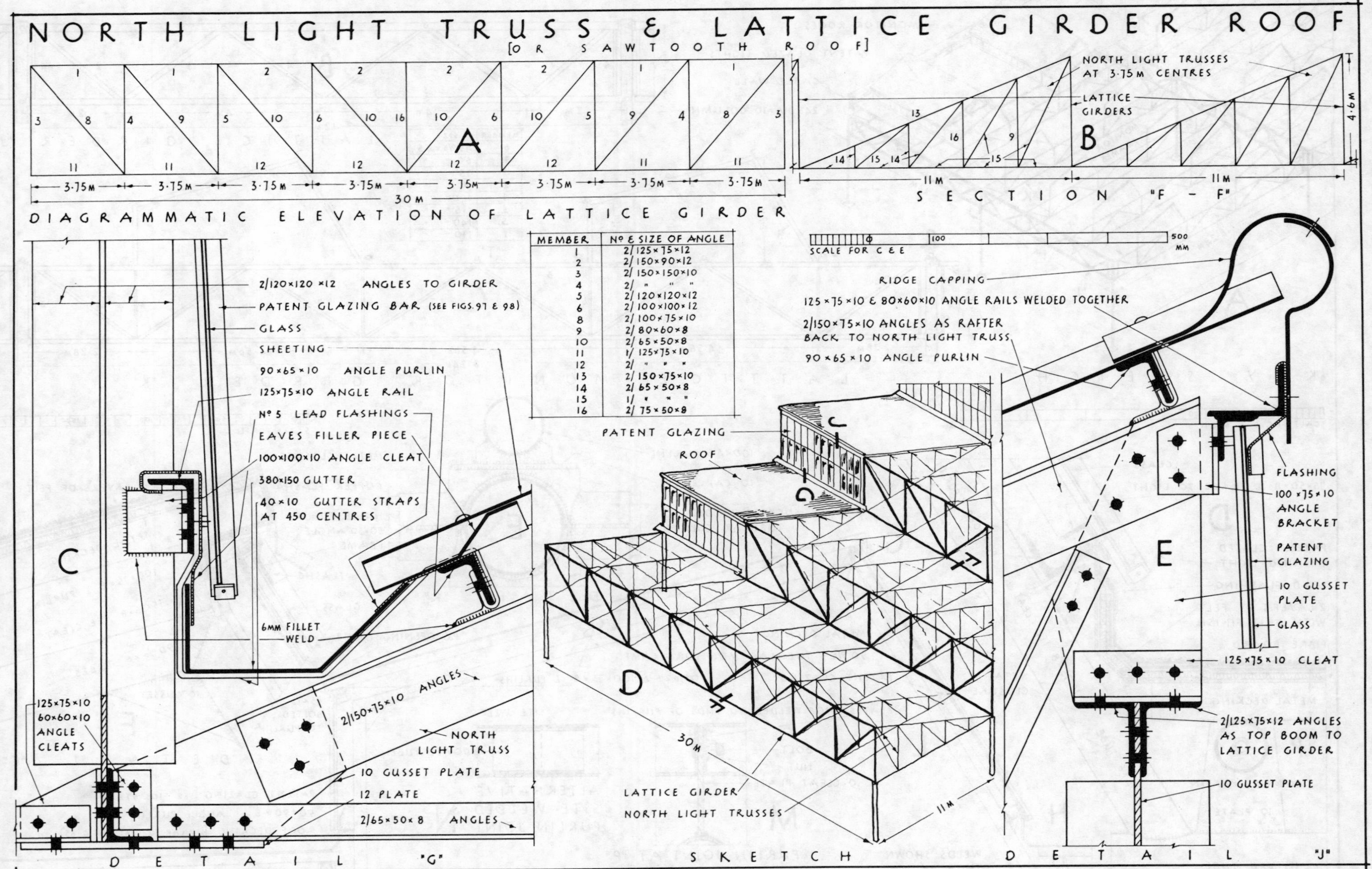

MEMBER	Nº & SIZE OF ANGLE
1	2/125×75×12
2	2/150×90×12
3	2/150×150×10
4	2/ " " "
5	2/120×120×12
6	2/100×100×12
8	2/100×75×10
9	2/80×60×8
10	2/65×50×8
11	1/125×75×10
12	2/ " " "
13	2/150×75×10
14	2/65×50×8
15	1/ " " "
16	2/75×50×8

FIGURE 15

TUBULAR STEEL MONITOR ROOF

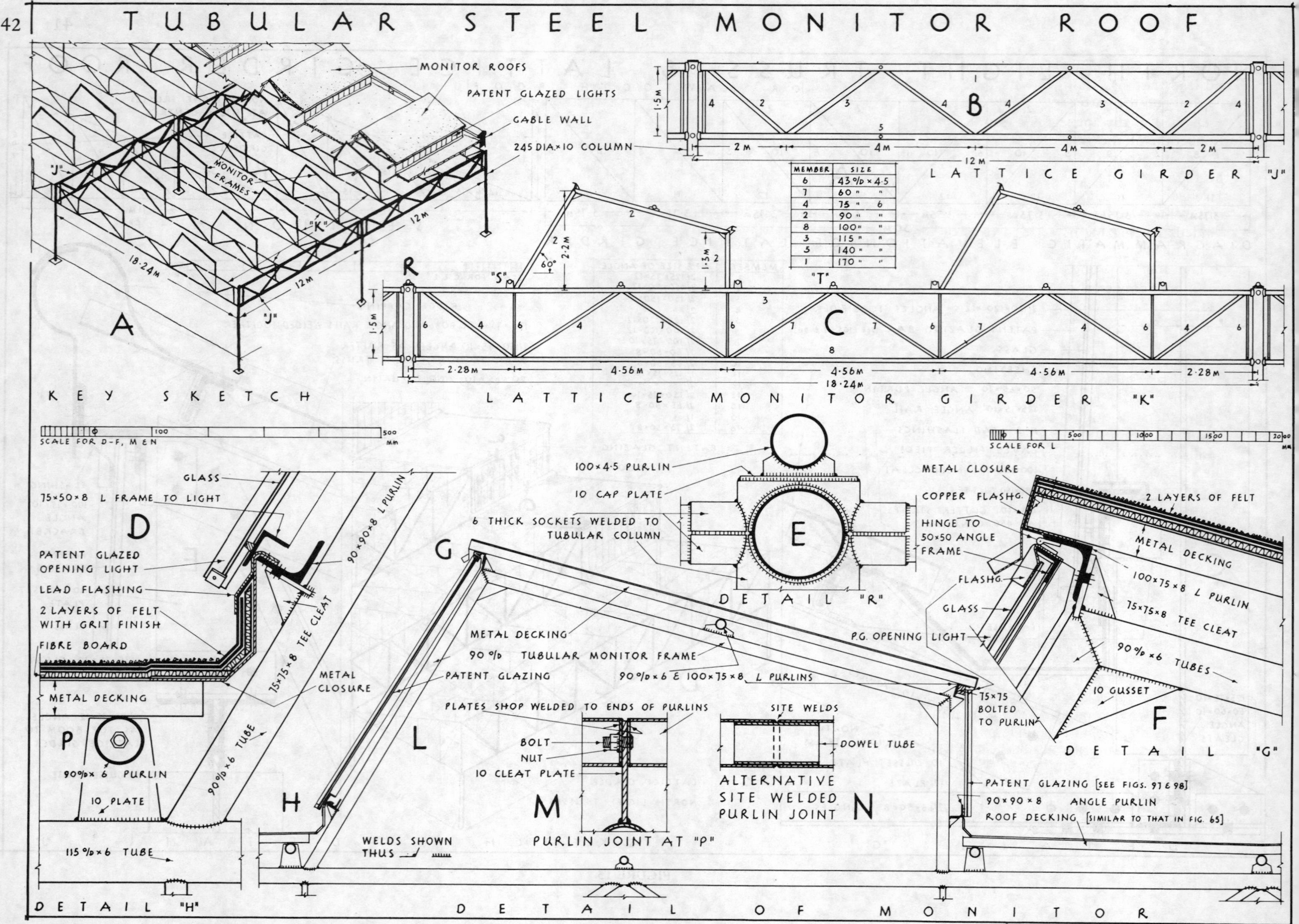

FIGURE 16

girder. The fibre-cement or steel gutter is slung from the angle rail and purlin and lead flashings seal the joints between the glazing and the gutter and between the roof and the gutter (patent glazing is described on pp. 221–224).

Detail J at the apex of the North light truss is drawn at E and shows the top connection of the two main components. The patent glazing is attached to a 75 mm by 50 mm by 8 mm angle which is welded to a larger angle round which the flashing is dressed and to which the wing of one of the ridge cappings is attached. The glazing bars should be fixed through slotted holes in the angle (to permit movement) so that when the girder deflects, damage to the glass is avoided. The glazing bars are in two lengths, being attached midway to another angle rail.

The roof covering is of fibre-cement sheeting which could be insulated with fibre-spray on the underside.

Tubular Steel Monitor Roof (Fig. 16). This is a flat roof with raised portions called *monitors* used to admit light. This type of roofing gives a more uniform level of daylighting than the previous North light system. In the example shown in the key sketch at A, columns are spaced at 18.24 m by 12 m centres with main lattice girders (J) spanning the shorter distance. At 4 m centres, lattice monitor girders (K) connect between the columns and intermediately to the main girders. Both girders are shown at B and C, they are 1.5 m deep (*i.e.*, about $\frac{1}{8}$ and $\frac{1}{12}$ of the span). The monitor frames of 90 mm o/d tubes are welded to the monitor girder, these are roofed on the top surface and have patent glazing to the sides, the left-hand panel of the glazing being openable for ventilation is the larger and faces north (see p. 176). The example is assumed to be for a large factory area where welding could be adopted economically for both site and shop joints.

The method of attaching the girder to the column is given in the detail at E. Curved socket plates are welded to the column in two halves, the column arrives on the site with the bottom sockets in position and the top ones are site welded after positioning of the girder.

The detail at D is at the foot of the glazed opening light. A metal closure plate is screwed to the roof decking and to the purlin angle; after the roofing felt is laid, the roof is sealed at the light by a lead flashing. The glazing bars are screwed to a 75 mm by 50 mm angle frame (50 mm by 50 mm at the top) to which the opening gear is attached.

Detail G shown at F is at the junction of the monitor roof and the top of the glazed opening light. The angle purlin is bolted to a tee cleat welded to the top tube of the monitor; alternatively, fillet welding would be used instead of bolting. The light is hinged to a 50 mm by 50 mm angle, a copper flashing is clipped between the angle and the hinge and is dressed over the glass. A further flashing of copper is screwed to the decking and shaped to clear the glazing bars when these are raised in the open position.

Two methods of joining adjacent purlin lengths are given at M and N. In the former, suitable for single bay lengths, the ends are sealed with plates, a threaded stud is welded to one and a nut to the other so that the lengths can be screwed together on site through the intervening 10 mm thick cleat plate; this application is shown at the connection "S" at C and at P in the detail at D. The joint at N, suitable for site welding random purlin lengths, employs a 150 mm long dowel tube; the lengths are brought almost together to leave a 10 mm gap which is filled with 5 mm fillet welds. 10 mm thick cleat plates shaped to the underside of the purlin are welded to the girder (as at "T" in the girder at C) in the shop, the purlin being site welded to the cleat.

LIGHT-GAUGE STEELWORK*

As an alternative to frameworks with the heavier hot rolled sections, light-gauge cold rolled channels and angles can be used in appropriate circumstances. These sections commonly differ from the corresponding hot rolled ones in that they are usually given outstanding narrow flanged edges (lips) so as to avoid local buckling of the thin sections normally employed (see U, Fig. 18). Light-gauge steelwork is particularly appropriate for single-storey buildings where the loadings are not too heavy, the shop connections are by welding with bolting for the site joints. As cold rolled sections are thin (3 and 4 mm thickness being common) adequate protection to prevent corrosion is important. Galvanizing is frequently adopted, but this is sometimes undesirable for long members for these tend to suffer distortion in the process; zinc spraying and phosphating are alternative protections (see pp. 29 and 30).

Figures 17 and 18 show the layout and construction of a single-storey steel-framed building having a framework of cold rolled sections. Stanchions are placed at 2.75 m by 11 m centres with trusses spanning the longer distance. The plan, cross section, longitudinal section, and elevation are given in the form of key diagrams at J; see also the sketch at O, Fig. 17.

The plan of a stanchion is shown at P, Fig. 17 and T, Fig. 18, it is a 230 mm by 175 m box section formed by two 230 mm by 50 mm by 3 mm thick channels on the long sides with two 75 mm by 25 mm channels on the shorter sides. The channels are welded together in a jig, the larger members being placed in the jig first and set at the correct distance apart. Four 5 mm thick diaphragm plates (one of which is shown at S and T, Fig. 18) are then spaced throughout the stanchion length and welded to the inside of the larger channels. Access for welding these plates is by means of the 75 mm gap in the shorter face of the column which is eventually filled with the smaller channels. The vertical joints between the channels is filled continuously with weld metal to exclude moisture from the inside of the stanchion. The stanchion base is a 300 mm by 250 mm by 8 mm plate welded to the end, 100 mm by 75 mm channel cleats are welded to the stanchion side and the base, and are holed for the fixing down bolts.

At the various heights noted in the key section, 75 mm by 50 mm by 12 mm lugs are welded to the sides of the column, the lugs are holed for fixing the

* See Introduction in Vol. I.

LIGHT-GAUGE STEELWORK

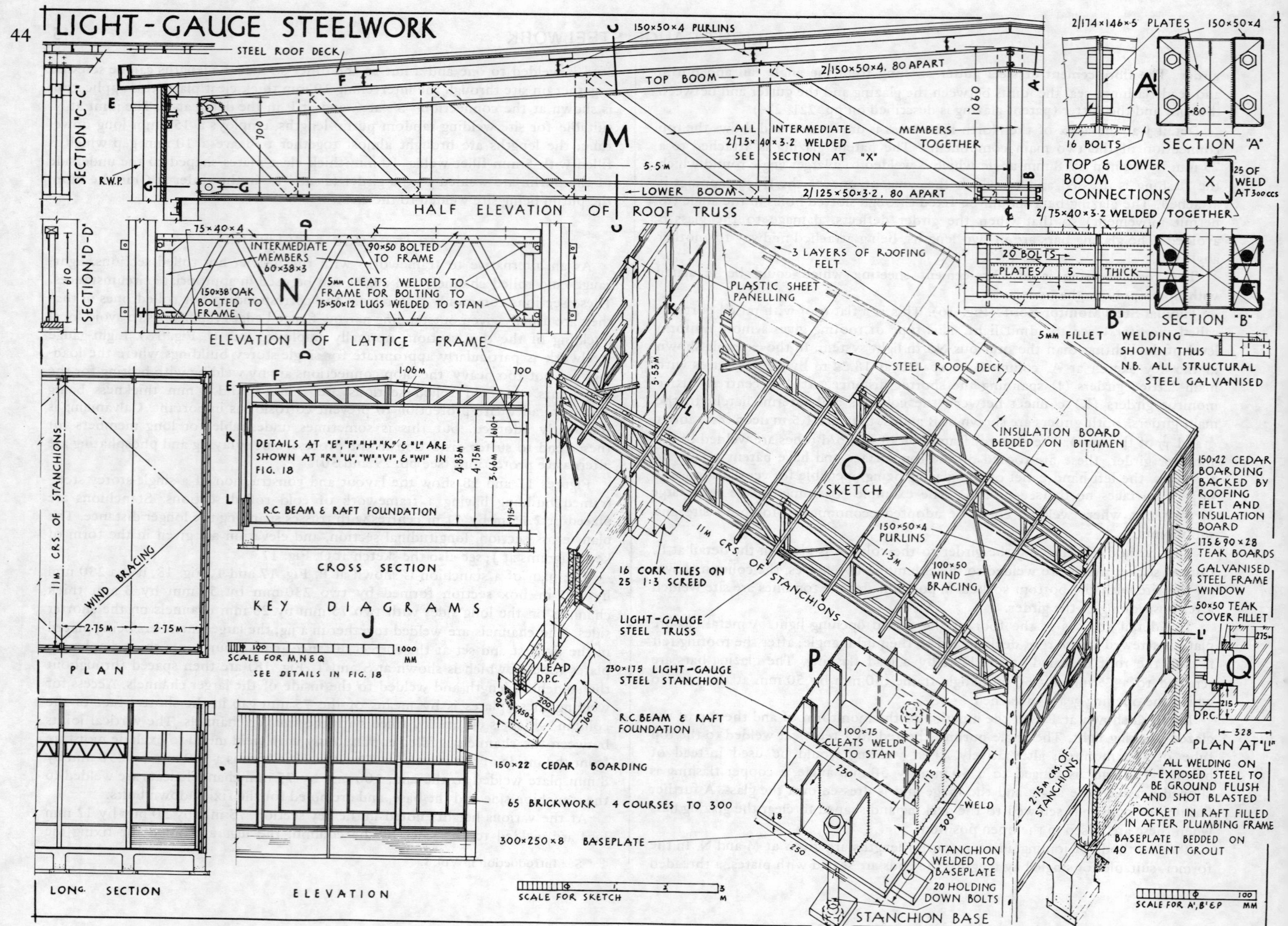

FIGURE 17

DETAILS OF LIGHT GAUGE STEEL FRAME

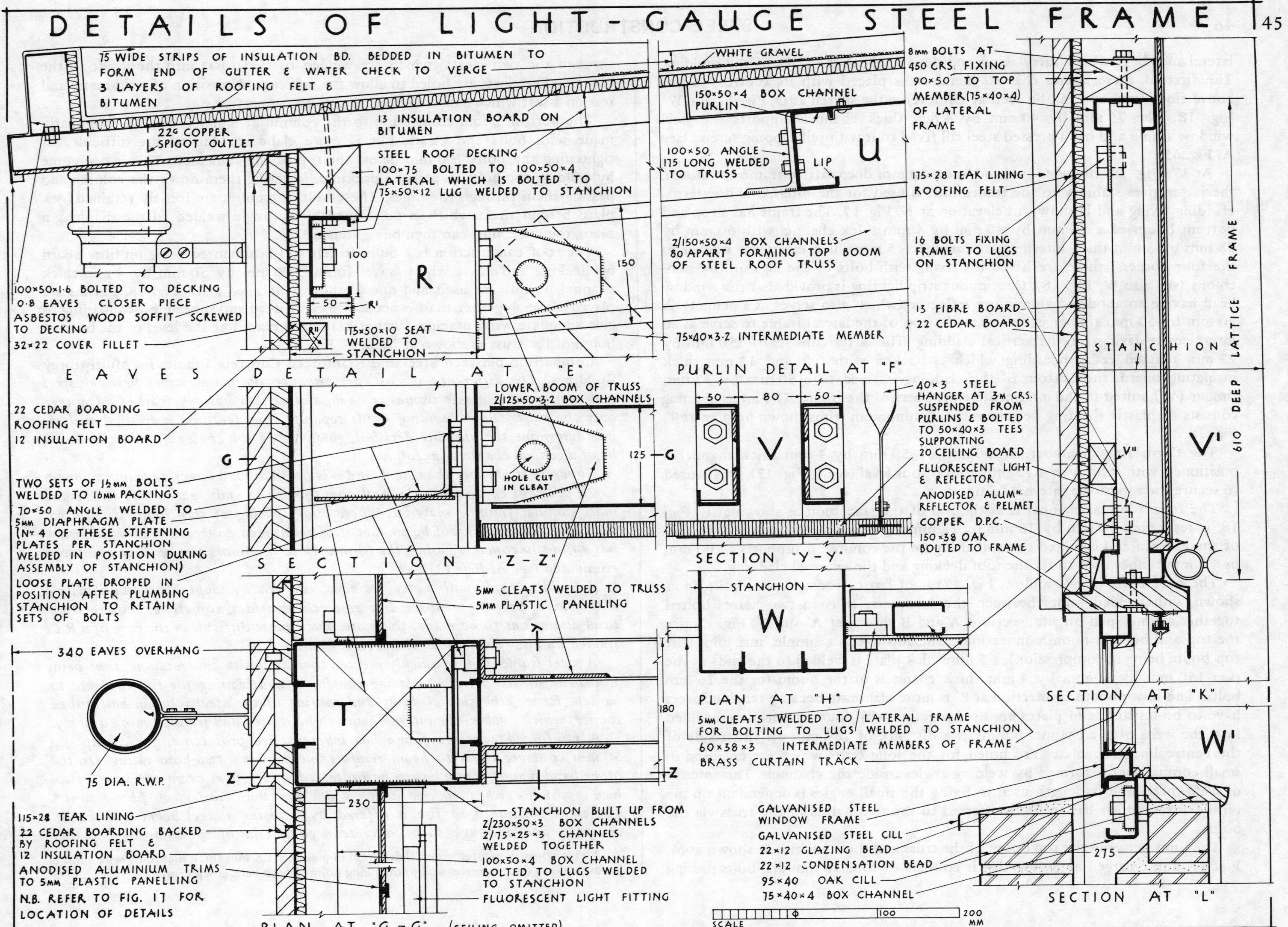

FIGURE 18

lateral members which carry wind and dead loads at the sides of the building. The first of these lateral channel members is placed with its centre 915 mm above floor level and can be seen at cill level in the sketch at O, Fig. 17 and W′, Fig. 18. The 75 mm by 40 mm by 4 mm thick channel supports the steel window frame and has a pressed steel cill fixed to it with self tapping screws (see A, Fig. 65).

At V′, Fig. 18, the window head and 610 mm deep lattice frame are shown, the latter gives stability to the stanchions, is used for the internal and external cladding fixing and is shown in elevation at N, Fig. 17. The frame has a top and bottom boom of a 75 mm by 40 mm by 4 mm thick channel with 60 mm by 38 mm by 3 mm thick intermediate members; 5 mm thick cleats are welded to the four corners, these are holed for fixing with bolts to the lugs on the stanchions (see also W, Fig. 18). Continuous strip lighting is provided at the window head having an anodized aluminium reflector (which also serves as a pelmet). A 90 mm by 50 mm timber is bolted to the top of the lateral frame to serve as an intermediate fixing for the vertical cladding. The latter consists of 150 mm by 22 mm rebated cedar boarding which is backed with felt and 12 mm thick insulating board, the bottom of the cladding is fixed to a 50 mm by 32 mm timber (V″) bolted to the intermediate members of the frame. The internal lining consists of plastic sheeting held in vertical aluminium trims shown on plan at T, Fig. 18.

The third lateral member, a 100 mm by 50 mm by 4 mm thick channel is positioned with its centre 4.75 mm above floor level (see J, Fig. 17), this is used to secure the top of the internal lining.

The fourth lateral channel is at the top of the stanchion as shown at R, Fig. 18, it rests on a 50 mm by 25 mm by 12 mm lug (R′) welded flat on to the side of the column and is bolted to another lug on the column; it supports a 100 mm by 75 mm timber used to fix the roof decking and the external cladding.

The roof truss (see O and M, Fig. 17) is of lattice construction, built up as shown with welded joints between the members. It is in two halves bolted together at mid span on site; sections A and B shown at A′ and B′, Fig. 17 give the top and bottom boom connections. The top one is a simple butt joint (the top boom being in compression), a 5 mm thick plate is welded to the ends of the two 150 mm by 50 mm by 4 mm thick channels of the boom for the 16 mm bolts. The lower boom connection at B′ is more elaborate because tension forces have to be resisted, end plates are used together with four smaller plates welded into the webs of the channel booms at a distance of 180 mm on either side of the centre line. The plates are holed for the long bolts which are enclosed in small compartments formed by welding angles inside the channels. The amount of weld metal and its length used in fixing the small angles is dependent on the tensile force which has to be transferred to the two halves of the truss via the bolts.

The joint between the top boom of the truss and the stanchion is shown at M, Fig. 17, and enlarged at R, Fig. 18; it consists of four 16 mm dia. bolts passing through the two cleats (which are welded to the truss) into the inside of the column. The cleats are holed to allow for sufficient deposition of weld metal and rest on a seat which assists in making the site connection.

The bottom boom connection to the column at S and T, Fig. 18, is similarly made with bolts and cleats, but is more elaborate due to the difficulty of tightening the bolts 700 mm below the top of the stanchion. This is overcome by welding the bolts in pairs to packings, lowering them down the column and passing them through the holes. These bolt assemblies are loosely retained by a plate behind them which is positioned by an angle welded to the diaphragm plate, the outer nuts can then be tightened.

The roof construction is a built-up felt and bitumen covering on fibre board on decking and has a white gravel finish. 100 mm by 50 mm by 4 mm thick channel purlins are used and one of these is detailed at U, Fig. 18. Purlins are placed closer together than is needed to carry dead and superimposed loading to give adequate wind bracing, further bracing is placed at the level of the bottom boom of the truss as shown at J and O, Fig. 17.

Comparison between Steel and Reinforced Concrete Frames for Multi-storey Buildings. *The difference in cost, performance and maintenance between steel and reinforced concrete frames is small, and neither has any marked advantage over the other. Each building needs separate consideration; individual analysis will determine the ultimate decision, guidance on the choice of frame can only be of a general character as follows.*

Concrete is cheaper than steel, and it is possible for a concrete frame to be up to 20 per cent cheaper than a steel one; this is the main reason why R.C. is the most popular framing material. Where wide spacing of stanchions is required, these and the beams will be smaller if of reinforced concrete. Where steelwork has an in-situ concrete casing, the formwork to the floors can be slung and props eliminated (see A, Fig. 33).

A building made with a steel frame is more readily adaptable than one with a R.C. frame. Certain premises, like research institutes, sometimes require structural alterations to be made; these are much more difficult in the case of a R.C. framed building than one having a steel frame.

A steel frame is more quickly erected than an in-situ concrete one, time being absorbed for the latter in placing the forms and waiting for the concrete to harden. Hence, the side cladding and roofing of the steel job can be finished sooner, which enables the internal work to be started and finished more quickly.

A reinforced concrete frame has inherent fire protection, for example, a 50 mm concrete cover to beam reinforcement gives a two-hour rating. On the other hand a steel frame has to be protected, and a steel beam can have a two-hour resistance when covered with a 38 mm thick casing of fibre-cement. The same resistance to fire is offered by encasing a steel beam with in-situ concrete, and although such concrete need not be of the same high quality*

* This consists of preformed slabs, held in place by 1.6 mm thick nichrome wire sunk in grooves 9 mm deep, grooves and joints being pointed with refractory cement.

demanded for reinforced concrete work, the casing enables higher stresses to be used in the design of the steel frame. This results in smaller steel sections being used but it greatly increases the erection time and formwork is needed. The use of concrete casings to permit greater stresses is probably only worth while in the taller buildings. Alternative lighter casings, such as the one given above (see also C, H, K, L and M, Fig. 34), ought to be used with greater frequency where analysis shows that the adoption of concrete casings would not permit a reasonable saving to be made in the size of sections.

REINFORCED CONCRETE

An introduction to this subject has been given in Vol. I, and the different types of cement, their manufacture, types of concrete and mixing have all been covered in Vol. II.

Symbols

A_c = cross-sectional area of concrete.
A_s = cross-sectional area of steel in tension.
b = width of section.
b_t = breadth of section.
D = diameter generally.
d = effective depth to the tensile reinforcement in a beam or slab.
f_{cu} = characteristic concrete cube strength.
f_y = characteristic strength of steel reinforcement.
M = bending moment due to ultimate loads.
M_u = ultimate resistance moment.
z = lever arm of the resistance moment.

There are two main types of reinforced concrete: ordinary reinforced concrete and prestressed reinforced concrete as in B.S. 8110: Structural Use of Concrete.

ORDINARY REINFORCED CONCRETE

This material has been in use since 1900, it is commonly used for the making of structural frames, walls and floors in either precast or in-situ form. In more recent times, there have been many advances in the making of thin precast slabs for the external cladding of buildings. The constituents of reinforced concrete are the concrete and the reinforcement.

Concrete. The type, or grade, of concrete required for a structure depends upon the particular use, the strength (known as the characteristic strength) needed to prevent structural collapse, the exposure conditions and the cover needed for the reinforcement. The two grades commonly used for reinforced concrete work are grades 20 and 25 where these two numbers are the values of the characteristic strengths in N/mm^2. The term *characteristic strength* means that value of the concrete cube strength below which not more than 5 per cent of the cube test results fall. The *cube strength* of the concrete is determined from 150 mm square cubes tested at 28 days.

Concrete durability increases as its permeability decreases. Low permeability is achieved with a low water/cement ratio, good compaction and proper curing. So sufficient cement must be provided in the mix to provide adequate workability with a water/cement ratio which is low enough for the conditions of exposure of the hardened concrete. For example, concrete having a 20 mm maximum size of aggregate, only 250 kg of cement per m^3 of concrete is required for a workable concrete completely protected from the weather compared with 360 kg needed for concrete exposed to severe weather near the sea. Concrete subject to sulphate attack (see p. 9) must be made with sulphate resisting cement.

For specification purposes structural concrete is classified in one of four ways: (1) designed mix for ordinary structural concrete; (2) prescribed mix for ordinary structural concrete; (3) designed mix for special structural concrete and (4) prescribed mix for special structural concrete.

Ordinary structural concrete is of any grade which does not contain admixtures or materials other than Portland cements to B.S. 12 (ordinary and rapid hardening), B.S. 146 (blastfurnace) and B.S. 4027 (sulphate resisting), normal weight aggregates and clean water.

Special structural concrete is one which contains admixtures or materials other than those above (*e.g.*, light-weight aggregates).

Designed mix is one for which the contractor or manufacturer is responsible for selecting the mix proportions to achieve the required strength and workability but the engineer specifies the minimum cement content and any other properties to ensure durability.

Prescribed mix is one for which the engineer specifies the mix proportions. A typical prescribed mix for grade 20 ordinary structural concrete might be 320 kg of cement: 600 kg of sand: 1 200 kg of coarse aggregate which approximates to a nominal 1:2:4 mix. The amount of water used would be that which gives a w/c ratio of about 0.6 corresponding to a slump of 25 to 75 mm.

The amount of water used should be the minimum to ensure proper workability in the production of a dense concrete. As the amount of water in the aggregates varies, periodic tests must be taken to ensure that the correct amount of mixing water is being used.

The most usual maximum size of coarse aggregate for R.C. work is 20 mm. The weight of reinforced concrete is usually taken as 25 kN/m^3.

Concrete cover to reinforcement. This is determined by the degree of fire resistance required (see pp. 91 and 103) and the durability needed to withstand the conditions of exposure; the cover should be not less than the bar diameter and will vary in thickness depending on the grade of concrete used in accordance with Table 4.

TABLE 4 CONCRETE COVER

Conditions of exposure	Concrete grade 20	25	30	40	50 and over
	Nominal cover in mm				
Mild: *e.g.*, completely protected	25	20	15	15	15
Moderate: sheltered from severe rain and frost. Concrete buried or in water	–	40	30	25	20
Severe: exposed to driving rain, frost, heavy condensation and corrosive fumes	–	50	40	30	25
Very severe: exposed to sea water or moorland water			–	60	50

There is an increased tendency now towards the use of "ready mixed" concrete which is produced at depots adjacent to large cities. At such places, special equipment consisting of a *weight-batching* mixer is used, where the ingredients are carefully measured and mixing occurs under close supervision. For example, electrical measuring devices are used to determine the water content of aggregates. The water/cement ratio (and therefore the strength) can be controlled easily and the production of a uniform quality is obtained more readily than is possible on some sites. The vehicles delivering the concrete have their own water containers so that, if necessary, mixing can be done *en route* to the site. It is known that there is no deterioration in the strength of concrete which is not placed within the initial setting time of the cement (30 to 40 minutes). On the contrary, tests have shown that for a period of six hours after the addition of water, there is actually a slight gain in strength over this period. Also, such concrete shrinks much less than that placed within the initial setting time. This is an additional factor contributing towards the use of ready mixed concrete, and it also frees the considerable space needed for site mixing. The concrete that is made in the mixing drum of the vehicle is not subject to loss of water by evaporation, it can be ready for placing as soon as it arrives on site.

Reinforcement. This is in five main categories, all in steel of various types, see Fig. 19, where a note is given of the relevant British Standards: (1) Plain round and plain square bars. (2) Wire. (3) Deformed bars. (4) Steel fabrics. (5) Proprietary materials.

(1) *Plain Round and Plain Square Bars*. These can be made of mild steel having an ultimate stress of 432 to 510 N/mm^2 or medium tensile steel having an ultimate stress of 510 to 586 N/mm^2 or high tensile steel having an ultimate stress of 571 to 664 N/mm^2. Much reinforced concrete work is done with plain round bars to B.S. 4449 as these are often the cheapest of all types of reinforcement. The characteristic strength (see p. 47) of these is 250 N/mm^2.

(2) *Wire*. This is cold drawn from mild steel so as to have an ultimate stress of 571 to 649 MN/mm^2.

(3) *Deformed Bars. Square twisted bars*. See Q, they have an ultimate stress of 478 MN/mm^2 or more. They are bars which have had their load-carrying capacity increased by a cold drawing process which twists and elongates the original square bar or they may be hot rolled high-yield bars. Such a bar provides a better bond or adhesion to the concrete and thus hooks (see G, Fig. 21) can be reduced or eliminated. When these bars are used, the bond stress with the concrete can be increased and this can lead to an economy in the use of reinforcement. The amount of twist or pitch is between 8 and 14 times the bar thickness, a twist being defined as a complete turn through 360 degrees. *Twin twisted round bars*. See R, these are made by stretching and twisting together two bars of the same size, they have an ultimate stress of 432 MN/mm^2. The pitch and permissible increase in bond stress is as above for square twisted bars. The deformed bar at W is made from a special rolled bar which has two parallel longitudinal ribs with transverse diagonal ribs. It is twisted and stretched so that the permissible working strength is increased. The ribs increase the nominal diameter by 10 per cent and a 25 per cent increase in bond stress over that for plain bars is permitted. The makers of the bar claim that a cost economy over plain round bars of 15 per cent is possible with this bar, it conforms to B.S. 4461 (except for pitch of twist – it being additionally stretched).

(4) *Steel Fabrics. Hard drawn steel wire fabric* to B.S. 4483 in either square or oblong mesh. These are shown at A and B and in detail at E, F. J and K. The wires are electrically welded together at all junctions to make a mat or *fabric*. The fabrics are made into rolls and sheets of various sized bars as shown, the main bars run the length of the sheet. *Twisted steel fabrics* are made of twisted square bars, woven into a square mesh mat as shown at C and G, the bars are hooked at the ends. The bars are not welded at the intersections, but due to the twist, they interlock and grip each other. The oblong mesh type is shown at D, H and L, it is made from square twisted main bars with twin twisted cross bars interlocking as before. *Expanded metal fabric*, see M, X and X′. This is commonly known as XPM and is made from sheet steel which is cut and expanded so as to form a diamond-shaped mesh as shown at X and X′, it is produced from blank steel sheet having an ultimate stress of 400 to 494 N/mm^2. The basic sheet sizes are given on the drawing and certain sizes are obtainable in rolls. One of the firms* that produce this material makes a large number of different types of fabric having a multitude of other uses such as a backing for suspended plaster ceilings, and in the flattened form, for machinery guards, vents, filters and radiator grilles, etc. It is available in aluminium alloy, copper and brass as well as steel. 6 mm s.w.m. (the short-way mesh size) is also used as shuttering for "no-fines" concrete walls.

(5) *Proprietary Materials*. Two common types are given below, both of them can serve the dual purpose of reinforcement and formwork. *Riblath*,* see N, T and Y, is made from small-gauge expanded metal having the s.w.m. size of

*** Manufactured by the Expanded Metal Co. Ltd., see also p. 79.**

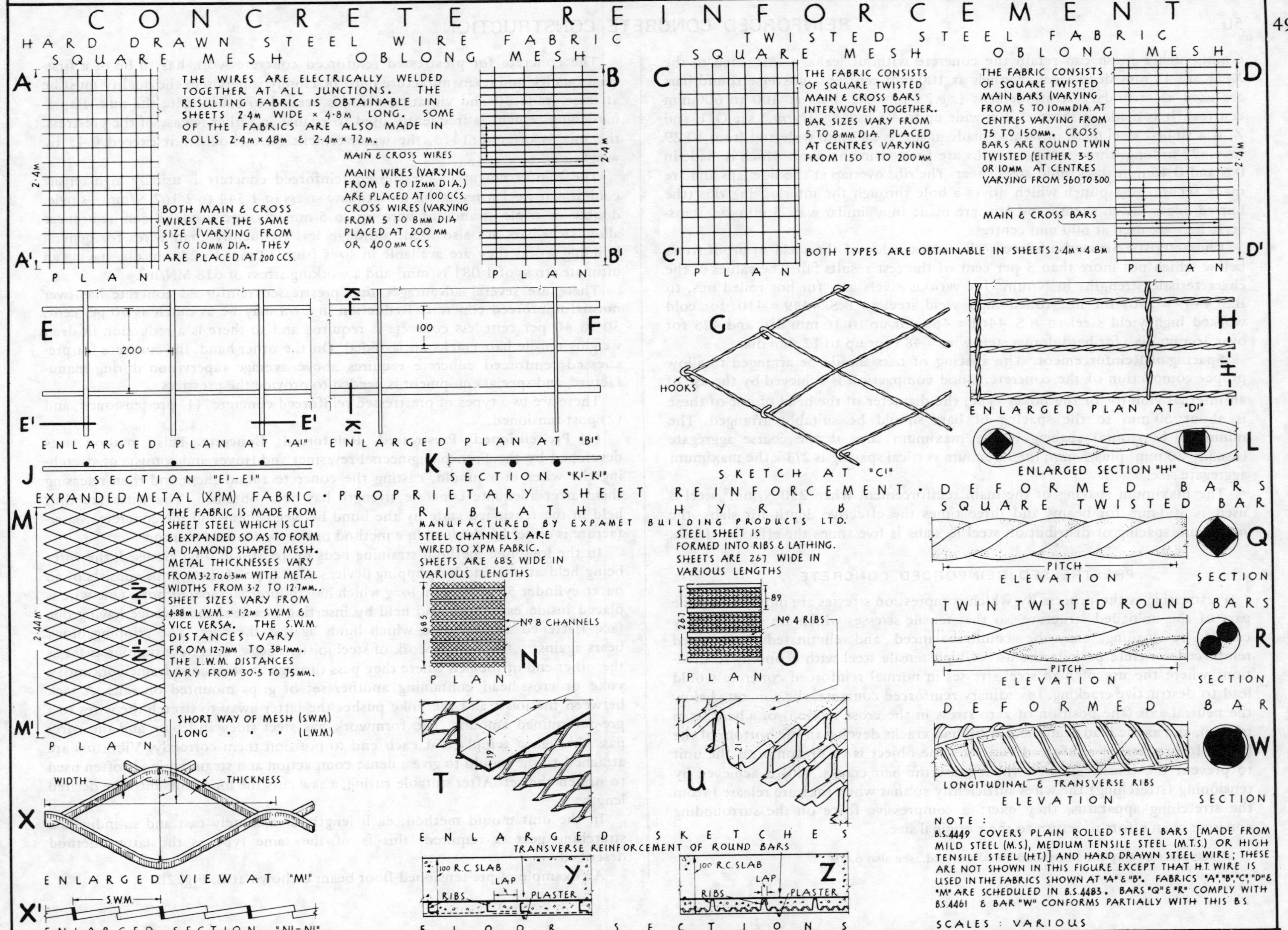
CONCRETE REINFORCEMENT
HARD DRAWN STEEL WIRE FABRIC
SQUARE MESH
OBLONG MESH
A
A'
B
B'
THE WIRES ARE ELECTRICALLY WELDED TOGETHER AT ALL JUNCTIONS. THE RESULTING FABRIC IS OBTAINABLE IN SHEETS 2·4m WIDE × 4·8m LONG. SOME OF THE FABRICS ARE ALSO MADE IN ROLLS 2·4m × 48m & 2·4m × 72m.
MAIN & CROSS WIRES
MAIN WIRES (VARYING FROM 6 TO 12mm DIA.) ARE PLACED AT 100 CCS. CROSS WIRES (VARYING FROM 5 TO 8mm DIA PLACED AT 200mm OR 400mm CCS.
BOTH MAIN & CROSS WIRES ARE THE SAME SIZE (VARYING FROM 5 TO 10mm DIA. THEY ARE PLACED AT 200 CCS.
2·4m
PLAN
PLAN
TWISTED STEEL FABRIC
SQUARE MESH
OBLONG MESH
C
C'
D
D'
THE FABRIC CONSISTS OF SQUARE TWISTED MAIN & CROSS BARS INTERWOVEN TOGETHER. BAR SIZES VARY FROM 5 TO 8mm DIA. PLACED AT CENTRES VARYING FROM 150 TO 200mm
THE FABRIC CONSISTS OF SQUARE TWISTED MAIN BARS (VARYING FROM 5 TO 10mm DIA AT CENTRES VARYING FROM 75 TO 150mm. CROSS BARS ARE ROUND TWIN TWISTED (EITHER 3·5 OR 10mm AT CENTRES VARYING FROM 560 TO 300.
MAIN & CROSS BARS
BOTH TYPES ARE OBTAINABLE IN SHEETS 2·4m × 4·8m
PLAN
PLAN
E
E'
F
100
200
K
K
ENLARGED PLAN AT "A"
ENLARGED PLAN AT "B"
J
SECTION "E-E"
K
SECTION "K-K"
G
H
HOOKS
SKETCH AT "C"
ENLARGED PLAN AT "D"
L
ENLARGED SECTION "H"
EXPANDED METAL (XM) FABRIC
PROPRIETARY SHEET
RIBLATH
MANUFACTURED BY EXPAMET BUILDING PRODUCTS LTD.
STEEL CHANNELS ARE WIRED TO XPM FABRIC. SHEETS ARE 685 WIDE IN VARIOUS LENGTHS
M
M'
THE FABRIC MADE FROM SHEET STEEL WHICH IS CUT & EXPANDED SO AS TO FORM A DIAMOND SHAPED MESH. METAL THICKNESSES VARY FROM 3·2 TO 6·3mm WITH METAL WIDTHS FROM 3·2 TO 12·7mm. SHEET SIZES VARY FROM 4·88m S.W.M. × 1·2m S.W.M. & VICE VERSA. THE S.W.M. DISTANCES VARY FROM 12·7mm TO 38·1mm. THE L.W.M. DISTANCES VARY FROM 30·5 TO 75mm.
2·44m
N
N
Nº 8 CHANNELS
685
N
PLAN
SHORT WAY OF MESH (SWM)
LONG " " " (LWM)
PLAN
HYRIB
STEEL SHEET FORMED INTO RIBS & LATHING. SHEETS ARE 267 WIDE IN VARIOUS LENGTHS
89
267
Nº 4 RIBS
O
PLAN
REINFORCEMENT
DEFORMED BARS
SQUARE TWISTED BAR
P
Q
PITCH
ELEVATION
SECTION
TWIN TWISTED ROUND BARS
R
PITCH
ELEVATION
SECTION
DEFORMED BAR
W
LONGITUDINAL & TRANSVERSE RIBS
ELEVATION
SECTION
X
WIDTH
THICKNESS
T
U
ENLARGED VIEW AT "M"
X'
SWM
ENLARGED SECTION "N-N"
ENLARGED SKETCHES
TRANSVERSE REINFORCEMENT OF ROUND BARS
100 R.C. SLAB
LAP
RIBS
PLASTER
Y
100 R.C. SLAB
LAP
RIBS
PLASTER
Z
FLOOR SECTIONS
NOTE:
BS.4449 COVERS PLAIN ROLLED STEEL BARS [MADE FROM MILD STEEL (M.S), MEDIUM TENSILE STEEL (M.T.S) OR HIGH TENSILE STEEL (H.T.)] AND HARD DRAWN STEEL WIRE; THESE ARE NOT SHOWN IN THIS FIGURE EXCEPT THAT H.T. WIRE IS USED IN THE FABRICS SHOWN AT "A" & "B". FABRICS "A", "B", "C", "D" & "M" ARE SCHEDULED IN B.S. 4483. BARS "Q" & "R" COMPLY WITH BS.4461 & BAR "W" CONFORMS PARTIALLY WITH THIS B.S.
SCALES: VARIOUS

FIGURE 19

6 mm, such a mesh can retain the concrete without leakage. Attached to the XPM are 19 mm deep steel channels at 100 mm centres, transverse round bars are used as secondary reinforcement (*e.g.*, 6 mm dia. bars at 400 to 600 mm centres). It is made in sheets 1.2 m wide up to 4.8 m long. *Hyrib*,* see O, U and Z, is a ribbed steel mesh or lathing made in sheets 267 mm wide and from 1.829 to 4.877 m long; three composite ribs are formed in the mesh which is made in 0.6 and 0.46 mm thick mild steel sheet. The ribs overlap at the side laps and are made secure by a punch which drives a hole through the interlocking ribs (the burred edges fasten them), end laps are made in a similar way. 5 mm dia. transverse bars are used at 600 mm centres.

Characteristic Strength of Steel. This is the value of the yield or proof stress below which not more than 5 per cent of the test results fall. The values of the characteristic strengths in N/mm^2 for various steels are: for hot rolled m.s. to B.S. 4449 = 250; for hot rolled high yield steel to B.S. 4449 = 410; for cold worked high yield steel to B.S. 4461 = 460 for up to 16 mm dia. and 425 for over 16 mm dia.; for hard drawn steel wire = 485 for up to 12 mm dia.

Spacing of Reinforcement. The spacing of bars should be arranged to allow proper compaction of the concrete. Good compaction is achieved by the use of an internal vibrator of the poker type; the diameter of the head of one of these is about 60 mm so the spacing of bars should be suitably arranged. The minimum horizontal spacing is the maximum size of the coarse aggregate (usually 20 mm) plus 5 mm; the minimum vertical spacing is 2/3 × the maximum aggregate size.

The maximum spacing of the main reinforcement when 250 N/mm^2 steel is used is 300 mm for beams and three times the effective depth for slabs; the maximum spacing of distribution steel in slabs is five times the effective depth.

PRESTRESSED REINFORCED CONCRETE

Prestressing is the process by which compression stresses are induced in some part of the unloaded structure, so that tensile stresses which are subsequently caused by loading, may be counterbalanced and eliminated. Prestressed reinforced concrete permits the use of high tensile steel with economy in situations where the use of high steel stresses in normal reinforced concrete would lead to destructive cracking. In ordinary reinforced concrete, the concrete below the neutral axis (the position of zero stress in the cross section) of a beam is in tension, and as the load is applied, small hair cracks develop in the bottom of the beam. In prestressed reinforced concrete, the object is to precompress the unit to prevent the tensile stresses which cause the hair cracks. This is achieved by tensioning (stretching) the wires sufficiently so that when they are released from the stretching apparatus, they exert a compressive force on the surrounding concrete in an effort to return to their original size.

* **Manufactured by the Expanded Metal Co. Ltd., see also p. 79.**

The concrete for prestressed reinforced concrete work has to be of a first-class quality and its manufacture must be closely supervised; the quality must be at least grade 30 and vibrating plant is needed to consolidate the mix. Rapid-hardening cement is frequently used to enable an earlier release of the prestress, the mix is often $1:1\frac{1}{2}:3$, the water/cement ratio should not exceed 0.45 by weight.

The reinforcement in prestressed reinforced concrete is usually high tensile cold-drawn steel wire, having an ultimate stress of 1 544 to 2 162 N/mm^2; single, double or triple strands of wire up to 5 mm dia. are used. Silicon-manganese alloy steel bars are also used, although less frequently than wires for general building work, they are available in sizes from 12 mm to 28 mm dia. having an ultimate stress of 1 081 N/mm^2 and a working stress of 618 MN/m^2.

There are several advantages that prestressed reinforced concrete has over normal reinforced concrete. Reduction in steel may be as much as 70 per cent, 30 to 40 per cent less concrete is required and so there is a reduction in dead weight, tensile hair cracks are avoided. On the other hand, the concrete for prestressed reinforced concrete requires above average supervision during manufacture, and special equipment is needed to provide the prestress.

There are two types of prestressed reinforced concrete: (1) pre-tensioned, and (2) post-tensioned.

(1) Pre-tensioned Prestressed Reinforced Concrete. This method was developed by the French engineers Freyssinet and Hoyer and consists of stretching the wires in a mould, casting the concrete round them and then releasing them after adequate concrete strength has been obtained. The wires are thus held in the tensioned state by the bond between them and the concrete. Manufacture is either by the *long line* method or the *unit mould* method.

In the long line method, straining beds up to 300 m long are used, the wires being held at one end by gripping devices. One type of these grips consists of an outer cylinder 50 to 75 mm long which has an internal tapered bore. One wire is placed inside each bore and held by inserting a cone-shaped wedge having one face flattened and serrated which binds against the wire. The gripping block bears against a fixed framework of steel joists. The wires are continuous as far as the other end of the bed where they pass through another joist framework into a yoke or cross-head containing another set of grips mounted on rails. A jack between the joists and the yoke pushes the latter away to stretch the wires to a pre-determined amount. The formwork has steel sides and base and the wires pass through a template at each end to position them correctly. Vibrators are attached to the mould to give a dense compaction and steam curing is often used to hasten the set. After suitable curing, a saw cuts the long units into the desired lengths.

In the unit mould method, each length is separately cast and so individual stretching gear is required, this is of the same type as the latter method described.

An example of pre-tensioned floor beam is shown at C, Fig. 28.

(2) Post-tensioned Prestressed Reinforced Concrete. With this type the wires are not stretched until the concrete has set, the wires may be bonded to the concrete or left unbonded. They are placed in ducts formed in the unit by inflatable rubber tubing, which is recoverable, or by flexible steel tubing. As soon as the concrete has hardened the wires are introduced to the ducts, gripped by special devices which anchor them to the concrete and then tensioned. Grout is usually subsequently injected to protect the wires from corrosion.

DESIGN* OF REINFORCED CONCRETE

One of the advantages of reinforced concrete is that it is a plastic material capable of being cast into almost any shape, in large areas, with slabs and beams continuous over relatively large distances. This continuity leads to the economy in the sizing of some members because they share the moments induced by a load. Whilst it is normally an advantage in this respect, continuity does also raise problems of sound insulation by providing direct paths for the transmission of noise. Where a large slab cannot be cast in one day, then the work has to be stopped across the centre of beams and at the mid-span of slabs. This is done by inserting a stop board (which can be of the type that will form a tongued joint as at G, Fig. 33) so as to make a *construction joint*. Before placing the new concrete against the joint, the surface of the old concrete is well roughened, hacked clean and washed to remove the cement skin. It is then plastered with a layer of cement and sand mortar (of the same proportion as the concrete mix) to a thickness of 25 mm, and the new concrete placed against it.

Concrete expands and contracts due to variations in temperature and moisture. In a building, the roof is susceptible to these changes, so *expansion joints* should be left in roof slabs at 30 m intervals. At such joints (see also pp. 60, 77 and 78, the construction adopted is to allow a gap of about 50 mm; weathering is obtained by forming a concrete upstand on either side of the gap and covering it with a copper flashing fixed to one side only (see N, Fig. 25).

For the greatest economy to be achieved, the aim of the reinforced concrete designer is to provide just enough concrete and steel which will be stressed *to the maximum* in resisting the applied and dead loads. It is obviously more satisfactory to have relatively small amounts of steel and concrete working to maximum capacity, than larger amounts which become only lightly stressed.

Reinforced concrete is designed in accordance with B.S. 8110: *The Structural Use of Concrete.*

* This volume is concerned only with the design of small lintels and simple slabs, serving as an introduction to the subject of design. A more extended treatment of the design of slabs, beams, columns, foundations and other reinforced concrete members is given in Vol. V. These parts of the structural frame are considered here only in typical form, so that the student will have a knowledge of the shape of members and the general arrangement of reinforcement. The design of reinforced concrete is the responsibility of the structural engineer, but the framework that he provides cannot be divorced from the larger subject of building construction.

The main purpose in the design of a reinforced concrete building is to produce a structure which will remain serviceable for its full design life. A structure which has become unfit for use is said to have reached a *limit state*. There are several such states, the most important being: (1) Structural collapse of the whole structure or of individual members; (2) Excessive deflection; (3) Excessive concrete cracking. B.S. 8110 calls these states the Ultimate Limit State, the Deflection Limit State and the Cracking Limit State respectively; the last two are also referred to as Serviceability Limit States.

The loads used in design are called characteristic loads and two of these loads are the *characteristic dead load* which is the weight of the structure complete with finishes, fixtures and partitions and the *characteristic imposed load* (or *live load*) which is the load produced by the intended occupancy including snow but excluding wind. Limit state design requires that safety factors, called *partial safety factors* in B.S. 8110, are applied to both the characteristic loads and the characteristic material strengths (see pp. 47 and 50). Many values of these partial safety factors are given varying from 0.9 to 1.6 but it is only necessary here to use four: 1.4 for dead loads; 1.6 for live loads; 1.5 for concrete strength; and 1.15 for steel strength. The partial safety factors for concrete and steel strengths are incorporated within the design equations which follow and so do not need to be used directly. The use of the dead and live load factors are illustrated in the examples below.

Ultimate Limit State. It can be shown that the bending strength of a R.C. member; *i.e.*, the ultimate resistance moment (M_u) is the lesser of the values obtained from the following equations:

$$M_u = 0.15 \times f_{cu} \times b \times d^2 \text{ N mm}$$

$$M_u = 0.87 \times f_y \times A_s \times z \text{ N mm}$$

If we put $z = z'd$ and call z' the lever arm factor the two equations for resistance moment can be rearranged to give a relationship between z' and $\dfrac{M}{b \times d^2 \times f_{cu}}$. This relationship is given in numerical form in the Table below.

z'	$\dfrac{M}{b \times d^2 \times f_{cu}}$	z'	$\dfrac{M}{b \times d^2 \times f_{cu}}$
1.0	0	0.85	0.101
0.95	0.037	0.80	0.128
0.90	0.072	0.75	0.150

In design one has to check that the moment on the member is not greater than the resistance moment of the concrete by using the first equation above for M_u then to put the second equation in the form $A_s = \dfrac{M}{0.87 f_y z' d}$ where M is now the design moment. The method is illustrated in the examples below.

Limit State of Deflection. Deflection requirements can be satisfied generally by ensuring that the values of the ratio: (span ÷ depth) do not exceed 7 for cantilevers, 20 for simply supported members and 26 for continuous members; provided that the spans are not greater than 10 m. Deflection is directly influenced by the amount of load so the basic (span ÷ depth) ratios can be modified by further factors which are dependent on the kind of load. For instance a lightly loaded roof slab might have a (span ÷ depth) modification factor of 1.5 or 2 but for a heavily loaded warehouse floor the factor might be as low as 0.67. The ratios only give a rough control over deflection and more refined methods for conforming with this limit state are given in B.S. 8110.

Limit State of Cracking. This can be taken as satisfied if the members are designed according to the procedures set out for the above two limit states and the further restrictions on the spacing of reinforcement (see p. 50).

Design of Slabs (Fig. 20). Normally, a slab will be designed to span the shortest distance* so that the main reinforcement will be placed in this direction the load being transmitted to supports on two sides. At right angles to the main bars, and wired to them, secondary reinforcement (sometimes called distribution steel) is laid (see B). Slabs are of four types: (1) simply supported, (2) with ends restrained, (3) continuous over one or more supports, and (4) cantilevers.

In all cases, the minimum reinforcement in either direction is to be not less than 0.15 per cent of A_c for m.s. and 0.12 per cent of A_c for high yield steel.

(1) *Simply Supported Slabs* (A and F). The roof slab is considered to be formed of 1 m wide strips of 3 m clear span.

Use concrete which has $f_{cu} = 25$ N/mm^2 and steel $f_y = 250$ N/mm^2.

The effective depth of the slab is estimated from the span ÷ depth ratio; as the slab is lightly loaded the span ÷ depth modification factor is taken as 1.5.

Therefore the effective depth must be not less than $\dfrac{3\,000}{20 \times 1.5} = 100$ mm.

Overall depth of slab = 100 + cover of 20 + 6 ($\frac{1}{2}$ bar dia.) = 126 (say 130 mm).
Effective span = 3 000 + 100 = 3 100 mm.

Characteristic dead loads: (kN/m^2)

Concrete = $\dfrac{130}{1\,000} \times 1 \times 1 \times 25 = 3.25$

19 mm asphalt = 0.32
12 mm plaster = 0.2
38 mm average screed = 0.86
Total = 4.63

For design purposes this dead load is multiplied by the partial safety factor for dead loads to give a design load = 4.63 × 1.4 = 6.482 kN/m^2.

* Slabs can also be designed to span in two directions, so that they are supported on four sides – see Vol. V. The effective span l of a slab is the lesser of the following: (1) distance between centres of bearings, (2) clear distance between supports, plus the effective depth d_1.

Characteristic live load:

Superimposed roof load = 0.75 kN/m^2
Partial safety factor = 1.6
Therefore design live load = 0.75 × 1.6 = 1.2 kN/m^2
Hence total design load = 6.482 + 1.2 = 7.682 kN/m^2.

This load is carried on an effective span of 3.1 m and so a 1 m wide strip of slab of this length will carry 7.682 × 3.1 × 1 = 23.81 kN.

$$\text{B.M.} = \frac{W \times L}{8} = \frac{23.81 \times 3.1}{8} = 9.23 \text{ kN m.}$$

Resistance moment of concrete $M_u = 0.15 \times f_{cu} \times b \times d^2$ N mm
$= 0.15 \times 25 \times 1\,000 \times 100^2$ N mm
$= 37.5 \times 10^6$ N mm

Note re $\dfrac{M}{bd^2 f_{cu}}$. It is not really necessary to calculate this value of M_u since it follows from the equation that providing the value of $\dfrac{M}{bd^2 f_{cu}}$ is equal to or less than 0.15 the resistance moment of the concrete is always satisfactory.

$$\frac{M}{bd^2 f_{cu}} = \frac{9.23 \times 10^6}{1\,000 \times 100^2 \times 25} = 0.037.$$

From the table on p. 51 z = 0.95.

$$\text{The area of reinforcement } A_s = \frac{M}{0.87 \times f_y \times z' \times d}$$

$$= \frac{9.23 \times 10^6}{0.87 \times 250 \times 0.95 \times 100} = 447 \text{ mm}^2 \text{ per m width of slab.}$$

Using 12 mm dia. m.s. bars, the area of one bar = 113 mm^2. 447 mm^2 of steel is required per 1 000 mm width of slab, therefore to provide this the spacing of 12 mm bars would be $\dfrac{1\,000}{447} \times 113 = 253$ mm.

So use 12 mm dia. main bars at 250 mm centres.

The area of distribution steel required = $\dfrac{0.15}{100} \times 1\,000 \times 100 = 150$ mm^2 per m width of slab.

Using 8 mm dia. bars, the area of one such bar = 50.26 mm^2. 150 mm^2 of distribution steel is required per 1 000 mm width of slab, therefore to provide this the spacing of 8 mm dia. bars would be $\dfrac{1\,000}{150} \times 50.26 = 335$ mm.

So use 8 mm dia. distribution bars at 335 mm centres.

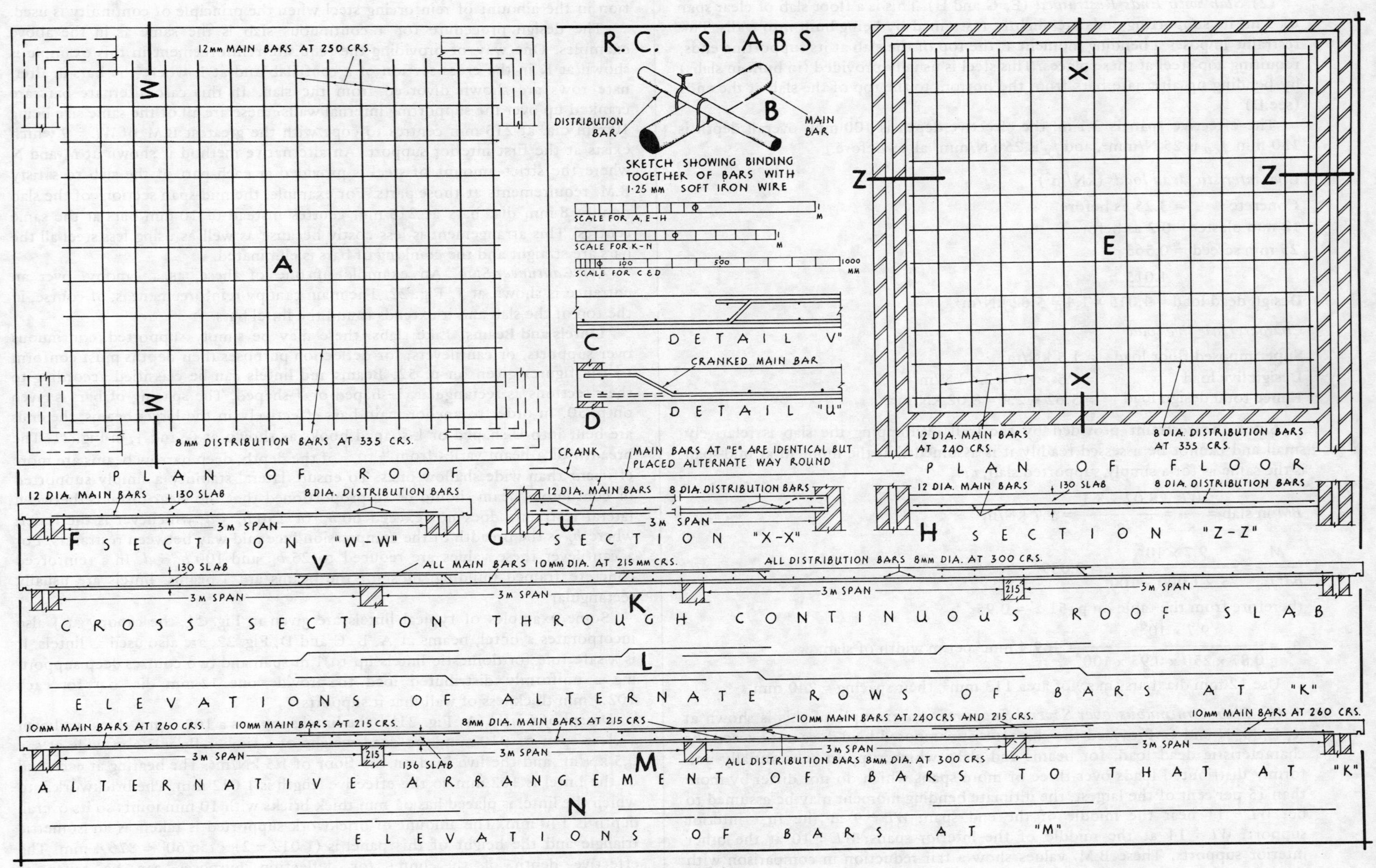

R.C. SLABS
12mm MAIN BARS AT 250 CRS.
W
W
A
8mm DISTRIBUTION BARS AT 335 CRS.
PLAN OF ROOF
DISTRIBUTION BAR
B
MAIN BAR
SKETCH SHOWING BINDING TOGETHER OF BARS WITH 1·25 mm SOFT IRON WIRE
SCALE FOR A, E–H
M
SCALE FOR K–N
M
SCALE FOR C & D
100
500
1000 MM
C
DETAIL "V"
CRANKED MAIN BAR
D
DETAIL "U"
CRANK
MAIN BARS AT "E" ARE IDENTICAL BUT PLACED ALTERNATE WAY ROUND
X
Z
Z
E
X
12 DIA. MAIN BARS AT 240 CRS.
8 DIA. DISTRIBUTION BARS AT 335 CRS.
PLAN OF FLOOR
12 DIA. MAIN BARS
130 SLAB
8 DIA. DISTRIBUTION BARS
3m SPAN
F
SECTION "W-W"
12 DIA. MAIN BARS
8 DIA. DISTRIBUTION BARS
U
3m SPAN
G
SECTION "X-X"
12 DIA. MAIN BARS
130 SLAB
8 DIA. DISTRIBUTION BARS
H
SECTION "Z-Z"
130 SLAB
ALL MAIN BARS 10mm DIA. AT 215mm CRS.
V
3m SPAN
3m SPAN
ALL DISTRIBUTION BARS 8mm DIA. AT 300 CRS.
3m SPAN
215
3m SPAN
K
CROSS SECTION THROUGH CONTINUOUS ROOF SLAB
L
ELEVATIONS OF ALTERNATE ROWS OF BARS AT "K"
10mm MAIN BARS AT 260 CRS.
10mm MAIN BARS AT 215 CRS.
8mm DIA. MAIN BARS AT 215 CRS.
10mm MAIN BARS AT 240 CRS AND 215 CRS.
10mm MAIN BARS AT 260 CRS.
3m SPAN
215
136 SLAB
3m SPAN
3m SPAN
3m SPAN
M
ALL DISTRIBUTION BARS 8mm DIA. AT 300 CRS
ALTERNATIVE ARRANGEMENT OF BARS TO THAT AT "K"
N
ELEVATIONS OF BARS AT "M"

FIGURE 20

(2) *Slab with Ends Restrained* (E, G and H). This is a floor slab of clear span of 3 m, its supporting ends are slightly restrained by being built into walls. This restraint imposes a bending moment at the top of the slab at its supporting ends, requiring top steel at these places. This steel is usually provided (in built-in slabs) by bending up alternate bars from the bottom to the top of the slab at the ends (see D).

The effective span is 3.1 m, the effective depth is 100 mm, overall depth is 130 mm, f_{cu} is 25 N/mm², and f_y is 250 N/mm² all as before.

Characteristic dead loads (kN/m²)

Concrete = 3.25 as before
12 mm plaster = 0.2 as before
25 mm screed = 0.565

4.015

Design dead load = 4.015 × 1.4 = 5.62 kN/m²

Characteristic live load

Superimposed floor load = 1.5 kN/m²
Design live load = 1.5 × 1.6 = 2.4 kN/m²
Hence total design load = 5.62 + 2.4 = 8.02 kN/m².

Since the restraint provided by the wall overlapping the slab is relatively small and cannot be assessed readily it is assumed that the moment at mid-span is the same as for a simply supported slab; *i.e.*,

$$BM \text{ in slab} = \frac{WL}{8} = \frac{8.02 \times 3.1^2}{8} = 9.7 \text{ kN/m}$$

$$\frac{M}{bd^2 f_{cu}} = \frac{9.7 \times 10^6}{25 \times 1\,000 \times 100^2} = 0.039$$

therefore from the table on p. 51 $z' = 0.95$

$$A_s = \frac{9.7 \times 10^6}{0.87 \times 250 \times 0.95 \times 100} = 469.4 \text{ mm}^2 \text{ per m width of slab.}$$

Use 12 mm dia. bars (m.s.) of area 113 mm², their spacing = 240 mm.

(3) *Slab Continuous over Several Supports.* An example of this is shown at K, L, M, N and C. Provided the characteristic imposed load does not exceed the characteristic dead load, for beams and slabs which support substantially uniformly distributed loads over three or more spans which do not differ by more than 15 per cent of the largest, the ultimate bending moment may be assumed to be: $WL \div 11$ near the middle of the end span; $WL \div 9$ at the first interior support; $WL \div 14$ at the middle of the interior spans; $WL \div 10$ at the other interior supports. These B.M. values show a fair reduction in comparison with the B.M. in a simply supported slab of $WL \div 8$ creating a corresponding reduction in the amount of reinforcing steel when the principle of continuity is used.

The design procedure for a continuous slab is the same as in the above examples. One way of providing the requisite reinforcement in this example is shown at K in the cross section of a roof slab and at L where the bars in alternate rows are shown divorced from the slab. In this case alternate bars are cranked up over the supporting internal walls; these are all of the same size being 10 mm dia. at 215 mm centres to cope with the greatest B.M. of $WL \div 9$ which exists at the first interior support. An alternative method is shown at M and N where the strict amount of steel is provided at each part of the slab to satisfy B.M. requirements at those parts. For example, the mid-span sections of the slab require 8 mm dia. bars at 215 mm centres instead of 10 mm bars at the same centres. This arrangement is less costly because as well as using less steel all the bars are straight and the cranking of bars is eliminated.

(4) *Cantilever Slab.* An example of one of these, as a canopy, over an entrance is shown at J, Fig. 22. The main canopy reinforcement is, of course, in the top of the slab and it extends round the lintel bars.

Lintels and Beams. Like slabs, these may be simply supported, continuous over supports, or cantilevers; for deflection purposes their depths must conform to the figures given on p. 52. Beams and lintels can be classified according to their sections as rectangular, L-shaped or T-shaped. The spacing of bars is given on p. 50. In order to anchor main bars effectively in the larger beams, the ends are bent into U-shaped or L-shaped hooks as shown at G and J, in Fig. 21. The breadth of a beam varies from $\frac{1}{3}$ to $\frac{1}{2}$ of the depth, deep narrow beams are more efficient than wide shallow ones. To ensure lateral stability a simply supported or continuous beam should be so proportioned that the clear distance between lateral restraints does not exceed $60\, b_c$ or $250\, b_c^2 \div d$, whichever is the lesser, where b_c is the breadth of the compression face mid-way between restraints. For a cantilever these values are reduced to $25\, b_c$ and $100\, b_c^2 \div d$. In a reinforced concrete framed building, most of the beams are T-beams, lintels are usually rectangular.

Some examples of typical lintels are given in Fig. 21; the canopy at J also incorporates a lintel, beams at A, B, C and D, Fig. 22, are also used as lintels. It is a safe rule for domestic lintels up to 1 m span and two courses deep supporting a uniformly distributed load to provide one 12 mm dia. bar for each 102.5 mm thickness of wall that it supports.

Design of Lintel (A, Fig. 21). The lintel supports a 102.5 mm thick wall over a clear span of 910 mm, the dead weight of a timber floor 3.6 m wide at say 0.5 kN/m² and the live load on the floor of 1.5 kN/m². The bearing at each end of the lintel is 102 mm so the effective length is 1 012 mm. The brickwork into which the lintel is placed has 65 mm thick bricks with 10 mm joints so its overall depth is 140 mm. The amount of brickwork supported is taken as an isometric triangle and the height of this panel is (1 012 ÷ 2) × tan 60° = 876.4 mm. The effective depth of the lintel for deflection purposes can be taken as 1 012 ÷ 20 = 50.6 mm and the overall depth provided is 140 mm.

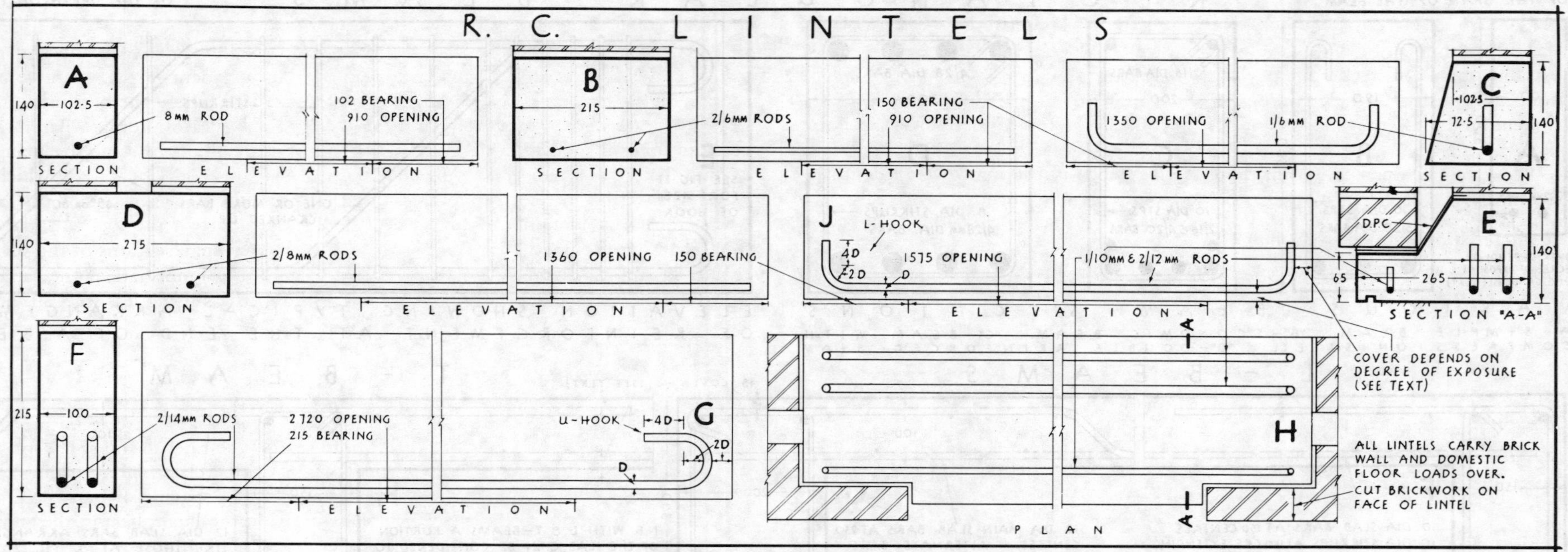

FIGURE 21

$$\text{Weight of brick panel and lintel} = \frac{1.012}{2} \times 0.8764 \times 0.1025 \times 20 = 0.91 \text{ kN}$$

$$\text{Dead weight of floor} \quad = 1.012 \times \frac{3.6}{2} \times 0.5 \quad = \underline{0.91}$$

$$1.82$$

$$\text{Design dead load} \quad = 1.82 \times 1.4 \quad = 2.548$$

$$\text{Live load} \quad = 1.012 \times \frac{3.6}{2} \times 1.5 \quad = 2.732$$

$$\text{Design live load} \quad = 2.732 \times 1.6 \quad = 4.371\,2$$

$$\text{B.M. is approximately } WL \div 8 = \frac{(2.548 + 4.371\,2) \times 1.012}{8} = 0.875 \text{ kN m}$$

A grade 20 concrete is adequate for this purpose and the effective depth is taken as 110 mm.

$$\frac{M}{b \times d^2 \times f_{cu}} = \frac{0.875 \times 10^6}{102.5 \times 110^2 \times 20} = 0.036$$

Therefore from the table on p. 51 $z' = 0.95$.

$$A_s = \frac{0.875 \times 10^6}{0.87 \times 250 \times 0.95 \times 110} = 38.5 \text{ mm}^2$$

Therefore use one 8 mm dia. m.s. bar (A_s = 50.26 mm²).

Other lintels are given in the Figure; the one at C is commonly used on the internal leaf of a cavity wall, by sloping the outer face the d.p.c. width is reduced (see R, Fig. 69). The one at E is termed a boot-lintel, being only one course deep on the outside and two courses deep on the inside.

Beams (see Fig. 22). Four sections at the mid-span of different rectangular beams are shown at A to D. As well as resisting compression, the concrete in a beam resists the shear forces, the concrete shear resistance at any section being the product $v \times b \times d$, where v = the shear stress in the concrete having a value between 0.35 and 1 N/mm², depending on the value of f_{cu} and the amount of reinforcement of the member. When insufficient concrete area is provided to resist shear, then steel shear reinforcement has to be introduced. This can be of two types, stirrups (see B to E) or bent up bars (see E). Shear stirrups should be placed not further apart than the *lever arm* of the beam which is the distance between the centre of action of the concrete stress area (the concrete stress varies from zero at the neutral axis to a maximum at the top of the beam) and the centre of the steel reinforcement. In large beams, stirrups are normally provided in any case as they help to retain the main bars in position, they can be shaped as at B or C.

Bars can be conveniently bent up to resist shear towards the end of the span where positive bending moments are less and shear is at its maximum, this is

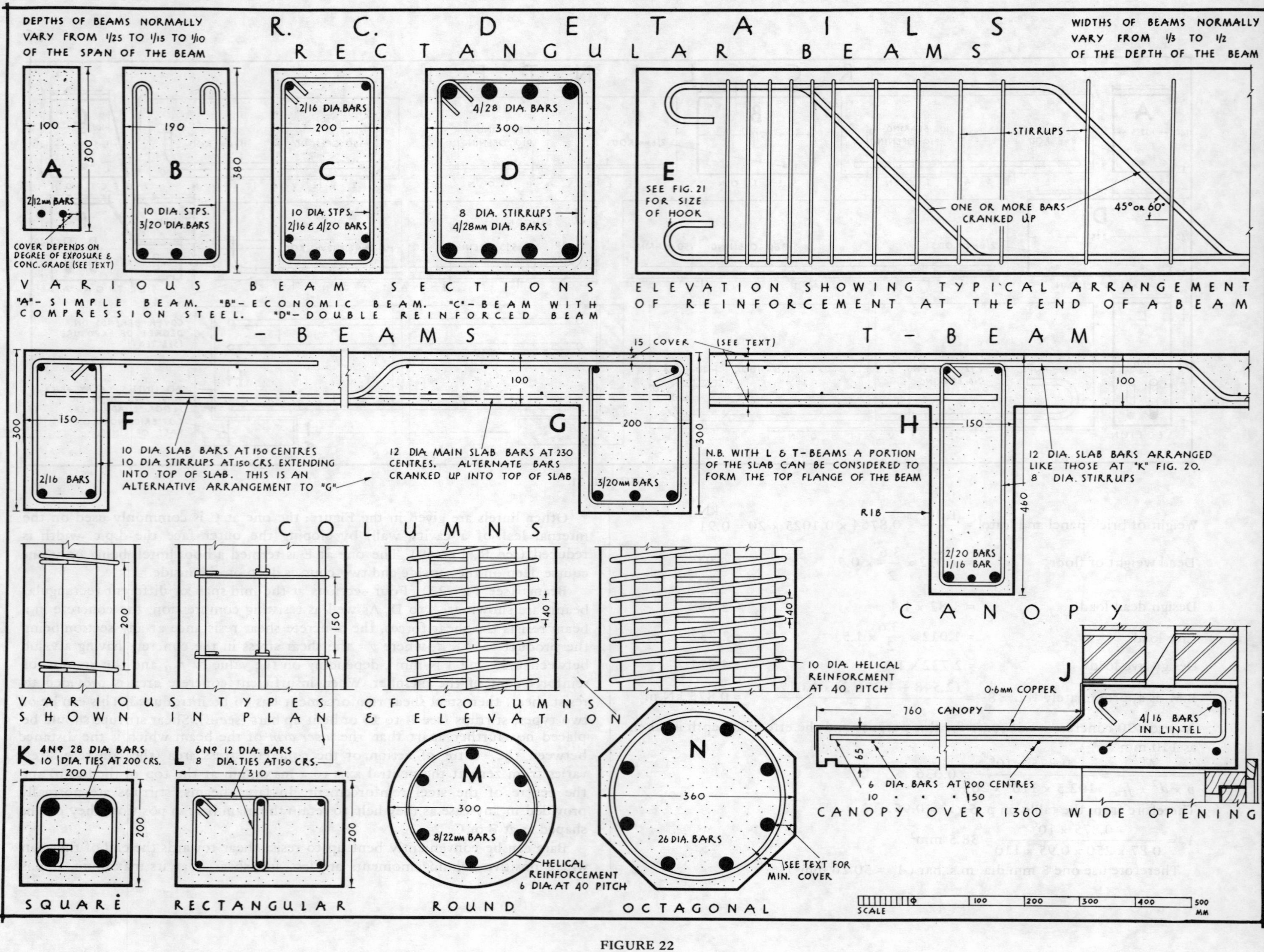

DEPTHS OF BEAMS NORMALLY VARY FROM 1/25 TO 1/15 TO 1/10 OF THE SPAN OF THE BEAM

R.C. DETAILS

RECTANGULAR BEAMS

WIDTHS OF BEAMS NORMALLY VARY FROM 1/3 TO 1/2 OF THE DEPTH OF THE BEAM

A
100
300
2/12mm BARS
COVER DEPENDS ON DEGREE OF EXPOSURE & CONC. GRADE (SEE TEXT)

B
190
10 DIA. STPS.
3/20 DIA. BARS

380

C
2/16 DIA. BARS
200
10 DIA. STPS.
2/16 & 4/20 BARS

D
4/28 DIA. BARS
300
8 DIA. STIRRUPS
4/28mm DIA. BARS

VARIOUS BEAM SECTIONS

"A"– SIMPLE BEAM. "B"– ECONOMIC BEAM. "C"– BEAM WITH COMPRESSION STEEL. "D"– DOUBLE REINFORCED BEAM

E
SEE FIG. 21 FOR SIZE OF HOOK
STIRRUPS
ONE OR MORE BARS CRANKED UP
45° or 60°

ELEVATION SHOWING TYPICAL ARRANGEMENT OF REINFORCEMENT AT THE END OF A BEAM

L-BEAMS

F
300
150
10 DIA. SLAB BARS AT 150 CENTRES
10 DIA STIRRUPS AT 150 CRS. EXTENDING INTO TOP OF SLAB. THIS IS AN ALTERNATIVE ARRANGEMENT TO "G"
2/16 BARS

15 COVER (SEE TEXT)
100

G
12 DIA. MAIN SLAB BARS AT 230 CENTRES. ALTERNATE BARS CRANKED UP INTO TOP OF SLAB
200
300
3/20mm BARS

T-BEAM

H
100
150
N.B. WITH L & T-BEAMS A PORTION OF THE SLAB CAN BE CONSIDERED TO FORM THE TOP FLANGE OF THE BEAM
12 DIA. SLAB BARS ARRANGED LIKE THOSE AT "K" FIG. 20.
8 DIA. STIRRUPS
RIB
460
2/20 BARS
1/16 BAR

COLUMNS

200
150
40
40

VARIOUS TYPES OF COLUMNS SHOWN IN PLAN & ELEVATION

K
4No 28 DIA. BARS
10 DIA. TIES AT 200 CRS.
200
200
SQUARE

L
6No 12 DIA. BARS
8 DIA. TIES AT 150 CRS.
310
200
RECTANGULAR

M
300
8/22mm BARS
HELICAL REINFORCEMENT 6 DIA. AT 40 PITCH
ROUND

N
10 DIA. HELICAL REINFORCMENT AT 40 PITCH
360
26 DIA. BARS
SEE TEXT FOR MIN. COVER
OCTAGONAL

CANOPY

J
0·6mm COPPER
760 CANOPY
4/16 BARS IN LINTEL
65
6 DIA. BARS AT 200 CENTRES
10 " " 150 "

CANOPY OVER 1360 WIDE OPENING

SCALE 0 100 200 300 400 500 MM

FIGURE 22

particularly so in continuous beams where top steel is required at the supports to withstand negative moments.

The beam at A is an ordinary one without stirrups. The one at B could be an "economic" beam where the amount of tension steel and compression concrete are related so that they are stressed to the maximum in resisting the moment. The one at C includes compression steel where there is insufficient concrete to resist the bending compression, it is sometimes called a doubly reinforced beam. At D, the beam has equal amounts of top and bottom steel, these behave in a similar way to the flanges of a steel beam (resisting compression and tension); it is a true doubly reinforced beam. The elevation at E shows how the stirrups are spaced closer together towards the end of a beam as the shear increases.

An L-beam includes part of the slab, and two examples are shown at F and G. It is permissible to consider that a fair proportion of the slab acts as forming the compression flange of the beam, providing the slab is effectively tied to the beam. Where the slab spans on to the L-beam as shown, it becomes partly restrained and top slab steel is required, two different ways of providing this are shown. L-beams occur frequently at the edge of slabs in reinforced concrete buildings and also in bridge construction.

The cross section of a T-beam is shown at H where, again, a proportion of the slab acts as the flange of the beam. Most beams supporting floors of reinforced concrete buildings are of this type, except at the supports of continuous beams where reversal of moment from positive to negative results in their acting with compression at the bottom and tension at the top.

Columns (see Fig. 22). The area of reinforcement required in a column is between 1 and 10 per cent of the gross column area, about 4 per cent is a normal maximum and this is usually not exceeded except when bars are lapped as at splices. The main longitudinal bars are held together by lateral ties or helical reinforcement as shown at the elevations K and M respectively. The diameter of this transverse reinforcement is to be not less than one-quarter of the diameter of the main bars and in no case less than 5 mm dia. Main bars should not be less than 12 mm dia. and should have adequate cover as given in Table 4.

The four most usual column sections are square, rectangular, round and octagonal as at K to N; dog-leg columns as at P, Fig. 29, are sometimes needed on awkward-shaped city sites. In the one at K, the amount of steel is about the maximum allowed; in the one at L, near the minimum; and average steel is included in M and N.

REINFORCED CONCRETE FRAMES*

The main details of a R.C. frame are given in Fig. 23, a key plan and section at G and J show main beams at 7.3 m centres supported on columns, intermediate secondary beams also are used.

* The great majority of reinforced concrete frames are cast in-situ as shown in this Volume. A precast R.C. building system is shown in Fig. 54.

At A, the section L–L shows the steel bars† in a secondary beam, 690 mm overall deep and 280 mm wide. Its reinforcement at mid-span is three cranked bars (V) and three straight bars (S′), the latter are actually cranked on plan at the column junction shown at D so as to pass three similar bars (S) from the adjoining span. Also at mid-span, at the top, there are two straight bars (Z) which are used to fix the stirrups. Where there are two rows of bottom bars, the stirrups pass alternately round the top and the bottom rows. At the right-hand support there are two rows of top steel, the upper having three straight bars (U) and one bar (T) cranked up from the next bay, the lower row consists of three bars (V), this arrangement can also be seen at H and B.

At E, the section M–M shows the steel bars in a main beam of 915 mm overall depth and 310 mm width. At mid-span, the reinforcement is in two rows, the upper row of bars (X) are cranked near the supports and the bottom row (W) extend to the columns. The latter are not cranked on plan at the right-hand support like the similar ones S′ above, due to lack of space, instead they are bent up, lapped and wired to the bars W′ from the adjacent span, hooks being omitted.

Also at E and E′, the column reinforcement and the pad foundation is shown. Short starter bars from the foundation are lapped and wired to the column bars, the use of these short bars is advocated when the column cannot be cast soon after the foundation. In such circumstances, this is a better method than having the long column bars cast in the foundation and left free to move until completion of the column. So as to simplify the shuttering (see p. 66), it is usual to have the same sized column extending through two or three storeys with varying steel content for the different loading in each storey length.

The sketch at H has been made to show the concentration of reinforcement that is present at the intersection of two beams and a column and illustrates the need for careful detailing and positioning of bars.

The arrangement shown in Fig. 23 is the most usual method of framing, but there is another one known as the flat slab method, where beams can be omitted. In this, the column spacings must be closer, the bays are more or less square and the slabs are thicker and have main reinforcement in both directions. The columns are usually provided with an enlarged head and the slab increased in depth in the vicinity of the column to form a "drop" at this point.

REINFORCED CONCRETE SHELL ROOFS

As permanent construction for the roofing of large areas, the shell has much to commend it both as a pleasing form and for the economy of steel and concrete. Shell construction is a type of structural arch membrane and roof cladding, covered* with felt or asphalt. The forces in the shell are mainly

† All the main bars are hooked at each end as at G, Fig. 21.

* The roof could be insulated by a vermiculite screed sealed with cement grout. The screed could consist of 1 part cement to 8 parts of vermiculite (density = 480 kg/m^3 and the grout covering of 1:4 cement and sand. The latter prevents the absorption of rain water prior to the asphalting or other sealing).

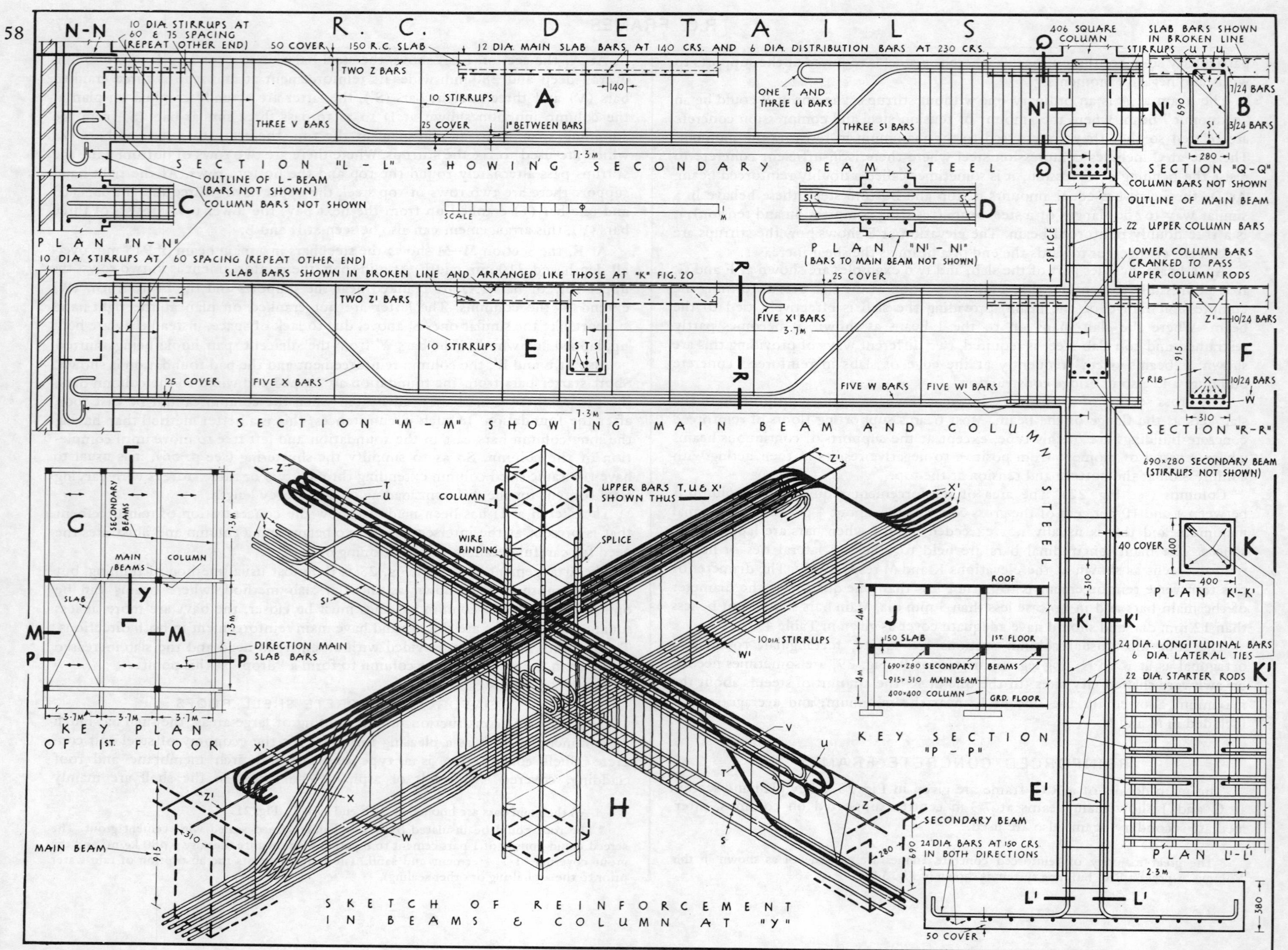
R. C. DETAILS
N-N
10 DIA. STIRRUPS AT 60 & 75 SPACING (REPEAT OTHER END)
50 COVER
150 R.C. SLAB
12 DIA. MAIN SLAB BARS AT 140 CRS. AND 6 DIA. DISTRIBUTION BARS AT 230 CRS.
TWO Z BARS
140
10 STIRRUPS
A
ONE T AND THREE U BARS
THREE V BARS
25 COVER
1" BETWEEN BARS
THREE S' BARS
SECTION "L-L" SHOWING SECONDARY BEAM STEEL
OUTLINE OF L-BEAM (BARS NOT SHOWN)
COLUMN BARS NOT SHOWN
C
SCALE
D
PLAN "N-N"
PLAN "N'-N'" (BARS TO MAIN BEAM NOT SHOWN)
406 SQUARE COLUMN
SLAB BARS SHOWN IN BROKEN LINE
STIRRUPS U T U
7/24 BARS
B
3/24 BARS
280
SECTION "Q-Q"
COLUMN BARS NOT SHOWN
OUTLINE OF MAIN BEAM
22 UPPER COLUMN BARS
LOWER COLUMN BARS CRANKED TO PASS UPPER COLUMN RODS
10 DIA. STIRRUPS AT 60 SPACING (REPEAT OTHER END)
SLAB BARS SHOWN IN BROKEN LINE AND ARRANGED LIKE THOSE AT "K" FIG. 20
TWO Z' BARS
25 COVER
FIVE X' BARS
10 STIRRUPS
E
FIVE X BARS
FIVE W BARS
FIVE W' BARS
Z' 10/24 BARS
F
RIB
10/24 BARS
310
SECTION "R-R"
SECTION "M-M" SHOWING MAIN BEAM AND COLUMN STEEL
SPLICE
690×280 SECONDARY BEAM (STIRRUPS NOT SHOWN)
G
SECONDARY BEAMS
MAIN BEAMS
COLUMN
SLAB
DIRECTION MAIN SLAB BARS
KEY PLAN OF 1ST. FLOOR
COLUMN
UPPER BARS T, U & X' SHOWN THUS
WIRE BINDING
SPLICE
K
40 COVER
400
PLAN K-K'
ROOF
J
150 SLAB
1ST. FLOOR
690×280 SECONDARY BEAMS
915×310 MAIN BEAM
400×400 COLUMN
GRD. FLOOR
KEY SECTION "P-P"
10 DIA STIRRUPS
24 DIA. LONGITUDINAL BARS
6 DIA. LATERAL TIES
22 DIA. STARTER RODS
H
MAIN BEAM
SECONDARY BEAM
24 DIA BARS AT 150 CRS. IN BOTH DIRECTIONS
PLAN L'-L'
2·3m
380
50 COVER
SKETCH OF REINFORCEMENT IN BEAMS & COLUMN AT "Y"

FIGURE 23

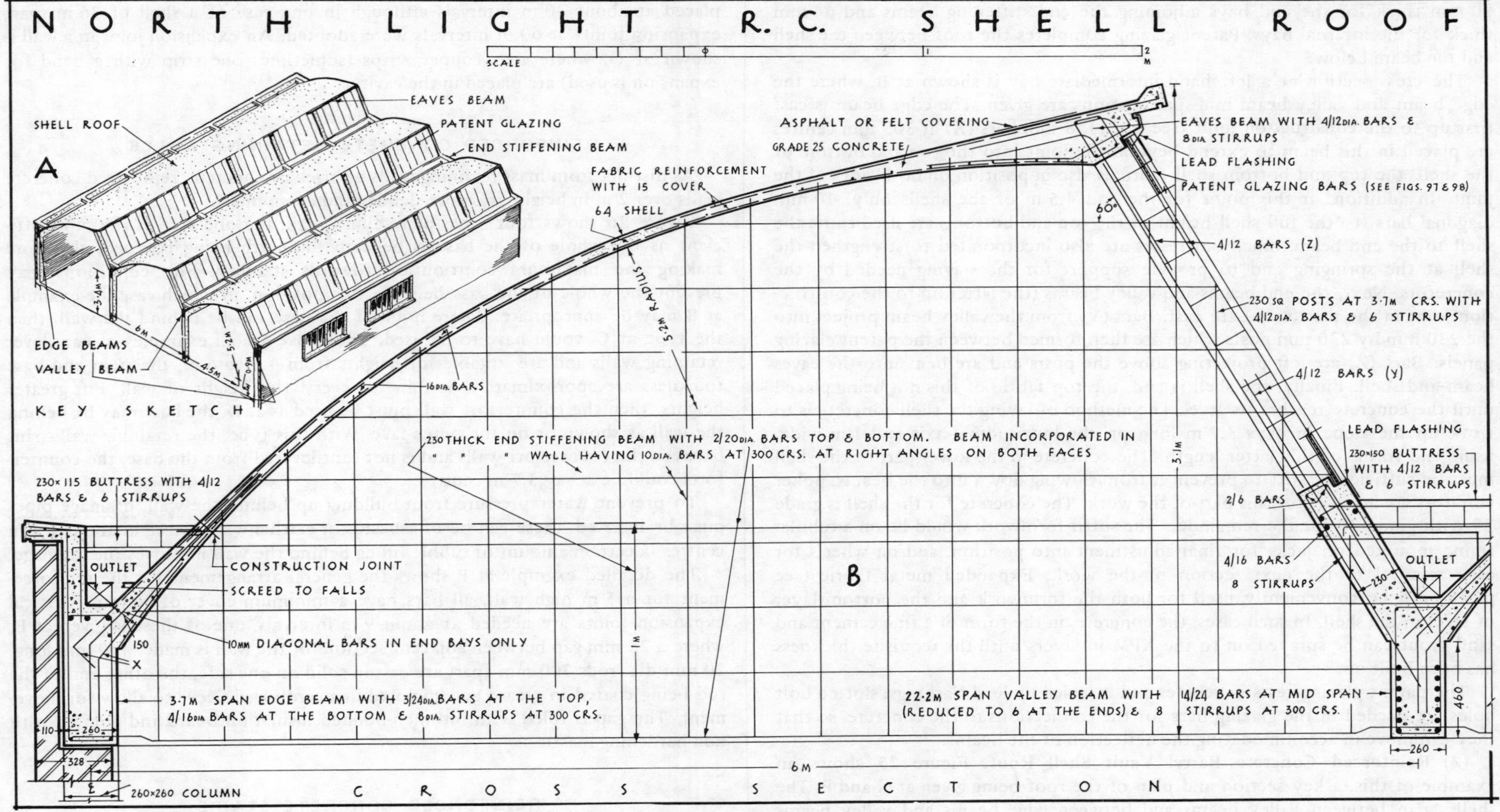

FIGURE 24

compressive and it is restrained in its position and shape by perimeter beams where the forces are mainly tensional. These beams (edge and end beams – see below) act as T-beams with the shell forming the compressive flange. As a result of the tensional stresses in the end beams particularly, these members can be economically provided with cables and prestressed. Of the types† of shell roof, two are most popular, (1) the North light shell and (2) the barrel vault shell.

(1) North Light Shell Roof. Fig. 24 shows an example of a building three bays wide with such a shell over each bay, the general arrangement being given at A. The shells extend from an edge or valley beam on the left to an eaves beam carried on 260 mm by 260 mm posts which rest on a valley or an edge beam. The beams run longitudinally and are framed at their ends into end stiffening beams, they rest on columns at 3.7 m centres for the edges and columns at 22.2 m centres for the intermediate valley beams. Each shell has a 5.2 m radius, is

† Another common type is the *hyperbolic paraboloid* shell, formed by raising the opposite corners of a square roof as described for the timber shell on pp. 167–171.

90 mm thick for the end bays adjoining the end stiffening beams and 64 mm thick for the internal bays. Patent glazing completes the roof between the shell and the beam below.

The cross section at a left hand intermediate bay is shown at B, where the edge beam and valley beam mid-span sections are given. The edge beam is cast first up to the construction joint (see p. 51), 8 mm bars (X) at 305 mm centres are placed in this beam to extend beyond the joint into the top and bottom of the shell, the top and bottom shell fabric is also in position on both sides of the joint. In addition, at this point for the end 4.5 m of the shells only, 10 mm diagonal bars (to the full shell height in the top and bottom) are used to tie the shell to the end beam. Small buttresses are also incorporated to strengthen the shell at the springing and to provide support for the staging needed by the concretors. Next, the end beams and valley beams (the latter up to the construction joint in the next shell) are cast. Bars (Y) from the valley beam project into the 230 mm by 230 mm posts which are then formed between the patent glazing panels. Bars (Z) are left projecting above the posts and are bent into the eaves beam and shell. Finally, the shell is laid, the top fabric of this not being placed until the concrete reaches its level. The method of laying the shell concrete is to work up the slope in bays 3.7 m long on the longitudinal axis and 1 m wide, using end forms of this latter length. The concrete in the lower part of the shell must be sufficiently stiff to prevent it from flowing down into the beams, poker vibrators are an asset for this part of the work. The concrete for the shell is grade 25 with grade 20 for the remainder. The soffit formwork would be on a tubular frame mounted on jacks for final adjustment into position, and on wheels for easy removal to the next section of the work. Expanded metal fabric (see p. 48) can be conveniently used for both the formwork and the bottom layer of steel in the shell. In such cases, the concrete, in the form of a fine cement and sand grout can be sprayed on to the XPM in layers until the requisite thickness has been built up.

The patent glazing rests in rebates and is sealed by lead flashings; slotted bolt holes are needed in the glazing bars for the connections to the concrete, so that they can move in accommodating the deflection of the beams.

(2) Reinforced Concrete Barrel Vault Shell Roof. Figure 25 shows an example of this, a key section and plan of the roof being given at G and P. The shells span between valley beams and between edge beams and valley beams which are at 9 m centres. Cross arch ribs are provided at 18 m centres, so the columns are on a basic grid 9 m by 18 m with intermediate columns at 3.6 m centres along the edge beams only. The inner radius of the shells is 8 m and they are 64 mm thick except for a distance of 2.1 m on either side of the arch ribs where they are 90 mm thick. A roof light is formed at the crown of the shells for most of the longitudinal distance.

The section C at J is through the edge beam showing the springing thickness of the shell of 150 mm, and the various other details are given. The detail at N is of one of the expansion joints in a long roof, these are 75 mm wide and are placed at about 30 m intervals although in one case of a shell of 36 m span, expansion joints at 60 m intervals were adopted. An expansion joint in a wall is shown at O, where two copper strips (sometimes one strip with a bend for expansion is used) are placed in the cavity.

REINFORCED CONCRETE RETAINING WALLS

As distinct from mass retaining walls of brick or concrete, reinforced concrete walls over 2 m in height are more slender and economical.

Figure 26 shows four types of retaining wall, the one at A is the most efficient as the whole of the base is beneath the earth being retained, therefore making the maximum contribution towards stability. Site conditions may prevent the whole of the base being in this position, in which case the example at B may be appropriate. Where none of the base can be behind the wall, then the type at C would have to be used. The above are all examples of cantilever retaining walls and are suitable for heights from 4.5 to 6 m, the stem and base thickness are approximately 85 mm for every 1 m height of wall. For greater heights, then the counterfort wall must be used as at D, the base may be behind the wall as shown or on the outer face. With this type, the retaining wall spans between the counterfort walls and is not cantilevered from the base, the counterforts could be at say 3.7 m centres.

To prevent water pressure from building up behind the wall, drainage pipes must be inserted, these can be of asbestos or earthenware placed at about 1.2 m centres, a certain amount of rubble filling behind the wall improves the drainage.

The detailed example at B shows the general arrangement for the reinforcement for a 5 m high wall, all bars have a minimum cover of 50 mm. Vertical expansion joints are needed at about 9 m intervals, one of these is given at E, where a 25 mm gap between adjacent sections of the wall is made. 400 mm long, 20 mm dia. rods 300 mm apart are cast in solid on one side, the other end of the rod being coated in grease and enclosed in a cardboard sleeve to allow for movement. The gap is filled with bitumen-bonded insulation board and pointed with non-hardening mastic.

REINFORCED CONCRETE STAIRS

These may be designed to span in the direction of the flight if this is not too long, or, across the flight either as a cantilever or built into side walls or on side string beams. The first-named type is usually made of in-situ concrete, and for the longer types, the stair would span on to beams at the top and bottom. Where the flight is short as at A and B, Fig. 27, then the flight and the landing can be considered as one unit spanning from K to L at B. Cantilever steps or those spanning between walls or strings can be in-situ or precast. Examples of precast cantilevered types are shown at E and F, Fig. 27 (where the stair is cantilevered from a 215 mm wall) and in Figs. 38 and 39.

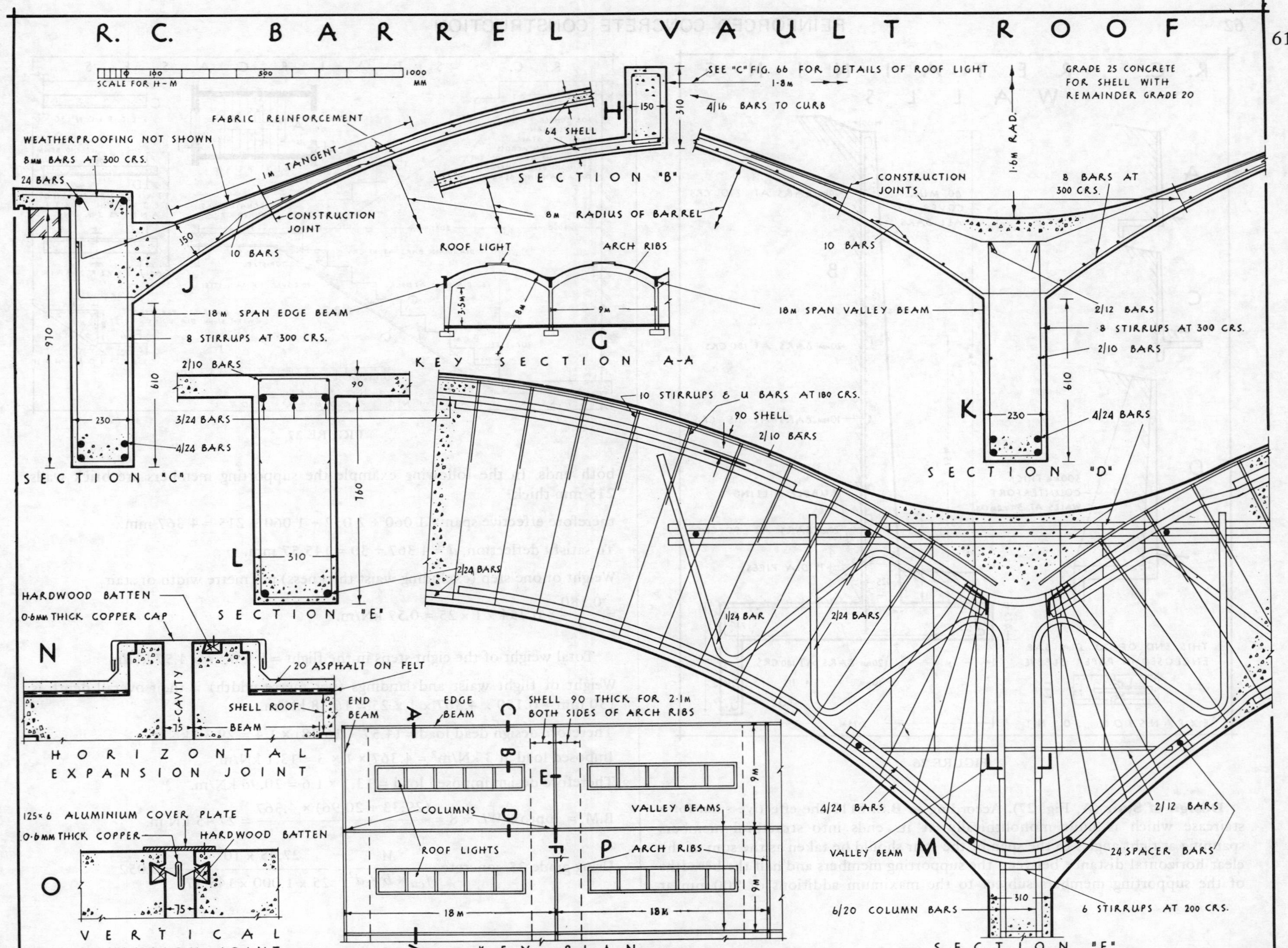
R. C. BARREL VAULT ROOF
SCALE FOR H–M
100
500
1000 MM
SEE "C" FIG. 66 FOR DETAILS OF ROOF LIGHT
1·8m
GRADE 25 CONCRETE FOR SHELL WITH REMAINDER GRADE 20
FABRIC REINFORCEMENT
64 SHELL
150
310
4/16 BARS TO CURB
H
SECTION "B"
WEATHERPROOFING NOT SHOWN
8mm BARS AT 300 CRS.
24 BARS
1m TANGENT
CONSTRUCTION JOINT
8m RADIUS OF BARREL
1·6m RAD.
CONSTRUCTION JOINTS
8 BARS AT 300 CRS.
150
10 BARS
10 BARS
J
ROOF LIGHT
ARCH RIBS
3·5m
8m
9m
18m SPAN EDGE BEAM
18m SPAN VALLEY BEAM
2/12 BARS
8 STIRRUPS AT 300 CRS.
8 STIRRUPS AT 300 CRS.
2/10 BARS
970
610
G
KEY SECTION A-A
2/10 BARS
90
610
3/24 BARS
230
4/24 BARS
SECTION "C"
10 STIRRUPS & U BARS AT 180 CRS.
90 SHELL
2/10 BARS
K
230
4/24 BARS
610
SECTION "D"
760
L
310
2/24 BARS
SECTION "E"
HARDWOOD BATTEN
0·6mm THICK COPPER CAP
N
20 ASPHALT ON FELT
CAVITY
SHELL ROOF
BEAM
75
HORIZONTAL EXPANSION JOINT
END BEAM
EDGE BEAM
SHELL 90 THICK FOR 2·1m BOTH SIDES OF ARCH RIBS
A
B
C
D
E
F
9m
9m
1/24 BAR
2/24 BARS
125×6 ALUMINIUM COVER PLATE
0·6mm THICK COPPER
HARDWOOD BATTEN
O
75
VERTICAL EXPANSION JOINT
COLUMNS
ROOF LIGHTS
VALLEY BEAMS
P
ARCH RIBS
18m
18m
KEY PLAN
A
4/24 BARS
2/12 BARS
VALLEY BEAM
M
24 SPACER BARS
310
6/20 COLUMN BARS
6 STIRRUPS AT 200 CRS.
SECTION "F"

FIGURE 25

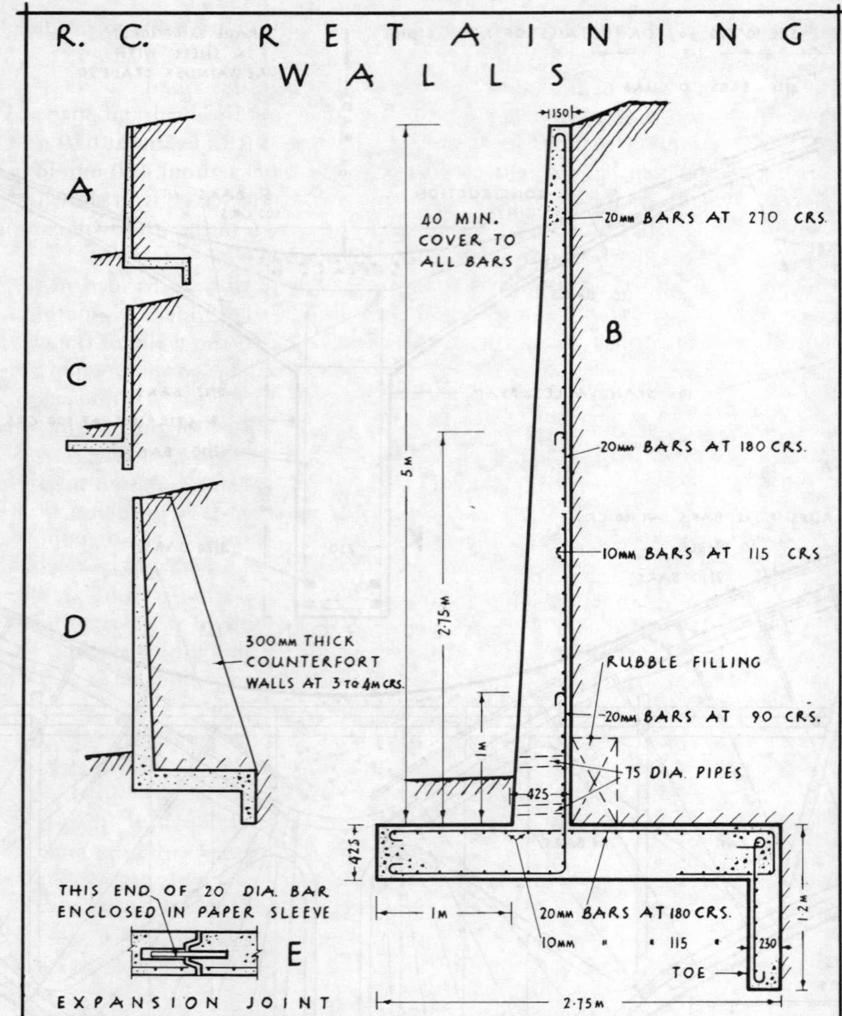

FIGURE 26

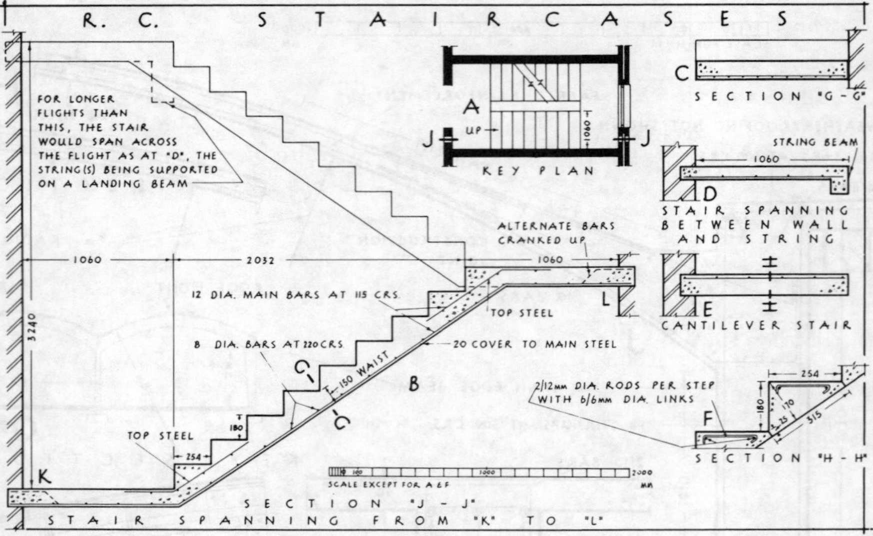

FIGURE 27

Design of Stair (A, Fig. 27). According to B.S. 8110 the effective span for a staircase which is built monolithically at its ends into structural members spanning at right angles to the span of the stair should be taken as the sum of the clear horizontal distance between the supporting members and half the breadths of the supporting members subject to the maximum additions of 900 mm at both ends. In the following example the supporting members are brick walls 215 mm thick:

therefore effective span = 1 060 + 2 032 + 1 060 + 215 = 4 367 mm.

To satisfy deflection, $d = 4\,367 \div 30 = 145.57$ mm.

Weight of one step (excluding waist thickness) per metre width of stair

$$= \frac{0.180}{2} \times 0.254 \times 1 \times 25 = 0.57 \text{ kN/m}.$$

Total weight of the eight steps in the flight = 8 × 0.57 = 4.57 kN/m.

Weight of flight waist and landings (per metre width) if their overall depth is 150 mm = 0.150 × 4.367 × 1 × 25 = 16.38 kN/m.

Therefore design dead load = (4.57 + 16.38) × 1.4 = 29.33 kN/m.

Imposed load at 3 kN/m^2 = 4.367 × 1 × 3 = 13.1 kN/m.

Therefore design imposed load = 13.1 × 1.6 = 20.96 kN/m.

$$\text{B.M.} = \text{approx. } WL \div 8 = \frac{(29.33 + 20.96) \times 4.367}{8} = 27.45 \text{ kN m}.$$

$$\text{Using grade 25 concrete, } \frac{M}{f_{cu} \times b \times d^2} = \frac{27.45 \times 10^6}{25 \times 1\,000 \times 145.57^2} = 0.052$$

Therefore from the table on p. 51 $z' = 0.92$.

$$A_s = \frac{M}{0.87 \times f_y \times z' \times d}$$

$$= \frac{27.45 \times 10^6}{0.87 \times 250 \times 0.92 \times 145.57} = 942.4 \text{ mm}^2\text{/m width of stair.}$$

Using 12 mm dia m.s. bars of area 113 mm², the spacing

$$= \frac{1\,000}{942.4} \times 113 = 119.9 \text{ mm, say } 115 \text{ mm.}$$

$$\text{Distribution steel} = \frac{0.15}{100} \times 150 \times 1\,000 = 225 \text{ mm}^2.$$

Using 8 mm dia. m.s. bars of area 50.26 mm² the spacing

$$= \frac{1\,000}{225} \times 50.26 = 223 \text{ mm.}$$

So use 8 mm dia. m.s. bars at 220 mm centres for the distribution steel.

PATENT REINFORCED CONCRETE FLOORS AND ROOFS

In an ordinary in-situ reinforced concrete floor or roof slab, the concrete below the neutral axis is in tension and contributes little to the strength. In designing these members, the capacity of the concrete to resist tensile forces is ignored. The functions of the concrete are to resist compression, to resist shear (which is small) and to retain the steel (which resists the tension) in position. Most patent floor systems take advantage of this fact by omitting unwanted concrete in the bottom of the slab between the reinforcing bars and thereby reducing the dead weight of the floor. The floor thus becomes a series of closely spaced ribs with a thin slab 25 to 50 mm thick connecting them and can be achieved in two main ways shown in Fig. 28. (1) Using light-weight hollow blocks (as B) to form thin slabs and ribs. (2) Using precast reinforced concrete or prestressed reinforced concrete beams with the joints filled with grout (as C and E) or precast beams at about 600 mm centres with light-weight blocks between (as A). In all cases, where the floor spans on either side of a main beam, continuity steel (required to resist the negative bending moment at the support) must be placed in top of the in-situ slab (or between the joints of precast units), this steel should extend for one-fifth of the span on either side of the support (see E and G, Fig. 28).

In comparison with an in-situ slab, the precast floor has the advantages of giving a more rapid completion of the floor with reduction of site concreting (including the space required for aggregates) and the benefits of a high quality concrete cast under factory supervision. It is also lighter in weight, this is structurally desirable but less soundproof.

Unless precautions are taken these patent constructions are liable to produce "pattern staining" in the ceilings (see pp. 257, 259).

The examples of patent floor and roof systems are now described.

In all the systems the depth of the floor increases as the load and span increases. The example at A consists of precast prestressed R.C. beams at 610 mm centres between which light-weight clay or concrete blocks about 400 mm long are placed. The top of the floor is finished with a concrete screed (not shown in the figure). Using a beam depth of 180 mm on a span of 6 m the floor will carry an imposed load of 3.8 kN/m², its dead load is 1.9 kN/m².

The one at B and G is an in-situ arrangement where ribs are formed in the concrete (which enclose the reinforcement) by hollow clay blocks. Sometimes the bottom of the rib has a clay tile of thickness equal to the walls of the clay block. Both methods are satisfactory if a suspended ceiling is adopted when the ceiling is suspended by steel straps like that shown at B, Fig. 90. If, however a plastered ceiling is placed against the floor soffit then the bottom of the rib should be cast against a fibreboard strip to avoid "pattern staining" – see p. 255. Such a floor 160 mm deep over a span of 4.7 m will take an imposed load of 3.8 kN/m², the dead load is 1.7 kN/m². Note that as shown at G such a floor must have continuity rods when the floor is continuous over a beam support; this applies to both in-situ or precast floors in every case. Such rods are needed to carry the negative bending moment which occurs at supports; similar provisions apply if the floor is built into a wall thickness as shown at the right hand side at G: the rods are placed in the top of the rib for this in-situ system; for precast beam floors this "negative steel" is placed between the beams as at E or in the screed over the support.

At C is given the cross-section of a precast prestressed floor or roof beam; this of an inverted U-shape but beams of rectangular cross-section as drawn at E are available also. The unit at C when 150 mm deep will take the same load as A. The hollow in the rectangular cross-section type can be left open or filled with urea formaldehyde foam. The detail at D shows rectangular units the ends of which are made with part of the top omitted; these are used with precast beams of the main structural frame, the top of the structural beam and upper ends of the adjacent floor units are filled with in-situ concrete and continuity steel to form T-beam construction. A T-beam is more efficient than a rectangular beam for part of the floor slab can be considered to act as part of the beam – see p. 57. It is possible to obtain (*e.g.*, from Concrete Ltd., Hounslow) wide precast floor units (up to 2.7 m wide) using the rectangular cross-section unit principle. These wide units have upper and lower horizontal concrete flanges and vertical concrete ribs at about 400 mm centres with voids filled with foam between. They thus resemble a series of the narrower beam units placed side by side but cast as one wide slab; they can be made to include thermal insulation and embedded electrical floor heating cables (see p. 268) incorporated in the factory.

The example at F, named "Bison plank" by the firm mentioned above, comprises a precast prestressed R.C. slab 400 mm wide as shown or 1.2 m wide in 50

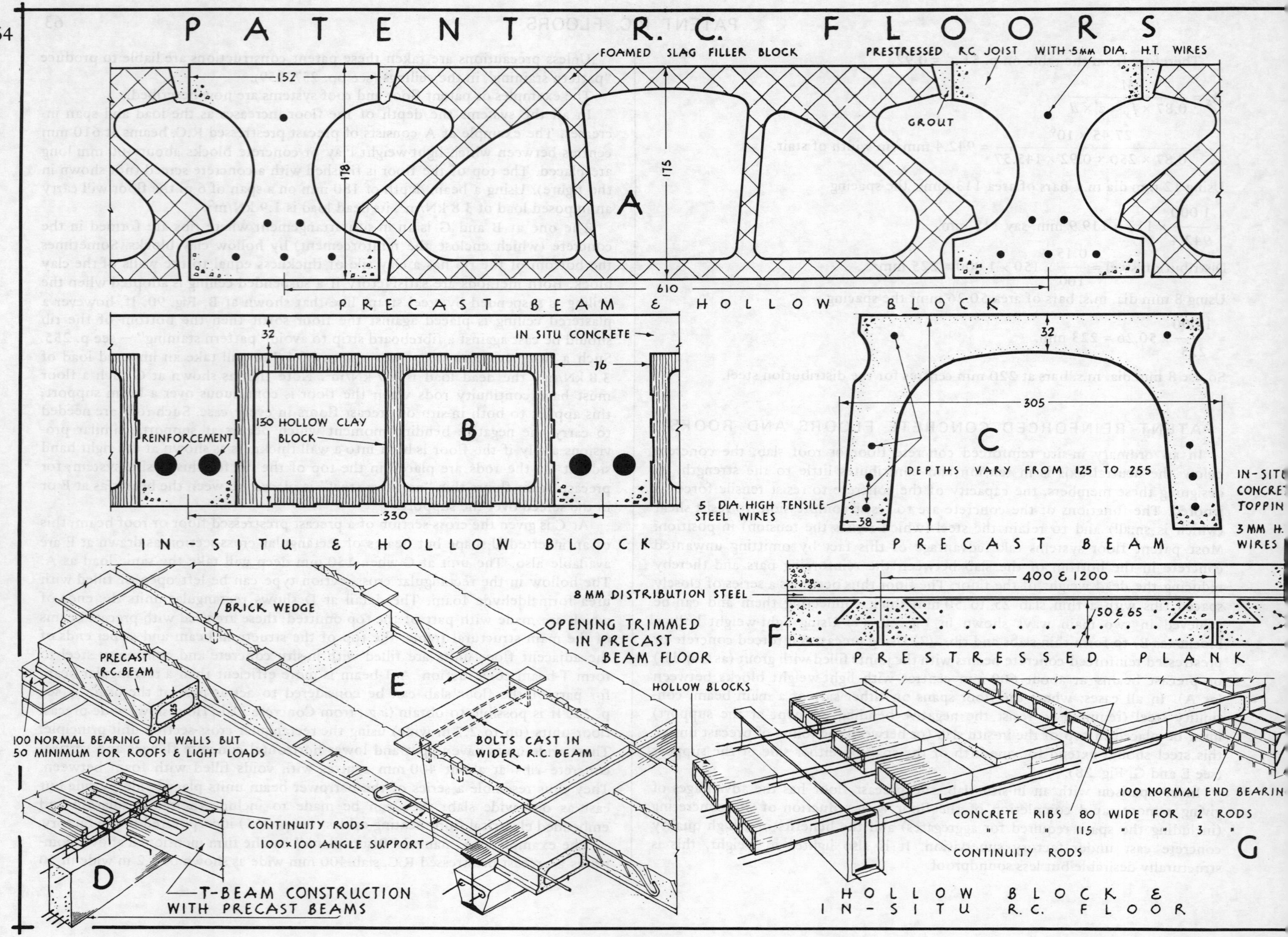

PATENT R.C. FLOORS

FOAMED SLAG FILLER BLOCK

PRESTRESSED R.C. JOIST WITH 5mm DIA. H.T. WIRES

152

178

115

GROUT

A

610

PRECAST BEAM & HOLLOW BLOCK

32

IN SITU CONCRETE

76

REINFORCEMENT

150 HOLLOW CLAY BLOCK

B

330

IN-SITU & HOLLOW BLOCK

32

305

C

DEPTHS VARY FROM 125 TO 255

5 DIA HIGH TENSILE STEEL WIRES

38

PRECAST BEAM

IN-SITU CONCRETE TOPPING

3 MM H.T. WIRES

400 & 1200

50 & 65

F

PRESTRESSED PLANK

8 MM DISTRIBUTION STEEL

BRICK WEDGE

OPENING TRIMMED IN PRECAST BEAM FLOOR

PRECAST R.C. BEAM

E

125

100 NORMAL BEARING ON WALLS BUT 50 MINIMUM FOR ROOFS & LIGHT LOADS

BOLTS CAST IN WIDER R.C. BEAM

CONTINUITY RODS

100×100 ANGLE SUPPORT

D

T-BEAM CONSTRUCTION WITH PRECAST BEAMS

HOLLOW BLOCKS

100 NORMAL END BEARING

CONCRETE RIBS 80 WIDE FOR 2 RODS
115 " 3 "

CONTINUITY RODS

G

HOLLOW BLOCK & IN-SITU R.C. FLOOR

FIGURE 28

or 65 mm thicknesses; it includes a structural R.C. topping. Using a total depth of 150 mm this floor will span 5.9 m carrying an imposed load of 5 kN/m^2, the dead load is 3.4 kN/m^2. The floor requires propping at 2.4 m centres during construction and the top and bottom surfaces are ready to receive final finishes.

The sketch at E shows a precast beam floor, brick wedges being used to adjust the position of the beams. It also shows how an opening can be trimmed in the floor; steel angles are fixed by bolts cast into special wide units, the angles rest on adjacent beams which are additionally reinforced.

All patent floor units should have a minimum bearing of 100 mm on brick walls and 50 mm on beams of framed buildings.

Sound Insulation of Floors. The Building Regulations require floors separating dwellings to have adequate insulation against airborne and impact sounds (see Chap. I, Vol. III). For concrete floors there are two ways of achieving adequate standards, and it makes no difference whether the floor is a solid slab or made of beams with hollow infilling blocks or consists of precast hollow beams: (1) A slab of mass 365 kg/m^2 (including screed and ceiling bonded to it but excluding a floating floor and suspended ceiling) covered with rubber on sponge rubber underlay not less than 4.5 mm thick, or 8 mm minimum cork tiles. (2) A slab of mass 220 kg/m^2 (excluding the mass of any floating floor or suspended ceiling) covered by one of the following: (*a*) rubber or cork as above but laid on a dense sealing layer on a 50 mm minimum screed of density not more than 1 100 kg/m^3 — *i.e.*, a light-weight screed; (*b*) boarding on battens on a quilt laid on the floor; (*c*) 38 mm minimum thick screed on a quilt laid on the floor. Types (*b*) and (*c*) are floating floors fully described in Vol. III.

FORMWORK*

Concrete structures require temporary supports and casings of the desired shape into which the concrete is deposited and contained until it has set sufficiently. For relatively small units, such as precast concrete lintels, window cills, cornices, etc., the casings are called *moulds*. For reinforced concrete columns, floors, walls and roofs, the terms *formwork* (abbreviated to *forms*), *falsework* and *shuttering* are applied to the temporary casings and supports; if the work is circular, such as arches and vault roofs, it may be referred to as *centering*.

In earlier years, formwork was exclusively of timber and classified under "temporary carpentry", but now such temporary carpentry to an increasing extent is being replaced by proprietary steel forms and appliances. Timber has the merit of being readily adapted, is cheaper in original outlay than patent systems and may be more economical where formwork is not repetitive.

The timbers used include Norwegian, Swedish, or Russian Whitewood, Spruce and third or fourth quality Douglas Fir. Better quality Douglas Fir and Columbian Pine are very suitable for members required to support heavy loads over large spans. As the timber is required to contain the wet concrete until it has attained an adequate set, it is important that members should be neither too dry nor have an excessive moisture content. If too dry, the timber will swell and become distorted by absorbing water from the concrete and causing honeycombing in the latter; if too wet, the wood will shrink in hot weather forming gaps between the boarding through which the concrete will flow producing ridges on the finished concrete surface. A moisture content of approximately twenty per cent is appropriate for timber formwork.

To be satisfactory, formwork must (1) be of adequate strength to support the dead load of the concrete and live load such as men with barrows, (2) be sufficiently rigid to permit consolidation of the concrete by tamping or vibration, (3) have tight joints between adjacent sections to prevent escape of liquid concrete, therefore provision must be made to cramp or tighten the members, (4) be capable of gradual and easy removal (an operation called *striking*) either completely or partially (such as the dismantling of the side boarding before the soffit boarding of beams), and (5) be capable of being re-used. The timber, especially when in contact with concrete should be planed, preferably on all four sides.

Two basic principles should be understood:

(1) The selection of sizes for members of formwork gives scope for far more precise and careful design than is generally appreciated. On the one hand, formwork is only temporary and so it is logical to use lower safety factors than for permanent structures. On the other hand it should be noted that failures of reinforced concrete formwork are by no means unknown, often being associated with collapse of compression members.

(2) Minimum cost in formwork is paramount, since it contributes nothing to the stability of the finished structure. Use of timber in its merchanted stock sizes is therefore desirable and re-use of complete units should be made wherever possible.

For ease of striking, the surfaces of sheeting in contact with wet concrete should be given a good coating of non-staining oil, whitewash, soft soap or proprietary solution. If this is not done the formwork may be difficult to *strike* (*i.e.*, remove) and patches of concrete may adhere to or come away with the formwork resulting in damage, time and money would be then wasted in making good. Where concrete surfaces are to be plastered oil should not be applied to the shutters as it prevents adhesion and one of the other substances should be used. The concrete to be plastered has eventually to be roughened to give a good key by power tool or small hand pick; or the concrete surface can have one of the proprietary mixes applied to it as a thin coating leaving a textured surface suitable for direct plastering. Yet another method to provide an adequate concrete surface for plastering is to apply a retardant solution to the shutters which prevents the outer skin of the concrete from setting, so that this skin can easily be removed later by a wire brush.

Formwork liners, placed inside the formwork, can be used to impart a textured or patterned surface finish to the concrete. Such linings are made of glass-reinforced plastic or high density expanded polystyrene: they are available in a wide variety of survaces.

* B.S. 5975 Code of Practice for Falsework is relevant.

The following is a description of the typical details of formwork shown in Figs. 29 to 33.

FORMWORK FOR COLUMNS

Reinforced concrete columns may be of the sections shown in Fig. 22. The formwork for a column is known as a *column box* and one for a square column is shown at C to F, Fig. 29. Each of the four sides consists of vertical boarding or sheeting which is nailed to cross battens or cleats, the sheeting is 25 to 38 mm thick and in widths from 125 to 225 mm. 25 mm thick stuff may be used for small columns or forms which are used only a few times. 32 mm thickness is generally adopted and 38 mm for the larger columns. The cleats are usually 32 mm thick like the boards unless, as shown at C to F, 75 mm by 50 mm stuff is used for the end shutters, see below. The cleats are spaced up to about 600 mm centres; if 32 mm sheeting is used for small columns, this maximum distance may be increased to 900 mm. Each side of the sheeting nailed to the cleats constitutes a shutter or panel, see F.

The four sides are securely held together by means of *yokes* or cramps of 75 mm by 50 mm or 100 mm by 75 mm stuff, which are drilled to take 16 mm dia. rods. As the pressure at the sides of the column box increases towards the base due to the weight of the wet concrete, the distance between yokes can reduce from about 600 mm at the top to about 300 mm at the bottom as indicated in the key section at A, Fig. 29. In practice, however, the yokes are usually spaced at a uniform distance apart, coinciding with the cleats as shown at C, D and E. Both ends of the rods are threaded and when the nuts are tightened (against washers) the opposite sides of the box are brought tightly against the edges of the sheeting of the other two sides, which are drawn in by driving down wedges between the rods and the 75 mm by 50 mm cleats. The shutters parallel to the yokes are called *side shutters*, the other pair being known as *end shutters* and the joints between them must be brought tightly together.

The head of the column box is shaped to allow for the reinforced concrete floor beams. In the example shown at D and E provision is made for a beam which will be parallel to the yokes. An opening is formed in each end shutter of width equal to the thickness of the beam plus twice the thickness of the boarded sides of the beam formwork, the depth of the opening would equal the depth of the beam plus the thickness of the soffit boarding formwork; 50 mm by 50 mm pieces are nailed to the forms round each opening, see F. Alternatively the sheeting of all four panels is stopped short to the underside of the beam (after allowance has been made for the boarded soffit) and a separate head is formed of sheeting to the height of the floor decking with openings, as required, for beams; the head sheeting is secured to the column sheeting by means of vertical cleats, two to each side.

In setting out the columns a steel tape is used to ensure accuracy and measurements are taken to the centres. At each centre a *profile* (or *kicker*) is used, one being shown at E, Fig. 29. This is a 75 mm thick slab of concrete of shape and size slightly less than the column and which is formed on the floor by the use of a mould. Before erecting a column box on say an upper floor, the reinforcements will have been assembled (namely, a *cage* formed by vertical bars and ties, see p. 57) and hoisted over the projecting main bars (or splice bars) of the column below (see E, Fig. 23), the upper and lower lengths of reinforcement being then wired together. Each shutter is erected separately round the cage in the case of heavy ones or as a complete box and hoisted over the reinforcement if it is not too heavy. After being accurately plumbed, the box is retained in position by inclined struts or braces secured to sole pieces at the floor and nailed to the upper cleats – see A, Fig. 29.

It is generally advisable to provide for the removal of debris which may have collected at the bottom of column boxes before concrete is deposited. For this purpose a *cleanout hole* or *washout hole* is provided at the bottom of one of the shutters, it is one or two boards wide, the short piece(s) being lightly nailed near the hole until the box has been erected. When formwork erection has been completed the base of the box can be washed out with water or compressed air immediately prior to the placing of the concrete. A washout door is shown at K, it has a short cleat fixed to it near the top and it slides down behind the shutter cleat, the ends of the short cleat are nailed to the shutter when all is ready for concreting.

In order to allow formwork to be used over and over again the column boxes should be designed so that with small adaption they can be re-used for smaller columns at higher floor levels. A column box is removed by easing and removing the wedges and so nailing of the separate members should be avoided as much as possible. When nails are used they should be regarded as temporary fixings only, with the heads left projecting for easy withdrawal by the claw hammer; formwork is damaged during dismantling if the nails are driven home and time is wasted in extracting them. Double headed nails are sometimes used and these give a better fixing, in using them the nail is driven in as far as the first head thus leaving the outer head available for subsequent withdrawal by a claw hammer.

A column box suitable for a rectangular reinforced concrete column (see L, Fig. 22) may be similar to that shown at C but having internal dimensions as required. Alternatively, it may be as shown at H to L, Fig. 29, where it consists of four shutters each with 32 mm thick sheeting and cleats and having a pair of yokes and rods as noted above. Continuous stop boards (see H) are provided to position the end shutters, the edges of which are lightly nailed through the side shutters. The plan at L shows the reinforced concrete column and the shutters removed after completion. If the column requires to have chamfered arrises each side shutter will have two triangular fillets nailed to it – see N. If rounded arrises are needed, the side shutters are made with narrow corner boards or coved mouldings – see M.

The need has been mentioned above for column boxes to be constructed so that their size can readily be reduced when they can be used in making the smaller columns which occur at higher floor levels. The key section at B shows

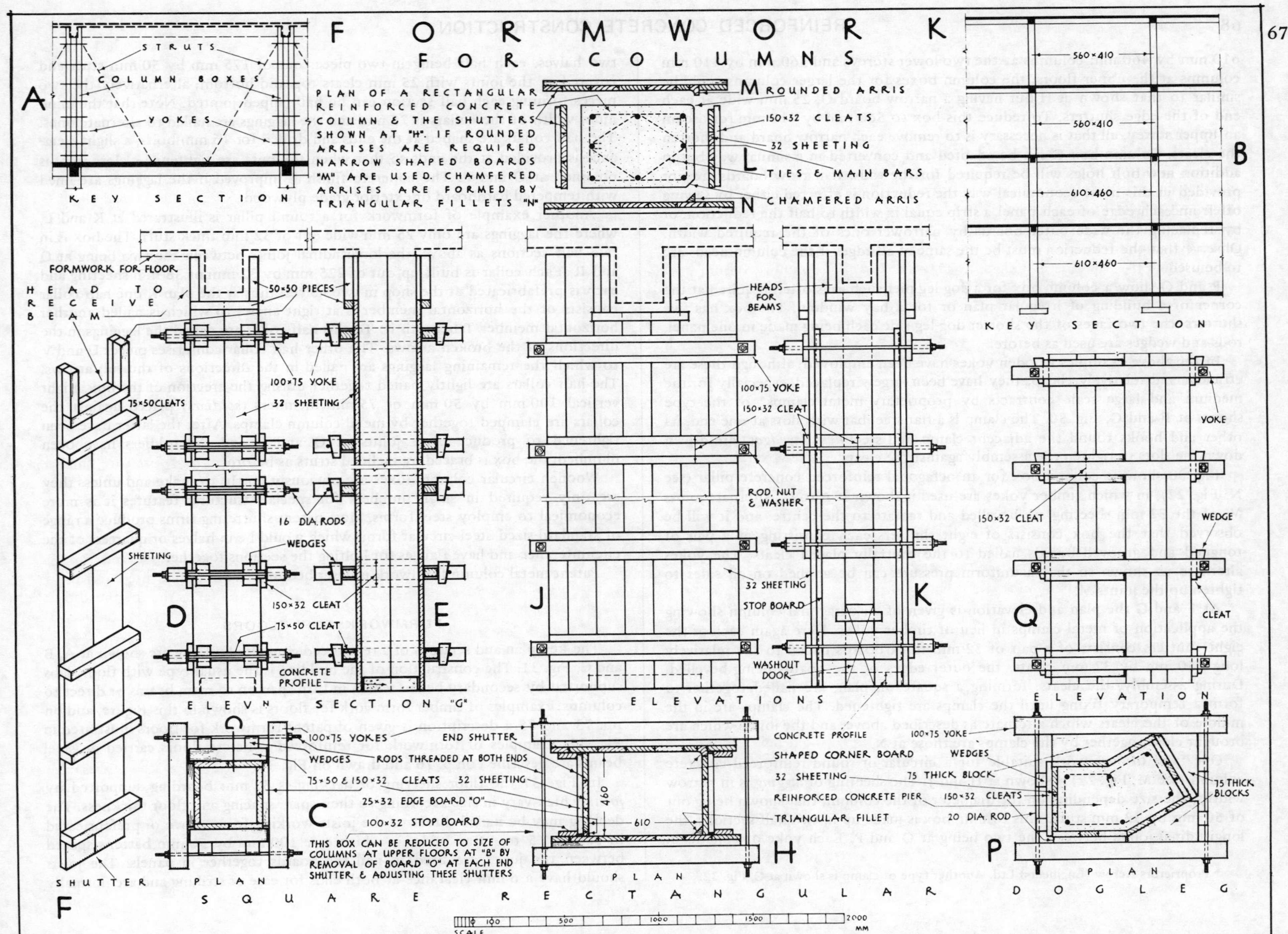
FORMWORK FOR COLUMNS
A
STRUTS
COLUMN BOXES
YOKES
KEY SECTION
PLAN OF A RECTANGULAR REINFORCED CONCRETE COLUMN & THE SHUTTERS SHOWN AT "H" IF ROUNDED ARRISES ARE REQUIRED NARROW SHAPED BOARDS "M" ARE USED. CHAMFERED ARRISES ARE FORMED BY TRIANGULAR FILLETS "N"
M
ROUNDED ARRIS
150×32 CLEATS
32 SHEETING
L
TIES & MAIN BARS
N
CHAMFERED ARRIS
560×410
560×410
B
610×460
610×460
KEY SECTION
FORMWORK FOR FLOOR
HEAD TO RECEIVE BEAM
50×50 PIECES
HEADS FOR BEAMS
100×75 YOKE
75×50 CLEATS
32 SHEETING
16 DIA. RODS
WEDGES
SHEETING
150×32 CLEAT
75×50 CLEAT
CONCRETE PROFILE
D
E
J
ELEVN
SECTION "G"
ELEVATIONS
100×75 YOKE
150×32 CLEAT
ROD, NUT & WASHER
32 SHEETING
STOP BOARD
K
WASHOUT DOOR
YOKE
150×32 CLEAT
WEDGE
CLEAT
Q
ELEVATION
G
100×75 YOKES
END SHUTTER
WEDGES
RODS THREADED AT BOTH ENDS
75×50 & 150×32 CLEATS
32 SHEETING
25×32 EDGE BOARD "O"
100×32 STOP BOARD
C
460
610
THIS BOX CAN BE REDUCED TO SIZE OF COLUMNS AT UPPER FLOORS AT "B" BY REMOVAL OF BOARD "O" AT EACH END SHUTTER & ADJUSTING THESE SHUTTERS
SHUTTER
PLAN
F
SQUARE
PLAN
RECTANGULAR
H
CONCRETE PROFILE
SHAPED CORNER BOARD
32 SHEETING
REINFORCED CONCRETE PIER
TRIANGULAR FILLET
100×75 YOKE
WEDGES
75 THICK BLOCK
150×32 CLEATS
20 DIA ROD
75 THICK BLOCKS
P
PLAN
DOGLEG
0 100 500 1000 1500 2000 MM
SCALE

FIGURE 29

610 mm by 460 mm columns at the two lower storeys and 560 mm by 410 mm columns at the upper floors; the column boxes for the larger columns could be similar to that shown at H but having a narrow board O, 25 mm wide at each end of the edge shutters. To reduce this box to 560 mm by 410 mm for use on an upper storey, all that is necessary is to remove each narrow board and shorten the cleats. Column box C can be adapted and converted in a similar way but in addition new bolt holes will be required for the rods. If narrow boards are not provided in this most economical way the reduction is effected either by sawing off from each edge of each panel a strip equal in width to half the reduction, or by replacing the wide outer boards by narrower ones of the required width. Observe that the reduction must be the same at all edges if the column heads are to be used.

P and Q show a column box for a dog-leg pier such as is often required at the corner of a building of irregular plan or for a bay window. The box has five shutters, the two faces of the shorter dog-leg side each being made in one panel, rods and wedges are used as before.

In the above examples wooden yokes have been employed; although these are efficient and relatively cheap, they have been largely replaced, especially for the medium and large scale contracts by proprietary metal clamps* of the type shown at F and G, Fig. 30. The clamp is a flat steel bar with slots at one end, its other end hooks round the adjacent clamp and steel *keys* (*wedges*) are driven down the slots to tighten the assembly against the cleats.

Fig. 30 shows a column box for an octagonal reinforced concrete pillar (see N, Fig. 22), in which timber yokes are used is shown at A to C. Alternate joints M, of the 32 mm sheeting are bevelled and radiate to the centre, and it will be observed that the box consists of eight shutters each consisting of a pair of tongued and grooved boards nailed to the centrally placed cleats. The yokes alternate as shown so that a uniform pressure can be applied on all sides to tighten up the joints M.

At F and G the plan and elevation is given of an octagonal column showing the application of metal clamps in lieu of timber yokes. Here again each of the eight shutters consists of a pair of 32 mm thick boards nailed to the relatively long 150 mm by 32 mm cleats, the outer edges of the boards being bevelled. During assembly, the cleats, forming a square on plan, are nailed together to form a temporary fixing until the clamps are tightened. The clamps are in the middle of the cleats which alternate as described above, and the joints which are brought close together by the clamps are those at N.

One type of formwork suitable for a circular or round reinforced concrete column (see M, Fig. 22) is shown at H and J. The sheeting or *lagging* is in narrow widths, the size depending on the diameter of the column, that shown being out of 50 mm by 32 mm stuff. This column box is made up in two half sections, the longitudinal joints between the two being at O and P. Each yoke or collar is in two halves, each half being in two pieces out of 175 mm by 50 mm stuff and covered at the joints with 25 mm cleats top and bottom; alternatively the two pieces forming each half section can be half-lapped jointed. Note that the minimum width of the collars is 75 mm and the laggings are nailed to alternate ones. The half collars are shaped at the ends and drilled for 16 mm bolts, a slight clearance is provided at the ends so that when the nuts are tightened a close joint is obtained at O and P. The concrete finish is improved if the laggings are lined with tempered hardboard or exterior grade plywood.

Another example of formwork for a round pillar is illustrated at K and L, where the laggings are only 25 mm wide out of 32 mm thick stuff. The box is in two half sections as above, the longitudinal joints between the two being at Q and R. Each collar is built up out of 225 mm by 32 mm or 38 mm sheeting and each is prefabricated at the shop in two halves; thus at the plan K one half collar consists of the horizontal member S at right angles to which is nailed another horizontal member T beneath it. To this half collar are nailed the laggings in the directions of the broken arrows. The other half collar comprises pieces U and V to which the remaining laggings are nailed in the directions of the full arrows. The half collars are lightly nailed together during the erection of the box. Eight vertical 100 mm by 50 mm or 75 mm members (*soldiers*) placed against the collars are clamped together by metal column clamps. After the latter have been tightened to produce close joints at Q and R and the soldiers have been plumbed, the box is braced by inclined struts as before.

Wooden circular column boxes are obviously costly to make and unless they are only required in small numbers for special structural features it is more economical to employ steel forms. Most patent shuttering firms produce a range of standard-sized steel circular forms which would be in halves or quarters of the circumference and have flanges for bolting the sections together.

Patent metal column formwork is described on p. 75.

FORMWORK FOR FLOORS

The key plan and sections of a reinforced concrete building are shown at A, B and C, Fig. 31. The construction of the building is the usual type with floor slabs supported by secondary beams which in turn span on to main beams or direct to columns; examples of timber formwork for floors is shown in this Figure, and on pp. 73 and 75 a description is given of patent formwork for floors illustrated in Fig. 32; examples of formwork for reinforced concrete floors carried on steel beams are described on p. 76 and drawn on Fig. 33.

In Fig. 31 the floor sheeting or *decking* is 32 mm boarding supported by *joists* which vary in size according to their span, spacing and floor thickness. The decking may be nailed direct to the joists working from above or prefabricated in panels 1.5 to 1.8 m wide, in which case 100 mm by 50 mm battens spaced between the joists are used to nail the boards together in panels. The joists should have a 6 mm clearance at both ends for ease of striking and are normally

* Proprietors Acrow (Engineers) Ltd. Another type of clamp is shown at C, Fig. 32.

FORMWORK FOR COLUMNS

FIGURE 30

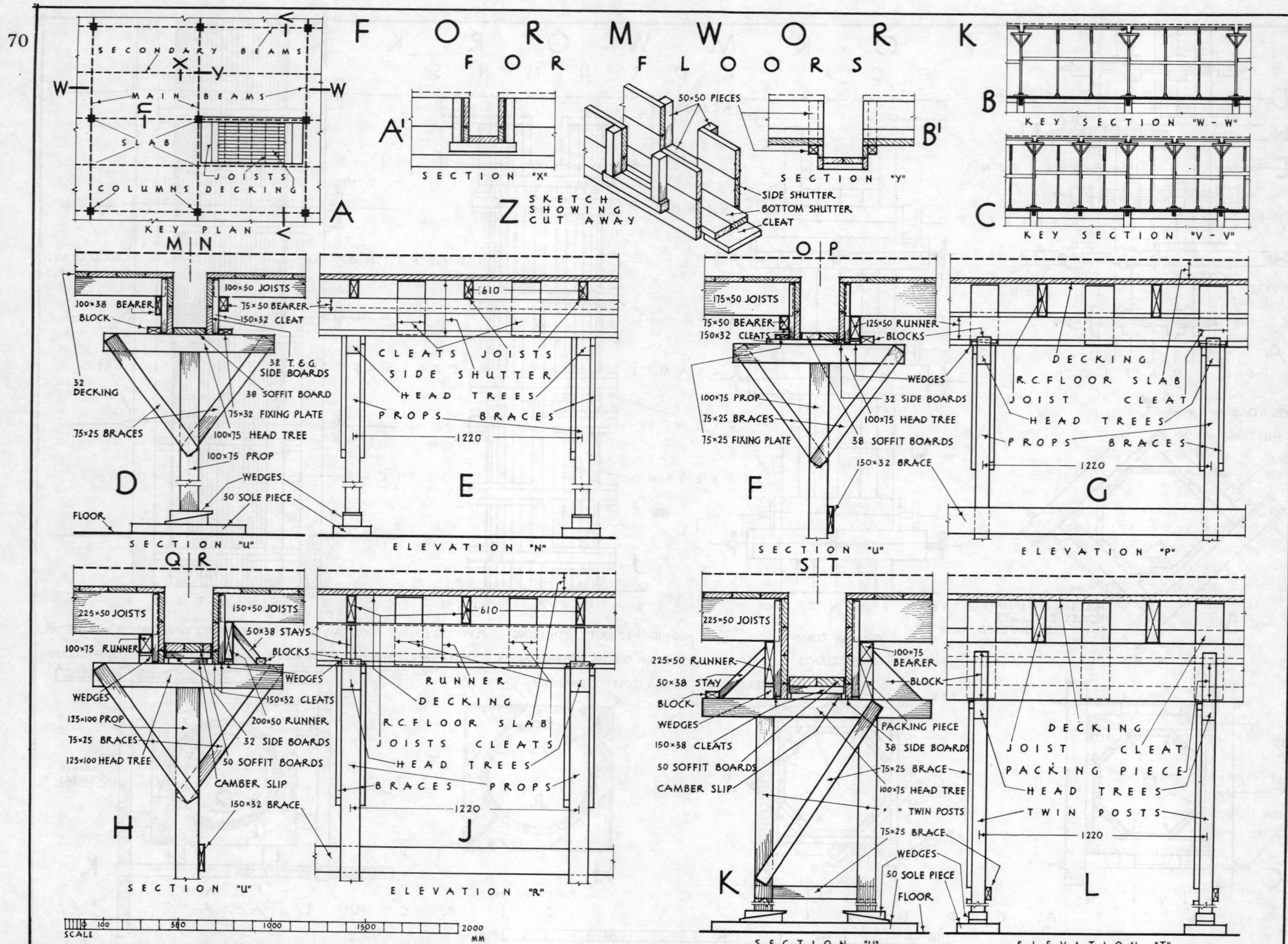
FORMWORK
FOR FLOORS
SECONDARY BEAMS
MAIN BEAMS
SLAB
JOISTS
COLUMNS DECKING
KEY PLAN
A
A'
SECTION "X"
Z
SKETCH SHOWING CUT AWAY
50×50 PIECES
SIDE SHUTTER
BOTTOM SHUTTER
CLEAT
B'
SECTION "Y"
B
KEY SECTION "W - W"
C
KEY SECTION "V - V"
100×38 BEARER
BLOCK
100×50 JOISTS
75×50 BEARER
150×32 CLEAT
32 T.&G. SIDE BOARDS
32 DECKING
38 SOFFIT BOARD
75×32 FIXING PLATE
75×25 BRACES
100×75 HEAD TREE
100×75 PROP
WEDGES
50 SOLE PIECE
FLOOR
D
SECTION "U"
610
CLEATS JOISTS
SIDE SHUTTER
HEAD TREES
PROPS BRACES
1220
E
ELEVATION "N"
175×50 JOISTS
75×50 BEARER
150×32 CLEATS
125×50 RUNNER
BLOCKS
WEDGES
100×75 PROP
32 SIDE BOARDS
75×25 BRACES
100×75 HEAD TREE
75×25 FIXING PLATE
38 SOFFIT BOARDS
150×32 BRACE
F
SECTION "U"
DECKING
R.C. FLOOR SLAB
JOIST CLEAT
HEAD TREES
PROPS BRACES
1220
G
ELEVATION "P"
225×50 JOISTS
150×50 JOISTS
100×75 RUNNER
50×38 STAYS
BLOCKS
WEDGES
150×32 CLEATS
125×100 PROP
200×50 RUNNER
75×25 BRACES
32 SIDE BOARDS
125×100 HEAD TREE
50 SOFFIT BOARDS
CAMBER SLIP
150×32 BRACE
H
SECTION "U"
610
RUNNER
DECKING
R.C. FLOOR SLAB
JOISTS CLEATS
HEAD TREES
BRACES PROPS
1220
J
ELEVATION "R"
225×50 JOISTS
225×50 RUNNER
100×75 BEARER
50×38 STAY
BLOCK
BLOCK
WEDGES
PACKING PIECE
150×38 CLEATS
38 SIDE BOARDS
50 SOFFIT BOARDS
75×25 BRACE
CAMBER SLIP
100×75 HEAD TREE
" TWIN POSTS
75×25 BRACE
WEDGES
50 SOLE PIECE
FLOOR
K
SECTION "U"
DECKING
JOIST CLEAT
PACKING PIECE
HEAD TREES
TWIN POSTS
1220
L
ELEVATION "T"
SCALE 0 100 500 1000 1500 2000 MM

FIGURE 31

placed at 610 mm centres to avoid deflection of the boards, the determination of the size of the joist is described later.

Formwork for beams is in three parts, two *side boards* and a *soffit board* and the simplest type is shown at D and E. A side board consists of 32 mm thick t. and g. boards nailed together with 150 mm by 32 mm cleats at 610 mm centres on the outside, the edge of the decking laps on to the edge of the side boards. Firmly nailed to the cleats are 100 mm by 38 mm or 75 mm by 50 mm bearers for the support of the ends of the joists. The soffit board is thicker at 38 or 50 mm because it has a greater weight to support, it rests directly on the *head tree* (see below) and has the side boards placed up against its edges. A 75 mm by 32 mm fixing plate is nailed to the top of the head tree on the right hand side (N) of the section to position the right-hand side board, the other side board is placed in position and a block is nailed on the head tree and used to tighten the joints between the soffit and sides.

The head tree is a 100 mm by 75 mm horizontal member placed centrally on top of the *prop* to which it is nailed and secured by 75 mm by 25 mm braces; 100 mm by 75 mm props are placed at 1.2 m centres centrally below the beams. The props rest on wedges used to place them at the correct height, 200 mm by 50 mm sole pieces 610 mm long are placed on the floor below the wedges, the latter being eventually nailed together and to the sole pieces to prevent them from becoming dislodged.

Similar beam formwork is shown at F and G, but in this case the soffit is made up of separate boards which are fixed to *one side* of a cleat 380 mm long so that the form can be easily adapted for later use for a beam of this width. At the left-hand side O of the section the joists rest on a continuous 75 mm by 50 mm bearer secured to the cleats of the side board. On the right-hand side at P the joists are supported on a 125 mm by 50 mm runner which bears on to the head tree via folding wedges used to position the runner at the correct level. Half-way down the prop, horizontal 150 mm by 32 mm braces are used to stiffen it and prevent it from bending.

At the details H and J, similar formwork for a deeper and wider beam is shown. On the left-hand side Q the construction is comparable to that described above; on the right at R, because only 150 mm by 50 mm joists are used for a shorter span and this entails a deeper 200 mm by 50 mm runner, the top of the latter needs bracing by 50 mm by 32 mm stays fixed back to blocks on top of the head tree. The soffit board is raised up above the level of the top of the head tree by means of a *camber slip*. The soffit of deep beams should be cambered to avoid the illusion of sagging which would otherwise be evident; the maximum camber is made at mid-span of the beam of an amount equal to 3 mm for every 1 m of span, and camber slips of determined thickness are placed at 1.2 m intervals coinciding with the head tree.

Camber slips are also shown in the details at K and L where the treatments show the formwork for heavier beams necessitating twin props. The construction on the right-hand side at T is different from any of the others described in that a shallow 100 mm by 75 mm bearer is used which is raised up on packing pieces from the head tree, the bearer and the block being braced by triangular-shaped blocks nailed to the head trees.

The details at A′, B′ and Z show the junction of formwork between the secondary and main beams. The main beam form is continuous over the junction but its sides are cut away to a profile corresponding to the outside of the minor beam formwork. 50 mm by 50 mm pieces are nailed round the "cut away" portion to secure the sawn edges of the main beam side forms and to position the ends of the minor beam forms.

Erection of Floor Formwork. After the column boxes have been set up, plumbed and stayed, the main beam soffits are placed in position working from the outside of the building to the centre, the soffits rest on the 50 mm by 50 mm pieces on the column boxes to which they are lightly nailed. A nail is partially driven in near the ends of the soffits so that when a builder's line is stretched along the centre line of the columns the nails will serve as guide on the centre line of the beams and columns (assuming that the two coincide, as they will for internal columns, but not always for external ones); a tape measure is then used to check that the top of the column boxes are accurately placed. The previously assembled head trees and props are then put in their places and centrally beneath the beam soffits, using the builder's line as a guide the soffits are now nailed centrally to the head trees (if camber slips are used the nail will pass through them). The posts must be carefully plumbed, and the hardwood wedges adjusted on the sole pieces. The main beam side boards are then erected, lightly nailed to the soffits and temporarily braced across the top. Sometimes the side boards are clamped together midway between the props by using patent metal cramps; alternatively this clamping may be done by wires tightened up beneath the soffit and attached to side board cleats left longer for this purpose. With very deep beams (say, 900 mm and over) wires may be similarly adopted which pass *through* horizontally half-way down the section of the beam.

The secondary beam soffits, props and head trees, and side boards are next fixed in the same way. Then, dependent on the type of formwork construction adopted (whether it be like D, F, H or K, Fig. 31), the various fixing plates, blocks, runners and wedges or bearers, and perhaps stays are positioned so that the joists can be lightly nailed in place ready to receive the decking. Sometimes one end decking board per bay is temporarily left out so that the decking can be easily swept clean.

The final operation after the placing of the decking is to fix the braces to the props; after the formwork has been swept clean, the oiling or similar treatment to the beam forms is done and the beam reinforcement cages are placed. The floor reinforcement is laid and wired together with the treatment of the floor decking proceeding simultaneously after traffic on the decking has ceased. All wedges are then checked, adjusted if necessary and nailed together and the concreting is done. When large long columns are used these are often cast before the floor and beams up to the level of the top of the 50 mm by 50 mm pieces on the column boxes.

Sizes of Floor Formwork. The loading to be supported by the shuttering will be the weight of the concrete (2 400 kg/m^3), plus the imposed load to cover constructional operations usually taken as 3.59 kN/m^2* of floor, which includes the weight of the formwork.

Providing the floor decking is 32 mm thick it will be satisfactory for a joist spacing of 0.6 m for all slabs up to 300 mm thick. In the case of beam soffits,

* This figure may be reduced to 1.92 kN/m^2 where heavy constructional loads are not allowed on the floor before it has set.

these should be 38 mm thick for small beams, as shown at D, Fig. 31, and 50 mm for the larger beams, providing the props are placed at centres not exceeding 1.2 m.

For joists, the size will be determined from considering the strength in bending, shear and deflection; and the section to use will be the largest that results from using the three following formulae:

(1) Bending, section modulus of joist $Z = \dfrac{BM}{f_{ppar}}$ mm^2 (see Chap. I, Vol. III).

(2) Shear, $b \times d = 1.5 \dfrac{Q}{p_q}$ mm^2.

(3) (*a*) For a uniformly distributed load and simple spans the deflection

$$= \frac{5}{384} \times \frac{WL^3}{E \times I} \text{ mm.}$$

(*b*) For a uniformly distributed load and continuous† spans the deflection

$$= \frac{3}{384} \times \frac{WL^3}{E \times I} \text{ mm.}$$

In normal cases the deflection of the formwork should not exceed 3.2 mm although the maximum permitted may be reduced to 1.6 mm in special cases where the concrete is to be left as a self finish.

Where

$Z = \dfrac{b \times d^2}{6}$ (b = breadth and d = depth of joist in mm).

BM = bending moment in kN m $= \dfrac{WL}{8}$ for simply supported spans and

$= \dfrac{WL}{10}$ for continuous* spans.

W = total load on the joist in N.

L = span of joist in millimetres.

f_{ppar} = permissible bending stress = 5.3 N/mm^2 for scotspine MGS grade timber (Table 26).

Q = maximum shear force in N.

p_q = permissible shear stress = 0.86 N/mm^2 for scotspine MGS grade timber.

E = modulus of elasticity = 10 200 N/mm^2 for scotspine MGS grade timber.

I = moment of inertia $= \dfrac{b \times d^3}{12}$ mm^4.

† This is an approximation.

* This value of BM applies strictly to end spans of continuous beams and as the formwork joists rarely have more than one prop in the centre this formula is appropriate. Actually for interior spans of continuous beams $BM = \dfrac{WL}{12}$.

The following is an example of the design of floor formwork.

A 150 mm thick floor slab is supported on 50 mm wide joists at 0.6 m centres spanning 3.7 m, with an intermediate prop giving an effective span of 1.85 m. Find the depth of the joist required.

Bending

Loading:

slab = 1 × 1 × 0.150 × 2 500 = 375 kg/m^2

$= \dfrac{375 \times 9.81}{10^3} = 3.7 \text{ kN/m}^2$

imposed = 3.59

total loading = 7.29 kN/m^2

Load on one joist = 1.85 × 0.6 × 7.29 = 8.09 kN

$BM = \dfrac{WL}{10} = \dfrac{8.09 \times 1.85}{10} = 1.5 \text{ kN m}$

From formula (1) $Z = \dfrac{1.5 \times 10^3 \times 10^3}{6.625}$ *

$= 0.226 \times 10^6 \text{ mm}^3$

$Z = \dfrac{bd^2}{6}$ and b = 50 mm

so $\dfrac{50d^2}{6} = 0.226 \times 10^6$

therefore d = 165 mm.

Shear

$Q = 8.09 \div 2 = 4.05$ kN

$p_q = 0.86 + 25\% = 1.075 \text{ N/mm}^2$

From formula (2)

$50 \times d = 1.5 \times \dfrac{4.05 \times 10^3}{1.075}$ therefore d = 113 mm.

Deflection

$I = \dfrac{bd^3}{12} = \dfrac{50d^3}{12} = 4.167d^3 \text{ mm}^4$

* In this formula the first 10^3 allows for the fact that BM is in kilos and the second 10^3 converts the metres to millimetres. The value of $f_{ppar} = 6.625 \text{ N/mm}^2$ is derived from the fact that the loading on flexural members may be increased by 25 per cent. When the loading is temporary (as in this case); *i.e.*, 5.3 + 25 per cent = 6.625 N/mm^2.

From formula (3) (*b*) by adopting a deflection of 3.2 mm max.,

$$3.2 = \frac{3}{384} \times \frac{8.09 \times 10^3 \times 1.85^3 \times 10^9}{10\,200 \times 4.167d^3}\ \ddagger, \quad \text{therefore } d = 143 \text{ mm.}$$

So the limiting condition is bending (165 mm deep joist) hence the joist will be 175 mm x 50 mm.

For runners supporting the ends of joists the design procedure will be the same except that the maximum *BM* in a runner will occur over a span of 1.2 m (the centres of the props) due to the central point load from the end of one joist. In these circumstances $BM = \frac{WL}{4}$ kN m and deflection $= \frac{WL^3}{48 \times E \times I}$ mm, the shear formula remaining the same.

An example of the design of a timber strut having a permissible compressive stress of 5.6 N/mm² (scotspine MGS grade timber) is now given; formwork props should be braced at mid-height and the effective length can be taken as half of the post length. Students will understand more clearly the following calculation if they first read the footnote on p. 161, and an example of the design of a compression member on p. 163.

Formwork props at 1.2 m centres are 3 m long (braced at mid point), the design of one to carry the formwork given in the above example plus a reinforced concrete beam 255 mm wide and 300 mm deep (excluding the floor thickness) is as follows:

Area of floor carried by prop = 1.85 x 1.2 = 2.22 m.

Loading

	kg
beam and slab formwork = 2.22 x 50 =	111
slab = 2.22 x 0.150 x 2 500 =	833
beam = 0.225 x 0.300 x 1.2 x 2 500 =	203
	1 147
	kN
$= \frac{1\,147 \times 9.81}{10^3}$	= 11.25
imposed = 2.22 x 1.92*	= 4.26
Total load	= 15.51 kN

$$r = \sqrt{\frac{I}{A}} = \sqrt{\frac{bd^3}{12} \times \frac{1}{bd}} = \frac{d}{2\sqrt{3}} \text{ mm}$$

Try a 75 x 75 mm post.

‡ In this expression the 10^3 converts the load from kN to N and the 10^9 converts the span from metres to millimetres.

* For posts a live load of 1.92 and not 3.59 kN/m² may be assumed.

$$\text{Therefore } r = \frac{75}{2\sqrt{3}} = 21.65 \text{ mm}$$

$$\text{Therefore } \frac{l}{r} = \frac{3 \div 2 \times 1\,000}{21.65} = 69.3$$

From Table 26 the modification factor for medium term loads = 0.9, therefore permissible compressive stress = 5.6 x 0.9 = 5.04 N/mm².

$$\text{The actual stress} = \frac{15.51 \times 10^3}{75 \times 75} = 2.76 \text{ N/mm}^2.$$

So the 75 mm x 75 mm post is satisfactory.

PATENT FORMWORK

This type of formwork comprises special forms and adjustable appliances which can be used many times. It is more expensive in the original outlay than timber methods previously described but as the patent systems are more quickly erected, the capital costs can soon be recovered. The labour costs in cutting and erecting timber formwork can be three times those entailed in fixing the patent systems, and the latter have a much longer life; it is for these reasons that the proprietary methods often are used for the larger reinforced concrete buildings.

Some of the products of two firms who manufacture patent formwork are given in Fig. 32, as follows:

Acrow (Engineers) Ltd. At A is shown one type of this firm's beam and floor formwork. The floor panels known as *V-Forms* are 1.8 m by 0.610 m down to 0.610 m by 0.610 m and comprise 16 mm plywood sheets with 19 mm steel angle edges welded to a 50 mm by 25 mm channel framework; running longitudinally underneath the plywood there is a further channel which is welded to the outer framework of channel and angle. In the centre of the form there is a hole passing through the plywood and central channel beneath, which allows the insertion of a hook bolt. The hooked part of the bolt extends in to the slab (see A), whilst the other threaded end permits the bolt to be fixed by a wing nut to the centre channel, a washer is welded half-way along the length of the bolt to retain it in position. The hook bolt holds the V-form in place after the steel joist supports and props have been removed, striking is thereby facilitated. On removal of the panels the hook bolts can be broken off or used to support pipes or false ceilings, etc.

These floor forms have their short sides carried on 152 mm deep steel beams which are available in lengths from 0.610 to 2.75 mm and have steel locating pins projecting above and below the flanges. The upper pins automatically locate themselves in corresponding holes in the channel framework of the V-forms, and the bottom pins fit similarly into holes provided in the top plate of the tubular steel props. The props are adjustable, consisting of an inner and an outer tube; the latter having an outside diameter of 60 mm and being slotted and threaded

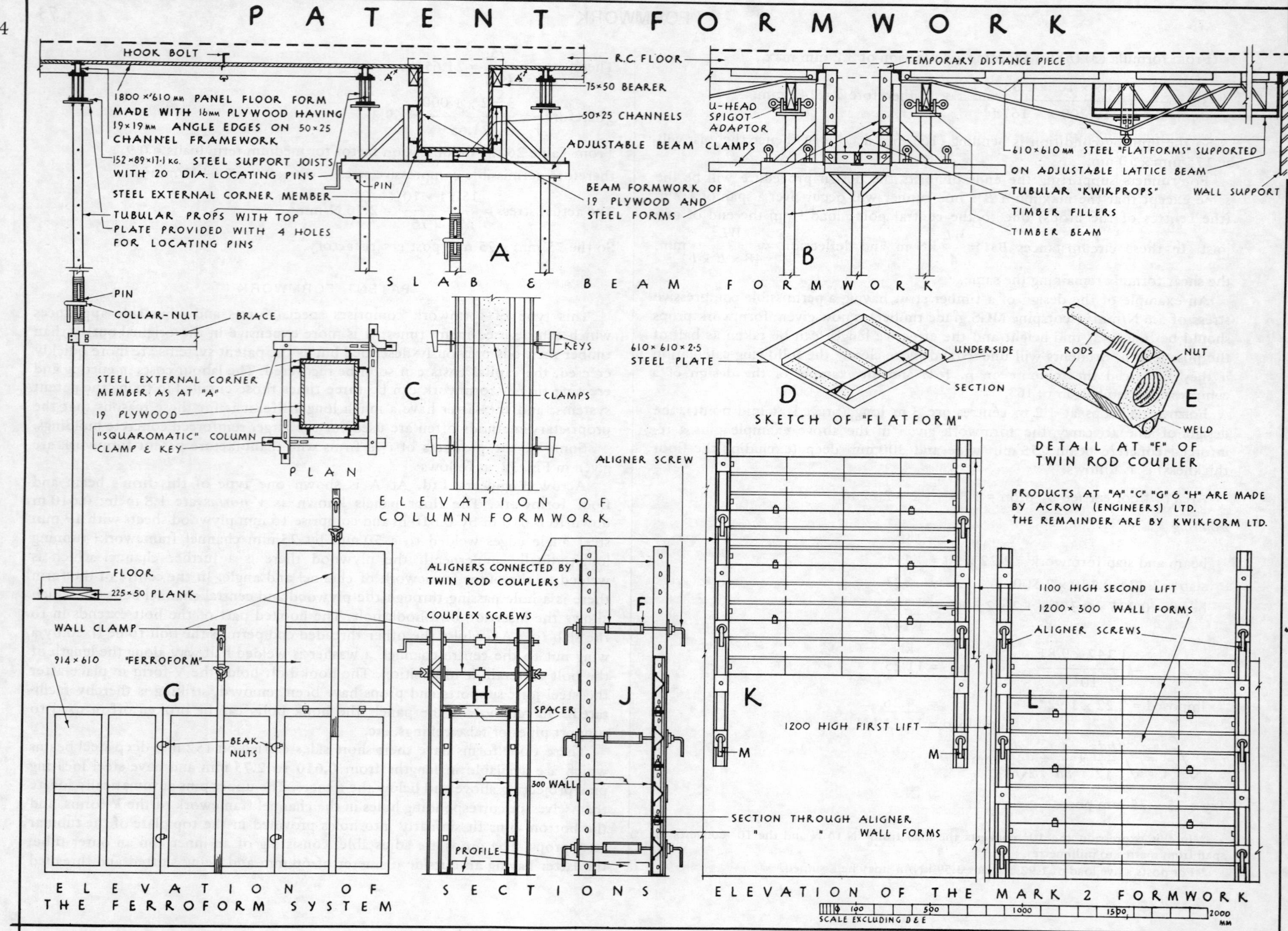

PATENT FORMWORK
HOOK BOLT
R.C. FLOOR
75×50 BEARER
1800×610 mm PANEL FLOOR FORM MADE WITH 16 mm PLYWOOD HAVING 19×19 mm ANGLE EDGES ON 50×25 CHANNEL FRAMEWORK
50×25 CHANNELS
ADJUSTABLE BEAM CLAMPS
152×89×17·1 KG. STEEL SUPPORT JOISTS WITH 20 DIA. LOCATING PINS
PIN
STEEL EXTERNAL CORNER MEMBER
TUBULAR PROPS WITH TOP PLATE PROVIDED WITH 4 HOLES FOR LOCATING PINS
BEAM FORMWORK OF 19 PLYWOOD AND STEEL FORMS
A
TEMPORARY DISTANCE PIECE
U-HEAD SPIGOT ADAPTOR
610×610 mm STEEL "FLATFORMS" SUPPORTED ON ADJUSTABLE LATTICE BEAM
TUBULAR "KWIKPROPS"
WALL SUPPORT
TIMBER FILLERS
TIMBER BEAM
B
SLAB & BEAM FORMWORK
PIN
COLLAR-NUT
BRACE
KEYS
STEEL EXTERNAL CORNER MEMBER AS AT "A"
19 PLYWOOD
"SQUAROMATIC" COLUMN CLAMP & KEY
C
CLAMPS
PLAN
ELEVATION COLUMN FORMWORK
610×610×2·5 STEEL PLATE
UNDERSIDE
SECTION
D
SKETCH OF "FLATFORM"
RODS
NUT
E
WELD
DETAIL AT "F" OF TWIN ROD COUPLER
ALIGNER SCREW
PRODUCTS AT "A" "C" "G" & "H" ARE MADE BY ACROW (ENGINEERS) LTD.
THE REMAINDER ARE BY KWIKFORM LTD.
FLOOR
225×50 PLANK
ALIGNERS CONNECTED BY TWIN ROD COUPLERS
COUPLEX SCREWS
F
WALL CLAMP
914×610
"FERROFORM"
G
BEAK NUTS
H
SPACER
J
300 WALL
PROFILE
SECTION THROUGH ALIGNER WALL FORMS
K
M
1100 HIGH SECOND LIFT
1200×300 WALL FORMS
ALIGNER SCREWS
1200 HIGH FIRST LIFT
L
ELEVATION OF THE FERROFORM SYSTEM
SECTIONS
ELEVATION OF THE MARK 2 FORMWORK
0 100 500 1000 1500 2000 MM
SCALE EXCLUDING D&E

FIGURE 32

at the top for a movable collar-nut, it has a 150 mm by 150 mm holed plate at the bottom for nailing to a sole piece or plank. The upper tube has holes as shown for a steel pin secured by a chain and ring which slides round its length. In setting up the prop, the upper tube is raised to the height required, the pin is passed through the slot in the lower tube and convenient hole in the upper tube, final tight adjustment is then made by turning the collar nut on the threaded tube. The collar nut is provided with a self-cleaning device which automatically removes dirt or concrete that has collected in the thread. Props are available in four lengths ranging from 1 m, when closed and 1.5 m when extended, to 3.2 m closed and 5 m extended; they are all provided with a holed steel plate just below the threaded portion so that horizontal braces may be fixed in the same way as braces are used for the timber props.

When using patent formwork it is usually necessary to employ timber to make up the difference between the sizes of the building and the fixed sizes of the forms. Hence for the beam at A a 16 mm thick piece of plywood (A′) is used, this rests on a 50 mm by 25 mm channel which is located on the pins of the steel beam at one end and a 75 mm by 50 mm bearer secured to the beam side forms.

The beam formwork is also of plywood, the soffit board being carried on two *external corner members* and a 50 mm by 25 mm channel (needed for wide beams). The corner member is a special unit consisting of channels which are welded to an angle corner plate. The unit is also holed for nailing to the plywood and provides an efficient means of support. A further filler channel is also situated approximately half way up the beam side forms. All the channels are in contact with the vertical or horizontal portions of the *adjustable beam clamp* which supports them in the correc position. The beam clamp is made with angle and channel components and has a handle which turns a synchronized screw to adjust the vertical arms giving distances from 150 mm to 860 mm between the arms. The underside of the clamp has projecting pins at the centre and both ends for fitting into a central hole in the top plate of the prop. In the example shown just one central prop is used, the two outer pins in the beam clamp enable two props to be used in the case of heavier beams.

The plan and elevation at C show formwork for a reinforced concrete column, consisting of plywood shutters with four external corner members as mentioned above. The forms are held rigidly by the *squaromatic column clamps* which are similar to those described on p. 68, except that they are bolted together in pairs.

The details at G and H show the elevation and section of *ferroforms* used to provide *climbing formwork* (see p. 78) for a reinforced concrete wall 300 mm thick. This is one type of formwork for walls, made by this firm, for use when bolts cannot be tolerated through the wall to hold the forms apart. Bolts or wires through the wall are the usual methods employed but these cannot always be permitted [for example in water retaining structures, or where the making good of holes (caused by bolts) would be left showing and therefore spoil the appearance]. In such cases the type illustrated would be used, where the forms are held apart by special *wall clamps*. The clamps are available in three sizes giving walls from 100 mm to 915 mm thick, they consist of 75 mm by 38 mm vertical channels and *couplex screws*, the latter are in two halves for ease of threading through the wall reinforcement. After the latter has been positioned and wired together, the base of the wall is cast 150 mm high using a profile mould of this height, the ferroforms are then placed and bolted together by the *beak nuts*. The wall clamps which fit into recesses in the top and bottom edges of the forms are then erected on the outside of the shuttering, the clamps are adjusted vertically by means of the special couplex screws and a timber spacer piece (see H) is used to keep the forms at the correct distance apart at the top.

Kwikform Ltd. Some of the patent formwork produced by this firm is illustrated in the remainder of the details in Fig. 32. Slab and beam formwork is shown at B, the former consists of steel *flatforms*, the sketch of one being given at D. The form is available in various sizes from 610 mm by 610 mm to 760 mm square it is made of 3 mm thick strip steel reinforced with a framework of 38 mm by 3 mm thick strip along two sides and down the centre, and a strip vee pressing along the two other sides. The flatforms rest on *lattice beams* placed at 610 mm centres, which, in effect, are adjustable joists that can be obtained in sizes to suit spans from 2 m upwards. The lattice beams have an internal portion which can be extended and locked in place on the site. In this example the left-hand end is supported on a timber beam which is carried on a tubular *kwikprop*. A special saddle arrangement known as a U-*head spigot head adaptor* slots into the top of the prop, and has two locking screws for securing the beam. The prop beneath the centre of the beam has a top plate reinforced with tubular stays. The props are similar to those described above.

The beam forms are metal shutters 1.2 m long by 300 mm and 100 mm wide with flanged edges having shaped holes for bolting the sections together. Timber fillers (to make up any desired dimensions) are also available with slotted holes for bolting to the metal forms; fillers are made in 25 mm, 38 mm and 50 mm thick sizes and three such pieces are shown in the detail. Metal external angle members are used at the corners. An adjustable beam clamp carried on a prop supports the beam side and soffit forms. The clamp is a horizontal tube over which slide two braced frames, the horizontal arm of these frames is tubular and has a locking screw; the vertical portion is a tee section with a tubular brace, all parts being welded together.

At L is shown the elevation of the first lift (see p. 78) of a 300 mm thick reinforced concrete wall shuttered with the Mark 2 Kwikform method, the section being shown at J. In this system 1.2 m by 0.3 m steel wall forms are bolted together horizontally one over the other, at their ends these forms are bolted to steel uprights or *aligners* which are coupled together in pairs. The aligner is 1.8 m long and is a lipped channel, its open outer side has plates welded at intervals through which bolts can pass. From the section at J it will be seen that the inside face of the aligner itself forms part of the shutter in contact with the concrete. The aligners are coupled together with *twin rod couplers*, the end of each coupler is the same and is shown at E, it consists of two nuts to which two rods are welded. Bolts pass through the aligner and screw into the nuts of the twin rod coupler which itself is left within the finished wall.

The second lift of the wall formwork is shown in elevation at K, this portion of the wall is 1.1 m high (allowing a 0.1 m lap of the shutters over the first lift). The aligners are raised and held in the new height by the bolts marked M which have been re-screwed in to the twin rod couplers left in this position. A construction joint (see p. 51) will be required between the two lifts and the holes left by the screws in the wall must be made good with cement mortar.

MISCELLANEOUS FORMWORK

This is shown for the following reinforced concrete elements in Fig. 33: (1) floors carried on structural steel beams, (2) stairs, (3) basements, and (4) walls.

(1) Formwork for R.C. Floors carried on Structural Steel Beams. For steel framed buildings with slab floors it is practicable to omit the props and suspend the floor shutters from the steel frame. This is shown at A where the steel beam is surrounded in concrete contained in 32 mm side and 38 mm soffit forms, concrete spacer blocks at 610 mm centres are used at the corners to give the correct amount of concrete cover to the steel beam. The formwork is suspended from 5 mm thick wire hangers at 610 mm centres which are wrapped round the beam, passing through the beam forms and round 100 mm by 50 mm joists at 610 mm centres underneath the beam soffit. The floor sheeting is supported on 150 mm by 50 mm joists resting at each end on a 150 mm by 50 mm runner carried on the 100 mm by 50 mm slung joists.

The arrangement at B is applicable where the steel beam is not required to be surrounded in concrete and is fireproofed in some other way (see p. 90), by expanded metal and plaster or perhaps sprayed asbestos. The floor decking is carried on timber frames at 610 mm centres, the frames comprise 100 mm by 75 mm joists with vertical and inclined struts of the same size resting on the bottom flange of the beam, continuous 125 mm by 50 mm cleats tie the joists together and act as abutments for the inclined struts.

(2) Formwork for Reinforced Concrete Stairs. This is shown at F, Fig. 33, in part section and elevation with cross-section E–E at H. The staircase abuts a wall on one side and has an open well on the other, it is a short flight with a landing. At the wall side a 225 mm by 50 mm plank is nailed to plugs in the wall so that its bottom edge is 50 mm clear of the nosing line of the treads, 100 mm by 50 mm cleats are nailed to the plank to provide a fixing for the 50 mm thick riser forms for the steps. The riser forms are nailed at the other end to a 300 mm by 50 mm outer string which has been cut to the profile of the steps. The bottom edge of the riser forms must be chamfered so that the step can be trowelled level right up to the next riser, the forms can be placed as shown for steps 1, 2 or 3 to give the profile required, in the latter case an additional form is used to provide an undercut finish.

The soffit of the stair has 32 mm thick decking carried on 100 mm by 75 mm joists running up the flight, these are bird's-mouthed on to 100 mm by 75 mm bearers resting on posts of the same size, the posts would be wedged up from sole pieces as described previously.

It is generally preferable to cast the stairs at the same time as the rest of the slabs so that they can be used for moving materials in the execution of the work. Sometimes however they are left until a later stage and when this happens a rebate should be left in the floor slab as shown on the left at F.

(3) Formwork for Reinforced Concrete Basements. One of the best arrangements for this type of formwork is shown at G, Fig. 33. The floor slab is cast first either direct on to the ground if it is hard and dry when building paper is used to prevent loss of water in the concrete, or alternatively hard core may be required; a further method is to apply a 50 mm thick layer of lean blinding concrete which provides a satisfactory clean surface for the men fixing the reinforcement for the floor slab itself.

The floor is cast working from the centre of the basement outwards and finishing at a construction joint (see below) about 300 mm to the left of the 150 mm by 150 mm baulk which will be eventually secured in the floor by bar hoops set in the concrete. This construction joint would be 150 mm away from the base of the sloping excavation (the preliminary line to which the excavation is taken, the slope being left to retain the sides until the vertical face is cut), the joint must be provided with splice bars which are left bent up until they can be connected to the bars in the remaining part of the slab. After the removal of the sloping portion of earth, the poling boards (see Fig. 21, Vol. III) are driven; walings, spacing blocks and struts (or props or shores) are all placed, struts being bird's-mouthed on to the baulk secured in to the floor. The remaining portion of the floor is cast up to the poling boards, finishing off at a construction joint 50 mm above the floor slab so as to provide a profile for the inner formwork.

The wall shuttering consists of the poling boards on the outside (and these are not normally recoverable) with a prefabricated panel shutter on the inside consisting of 32 mm thick sheeting 760 mm high fixed to 100 mm by 75 mm uprights at 610 mm centres, the uprights finishing off 50 mm above the boarding. The bottom of the panel form is held in place against the 50 mm profile concrete by a 100 mm by 75 mm timber laid on the floor which is tightened against the panel by wedges between it and other timbers of the same size which abut the baulk; 75 mm by 50 mm raking struts at 610 mm centres are used to brace the top of the panel. After the fixing of the panel another 225 mm by 100 mm waling (with attached shutter board having a chamfered bottom edge for a close fit) is positioned, a concrete spacer block the thickness of the wall is used between the poling boards and the chamfered board and the waling is strutted back to the baulk. It will be noticed that the 100 mm by 75 mm uprights of the panel form are not the full length at the bottom of the panel, they

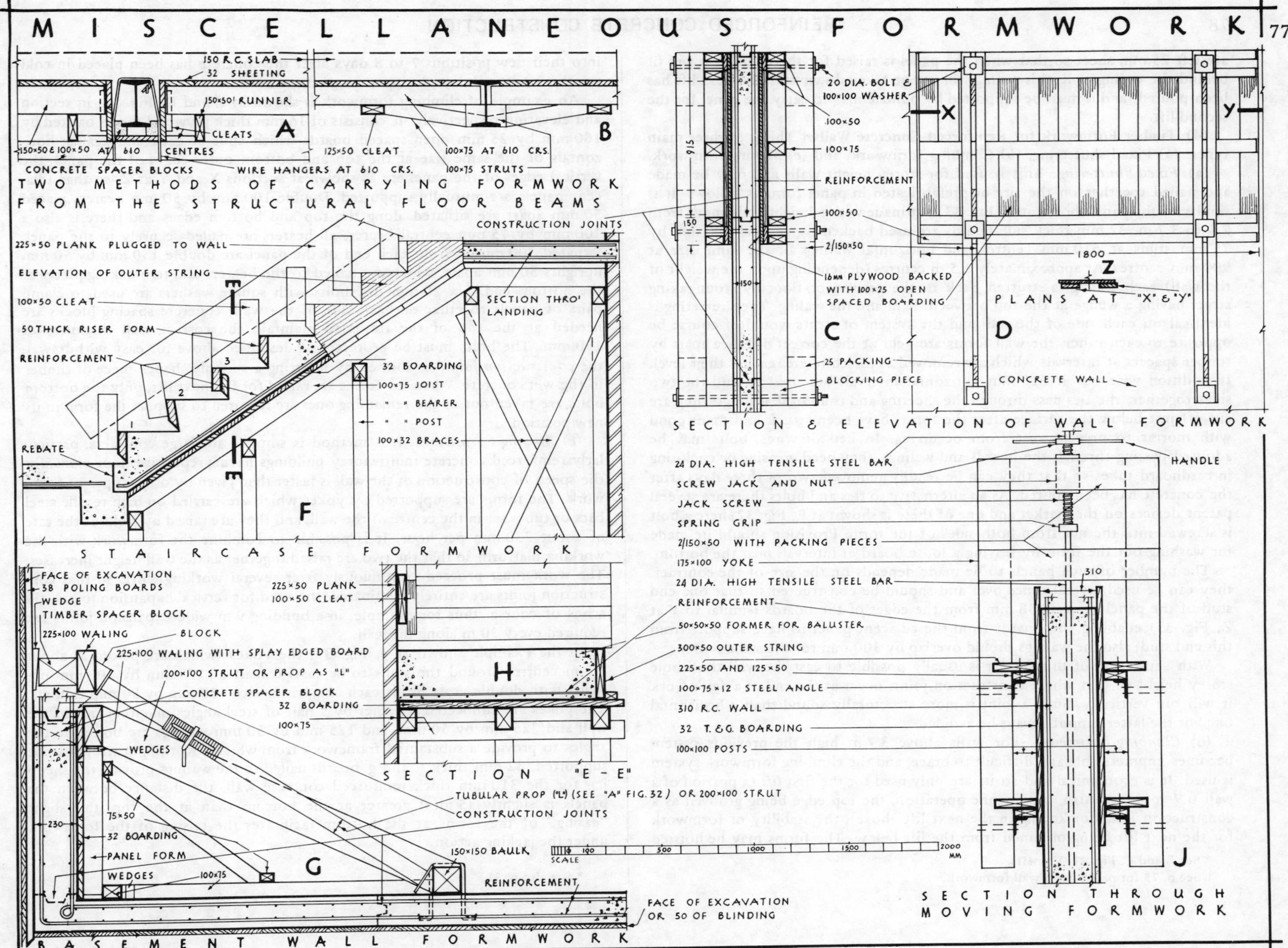
MISCELLANEOUS FORMWORK
150 R.C. SLAB
32 SHEETING
150×50 RUNNER
CLEATS
A
B
150×50 & 100×50 AT 610 CENTRES
CONCRETE SPACER BLOCKS
WIRE HANGERS AT 610 CRS.
125×50 CLEAT
100×75 AT 610 CRS.
100×75 STRUTS
TWO METHODS OF CARRYING FORMWORK FROM THE STRUCTURAL FLOOR BEAMS
CONSTRUCTION JOINTS
225×50 PLANK PLUGGED TO WALL
ELEVATION OF OUTER STRING
100×50 CLEAT
50 THICK RISER FORM
SECTION THRO' LANDING
REINFORCEMENT
32 BOARDING
100×75 JOIST
" " BEARER
" " POST
100×32 BRACES
REBATE
F
STAIRCASE FORMWORK
FACE OF EXCAVATION
38 POLING BOARDS
WEDGE
TIMBER SPACER BLOCK
225×50 PLANK
100×50 CLEAT
225×100 WALING
BLOCK
225×100 WALING WITH SPLAY EDGED BOARD
200×100 STRUT OR PROP AS "L"
CONCRETE SPACER BLOCK
32 BOARDING
100×75
H
K
WEDGES
SECTION "E-E"
TUBULAR PROP ("L") (SEE "A" FIG. 32) OR 200×100 STRUT
CONSTRUCTION JOINTS
75×50
32 BOARDING
PANEL FORM
WEDGES
100×75
150×150 BAULK
REINFORCEMENT
G
SCALE
FACE OF EXCAVATION OR 50 OF BLINDING
BASEMENT WALL FORMWORK
20 DIA. BOLT &
100×100 WASHER
100×50
100×75
REINFORCEMENT
100×50
2/150×50
16mm PLYWOOD BACKED WITH 100×25 OPEN SPACED BOARDING
25 PACKING
BLOCKING PIECE
C
D
X
Y
Z
1800
PLANS AT "X" & "Y"
CONCRETE WALL
SECTION & ELEVATION OF WALL FORMWORK
24 DIA. HIGH TENSILE STEEL BAR
SCREW JACK AND NUT
JACK SCREW
SPRING GRIP
2/150×50 WITH PACKING PIECES
175×100 YOKE
24 DIA. HIGH TENSILE STEEL BAR
REINFORCEMENT
50×50×50 FORMER FOR BALUSTER
300×50 OUTER STRING
225×50 AND 125×50
100×75×12 STEEL ANGLE
310 R.C. WALL
32 T.&G. BOARDING
100×100 POSTS
HANDLE
310
J
SECTION THROUGH MOVING FORMWORK

FIGURE 33

are left 25 mm short so that when the panel is raised for the next lift it will fit behind the waling at K; this waling will not be taken down until the next lift has been poured, and it must be supported by puncheons* to carry the panel for the second lift.

(4) Timber Formwork for Reinforced Concrete Walls.† This is of three main types: (*a*) Fixed shuttering, (*b*) Climbing formwork, and (*c*) Moving formwork.

(a) *Fixed Shuttering*. This is used for storey height walls and may be made and nailed together on the site or prefabricated in panel form as follows. It is similar to the panel shown at G, Fig. 33, but made with a height and length from 2.4 to 3.7 m, 32 mm thick side boards are used backed by vertical 100 mm by 75 mm studs at 610 mm centres, and horizontal walings of the same size at 900 mm centres. At approximately 1.5 m centres (depending upon the weight of the wall) each waling is strutted back to the ground or floor by stout raking struts having a wedge at the top between them and the waling. The shuttering is identical on each side of the wall and the system of struts would of course be opposite to each other, the wall forms are held at the correct distance apart by timber spacers at intervals which are removed as the concrete reaches their level. In addition wire ties at 610 mm horizontal intervals are used to pull the two sides together, the ties pass through the sheeting and round the walings; they are cut off just below the surface after the forms have been struck and made good with mortar to prevent rust from occurring. In lieu of wires, bolts may be adopted passing through the boards and walings, they need greasing or enclosing in cardboard tubes so that they can be readily removed two or three days after the concrete has been poured. As an alternative to ties and bolts there are several patent devices on the market and one of these is shown at E, Fig. 32; here a bolt is screwed into the nut from both sides of the form. Provision should be made for washing out the form by leaving a loose board at intervals near the bottom.

The number of such panels to be made depends on the size of the contract, they can be used several times over and should be constructed so that one end stud of the panel projects 38 mm from the edges of the boards (similar to Y at Z, Fig. 33) enabling the boards from the adjacent panel to have support from this end stud; also the walings should overlap by 300 mm for the same reason.

With shuttering of this type it is usually possible to cast the wall the whole storey height so that where construction joints occur at the end of a day's work it will run vertically. Such a joint is more structurally sound than a horizontal one but the latter cannot always be avoided.

(b) *Climbing Formwork*. For walls above 3.7 m high the previous system becomes impracticable and difficult to brace, and the climbing formwork system is used. It is economical and struts are only used for the first *lift* (a portion of a wall 0.9 to 1.2 m high cast in one operation, the top edge being grooved as a construction joint for keying in the next lift above), the stability of formwork for the next lift being obtained from the lift below. The forms may be hoisted into their new positions 7 to 8 days after the concrete has been placed in cold weather or after 3 days during normal temperatures.

* See B and C, Fig. 21, Vol. III.

† See p. 75 for patent steel wall formwork.

An example of climbing formwork is shown at C and D, Fig. 33, in section and elevation respectively, it consists of 16 mm thick plywood sheets backed by 100 mm by 25 mm open spaced boards which abut at each end against horizontals of the same size at the top and bottom outer edges of the panel; the vertical edges of the panel are as shown at sections X and Y at Z, so that adjacent panels are mutually supported. Double 100 mm by 50 mm bearers placed 50 mm apart are situated along the top and bottom edges and there is also a 100 mm by 75 mm central bearer, all bearers are nailed securely to the panel. Situated 300 mm in from each end of the panel are double 150 mm by 50 mm uprights 50 mm apart, which are nailed to the bearers and to blocking pieces at the bottom end. Six 20 mm dia. bolts with square washers are used to clamp pairs of panels together on each side of the wall, concrete spacing blocks are needed at the top of the forms to maintain the correct wall thickness of 150 mm. The bolts must be protected as described above for easy withdrawal; the *construction joint** is formed by inserting a suitably shaped piece of timber in the wet concrete. When the forms are raised for the next lift, only the bottom bolts are taken out as the remaining ones are required to support the form in its new position.

(c) *Moving Formwork*. This method is suitable for large contracts, particularly reinforced concrete multi-storey buildings having repetitive floor plans, for the speed of construction of the wall is faster than given by other types of formwork. The forms are supported by yokes which are carried on high tensile steel bars or tubes set in the centre of the wall, and they are raised by jacks at the rate of about 230 mm per hour. It is possible to combine the formwork with the working platform so that the two are raised together as the wall height increases. The work must proceed continuously over several working shifts so that construction joints are entirely eliminated; the need for vertical expansion joints still arises of course, thus for example, in a building 9 m wide expansion joints are required every 30 m along the wall.

In the example shown at J, Fig. 33, the yokes (which are placed at about 1.5 m centres around the walls to be cast) consist of 175 mm by 100 mm uprights with double cross heads each comprising two 150 mm by 50 mm timbers. The yokes are connected together by a pair of steel angles on either side of the wall and 225 mm by 50 mm, and 125 mm by 50 mm walings are bolted to the angles to provide a substantial framework from which a working scaffold can be supported. 32 mm thick t. and g. boards nailed to the walings provide the sheeting for the 310 mm thick reinforced concrete wall, the distance between the panels is slightly (5 mm) greater at the bottom than at the top; this slight "easing" of the forms at the bottom facilitates the raising of the formwork under the jacking action.

* See also p. 51.

The high tensile steel bars or tubes coincide with the yokes to which they are attached at about 1.5 m centres, the bars or tubes are supplied in three or more different lengths up to 5.5 m and they are jointed by means of sleeves and stud bolts. Differing lengths are needed so that joints in adjacent bars are not at the same level, this is necessary so as to avoid adjacent jacks being out of action at the same time whilst the splicing of the bars or tubes is accomplished; when these are being extended the load at that point is shared by the jack on either side.

The *screw jack* is in four parts: the *jack screw* which slides over the bar or tube and has a square thread for strength, the *nut* which is bolted to the cross head of the yoke and through which the screw rotates, a *handle* for turning the screw, and a *spring grip* or *clutch* which fits over the tube or bar transmitting the load to it from the jack. There are two kinds of grip, one being of the sliding sleeve type and the other of the dog-clutch type having a pair of spring-loaded dogs with serrated edges which bite in to the bar.

In operating the formwork and pouring the concrete care is required in organizing the work so that progress is smooth and continual; this is best effected by having four teams of workers who would have the following duties:

1st team, erecting and wiring the reinforcement; *2nd team*, mixing the concrete and hoisting it to scaffold level; *3rd team*, placing of the concrete which should have a slump not exceeding 75 mm; *4th team*, operating the screw jacks, two men would be responsible for about 12 jacks, the jacks are given a quarter turn in sequence which corresponds to a lift of about 3 mm depending on the size of the jack. The man in charge of the jacking gang would be an engineer whose main duty is to ensure that the forms are kept at the correct level.

The concrete should be placed at an even depth along the length of the formwork (which may encompass external and internal walls together) and after a height of 900 mm has been reached and the initial set of the concrete taken place (approximately half an hour after the addition of the water) the jacking can start.

It is a simple matter to use hydraulic jacks operated from an oil ring main using electrically driven oil pumps instead of the manual method outlined above, the adoption of this electrically operated system gives a more accurate control of the lift and allows the progress to be speeded up from 225 mm to 300 mm per hour.

$1:1\frac{1}{2}:3$ or $1:2:4$ normal Portland cement concrete mixes are used and internal vibrators to consolidate the mix should be employed. As the concrete is still green when the shutter has been raised the 900 mm height, the wall surface can be rubbed down as the work proceeds and a first class surface obtained.

Metal Fabric used as Formwork Sheeting. Certain of the concrete reinforcement materials given on pp. 48 and 50, can be used to replace the timber and metal formwork sheeting described above, *e.g.*:

Expanded Metal (see p. 48 and M, X and X′, Fig. 19). 6 mm short-way mesh fabric has been successfully used as a sheeting in formwork for the casting of "no-fines" concrete walls. Being light in weight in comparison with timber decking, large shutters can be employed; for example by using 6 mm s.w.m. expanded metal fabric and a timber framework, shutters equal in size to the length and height of the long walls of a pair of semi-detached houses can be made and hoisted in position with a crane. Construction can thus be very rapid and the shuttering for such a pair of houses and the placing of the 300 mm thick "no-fines" concrete walls can be done in a day. The textured surface of such walls gives an ideal finish and good adherence for internal plasterwork and external waterproofed rendering.

Dual-Purpose Formwork and Concrete Reinforcement. The materials illustrated at N and O, Fig. 19, can be used as sheeting for reinforced concrete slabs whilst at the same time acting as permanent slab reinforcement. In this dual capacity the need for close-boarded shuttering or metal panels is eliminated and supporting joists at relatively wide spacings are all that are required, plus the usual props and braces.

Riblath (see p. 48 and N, T and Y, Fig. 19). Timber joists are placed directly below the mesh at right angles to the ribs; for a 100 mm thick slab using 0.6 mm thick 6 mm s.w.m. fabric and 1 mm thick ribs with transverse reinforcement of 5 mm dia. bars at 450 mm centres, the joists are needed at 610 mm centres. The material is very suitable for light pitched concrete roofs and concrete shells (see p. 60).

Hyrib (see p. 50 and O, U and Z, Fig. 19). This is used in a similar way to *Riblath*, and for the same slab by adopting 0.6 mm thick Hyrib with 5 mm dia. transverse reinforcement at 610 mm centres, the joist spacing is 760 mm.

Striking of Formwork. The interval of time that must elapse between the placing of the concrete and the *striking* (stripping, or dismantling) depends upon several factors: (*a*) The setting time of the cement: normal Portland cement does not set as quickly as rapid-hardening cement. (*b*) Formwork for short spans can be struck before that for longer spans. (*c*) Shuttering below beams must be left in place longer than that under slabs, and the latter must remain in position longer than column boxes or wall sheeting. (*d*) The air temperature: the time interval being longer in cold weather than during warm periods. The site test of striking the concrete with a hammer to hear if it gives a hard ring is a useful indication of the hardness achieved. The following Table 5, showing the days that must elapse, can be used with discrimination as a general guide.

TABLE 5 STRIKING OF FORMWORK

Member Struck	Ordinary Normal Portland Cement	Rapid-hardening Portland Cement
	(Days after placing of concrete)	
1. Columns, beam sides and walls	1	½
2. Slabs (leaving props in place)	4	2
3. Beam soffits (leaving props in place)	8	4
4. Props to slabs	11	4
5. Props to beams	15	8

These times apply during normal weather conditions; when temperatures are just above freezing the number of days must be increased as follows: for items 1 and 2, by 4 days; item 3, by 7 days; item 4, by 11 days; item 5, by 12 days.

The column boxes are struck first by slacking off the wedges and yoke bolts and easing the forms away from the bottom first and working upwards, care should be taken to avoid damage to the corners of the column.

It is convenient to strike the shuttering as soon as it is safe to do so; it can then be moved to the new positions, modified in size if necessary and re-erected. Accordingly, the removal of the different components will follow the general order shown in the table. When the slab panels are required early they can be stripped after 4 days (when normal Portland cement is used) but the slab must remain supported by the immediate insertion of props for a further 7 days. The beam sides can be made available by easing the wedges under the beam props one at a time and turning it through 90° to make the head tree parallel and centrally beneath the beam. If the beam soffits are needed early (as is the normal case in the erection procedure), they can be taken down and temporary props inserted under the beam. The latter props must not be removed until 15 days have elapsed when normal Portland cement is used.

CHAPTER THREE

FIRE PROTECTON

Syllabus. Definitions. Tests. Rules for structural fire precautions. Effects of fire on materials. Fire-fighting equipment. Detection. Fire-resisting doors and shutters. Means of escape. Lifts.

In the first edition of this book it was stated that the subject of fire protection demands more consideration than it has received in the past. Whilst designers and users of buildings do now pay greater attention to the subject the financial loss directly attributable to fire damage is still very substantial. Eighty per cent of this damage occurs in business premises and factories and over 1000 people die annually in fires, most of them in the home.

Carelessness is responsible for a large proportion of fires so the owners and other users of buildings bear the major responsibility for the annual wastage. Obviously, a reduction in the number of outbreaks caused by carelessness will occur only when greater care is taken by the general public and by those engaged in industry, especially in those occupancies in which the hazards are high. However, the designer of a building has a prime duty to ensure that the premises comply with the various statutory enactments and regulations; this chapter is concerned mainly with this aspect.

The safeguarding of life and property, being the object of fire precautions, is achieved by preventing outbreaks of fire or reducing their number, by minimizing the spread of fire in the event of an outbreak, and by providing for the safety and escape of the occupants. Several factors contribute towards limiting fire spread, such as the satisfactory fire resistance of structural elements (walls, partitions, floors and roofs), the subdivision of large buildings into compartments, the adequate protection of door and window openings, the provision of external openings and other means of escape for the occupants and the ready access of firemen, and the provision of detecting, warning and extinguishing equipment for dealing with fires.

The main sources of information on fire precautions are:

(1) The Building Regulations which apply in England and Wales (except in the London Area which has its own similar provisions). These include a section devoted to structural fire precautions which specify the fire resistance required for the elements of structure for different types of building.

(2) The Building Standards (Scotland) Regulations which apply to that country and are similar to (1).

(3) The Factories Act 1961, which has similar provisions to the above-mentioned Act in regard to factories.

(4) C.P. 3: Chap IV. Precautions against Fire. Part 1, Flats and maisonettes over two storeys; Part 2, Shops and departmental stores; and Part 3, Offices. This Code deals with the planning of the various buildings and is concerned to safeguard the lives of occupants; it covers alarms and fire-fighting equipment and has sections on means of escape in the case of fire (see pp. 109 to 116).

(5) The Fire Precautions Act 1971. This (and the guide to it) deal with the protection of life in the event of fire in buildings which are used by the public; it is designed to ensure that people can escape from a building even before the fire brigade arrives. An important provision in the Act is that a *fire certificate* issued by the fire authority (normally the fire brigade service) is required for all premises designated in an Order made by the Secretary of State.

The first designation order, made in 1972, is in respect of hotels and boarding houses. Such premises are exempt if they do not offer sleeping accommodation for more than six persons providing this accommodation is not above first floor or below ground floor.

Designated premises are inspected by the fire authority who will issue a fire certificate as soon as the building has fulfilled the following conditions:

(*a*) The means of escape in case of fire are satisfactory (see p. 109). (*b*) Proper means of fire fighting by persons in the building are available (see pp. 101–102). (*c*) Means of giving warning in case of fire exist (see p. 102). The fire certificate will specify these requirements, state the maximum number of persons who can be in the building, give details of emergency lighting, direction signs, smoke stopping, and impose requirements for staff training and maintenance of fire precautions.

(6) The Health and Safety at Work etc. Act 1974 makes certain provisions for the protection of persons at work. The Act transfers to the Fire Precautions Act the powers formerly contained in the Offices, Shops and Railway Premises Act 1963 and the Mines and Quarries Act 1954 whereby such places must have a

satisfactory means of escape, alarm and fire fighting equipment and must be provided with a fire certificate before they are used.

The Health and Safety Act establishes a Commission and an Executive which have the duty of regulating the health, safety and welfare of persons at work and for controlling the use of dangerous substances and certain emissions to the atmosphere. It also gives powers to the Secretary of State to make Building Regulations to secure its provisions including fuel conservation and prevention of waste and contamination of water; and to make health and safety regulations.

(7) The Fire Protection Association issues publications on the subject.

(8) Mandatory Rules for Means of escape in Case of Fire.

(9) B.S. 5588: Fire precautions in the Design and Construction of Buildings.

(10) B.S. 8207: Energy Efficiency in Buildings.

(11) A document entitled Firecode issued by the Dept. of Health & Social Security regarding fire safety in health buildings.

(12) Fire Safety and Safety of Places of Sport Act gives local authorities power to *immediately* close football, rugby and cricket grounds with a seating capacity of more than 10,000 if they have serious fire hazards.

Glossary. The following define some of the terms used in this.

Calorie **or** ***Metric Heat Unit*** **is the quantity of heat required to raise the temperature of 1-gram of water by 1° C.**

Cavity Barrier. Material used to seal a cavity (concealed space) against penetration of smoke and flame.

Combustible Material. **That which takes fire and burns.**

Compartment. **A part of a building separated from other parts by one or more compartment walls or compartment floors (or both), including also any roof space above a top storey if that storey is within a compartment.**

Compartment Wall and Compartment Floor. **A wall and floor complying with Rule 2 provided as such for the purposes of that Rule (p. 86) or to divide a building into compartments.**

Conflagration. **A fire involving several buildings (not applied to a fire in a single building, however large).**

Elements of Structure or Construction. **Parts of the structure of a building such as the structural frame, external wall, separating wall, compartment wall, load-bearing wall, gallery, structure enclosing a protected shaft; all these must have the minimum period of fire resistance given in Tables 7 and 10.**

Escape Route. **See Travel Distance** p. 112.

Fire Certificate. **This is issued by a fire authority when certain buildings covered by Acts of Parliament have satisfactory fire precautions.**

Fire Load. **The amount of heat (expressed in MJ/m² of floor area) which would be produced by complete combustion of the combustible contents and any combustible parts of the building itself, calculated on the assumption that the contents are uniformly distributed over the total area of the floor (see** p. 91).

Fire Precautions. **Measures, both preventive and protective, taken to reduce the fire risk; they include the provision of adequate facilities for the escape of the occupants in the event of an outbreak and minimizing the spread of fire.**

Fire Prevention. **Steps taken to restrict the risk of an outbreak of fire.**

Fire Protection. **Measures taken to lessen the danger to the occupants of a building, to the public and firefighters, and to minimize the damage to a building and its contents.**

Fire Resistance. **That quality whereby an element of building structure resists fire for a specified period of time in accordance with B.S. 476: Part 8.**

Fire-resisting Floor, Wall or Partition. **That having a standard fire resistance specified** in terms of a grade laid down in B.S. 476: Part 8.

Fire-resisting Roof. That having fire resistance of a grade given in B.S. 476: Part 3.

Fire Stop. **A barrier or seal which prevents or retards the passage of smoke or flame within a cavity or around a pipe or duct passing through a wall, or at a junction between elements of structure.**

Flammable Material. **That which is readily set on fire.**

Grading Period. **The fire resistance of an element of structure which is most equal to,** but does not exceed, the test period for which the element satisfies all the relevant tests.

Hazards. **Risks to which fire may give rise.** ***Personal hazard*****: danger to occupants of a building.** ***Damage hazard*****: that concerned with a building and its contents.** ***Exposure hazard*****: that of a fire spreading to adjacent property or through the open air from one compartment to another in the same building.** ***Hazardous occupancy*****: business or industry in which a serious fire or explosion may occur unless special precautions are taken (such as in cotton and woollen mills, match factories, oil refineries, paint and varnish factories, paper mills, tar distilleries and wood-working shops).** ***Hazardous goods*****: materials which present serious risk of a fire or explosion owing to their being easily ignitable or difficult to extinguish or which might impede escape or handicap firefighters owing to emanation of poisonous or obnoxious gases (examples being asphalt felt, fats, films, fireworks, petrol and hydrochloric and sulphuric acids).**

Non-combustible Material. That which is incapable of being burnt or consumed by fire. **Specifically, material which neither flames nor produces flammable vapours when subjected to the test prescribed in B.S. 476: Part 4.**

Protected Opening. **An opening in an internal fire-resisting wall or floor which may be closed by a door, shutter or other protection of a specified grade of fire resistance** (see p. 94).

Protected Route. **A route for persons escaping from a fire which is separated from the remainder of the building by fire-resisting doors, walls and floors.**

Protected Shaft. **A stairway, lift, duct, etc., which enables persons, things or air to pass between different compartments and which complies with Rule 6** (p. 94).

Protecting Structure. is a wall, or floor or other parts enclosing a protected shaft which are not: (a) walls of the external, separating or compartment type; (b) a floor in contact with the ground or a compartment floor; (c) a roof.

Relevant Boundary. This can be the boundary of a site which is at an angle of not more than 80° to the external wall of a building which: (a) coincides with; or (b) is parallel to that wall. It could also be a *notional boundary* which is presumed to exist between 2 buildings on the same site, one of which is in the Assembly or Residential group and the second is of any other use; it should be notionally placed at a safe distance between the 2 buildings to prevent the spread of fire across the space between them.

Separated Part (of a building). A form of compartmentation that is a part which is separated from another part of the same building by a compartment wall which runs the full height of the part in one plane.

Separating Wall. **One which is common to two adjoining buildings.**

Travel Distance. **The distance between a point in a room (or space) and a fire-resisting door to an enclosed staircase (or lobby thereto) or an external door leading to the open air (see** p. 112).

Unprotected Area. **In relation to an external wall or side of a building this means a window, door or other opening, or part of an external wall which has a fire resistance less than that specified for the wall, or part of such a wall having a combustible material more than 1 mm thick attached or applied to its surface.**

Fire Growth. Students are reminded that the growth of a fire depends not only on the presence of combustible material but also upon the existence of oxygen. When such materials are heated to a sufficient temperature, carbon monoxide and steam are produced and the rate of burning varies directly with the volume of oxygen available from the atmosphere. The oxygen present in an enclosed room may be sufficient to burn but a small amount of the combustible material, although the gases of combustion will occupy a much greater space than the material burnt; if no more oxygen is supplied, the fire may become inactive and eventually peter out. If, however, the hot gases escape, fresh air is drawn in causing an extension of the fire. Thus, fresh air admitted through a door which has been left open or burnt out will cause growth of fire as the escaping hot gases are replaced by the incoming fresh air; openings closed by fire-resisting doors or shutters will reduce this hazard. An outlet for the hot gases, and an additional supply of oxygen, is provided if the heated glass in the windows of a compartment in which a fire has started has been broken; glass blocks and so-called "fire-resisting glazing", namely, metal window frames with wired glass in relatively small squares, afford a partial protection of window openings. Then again, a fire in the bottom storey of a building having fire-resisting external and division walls will penetrate relatively quickly an upper floor if it be of the wood-boarded and joisted type, the hot gases escaping into the upper storey being replaced by air at the lower level; it should be noted, however, that this traditional form of floor-construction is adequate for many smaller types of buildings, such as houses, the fire resistance being $\frac{1}{2}$ hr providing the correct type of boarding and ceiling is used – see Table 12.

It will be clear from the above that smoke is as much a personal hazard as is fire. In a conflagration the smoke rises and so floods the building in a downwards direction; hence smoke is less dense at floor levels than it is at the ceiling. This may seem a very obvious statement but in the panic ensuing from a fire it is not unusual for people to over-estimate the size of the fire because of the amount of smoke they encounter at face level. Frequently their reaction, if the fire is in a storey below, is to move upstairs and await the hazard of rescue from upper windows or the roof (hence if there is a door leading to the roof it should have a panic release latch). Evidence shows that it is often the case that escape could be made by going downstairs towards the fire; especially if occupants crawled along the floor, gave some protection to their clothes by wetting them and covered the head with a wet towel.

FIRE TESTS

The Building Regulations require that materials and methods of construction satisfy certain tests in B. S. 476: *Fire Tests*. At present this B.S. contains thirteen parts as follows: Part 3, External Fire Exposure Roof Tests. Part 4, Non-combustibility Test for Materials. Part 5, Ignitability Test for Materials. Part 6, Fire Propagation Tests for Materials. Part 7, Surface Spread of Flame Tests for Materials. Part 10, Guide to the Principles of Fire Testing. Part 13, Method of Measuring the Ignitability of Products subjected to thermal irradiance. Part 20, Method for Finding the Fire Resistance of Elements of Construction (general principles). Part 21, Methods of Finding the Fire Resistance of Load Bearing Elements of Construction. Part 22, Methods of Finding the Fire Resistance of Non-loadbearing Elements of Construction. Part 23, Methods of Findinᵍ the Contribution of Components to the Fire Resistance of a Structure. Part 24, Method of Finding the Fire Resistance of Ventilation Ducts. Part 31, Methods of Measuring the Smoke Penetration through door Sets. B.S. 2782: *Methods of Testing Plastics*: Part 5. Flammability is used to test plastic materials. The following is a brief description of these tests.

B.S. 476: Part 3. External fire exposure roof tests. **This is concerned with the hazard that exists from a fire spreading to a roof from an external source. Materials are given a designation of two letters; the first letter denotes the time of penetration of a flame and the second letter signifies the distance of the spread of flame along the external surface. Thus the designation AA means that penetration has not occurred within 1 hr and there is no spread of flame. Designation BB means penetration in not less than $\frac{1}{2}$ hr and flame spread does not exceed 533 mm. CC is penetration in less than $\frac{1}{2}$ hr and spread exceeds 533 mm; the least satisfactory is designation DD. The letters can, of course, be inter-**posed so as to grade a roof covering AB, CA, etc.; see Table 23, note 6.

B.S. 476: Part 4. Non-combustibility Test for Materials. **Three specimens are tested, the size of each being 40 mm wide, 50 mm high, volume 80 cm³. The specimens are conditioned and dried, before testing. The test is carried out in a small electric furnace, the temperature of which is determined by thermocouples. After this has been raised to 750° C a specimen is inserted and suspended in the 75 mm dia. heating tube of the furnace and maintained at this temperature for a period of 15 minutes. A gas pilot flame is provided centrally and at the top of the tube, and a small mica observation window forms part of the lower portion of the tube.**

The material is deemed non-combustible if, during the test, none of the three specimens either (i) causes the temperature reading of either of the thermocouples to rise by 50° C or more above the initial furnace temperature of 750° C or (ii) is observed to flame continuously for 10 seconds or more inside the furnace. Otherwise the material is classed as combustible.

B.S. 476: Part 5. Ignitability Test for Materials. **This is mainly intended for materials in sheet or slab form of a rigid or semi-rigid nature; it is not suitable for fabrics. It classifies combustible materials as "easily ignitable" or "not easily ignitable" and identifies easily ignitable materials of low heat contribution of which the performance in Part 6 below does not necessarily indicate the full hazard.**

Three specimens are used for each face tested, they are 228 mm square by the thickness of the material. The test apparatus has a gas flame which is applied to the surface of the sample for 10 seconds and then removed, a note is made of the subsequent duration of flaming.

If the specimen flames for more than 10 seconds after removal of the flame, or if burning extends to the edge of the specimen within 10 seconds it is classed "easily ignitable" and its performance indicated by the letter "X". If no specimen flames for more than 10 seconds after removal of the flame and burning does not extend to the edge of the sample it is classed "not easily ignitable" and given the performance index "P".

B.S. 476: Part 6. Fire Propagation Tests for Materials. **The extent to which wall and ceiling linings can contribute to the spreading of fire across their surfaces is assessed below by Part 7, the surface spread of flame test. The latter does not measure all the properties relevant for placing lining materials in the proper order of hazard. Hence the use of Part 6 which takes account of the amount and rate of heat evolved by a specimen whilst it is being subjected to heat in an enclosed space. The test is incomplete without a report on Part 5 of B.S. 476.**

The specimen is 228 mm square by the normal thickness of the material not exceeding 50 mm. If the material is thicker than this it is sliced to give a thickness not more than 50 mm. The sample is placed in a combustion chamber where gas jets deliver a flame of known heat output to its surface. A graph or "calibration curve" is first

obtained by plotting time against temperature for a standard test piece of asbestos board. A similar curve is obtained when the specimen being tested is substituted for the test piece (the average for three specimens being used). By subtracting the calibration curve from the mean curve of the samples under test a measure of the heat produced by the sample is obtained.

Materials are thus given a Performance Index, *I*, which is based on the summation of three sub-indices i_1, i_2 and i_3 calculated from heat release rates over three time divisions in the test (0–3 min., 4–10 min. and 12–20 min.). The lower the Performance Index the more satisfactory is the material, a high value of i_1 denotes easy ignition and flame spread. Examples are: 6 mm plywood has an *I* of 41 and i_1 of 20 compared with plaster-board having an *I* of 10 and i_1 of 6.

By using these indices and the letters P or X (see Part 5) and by making use of the spread of flame figures (see Part 7 below) the fire characteristics of a material can be assessed.

***B.S. 476: Part 7. Surface Spread Flame Test for Materials*. This test is applied to wall and ceiling lining materials which are classified according to the tendency for flame to spread over their surfaces from one part of a building to another. If such a surfacing material (see pp. 94–95) becomes ignited, it is essential to know how quickly the flame will spread across its surface and hence the length of time during which any occupants can escape.**

Six specimens are tested, each 230 mm by 900 mm by their normal thickness. The edges are sealed and the specimens are conditioned as regards moisture content. A specimen is fixed to a wood frame (which is faced with asbestos millboard) with its longest sides horizontal. Its test face is exposed to radiant heat, the source being at one end; the intensity of heat, measured by thermocouples placed along the length of the specimen, shall vary from 500° C at its hotter end to 130° C at the opposite end. At the same time a gas flame is applied to the specimen at its hotter end for a minute and observations are taken of the time of spread of the flame front for distances which are measured along a horizontal line, previously drawn, which is parallel to and 75 mm distant from the bottom side; these measurements are continued until the flame has died out or for 10 minutes, whichever is the longer time.

The following classifications in Table 6 are used to evaluate the effectiveness of materials in regard to flame spread:

TABLE 6 CLASSIFICATION OF FLAME SPREAD

Classification	Limit of flame spread at 1½ minutes (mm)	Final limit of flame spread (mm)
Class 1	165	165
Class 2	215	455
Class 3	265	710
Class 4	exceeding Class 3 limits	

***N.B.* One sample only out of the six specimens tested may exceed the limits by a tolerance not exceeding 25 mm.**

Note that there is an additional Class of surface which is better than Class 1 and which is defined in the Building Regulations as a Class O surface; it is one which when tested to B.S. 476: Part 6 has *I* not exceeding 12 and i_1 not exceeding 6 (see above). Non-combustible materials are of course better than Class O.

B.S. 476: Part 10. Guide to the Principles and Applications of Fire Testing describes the general principles and applications of methods in this B.S. series for fire testing of building products.

B.S. 476: Part 13. Method of Measuring the Ignitability of Products Subject to Thermal Irradiance specifies a method for examining the ignition characteristics of essentially flat materials and composites when subject to thermal irradiance.

B.S. 476: Part 20. Method for Determination of the Fire Resistance of Elements of Construction (general principles) gives general details of test conditions, apparatus and criteria for fire resistance testing, it replaces B.S. 476: Part 8.

B.S. 476: Part 21. Methods for Determination of the Fire Resistance of Loadbearing Elements of Construction gives test requirements for beams, columns, floors, walls and flat roofs; thus: This is suitable for testing the fire resistance of the following elements of building construction: walls and partitions, floors, flat roofs, columns, beams, suspended ceilings protecting steel beams, doors and shutters, glazing.

The fire resistance of the element is measured under the following headings: (1) *Stability* or the ability to resist change due to fire; (2) *Integrity* or the resistance to the passage of flame and hot gases; (3) *Insulation* or resistance to heat transmission.

Wherever possible the test specimen is full size; load-bearing elements are loaded before test to the amount they would encounter in the actual building. The sample is tested in a furnace which is heated to standard temperatures at given time intervals. Failure under the three headings above is noted when, in the case of stability, the element collapses; for integrity when cracks exist in the sample through which hot gases or flame can pass sufficient to cause flaming to a pad of cotton wool placed near to the unexposed surface; for insulation when the mean temperature of the unexposed surface increases by more than 140°C.

The fire resistance of the elements is the time in minutes from the start of the test until failure under one or all of the above headings. For example a test result with the following figures: stability 120, integrity 120, insulation 15 would mean that the specimen failed in respect of insulation after 15 minutes but complied with the other requirements for at last 120 minutes.

B.S. 476: Part 22. Methods for Determination of the Fire Resistance of Non-loadbearing Elements of Construction gives test requirements for partitions, ceilings, glazed elements, doorsets and shutters.

B.S. 476: Part 23. Methods for Determination of the Contribution of Components to the Fire Resistance of the Structure gives test requirements for the contribution made by suspended ceilings to beams and intumescent seals to door sets and shutters.

B.S. 476: Part 24. Method for Determination of the Fire Resistance of Ventilation Ducts.

B.S. 476: Part 31. Methods for Measuring Smoke Penetration through Doorsets and shutters gives a method for measuring air leakage round doors and shutters to establish the extent of smoke leakage.

***B.S. 2782: Methods of Testing Plastics: Part 5, Flammability*. Among the several methods in this B.S. are two methods 508A and 508D. They are now described.**

***Method 508A*. Three specimens are used, 150 mm long, 13 mm wide and 1.5 mm thick; two lines are drawn across each, one at 25 mm and the other at 127 mm from the end. A flame is applied to the specimen for 10 seconds and then removed.**

If the three specimens do not burn to the first mark and show no flame or afterglow 5 seconds after the flame has been removed the material is reported as self extinguishing. If they do not burn to the second mark it is classed as resistant to flame propagation.

***Method 508D*. Three specimens 150 mm square are used and heated by a small flame from a cup containing a measured amount of burning alcohol. When the alcohol has burnt out a note is made of the length of time the specimen glows. When it has ceased to glow a note is made of (*a*) whether the material that has dropped from the specimen continues to burn; (*b*) the percentage of the area on the underside of the sample that is charred or scorched and (*c*) the length of that part of the edge that is scorched.**

If the length of the scorched part of the edge of any three specimens exceeds 51 mm it is described as being flammable; if it does not so exceed it is described as having low flammability. If it satisfies the low flammability requirement and in addition each specimen, or five out of six of them, fulfil the following: (1) flaming or glowing does not continue after the alcohol has burnt out; (2) any material that may have dropped from the specimen does not continue to burn and (3) charring or scorching does not extend over an area exceeding 20 per cent of the underside of the specimen then the sample is described as having very low flammability.

RULES FOR STRUCTURAL FIRE PRECAUTIONS

The methods by which buildings are to be given adequate fire resistance are given in the Building Regulations (see p. 81) and the rules given below summarise these regulations. Briefly, the regulations: (1) stipulate the fire resistance required for elements of structure according to the purpose for which the building is used; (2) provide for certain buildings to be divided into compartments to prevent the internal spread of fire; (3) consider the fire hazard attributable to external walls and roofs and the prevention of the spread of fire from one building to another; and (4) means of escape.

The following are the rules for structural fire precautions:

Rule	*Title*
1.	Building groups.
2.	Provision of compartment walls and compartment floors.
3.	Fire resistance.
4.	External walls.
5.	Separating walls.
6.	Protected shafts.
7.	Fire protection of openings.
8.	Stairways.
9.	Fire-stopping and cavity barriers.
10.	Internal surfaces.
11.	Roofs.

TABLE 7 PROVISIONS OF TEST FOR FIRE RESISTANCE OF ELEMENTS OF STRUCTURE ETC.

Part of building	minimum provisions when tested to BS 476: Part 8 (minutes)			Method of exposure
	Stability	Integrity	Insulation	
1. Structural frame, beam or column	+	no provision	no provision	exposed faces
2. Loadbearing wall which is not also an external wall, separating wall, compartment wall or protecting structure	+	no provision	no provision	each side separately
3. Floors. (a) in upper storey of a 2-storey dwelling house (but not over a garage)	30	15	15	from underside (note 1)
(b) any other floor (incl. a compartment floor)	+	+	+	from underside (note 1)
4. External walls. (a) any part less than 1 m from any point on relevant boundary	+	+	+	each side separately
(b) any part of the wall of an assembly building 1 m or more from the relevant boundary and described in note 2	+ + max. 60	+ + max. 60	15 + max. 60	from inside from outside
(c) any part 1 m or more from the relevant boundary and is not a part described in (b) above	+	+	15	from inside
5. Separating wall	+ min. 60	+ min. 60	+ min. 60	each side separately
6. Compartment wall	+	+	+	each side separately
7. Protecting structure (a) any glazing to a Protected Shaft described in Rule 6, paragraph 3.	30	30	no provision	each side separately
(b) any other part between a Protected Shaft & a Protected lobby/corridor described in Rule 6, paragraph 3.	30	30	30	each side separately
(c) any part not described in (a) or (b) above	+	+	+	each side separately
8. Wall separating an attached or integral garage from a house	+	+	+	from garage side
9. Doors, (a) in a separating wall	no provision	+ + (min. 60)	no provision	each side separately
(b) in a Compartment wall if it separates a flat from a space in common use	no provision	20	no provision	each side separately
(c) in a Compartment wall or Compartment floor not described in (b) above	no provision	+ +	no provision	each side separately
(d) in a Protecting structure placed wholly or partly above the level of the adjoining ground in a building used for Flats, Other Residential, Assembly or Office purposes	no provision	30	no provision	each side separately

TABLE 7 – *continued*

(e) in a protecting structure not described in (d) above	no provision	+ + + (min. 30)	no provision	each side separately
(f) any other door (incl. one in a cavity barrier & one between a house and garage)	no provision	20	no provision	each side separately
10 Casing around a drainage system	30	30	30 + + + +	from outside
11. Cavity barriers (a) 1 m by 1 m or larger	30	30	15	each side separately
(b) any other cavity barrier + + + + +	30	30	no provision	each side separately
(c) fire resisting ceiling below a concealed space	30	30	30	from underside

Notes

\+ Period of fire resistance given in Table 10.

\+ + Period of fire resistance of the wall or floor in which the door is placed.

\+ + + Half the period of fire resistance for the wall or floor in which the door is placed.

\+ + + + No provision for insulation if the casing is more than 50 mm from any pipe in the enclosure (except a pipe passing through the casing)

\+ + + + + This refers to a cavity below a floor or roof. The ceiling surface facing the cavity to have a surface spread of flame at least Class 1. The exposed ceiling surface to have a fire propagation index I not more than 12 and a fire propagation index i_1 not more than 6. Additionally the ceiling should have no openings in it except for (a) a $\frac{1}{2}$ hr. fire resisting door, (b) a suitable pipe (see Rule 7), a cable or conduit, (c) one having an automatic fire shutter and (d) a duct which (unless it is of mild steel at least 0.7 mm thick and is continous throughout the cavity on both sides of the cavity barrier) is fitted with a automatic fire shutter where it passes through the cavity barrier.

1. A suspended ceiling should only be relied on to contribute to the fire resistance of the floor if the ceiling meets the provisions of Table 11.
2. Any part of the wall which is 7.5 m or less above ground, or above a roof or any other part of the building to which people have access, if it has 2 or more storeys.

TABLE 8. DESIGNATION OF PURPOSE GROUPS

Purpose for which building or compartment of a building is intended to be used	Purpose group
Residential group	
private dwelling house which does not include a flat or a building containing flats	Dwelling house[++]
a self-contained dwelling which is not a private dwelling house	Flat (includes a maisonette)
hospital, home, school or other similar establishment used as living accommodation for, or for the treatment care or maintenance of, persons disabled due to illness or old age, or under the age of 5 years, where these sleep on the premises	Institutional
hotel, boarding house, hostel and any other residential purpose not described above	Other residential
Non-residential group	
public building[+] or place of assembly of persons for social, recreational or business but not office, shop or industrial	Assembly
premises used for the purpose of administration, clerical work, drawing, handling money or telephone and telegraph operating	Office
premises used for the retail trade or business (including the sale of food & drink, auctions, book loans, hairdresser etc.)	Shop
a factory within the meaning of section 175 of the 1961 Factories Act	Industrial
place for storage, parking of goods & vehicles and any other non-residential purpose not described above[++]	other non-residential

\+ A theatre, hall, school and place of public worship.

\+ + A detached garage not more than 40 m^2 is included in the dwellinghouse purpose group; as is a detached open carport of not more than 40 m^2, or a detached building consisting of a garage and open carport where neither of them exceeds 40 m^2 in area.

"RULE 1. BUILDING GROUPS. This rule describes by reference to Table 7, which side(s) of, and for how long, an element of structure, door or casing has to satisfy B.S. 476: Part 21.

Rule 1 also divides buildings and compartments into nine groups according to the purposes defined in Table 8.

"RULE 2. PROVISION OF COMPARTMENT WALLS AND COMPARTMENT FLOORS. These are provided to divide buildings into compartments, they must have the fire resistance specified in Table 10.

The minimum period of fire resistance increases as the size of the building or compartment increases. It is often worthwhile reducing the size of compartments which will enable a lower standard of fire resistance to be provided. Spaces connecting compartments [known as *protected shafts* (see rule 6)] require provisions to restrict fire spread; fire resisting doors should be used at connections between compartments.

The following provisions for these walls and floors are common to all buildings.

The walls and floors should be constructed of materials of limited combustibility if they are required to have a fire resistance of 1 hour or more. However this provision does not apply if they are required to have 1 hour resistance because of note (1) in Table 10.

Any shaft passing from one compartment to another should meet the requirements of Rule 6 Protected Shafts.

The only openings permitted in these walls is a door provided as a means of escape in the event of fire specified in Table 7 item 9 (a) having fittings noted in Rule 7 Protection of Openings. A pipe passing through them must meet the requirements given in Rule 7. A refuse shute in them must be non-combustible.

TABLE 9 MAXIMUM DIMENSIONS OF BUILDING OR COMPARTMENT

Type of building	Height of building (m)	Floor area of any storey in building or compartment (m^2)	Cubic capacity of building or compartment (m^3)
		other residential	
single storey	no limit	3 000	no limit
multi storey	not more than 28 over 28⁺	3 000 2 000	8 500 5 500
		offices, shops etc	
single storey (any use)	no limit	no limit	
multi-storey office shop (not sprinklered) (sprinklered)	no more than 28 over 28⁺ no limit⁺ no limit⁺⁺	no limit no limit 2 000 4 000	no limit no limit 7 000 14 000
industrial	not more than 28 over 28⁺	no limit 2 000	28 000 5 500
other non-residential	no more than 28 over 28⁺⁺	no limit 1 000	2 100 no limit

+ Such buildings higher than 28 m having a floor more than 9 m above the ground or a floor over a basement must be constructed as compartment floors. (see text).

Where a compartment wall or compartment floor meets any other wall they should be bonded together or fire-stopped.

At the junction of a compartment wall with a roof the wall must project at least 375 mm above the roof or: (a) in the case of any building at any height and use having a roof slab the roof covering must be AA, AB, or AC for a distance of 1.5 m either side of the wall and the wall fire-stopped; or (b) in the case of a building in residential (except institution), office or assembly use not more than 15 m above ground, having a boarded, wood wool or roofing battens (fully bedded in mortar), the roof covering must be of limited combustibility or asphalt extending for 1.5 m either side of the wall and the wall fire stopped.

In the case of a *garage* attached or forming part of a house the wall and floor between the garage and the house should have ½ hour fire resistance. An opening in the wall to be at least 100 mm above the garage floor and fitted with a ½ hour fire resisting door.

Other provisions under this rule vary according to the use of the building thus:

Dwelling house. A floor over a basement in a house of 3 or more storeys (basements not counted) where the basement has an area of more than 100 m^2 must be a compartment floor having the fire resistance given in Table 10; it must be constructed of materials of limited combustibility.

Flat. The following walls and floors must be constructed as compartment walls and compartment floors: (a) a floor unless it is in a maisonette, (b) a wall separating a flat or maisonette from any other part of the building, (c) a wall enclosing a refuse storage chamber, (d) (in the case of a building, part of which is occupied mainly for a different purpose) any wall or floor forming a boundary with that part.

The following compartment walls and compartment floors should be constructed of materials of limited combustibility: in a building of 1, 2 or 3 storeys the floor over the basement and a wall within it; in a 4 storey building a floor over a basement and any compartment wall; in a building of more than 4 storeys any floor and compartment wall.

In the case of a *garage* attached or forming part of a house the wall and floor between the garage and the house should have ½ hour fire resistance. An opening in the wall to be at least 100 mm above the garage floor and fitted with a ½ hour fire resisting door.

A wall or floor noted in (d) above must also be constructed of materials of limited combustibility if it is required to have a fire resistance of 1 hour or more, but not if the provision arises solely from note (1) in Table 10.

Other residential. The following walls and floors must be compartment ones: (a) a floor over a basement having a floor area more than 100 m^2; (b) (if the building is more than 28 m high) any floor more than 9 m above the ground and any floor over a basement; (c) any wall and floor needed to divide the building into compartments within the size limits given in Table 9; (d) (in the case of a building, part of which is occupied mainly for a different purpose) any wall or floor forming a boundary with that part.

Compartment walls and compartment floors should be constructed of materials of limited combustibility if they are required to have fire resistance of 1 hour or more, but this does not apply to a floor or wall required to have 1 hour fire resistance only because of note (1) in Table 10.

Institutional. The following must be constructed as compartment walls and compartment floors: any floor; any wall needed to divide a building into compartments having a floor area of not more than 3 000 m^2 (single storey buildings), or 2 000 m^2 (multi-storey buildings); a wall or floor as in (d) above.

Assembly. The following must be constructed as compartment walls and floors: (a) (if the building is more than 28 m high) any floor more than 9 m above ground and a floor over a basement; (b) (in a building of 2 or more storeys, galleries counted but not basements) a wall or floor needed to divide the building into compartments having a capacity of more than 7 000 m^3; a wall or floor as in (d) above.

Office and shops. The following must be constructed as compartment walls and floors: (a) a floor in a shop having a floor area more than 100 m^2; (b) as (a) in Assembly buildings. (c) a wall and floor needed to divide the building into compartments within the size limits in Table 9; (d) in the case of a building part of which is mainly an office and part is used for other purposes the boundary wall and floor between the two parts.

TABLE 10. MINIMUM PERIODS OF FIRE RESISTANCE

Type of building	Maximum dimensions: Height of building or of separated part (m)	Floor area of each storey (m²)	Cubic capacity of building (m³)	Minimum period (hours) for elements of structure in a: Ground or upper storey	Basement storey incl. floor over	
single storey house or separated part (no basement)	no limit	no limit	no limit	½[1]	not applicable	
1, 2, or 3 storey house or separated part (basements not included)	no limit	no limit	not limit	½	1[2]	
4 storey house or separated part (basements not included)	no limit	250	no limit	1[3]	1	
house with any number of storeys	no limit	no limit	no limit	1	1½	
single storey flat or separated part (no basement)	no limit	3 000	no limit	½[1]	not applicable	
1 or 2 storey flat or separated part (basements not included)	no limit	500	no limit	½[1]	1	
3 storey flat or separated part (basements not included)	no limit	250	no limit	1[3]	1	
flat with any number of storeys	28	3 000	8 500	1	1½[4]	
	no limit	2 000	5 500	1½[4]	2[4]	
other residential buildings						
single storey building or separated part (no basement)	not limit	3 000	no limit	½[1]	not applicable	Z
1 or 2 storey building or separated part (basements not counted)	no limit	500	no limit	½[1]	1	X
3 storey building or separated part (basements not counted)	no limit	250	no limit	1[3]	1	
building with any number of storeys	28	3 000	8 500	1	1½	
	no limit	2 000	5 500	1½	2	
institutional buildings						
single storey building or separated part (no basement)	no limit	3 000	no limit	½[1]	not applicable	
building, or separated part which is not a single storey	28	2 000	no limit	1	1½	
	over 28	2 000	no limit	1½	2	
assembly buildings						
single storey building or separated part (no basement)	no limit	3 000	no limit	½[1]	not applicable	Z
	no limit	no limit	no limit	1	not applicable	
building or separated part which is not a single storey	7.5	250	no limit	½[1]	1[2]	X
	7.5	500	no limit	½[1]	1	
	15	no limit	3 500	1[3]	1	
	28	1 000	7 000	1	1½	
	no limit	no limit	7 000	1½	2	
Offices, shops etc						
single storey office or separated part (no basement),	no limit	3 000	no limit	½[1]	not applicable	Z
	no limit	no limit	no limit	1	not applicable	
office or separated part which is not single storey	7.5	250	no limit	½[1]	1[2]	X
	7.5	500	no limit	½[1]	1	
	15	no limit	3 500	1[3]	1	
	28	5 000	14 000	1	1½	
	no limit	no limit	no limit	1½	2	
single storey shop or separated part (no basement)	no limit	2 000	no limit	½[1]	not applicable	Z
	no limit	3 000	no limit	1	not applicable	
	no limit	no limit	no limit	2	not applicable	

TABLE 10 – *continued*

shop or separated part, not single storey (not sprinklered)[5]	7.5	150	no limit	½[1]	1[2]	X
	7.5	500	no limit	½[1]	1	
	15	no limit	3 500	1[2]	1	
	28	1 000	7 000	1	2	
	no limit	2 000	7 000	2	4	
shop or separated part, not single storey (sprinklered)	7.5	150	no limit	½[1]	1	X
	7.5	500	no limit	½[1]	1	
	15	no limit	3 500	1[3]	1	
	28	1 000	7 000	1	2	
	no limit	4 000	14 000	2	4	
single storey industrial building or separated part (no basement)	no limit	2 000	no limit	½[1]	not applicable	Z
	no limit	3 000	no limit	1	not applicable	
	no limit	no limit	no limit	2	not applicable	
industrial building or separated part not single storey	7.5	250	no limit	½[1]	1[2]	X
	7.5	no limit	1 700	½[1]	1	
	15	no limit	4 250	1[3]	1	
	28	no limit	8 500	1	2	
	28	no limit	28 000	1	4	
	over 28	2 000	5 500	2	4	

Notes.

1. (i) For a house, flat, assembly & office building this is increased to 1 hour for separating walls. (ii) The increase also applies to a compartment wall and compartment floor between a flat and a part of it and another part used for non-residentail purposes, or between it and a refuse chamber. (iii) For other residential buildings the increase applies for cases (i) and (ii), it also applies for a compartment wall and a compartment floor between 2 separate residential buildings. For institutional buildings the increase in (i) applies as it does for a compartment wall between the institute and a part of it used for non-residential purposes.
2. Reduced to ½ hour if basement is 50 m² or less.
3. Reduced to ½ hour for any floor (not being a compartment floor) but not for any part of the floor contributing to the support of the building.
4. Reduced to 1 hour for a compartment wall between a flat and any other part of the same building if the wall is (a) non load-bearing and does not form part of a protected shaft and, (b) is not part of the boundary with a different purpose group, where the minimum period of fire resistance for any element of structure in that other part exceeds 1 hour.
5. The whole building has an automatic sprinkler system.

Note the floor area & cubic capacity for other residential buildings, institutions, offices, and industrial buildings are defined thus: The floor area of each storey in the building or, where the building is compartmented, the floor area of each storey in the compartment of which the structure is a part. The cubic capacity of the building or, where the building is compartmented, the cubic capacity of the compartment of which the structure forms a part.

"RULE 3. FIRE RESISTANCE. Table 7 gives the methods of test for fire resistance for the different parts of a building, which test criteria are relevant and whether the element has to perform equally under test from all sides. It contains three requirements:– (1) *stability* – the resistance to collapse of load bearing elements, (2) *integrity* – resistance to fire penetration of fire separating elements, (3) *insulation* – resistance to the transfer of excessive heat of fire separating elements.

Table 10 gives the minimum periods of fire resistance for the elements of structure for the different types of building according to its height, area and cubic capacity. It will be noted that the provisions are generally more severe for basements than other storeys due to the greater difficulty in fighting fires in basements.

Where an element of structure forms part of more than one building or compartment it must be constructed to the greater of the relevant provisions.

As stated in Rule 2 the spread of fire can be reduced by dividing the building into compartments.

Structural frames, beams, columns, internal and external walls, floors and galleries require the fire resistance given in Table 10.

There are no requirements for fire resistance for a structural frame, beam, column or leadbearing wall, which are part of a single storey building (or part of the ground storey of a building with basements but has no storey above the ground storey) unless the element:– (a) is part of or supports an external wall in which the openings or other unprotected areas are limited; or (b) is part of or supports a separating wall, compartment wall or protecting structure; or (c) supports a gallery.

Table 11 sets out criteria appropriate to the different kinds of suspended ceilings that can contribute to the fire resistance of a floor according to the height of the building and type of floor.

TABLE 11 LIMITATIONS ON FIRE-PROTECTING SUSPENDED CEILINGS

Height of building or of separated part [m]	Type of floor	Provision for fire resistance of floor [hours]	Description of suspended ceiling
less than 15	not compartment	1 or less	Type A, B, C or D
	compartment	less than 1	
		1	Type B, C or D
15 or more	any	1 or less	Type C or D
no limit	any	more than 1	Type D

Notes

Ceiling Type	Description
A	Surface of ceiling exposed to the cavity should be Class 0 or Class 1.
B	Surface of ceiling exposed to the cavity should be Class 0. Supports and fixings should be non-combustible.
C	Surface of ceiling exposed to the cavity should be Class 0. Ceiling should be jointless (ie not contain access panels). Supports and fixings should be non-combustible.
D	Ceiling should be of a material of limited combustibility and be jointless (i.e. not contain access panels). Supports and fixings should be non-combustible. Any insulation above the ceiling should be of a material of limited combustibility.

TABLE 12 PERIODS OF FIRE RESISTANCE FOR ELEMENTS OF STRUCTURE

In this table:

(*a*) Class I aggregate means foamed slag, pumice, blast furnace slag, pelleted fly ash, crushed brick and limestone.

(*b*) Class 2 aggregate means flint-gravel, granite, and all crushed natural stones other than limestone.

(*c*) Any reference to plaster means (i) for an external wall 1 m or more from the relevant boundary, plaster applied on the internal face only; (ii) for any other wall, plaster applied to both faces; (iii) if to plaster of given thickness on the external face of a wall, except in the case of vermiculite-gypsum plaster, rendering on the external face of the same thickness; (iv) for vermiculite-gypsum plaster a mix within the range of $1\frac{1}{2}$ to 2 : 1 by volume.

Construction and Materials	Minimum Thickness in Millimetres (Excluding Plaster) for Period of Fire Resistance of									
	Loadbearing hours					Non-loadbearing hours				
	4	2	1½	1	½	4	2	1½	1	½
WALLS. *Masonry construction:*										
Reinforced concrete, 25 mm minimum conc. cover to main reinforcement:										
unplastered	180	100	100	75	75					
12.5 mm cement-sand or gypsum-sand plaster	180	100	100	75	75					
12.5 mm vermiculite-gypsum plaster	125	75	75	63	63					
No-fines concrete of Class 2 aggregate:										
12.5 mm cement-sand or gypsum-sand or vermiculite-gypsum plaster						150				
Bricks of clay, concrete or sand-lime:										
unplastered or 12.5 mm cement-sand or gypsum-sand plaster	200	100	100	100	100	170	100	100	75	75
Concrete blocks of Class 1 aggregate:										
unplastered	150	100	100	100	100	150	75	75	75	50
12.5 mm cement-sand plaster	150	100	100	100	100	100	75	75	75	50
12.5 mm gypsum-sand plaster	150	100	100	100	100	100	75	75	75	50
12.5 mm vermiculite-gypsum plaster	100	100	100	100	100	75	75	62	50	50
Concrete blocks of Class 2 aggregate:										
unplastered		100	100	100	100	150	100	100	75	50
12.5 mm cement-sand or gypsum-sand plaster		100	100	100	100	150	100	100	75	50
12.5 mm vermiculite-gypsum plaster	100	100	100	100	100	100	75	75	75	50
Autoclaved aerated concrete blocks: (density 475–1 200 kg/m^3)	180	100	100	100	100	100	62	62	50	50
Hollow concrete blocks one cell in wall thickness of Class 1 aggregate:										
unplastered		100	100	100	100	150	100	100	100	75
12.5 mm cement-sand or gypsum-sand plaster		100	100	100	100	150	100	75	75	75
12.5 mm vermiculite-gypsum plaster		100	100	100	100	100	75	75	62	62
Hollow concrete blocks one cell in wall thickness of Class 2 aggregate:										
unplastered						150	150	125	125	125
12.5 mm cement-sand or gypsum-sand plaster						150	150	125	125	100
12.5 mm vermiculite-gypsum plaster						125	100	100	100	75
Cellular clay blocks not less than 50% solid:										
12.5 mm cement-sand or gypsum-sand plaster									100	75
12.5 mm vermiculite-gypsum plaster						200	100	100	100	62
Cavity wall with outer leaf of bricks or blocks of clay, composition, concrete or sand-lime, minimum 100 mm thick and:										
inner leaf same as outer leaf	100	100	100	100	100	75	75	75	75	75
WALLS. *Framed and composite construction (non-loadbearing)*	Minimum Thickness of Plaster (mm) for Fire Resistance of									
1. Steel or timber frame with facings on each side of:										
(*a*) metal lathing with cement-sand or gypsum plaster									19	12.5
(*b*) metal lathing with vermiculite-gypsum or perlite-gypsum plaster							25	19	12.5	
(*c*) 9.5 mm plasterboard with vermiculite-gypsum plaster							25	16	10	5
(*d*) 12.5 mm plasterboard with gypsum plaster (ditto but unplastered has ½ hr resistance)									12.5	
(*e*) 25 mm wood-wool slabs with gypsum plaster									12.5	
(*f*) 12 mm fibre-cement board (unplastered) has ½ hr resistance										
2. Steel frame with external cladding of 100 mm conc. blocks and internal lining of 16 mm gypsum plaster on metal lathing has a 4 hr fire resistance.										

	Period of Fire Resistance in hours
3. Steel frame with external cladding of 100 mm thick clay, concrete or sand-lime bricks and internal lining of 9 mm thick fibre-cement board	3
4. 50 mm wood-wool slab with 12.5 mm plaster	1
(75 mm slab)	2
5. 50 mm strawboard slabs with 75 mm by 12.5 mm cover strips to joints	½
WALLS. *External walls more than 1 m from the relevant boundary (non-loadbearing)*	
1. Steel frame with external cladding of non-combustible sheets with internal lining of:	
9 mm fibre-cement board or 12.5 mm plaster on metal lathing	4
9.5 mm plasterboard with 12.5 mm gypsum plaster	½
2. Timber frame with 100 mm clay, concrete or sand-lime bricks as external cladding finished internally with fibre-cement board or 16 mm gypsum plaster on metal lathing	4
3. Timber frame with weather boarding or 9.5 mm plywood as external cladding and internal lining of 9 mm fibre-cement board or 16 mm gypsum plaster on metal lathing or 9.5 mm plasterboard finished with 12.5 mm gypsum plaster*	½
4. Same frame and weather boarding with internal lining of 62, 75 or 100 mm aerated concrete blocks*	4

* (The presence of a combustible vapour barrier within the wall will not affect the fire resistance.)

FLOORS. *Timber*	Fire resistance in hours
(a) Any structurally suitable flooring on joists 37 mm wide (min.) 9.5 mm plasterboard* ceiling & 10 mm gypsum plaster	$\frac{1}{2}$**
(b) 15 mm t & g boards, plywood or chipboard on joists as above, 12.5 mm plasterboard (joints taped & filled) or 9.5 mm plasterboard* & 5 mm gypsum plaster ceilings	$\frac{1}{2}$**
(c) Flooring as (b), 12.5 mm plasterboard* & 5 mm plaster ceilings	$\frac{1}{2}$
(d) 15 mm t & g boards, plywood or chipboard on joists 50 mm wide, 30 mm plasterboard* in two layers with joints staggered & exposed layer taped & filled ceiling	1

* Galvanised nails at 150 mm centres 30 mm long for 9.5 mm, 40 mm long for 12.5 mm and 60 mm long for 19–25 mm.

** Modified $\frac{1}{2}$ hour (stability 30 minutes, integrity 15 minutes, insulation 15 minutes, see p. 84).

FLOORS. *Concrete*

Construction and Materials	Minimum Thickness of Solid Substance incl. Screed (mm)	Ceiling Finish for a Fire Resistance of 4 hr	2 hr	1½ hr	1 hr	½ hr
Solid flat slab or filler joist floor. Units of channel or T section	90	25 mm V or A	10 mm V or 12.5 mm A	10 mm V or 12.5 mm A	7 mm V or A	nil
	100	19 mm V or A	7 mm V	7 mm V	nil	nil
	125	10 mm V or 12.5 mm A	nil	nil	nil	nil
	150	nil	nil	nil	nil	nil
Units of inverted U section with minimum thickness at crown	63					nil
	75				nil	nil
	100		nil	nil	nil	nil
	150	nil	nil	nil	nil	nil
Hollow block construction or units of box or I section	75				nil	nil
	90		nil	nil	nil	nil
	125	nil	nil	nil	nil	nil

V. Vermiculite-gypsum plaster.

A. Sprayed Limpet mineral fibre, see p. 102.

Note. Where no entry is given in the column relating to ceiling finishes, the period of fire resistance specified in that column is not applicable.

TABLE 12 – *continued*

REINFORCED CONCRETE COLUMNS Construction and Materials (for reference to details see Fig. 34)	Minimum Dimension of Column[1] without Finish (in mm) for Fire Resistance of hours: 4	2	1½	1	½
Unplastered (see N and O)	450	275	250	200	150
With 12.5 mm encasement of vermiculite-gypsum plaster	275	200	150	120	120
Built[2] into any separating wall, compartment wall or external wall[3] and					
(*a*) unplastered	180	100	100	75	75
(*b*) with 12.5 mm vermiculite-gypsum plaster	125	75	75	63	63

REINFORCED CONCRETE BEAMS Construction and Materials (for reference to details see Fig. 34)	Minimum Concrete Cover without Finish to Main Reinforcement (in mm) for Fire Resistance of hours: 4	2	1½	1	½
Unplastered (see D)	63	45	35	25	12.5
With 12.5 mm vermiculite-gypsum plaster	25	12.5	12.5	12.5	12.5
With 12.5 mm cement-sand or gypsum-sand plaster on mesh reinforcement fixed round beam	50	30	20	12.5	12.5

PRESTRESSED CONCRETE BEAMS WITH POST-TENSIONED STEEL

Cover Reinforcement	Additional Protection	Minimum Concrete Cover to Tendons (in mm) for Fire Resistance of hours: 4	2	1½	1
None	unplastered				38
	12.5 mm vermiculite concrete slabs (permanent shuttering)		38	25	25
	With 12.5 mm vermiculite-gypsum plaster or 10 mm sprayed fibre		38	25	25
Light mesh reinforcement (having 25 mm min. concrete cover) to retain the concrete in position around tendons	Unplastered	100	63	63	
	12.5 mm vermiculite slabs (permanent shuttering)	75			
	12.5 mm vermiculite-gypsum plaster	75			
	12.5 mm sprayed fibre	75			

ENCASED STEEL STANCHIONS (mass per metre not less than 45 kg) Construction and Materials (for reference to details see Fig. 34)	Minimum Thickness (mm) of Protection for Fire Resistance of hours: 4	2	1½	1	½
Solid protection[6] (unplastered)					
1.2.4 concrete, concrete not assumed to be loadbearing, reinforced[4] (see E and F)	50	25	25	25	25
1.2.4 concrete, concrete assumed to be loadbearing, reinforced[5]	75	50	50	50	50
Clay, composition or sand lime solid bricks (see G)	75	50	50	50	50
Foamed slag or pumice concrete solid blocks, reinforced[4] in every joint (see H)	62	50	50	50	50
Sprayed fibre of density 140–240 kg/m³	44	19	15	10	10
Sprayed vermiculite-cement		38	32	19	12.5
Hollow protection[6]					
Clay, composition or sand lime solid bricks, reinforced in horizontal joints, unplastered (see J)	115	50	50	50	50
9.5 mm plasterboard with 16 mm wire binding at 100 mm pitch with gypsum plaster of thickness (see L)				12.5	12.5
Metal lath with sprayed fibre of thickness	44	19	15	10	10
Vermiculite-cement slabs of 4.1 mix reinforced with wire mesh and finished with plaster skim. Slabs of thickness	63	25	25	25	25

STRUCTURAL STEEL ENCASED STEEL BEAMS (mass per metre not less than 30 kg)	Minimum Thickness (mm) of Protection for Fire Resistance of hours: 4	2	1½	1	½
Solid protection[6] (unplastered)					
1.2.4 concrete, concrete not assumed to be loadbearing, reinforced[4]	63	25	25	25	25
1.2.4 concrete, concrete assumed to be loadbearing, reinforced[5]	75	50	50	50	50
Sprayed fibre of density 140–240 kg/m³	44	19	15	10	10
Sprayed vermiculite-cement		38	32	19	12.5
Hollow protection[6]					
Metal lathing with gypsum plaster of thickness		22	19	16	12.5
Metal lathing with vermiculite-gypsum plaster of thickness	32	12.5	12.5	12.5	12.5

1. The minimum dimension of a circular column is the diameter.
2. No part of the column projecting beyond either face of the wall.
3. Having not less fire resistance than that of the column and extending to the full height of, not less than 600 mm each side of, the column.
4. Steel mesh weighing at least 0.48 kg/m².
5. 5 mm dia. wire stirrups at 150 mm maximum pitch attached to not less than four longitudinal bars.
6. In hollow protection there is a void between the steel and protective material; all hollow protection to columns must be sealed at each floor level. In solid protection the casing is bedded to the steel.

"Table 12 gives the periods of fire resistance for different types of construction and Figure 34 shows how steelwork and reinforced concrete may be protected.

Table 13 defines non-combustible materials and their applications, Table 14 gives the use of materials of limited combustibility.

There is another method, used in some countries, of determining the period of fire resistance a building element should have. This is to use the fire load as the basis. The method is known as:

Grading of Occupancies according to Damage Hazard. It is found by multiplying the weight of the combustible materials by their specific energy and dividing by the floor area of the compartment. The specific energy of some materials in MJ/kg are as follows: bitumen (35.4), coal (23.2 to 32.6), cotton (16.7), butter (31.2), leather (18.6), paper (16.3), rubber (39.6), softwoods and hardwoods (18.6) and raw wool (22.8). Thus, for example, if 18 000 kg of combustible material of calorific value of 21 MJ/kg is contained in part of a factory of 200 m² floor area, the fire load would be:

$18\ 000 \times 21 \div 200 = 1\ 890$ MJ/m²

and the occupancy would be graded as one of "Moderate Fire Load".

The following grading of occupancies has been proposed:

1. *Occupancies of Low Fire Load* are those in which the fire load does not exceed 1 130 MJ/m² over the net floor area of any compartment. Examples of such occupancies are domestic buildings, offices, schools, hotels, restaurants, hospitals and public libraries, and they require 1 hr protection.

2. *Occupancies of Moderate Fire Load* are those in which the fire load is between 1 130 and 2 260 MJ/m². Most retail shops, factories and workshops come within this class and require 2 hr protection.

3. *Occupancies of High Fire Load* are those in which the fire load is between 2 260 and 4 540 MJ/m². Examples of this type of occupancy are warehouses and other bulk storage buildings. They require 4 hr protection.

In the above three types of grading it is stated that buildings of low fire load, moderate fire load and high fire load require 1, 2 and 4 hr protection respectively. Thus, the elements of structure of a building of low fire load shall be sufficiently fire resistant to withstand a complete burn-out without collapse for 1 hr, if of moderate fire load 2 hr, and if of high fire load 4 hr. Such buildings are referred to as being of *fully protected construction*.

The designer of a building will be aware of the occupancy or purpose for which it is to be used. Therefore, having established the grading by calculating the fire load as described above and thereby arriving at the required period of protection (of 1, 2 or 4 hr), the minimum thickness of the proposed materials for the elements of structure which will give the necessary fire resistance can be found by consulting Table 12.

Whilst most occupancies are covered by the above classification, there are some which cannot be included in any of the three groups, namely, occupancies in which the fire load exceeds 4 540 MJ/m^2, churches (which have a low risk) and those which may have a very high risk, such as munition factories, underground car parks (because of the danger of explosion of petrol vapour) and buildings in which certain acids are stored. Special consideration should be given to such buildings and in those having a fire load in excess of 4 540 MJ/m^2 a fire resistance of 6 hr may be necessary.

TABLE 13 USE OF NON-COMBUSTIBLE MATERIALS.

Use		Material
1	solid construction forming External walls, Separating walls, Compartment walls, Compartment floors and Protecting structure where there is provision in various Rules for them to be constructed of materials of limited combustibility.	(a), (b) (c) or (d)
2	frames of hollow elements of structure referred to above.	
3	loadbearing elements of structure forming part of, or which carry, any element of structure referred to in 1 or 2 above.	
4	supports and fixings of any suspended ceiling meeting the provisions given in Table 11 (Types B, C and D).	
5	refuse chutes of non-combustible construction.	
6	flues going through a compartment wall or floor, or built into a compartment wall.	

Notes
(a) Any material which when tested does not flame and there is no rise in temperature on either the centre (specimen) or furnace thermocouples.
(b) Totally inorganic materials such as concrete, fired clay, ceramics, metals, plaster and masonry containing not more than 1 per cent by weight or volume of organic material. (Use in buildings of combustible metals such as magnesium/aluminium alloys should be assessed in each individual case).
(c) Concrete bricks or blocks meeting BS 6073: Part I.
(d) Products classified as non-combustible under BS 476: Part 4.

RULE 4, EXTERNAL WALLS. The external walls of a building must offer adequate resistance to the spread of fire over the walls and from one building to another. The spread of fire across an open space depends on the size of the fire in the building, the risk it presents to people in other buildings, the distance between the buildings and the fire protection given by their facing sides. The distance of the wall from the boundary and the extent of openings in the wall (these facilitate the spread of fire) must also be considered.

Certain provisions for externals walls depend on the use to which the building is put, these are described later.

The following provisions are common for the external walls of all buildings.

The internal surface material of any wall that should be constructed of material of limited combustibility may be combustible if it is not being relied on to contribute to the fire resistance of the wall and has at least the classification given in Table 14.

External cladding to a wall that should be constructed of materials of limited combustibility may also be combustible if it is not being relied on to contribute to the fire resistance of the wall and it meets the provisions of Table 15. However the total amount of combustible cladding may be limited by the provisions of space separation between buildings, see p. 93.

An external wall within 1 m from the relevant boundary should only have the permitted unprotected areas as described below. The extent to which unprotected areas need to be limited when the wall is 1 m or more from the relevant boundary is also given below.

Loadbearing external walls should meet the requirements of Table 10. Non-

TABLE 14 USE OF MATERIALS OF LIMITED COMBUSTIBILITY.

Use		Material
1	insulating linings to hollow elements of structure referred to under item 2 in Table 13.	(a), (b) or (c)
2	insulating linings to elements of structure referred to under item 3 in Table 13.	
3	class 0 materials.	
4	roof coverings meeting the provisions: (a) given in Note 1 of Table 23. (b) given in Table 21. (c) for the junction at separating and compartment walls with a roof in a building or compartment in residential (except institution), office or assembly use and not more than 15 m above mean ground level the roof covering must be either a material of limited combustibility or asphalt for at least 1.5 m either side of the wall; such covering can be over boarding or wood wool slabs, tiling battens bedded in mortar can be taken over the wall, the top of the wall fire-stopped; or (d) roof sheeting of limited combustibility, as much as possible of it in contact with insulation having both surfaces at least Class 1 surface spread of flame.	
5	roof slabs of limited combustibility over separating and compartment walls having a roof covering AA, AB or AC extending 1.5 m either side of the wall, the top of the wall fire stopped.	
6	cement mortar cavity barriers at least 25 mm thick.	
7	stairways where required to be constructed of materials of limited combustibility.	
8	insulation used in the cavity of hollow elements of structure referred to in 1 above, or behind linings referred to in 2 above.	(a), (b) (c) or (d)
9	insulation above any suspended ceiling, the ceiling being jointless and of limited combustibility	

Notes
(a) Any non-combustible material listed in Table 13.
(b) Any material of density 300 kg/m^3 or more, which when tested does not flame and the rise in temperature on the furnace thermocouple is not more than 20°C.
(c) Any material with a non-combustible core of 8 mm thick or more, having combustible facings (on one or both sides not more than 0.5 mm thick (Where a flame spread rating is specified, these materials must also meet the appropriate test requirements.)
(d) Any material of density less than 300 kg/m^3, which when tested does not flame for more than 10 seconds and the rise in temperature on the centre (specimen) thermocouple is not more than 35°C and the furnace thermocouple is not more than 25°C.

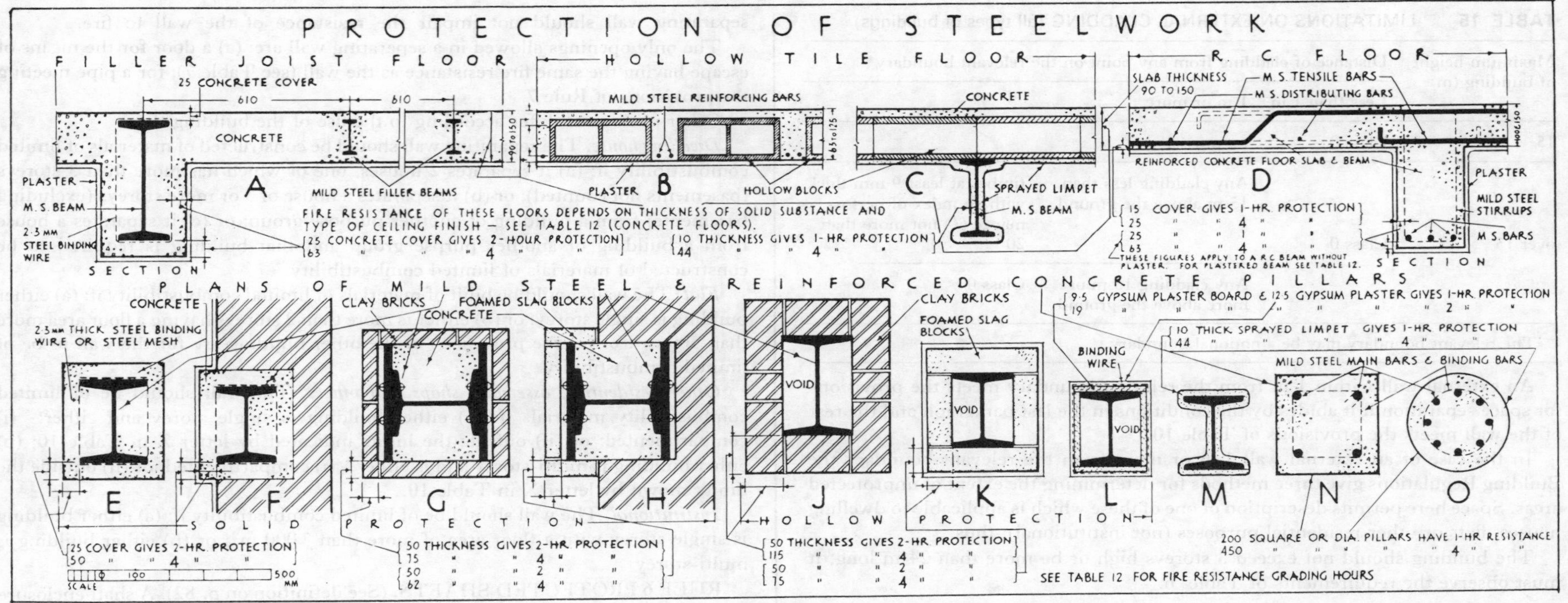

FIGURE 34

loadbearing walls, or parts of such walls, which should not form an unprotected area should meet the same requirements.

Certain other provisions for external walls depend on whether the building is a house, flat, other residential, institutional, assembly or office, thus:

Dwelling house. External walls should be constructed of materials of limited combustibility if: (a) the wall is less than 1 m from any point on the relevant boundary and the house has more than 3 storeys (basements not counted), or (b) the house is more than 15 m high, whatever the distance from the relevant boundary.

Flat. External walls should be constructed of materials of limited combustibility if the building, or separated part, is more than 15 m high (whatever the distance from the relevant boundary) or has more than 3 storeys (basements not counted) and is also, within 1 m from the relevant boundary.

Other residential. External walls should be constructed of materials of limited combustibility if: (a) the building is more than 15 m high (whatever the distance from the relevant boundary), but *not* for any wall to a separated part which does not exceed 15 m in height if that wall is 1 m or more from any point on the relevant boundary, or (b) the wall of a single storey building is less than 1 m from any point on the relevant boundary and the building is either compartmented, or outside the limits indicated by the letter Z in Table 10, or (c) the wall of a multi-storey building is less than 1 m from any point on the relevant boundary and the building is outside the limits shown by the letter X in Table 10.

Institutional. External walls should be constructed of materials of limited combustibility if the building is like (a) in other residential, or (b) the wall is less than 1 m from any point on the relevant boundary and the building is – (i) single storey and divided into compartments or has a floor area more than 3 000 m² or (ii) multi-storey.

Assembly, Office and Shops. External walls should be constructed of materials of limited combustibility as for (a) (b) and (c) in other residential buildings.

An important safeguard against the spread of fire is to ensure that adequate space separation between buildings is maintained. This fire risk increases as the area of unprotected areas (see p. 82) increases. The permitted size of such areas depends on the distance from the external wall to the boundary facing it; a wall is treated as facing a boundary if it makes an angle with it of 80° or less.

TABLE 15 LIMITATIONS ON EXTERNAL CLADDING (all types of buildings)

Maximum height of building (m)	Distance of cladding from any point on the relevant boundary*		
	Less than 1 m	1 m or more	
15	Class 0	no provision	
over 15	Class 0	Any cladding less than 15 m above the ground	timber at least 9 mm thick with an index of performance (I) not more than 20
		Any cladding 15 m or more above the ground	Class 0

* The relevant boundary may be a notional boundary.

An external wall within 1 m from the relevant boundary meets the provisions for space separation if it abides by the conditions in the last paragraph and the rest of the wall meets the provisions of Table 10.

In the case of an external wall 1 m or more from the relevant boundary the Building Regulations give three methods for determining the extent of unprotected areas. Space here permits description of one of these which is applicable to dwelling houses, flats or other residential purposes (not institutional); thus:

The building should not exceed 3 storeys high or be more than 24 m long, it must observe the requirements of Table 6.

TABLE 16 PERMITTED UNPROTECTED AREAS IN SMALL RESIDENTIAL BUILDINGS

Minimum distance between side of building and boundary (m)	Maximum length of side of building (m)	Maximum total area of unprotected area (m^2)
1	24	5.6
2.5	24	15
5	12	no limit
6	24	no limit

RULE 5. SEPARATING WALLS. A wall of this kind must form a vertical fire barrier between the buildings it separates and satisfy the provisions of Table 10. The permissible openings in it are as described in Rule 2 and the provisions for the junctions of separating walls with a roof are the same as those given in Table 14.

The surface material of the wall that must be of limited combustibility may be combustible if it is not relied on to contribute to the fire resistance of the wall and meets the provisions of Table 19.

Where a separating wall joins an external wall the walls must be bonded together or fire-stopped. Combustible material carried through, or across, or built into a separating wall should not impair the resistance of the wall to fire.

The only openings allowed in a separating wall are: (a) a door for the means of escape having the same fire resistance as the wall (see Table 7); for a pipe meeting the provisions of Rule 7.

Other provisions differ according to the use of the building thus:

Dwelling house. The separating wall should be constructed of materials of limited combustibility if: (a) it separates 2 houses, one of which has more than 3 storeys (basements not counted); or (b) it separates a house of 3 or more storeys (excluding basements) from a building of another purpose group; or (c) it separates a house from a building of another purpse group and that building is required to be constructed of materials of limited combustibility.

Flat. The wall should be built of materials of limited combustibility if: (a) either building is single storey; or (b) either is more than 2 storeys having a floor area more than 500 m²; or (c) the provisions of the other building are for the wall to be of limited combustibility.

Other residential, assembly, shops and offices. The wall should be of limited combustibility materials if: (a) either building is single storey and either:– (i) compartmented; or (ii) outside the limits indicated by letter Z in Table 10; (b) either building is multi-storey and is either – (i) compartmented, or (ii) outside the limits shown by letter X in Table 10.

Institutional. The wall should be of limited combustibility if: (a) either building is single storey with a floor area of more than 3 000 m²; or (b) either building is multi-storey.

RULE 6 PROTECTED SHAFTS. (See definition on p. 82). A shaft enclosure must form a complete barrier to fire. The shaft enclosure must meet the fire resistance requirements of Table 10, if this is more than 1 hour the enclosure should be made of materials of limited combustibility (Table 14); if it is so made the surface material of the enclosure may be combustible if it is either part of a separating wall, compartment wall or compartment floor meeting the provisions of Rules 5 and 2 respectively, or of a protecting structure (see p. 82) meeting the provisions of Table 19.

They should be ventilated and if it contains a lift this must be a permanent opening at the top of 0.1 m² per lift.

When a shaft contains a stair and is approached by a corridor or lobby, that part of the enclosure between those approaches and the shaft may be fitted with ½ hour fire resisting glass if that part of the protecting structure is not required to have more than 1 hour fire resistance and the corridor or lobby is separated from the rest of the floor by ½ hour fire-resisting construction, including any openings in it. A shaft enclosing a stair or lift should not contain a oil pipe or ventilating duct, gas pipes in protected shaft should have screwed or welded joints.

The only openings in a shaft as those given in Rule 2, those for a pipe as per Rule 7, those for the inlets and outlets (fitted with automatic fire shutters) of a shaft which also serves as a ventilation duct, those for lift cable to the motor room.

All the above requirements are common to all buildings; in addition in the case of flats: the enclosure should be constructed with materials of limited combustibility if the shaft is in a basement or on the ground and upper storeys of a building or separated part which has more than 3 storeys (basements not counted)

RULE 7. FIRE PROTECTION OF OPENINGS. The provisions are described under the following headings: doors, pipes, ventilating ducts and flues etc. *Doors*. Fire resisting doors should comply with Table 7 (however 2 fire-resisting doors may be used in an opening if each can close the opening and the 2 doors together satisfy the fire resistance required).

They should be fitted with an automatic self-closing device although this is not needed in a protected shaft containing a lift if the opening is protected by either: (a) a single door of the same fire resistance as the structure; or (b) 2 doors in the opening, one with a self closer and fusible link to hold it open and of the same fire resistance as the structure; and one door of ½ hour resistance but not necessarily self closing.

Where a self-closing device would be a hindrance to normal usage in the building, a door may be held open by a fusible link, or (if the door can be opened manually) it can be fitted with electro-magnetic or electro-mechanical devices susceptible to smoke.

Hinges should be of non-combustible material having a melting point of at least 800°C (like steel).

TABLE 17 MAXIMUM NOMINAL INTERNAL DIAMETER OF PIPES

Situation	Pipe material & maximum internal diameter (mm)		
	Non-combustible material[1] (a)	Lead, aluminium, aluminium alloy fibre-cement or upvc[2] (b)	Any other materal (c)
1 structure (not a separating wall) enclosing a protected shaft which is not a stair or lift shaft	160	110	40
2 separating wall between houses or compartment wall or compartment floor between flats	160	160 (stack pipe)[3] 110 (branch pipe)[3]	40
3 any other situation	160	40	40

Notes to Table 17.
1. A non-combustible material (like cast iron or steel) which if exposed to a temperature of 800°C will not soften or fracture.
2. Upvc pipes to BS 4514.
3. Pipes in an above ground drainage system within an enclosure.

A door in an opening provided as a means of escape should be easily opened by hand and held open by the above items susceptible to smoke. Where 2 fire resisting doors are fitted in such an opening as a means of escape, one may have an automatic self-closing device and be held open by a fusible link if the other has ½ hour fire resistance and is easily opened.

Pipes passing through a separating wall, comparment wall or comparment floor (unless they are in a protected shaft), protecting structure or cavity barrier must meet the following requirements: (1) be sealed to maintain the fire resistance of the part through which they pass; (2) the internal diameter of the pipe should not be more than the relevant size given in Table 17 and be fire stopped round it; (3) the diameters in the Table for pipes of specification (b) used in situation 2 assume the pipes are in an above ground drainage system and are enclosed as described below. If they are not, the smaller diameter given in situation 3 should be used instead.

There are two methods of providing an *enclosure* for drainage and water pipes: (1) The enclosure should be bounded by a separating wall, compartment wall or floor, an outside wall, an intermediate floor. (2) By a *casing* (see below). In both methods the enclosure should have Class O internal surfaces (except framing members), be used only for drain and water pipes, *not* have an access panel opening into a circulation space or bedroom.

A casing should be imperforate except for pipes and an access panel, have not less than ½ hour fire resistance (including the access panel), *not* be of sheet metal.

The opening for a pipe in the structure or casing to be as small as possible and fire stopped.

A common drainage stack is sometimes used for *adjoining* houses, flats or maisonettes so that some branch pipes will pass through a separating wall, others through a casing.

Ventilation ducts. These which pass from one compartment to another must meet the following provisions.

If it does not form a protected shaft (or is not within one) it should have an automatic fire shutter where it passes through a compartment wall or compartment floor; the opening for the duct to be as small as possible and space round it fire stopped.

If the duct forms a protected shaft (or is within one) it must have automatic fire shutters at inlets and outlets to it and be lined with materials which minimise the risk of fire spread. Where the shaft is also used for other purposes the ventilating duct should enclosed.

If the duct forms part of an air circulating system it should be fitted with optical smoke detectors capable of changing the operation of the ventilating system so that any smoke can be diverted to the outside.

Flues etc. Flues in chimneys, passages in appliance ventilation ducts and spaces within ducts encasing flue pipes which pass through, or form part of, a compartment wall or compartment floor must be enclosed in a separate wall.

Rule 8. STAIRWAYS. (see also p. 94) Stairs and landings should be constructed of materials of limited combustibility if they are external and connect the ground floor with a floor or flat roof more than 6 m above ground. Combustible materials *may* be added to the upper surface of stairs and landings.

Other provisions depend on the use of the building thus:

Dwelling house. Stairs and landings should be of limited combustibility construction if they are within a house of more than 4 storeys (basements not included).

Flat. Stairs and landings should be constructed of materials of limited combustibility (unless they are within a maisonette) if they are: within a basement storey; or within a storey of a building or separated part which has more than 3 storeys (basements not counted).

Other residential and assembly. Stairs and landings should be constructed of materials of limited combustibility if they are within a storey which comprises elements of structure requiring fire resistance of 1 hour or more.

Institutional. Internal stairs and landings should be constructed of materials of limited combustibility.

Offices and shops. Stairs and landings should be constructed of materials of limited combustibility if they are within a storey which comprises an element of structure requiring fire resistance of 1 hour or more, but not for any stair in a building or compartment used as a shop if the stair is not within a protected shaft.

RULE 9. FIRE-STOPPING AND CAVITY BARRIERS. In addition to provisions for this given in Rule 2, the following also apply:

Fire stopping is required round pipes, ducts, conduits or cables passing through an element of structure (but not a part required to be fire-resisting because it is load-bearing; it and cavity barriers should be kept as small and few as possible and fire-stopped (in the case of a pipe or duct which will allow thermal movement).

To prevent dislodgement fire stopping materials should be reinforced with, or supported by, materials of limited combustibility where the unsupported span is greater than 100 mm or where non-rigid materials are used unless tests have shown them to be satisfactory.

The following fire-stopping materials are satisfactory: cement mortar; gypsum plaster; cement or gypsum based vermiculite/ perlite mixes; glass; crushed rock; blast furnance slag or ceramic products; and intumescent mastics.

Cavity barriers. (see Table 7) The restriction of the spread of smoke and flame in a building is assisted if concealed spaces (e.g. above a suspended ceiling*) and like cavities, are properly constructed thus:

Barriers should be placed at the edges of cavities, at around openings in a wall or floor and to separate one cavity from another. Roof spaces are vulnerable; where a fire resisting wall, floor, ceiling or roof abut a roof cavity at ceiling (or roof) level a barrier in the space must be used. Those provisions do not apply to a cavity: (i) below a ground floor; (ii) enclosed on the lower side by a ceiling constructed as given in Table 7, item 11 (c) and note thereto; (iii) within the roof of a house up to 2 storeys high; if it has 3 or more storeys with a fire-resisting enclosure to the stair then that enclosure must extend through the roof space or the top ceiling constructed as (ii); (iv) in a roof space at its junction with an external wall, where a cavity barrier would prevent ventilation between roof space and outside air.

* see also Table 11.

Large cavities (as in some roof spaces) need to be sub-divided by a barrier as noted in Table 18. A barrier must be placed between the leaves of a cavity wall at the top of the wall and at the *head* of openings in the wall. Barriers are not required: (i) below a floor next to the ground if access to that cavity is not provided and its height is not more than 1 m, or (ii) below roof of limited combustible sheeting which is in contact with insulation and both surfaces of the insulation have a Class 1 surface.

Table 18 MAXIMUM DIMENSIONS OF CAVITIES

Location of cavity	Purpose group of building or compartment	Class of surface exposed in cavity (excl. surface of any pipe, cable or conduit, or insulation to any pipe)	Max. dimension in any direction (m)
Between a roof and ceiling	house and flat	any	no limit
	other residential and institutional	any	15 with area limited to 100 m²
	assembly, office, shop, other residential and industrial	any	20
Any other cavity	any	Class 0	20
		any other Class	8

The permitted openings in a cavity barrier are: a ½ hour fire resisting door with fittings as per Rule 7; a pipe in the same Rule; a cable or conduit; an opening fitted with an automatic fire shutter; and a duct similarly fitted or made of 0.7 mm thick mild steel being continuous throughout the cavity and on both sides of it.

Barriers must fit tightly to rigid construction or be fire stopped. Their performance must not be affected by shrinkage or thermal movement; or by collapse in a fire of services penetrating them; or by failure in any material they abut.

If a cavity barrier is at least 1 m by 1 m it should have at least ½ hour fire resistance, see Table 7, item 11(a). Smaller barriers should be the same, see same Table item 11(b) OR of: (i) fibre-cement board of the same rating as 9 mm thick fibre-cement board (*not* asbestos-cement); or (ii) 12.5 mm thick plasterboard; or steel at least 3 mm thick; or (iii) 38 mm thick timber; or 50 mm thick wire-reinforced mineral wool; or (iv) cement mortar or plaster 25 mm thick.

RULE 10. INTERNAL SURFACES. The spread of fire over surfaces can be restricted by the use of materials with a low rate of surface spread of flame (see p. 84), and in some cases these restrict the rate of heat produced. The provisions apply to walls and ceilings (including the underside of roof lights) as given in Table 19; they do *not* apply to the upper surface of floors and stairs; see also Rule 3 and Table 11.

TABLE 19 MINIMUM PROVISIONS FOR SURFACES OF WALLS AND CEILINGS

Classification of flame spread for walls (W) & ceilings (C)		
Small rooms	Other rooms	Circulation spaces & protected shafts
	one or two storey house (basements not counted)	
3 (floor area not more than 4 m²)	W: 1* C: 3	W: 1 C: 3
	house with 3 or more storeys (basements not counted), flats and other residential buildings	
3 (floor areas not more than 4 m²)	W: 1* C: 1**	0**
	insitutional buildings	
W: 1* C: 1** (floor area not more than 4 m²)	W: 0* C: 1**	0**
	assembly & office buildings	
3 (floor areas not more than 30 m²)	W: 1* C: 1**	0**

Notes.
* Part of the walls may be of a lower Class (Class 3 min.) but the area of the part (or total area if there is more than one part) should not be more than one half of the floor area of the room and not more than 20 m² (for houses, flats, other residential and institutional buildings; and 60 m² for assembly and office buildings).
** Rooflights in rooms and circulation spaces may be of a lower Class (Class 3 min.) if they meet the provisions of Table 21.

Suspended ceilings in rooms and circulation spaces, provided they are not fire-protecting suspended ceilings – Table (11), may have one or more panels of pvc if a specimen when tested by B.S. 2782: Method 508D satisfies the following: (i) the specimen does not flame or glow for more than 5 seconds; (ii) any material dropped from the specimen does not continue to burn after reaching the base of the apparatus; (iii) charring or scorching does not extend over more than 20% of the area of the underside of the specimen; and (iv) the length of the charred or scorched edge on the underside should not be more than 50 mm, (see p. 84).

Alternatively, the suspended ceiling (with the same proviso as above) may be of thermoplastic materials if a 3 mm thick specimen when tested to B.S. 2782: Method 508A does not burn at a rate of more than 50 mm a minute.

Whether the ceiling is of pvc or thermoplastic it must observe Table 20.

TABLE 20 CONCESSIONS FOR SUSPENDED CEILINGS OF PLASTIC MATERIALS

	Limitations			
			Maximum area	
Material	Max. length of side of panel (m)	Max. distance between panels (mm)	Any one panel (m²)	Total area as % age of floor area below ceiling
Pvc as described above 1 mm max. thickness	no limit	no limit	4	no limit
Thermoplastic + 3 mm max. thickness	5	575 + +	circulation spaces: 2	15%
			rooms: 4	flats, other residential, institutional and assembly groups: 30% elsewhere: 50%

Notes.
\+ Panels to be loosely mounted so they fall if softened by heat.
\+ + Panels may be closer if in a group (or groups) which each meet the limitations on length, distance apart and area as a single panel.

The provisions given above apply to all buildings, in addition the ceiling to the top floor of a house of 3 or more storeys which has a fire resisting enclosure to the stair must be constructed thus: (a) have $\frac{1}{2}$ hour fire resistance; (b) extend throughout the building or compartment; (c) not be demountable and (d) be imperforate except for a $\frac{1}{2}$ hour fire resisting door with fittings as given in Rule 7, or a pipe given in the same Rule, or a cable or conduit, or an opening or duct having an automatic fire shutter. The surface of the ceiling facing the cavity must have a surface spread of flame at least Class 1; its exposed surface must have a fire propagation index I not more than 12 with i_1 not more than 6.

TABLE 21 CONCESSIONS FOR ROOFLIGHTS OF PLASTIC MATERIALS

Material or minimum surface spread of flame on lower side	Space which rooflight serves	LIMITATIONS Maximum area of each rooflight (m²)	Rooflight area as % age of floor area of space in which rooflight situated	Separation of rooflight by material of limited combustibility (m)	For rooflight with external surface of Rigid pvc as described above	AD, BD, CA, CB, CC, CD or no designation+	DA, DB, DC or DD
					minimum distance from any point on the boundary (m)		
1 Rigid pvc as described in Rule 10	any space except a protected shaft	no limit	no limit	no limit	6*	not applicable	not applicable
2 Class 3	(a) balcony, verandah, carport, covered way which has one longer side open, or detached swimming pool	no limit	no limit	no limit	not applicable	6	22
	(b) garage, conservatory or outbuilding with max. floor area of 40 m²	no limit	no limit	no limit	not appliable	6	22
	(c) circulation space++ (d) room in a++ residential, assembly, office or shop	5	no limit	2.8 min. (if rooflight is constructed as below) 3.5 min. (if not)	not applicable	6	22
	(e) room in an++ industrial or other non-residential building	5	20% max. (evenly distributed)	1.8 min.	not applicable	6	22

Notes.
\+ A material which canot be designated because of its low softening temperature.
\+ + Single skin material only.
*no limit in the case of any space which rooflight serves in item 2(a) or (b).

If windows, rooflights and suspended ceilings of *plastic materials* having surface classification lower than those in Table 11, or with no classification they may be used under the following conditions:

Windows may be of a single layer of rigid pvc sheeting if this is tested to BS 2782, method 508A and the test flame does not reach the first mark, and the duration of flaming or afterglow does not exceed 5 seconds following removal of the burner.

Rooflights of plastics may be used in compliance with Table 21 provided the height of the curb to the rooflight is at least one-quarter of its width.

RULE 11. ROOFS. On p. 83 the various designations (AA, BB etc.) for roof coverings is given. Table 22 allocates these designations to the different coverings and roof constructions.

Rules 2 and 5 give certain provisions for the junction between compartment walls and separating walls with a roof.

Table 23 gives the limitations on roof coverings according to the distance of different buildings from the boundary.

Certain provisions for rooflights are given in Rule 10, Internal Surfaces.

TABLE 22 NOTIONAL DESIGNATIONS OF ROOF CONSTRUCTIONS (RULE 11) (see note 6, Table 23)

Part I: Pitched Roofs Covered With Slates or Tiles

Covering Material	Supporting Structure	Designation (see p. 83)
Natural slates Asbestos-cement slates Clay tiles Concrete tiles	Timber rafters with or without underfelt on sarking or boarding, wood-wool slabs, compressed straw slabs, wood chipboard or insulating fibreboard	AA
Bitumen felt strip slates, asbestos or fibre based	Timber rafters and boarding	CC
Bitumen felt strip slates, asbestos based, mineral surfaced with an underlayer of self-finished asbestos felt minimum of weight 13 or 16 kg/10 m²	Timber rafters and boarding	BB

Part II: Pitched Roofs Covered With Preformed Self-Supporting Sheets

Covering Material	Supporting Structure	Designation
Corrugated sheets of: galvanized steel, or aluminium, or composite steel and asbestos sheets, or asbestos-cement, or p.v.c. coated steel	Main structure of timber, steel or concrete and covering in either: (*a*) single-skin construction without underlay or with underlay of: (i) asbestos insulating board, or (ii) plasterboard, or (iii) fibre insulating board, or (iv) compressed straw slab, or (v) wood-wool slab, *or* (*b*) double-skin construction without interlayer or with interlayer of resin-bonded or bitumen-bonded glass fibre or mineral wool or polystyrene or polyurethane.	AA

Part III: Pitched or Flat Roofs Covered With Fully Supported Material

Covering Material	Supporting Structure			
	Timber Joists and Boarding		Steel or timber joists with deck of: (*a*) wood-wool slabs, or (*b*) compressed straw slabs or (*c*) wood chipboard or (*d*) insulating fibreboard or (*e*) 9.5 mm plywood	Slab of concrete or clay pot, in-situ or precast concrete; or non-combustible deck of steel, aluminium or asbestos-cement with or without insulation
	Tongued and Grooved	Plain Edged		
Aluminium, copper or zinc sheets, mastic asphalt	AA	AA	AA	AA
Lead sheet	AA	BA	AA	AA

Part IV: (A) Flat Roofs Covered With Bitumen Felt. These roofs (irrespective of the type of felt are designated AA if the felt is laid on a deck of any of the materials prescribed in Part IV (B) of the Table below and has a surface finish of: (*a*) bitumen bedded stone chippings covering the whole surface to a minimum depth of 12.5 mm; (*b*) bitumen bedded tiles of non-combustible material; (*c*) sand and cement screed; or (*d*) macadam.

Part IV (B) Pitched Roofs Covered With Bitumen Felt

Details of Felt			Combustible Deck			Non-combustible Deck		
Number of layers	Type of upper layer	Type of underlayer(s)	Deck of any of the following (having minimum thickness stated); 6 mm plywood; 12.5 mm chipboard; 16 mm t. & g. boarding; 19 mm p.e. boarding	Deck of compressed straw slab	Deck of screeded wood-wool slab	Asbestos-cement or steel single skin or cavity deck (with or without overlay of fibre insulating board)	Aluminium single skin or cavity deck (with or without overlay of fibre insulating board)	Concrete or clay pot slab
2 or 3	1. Type 1E	Type 1B*	CC	AC	AC	AC	AC	AB
	2. Type 2E	Type 1B*	BB	AB	AB	AB	AB	AB
	3. Type 2E	Type 2B*	AB	AB	AB	AB	AB	AB
	4. Type 3E	Type 3B or 3G	BC	AC	AB	AB	AB	AB
Single layer	Type 1E		CC	AC	AC	AC	AC	AC

The following are the types of bitumen felt quoted above with the relevant weights in kg per 10 m².
1E – mineral surfaced fibre base, 36. 1B – fine sand surfaced, 17. 1C – self finished, 13. 1D – coarse sand surfaced, 20 and 30. 2B – fine sand surfaced, 16. 2C – self finished, 13. 2E – asbestos based, mineral surfaced, 36.
3B – fine sand surfaced glass fibre, 18. 3E – glass fibre based, mineral surfaced, 27. 3G – venting base glass fibre, 32.

* or minimum mass 13kg/10 m².

TABLE 23 LIMITATIONS ON ROOF CONSTRUCTION

Building	Designation or covering of roof, or part of roof	Minimum distance from boundary less than 6 m	at least 6 m	at least 12 m	at least 22 m
House (other than terraced) and building of any other use, all of capacity not more than 1500 m^3	AA, AB or AC	a	a	a	a
	BA, BB or BC	na	a	a	a
	AD, BD+, CA, CB, CC or CD	na	a[1](X)	a	a
	DA, DB, DC or DD+	na	na	na	a[1]
	thatch or wood shingles	na	a[1]	a	a
	glass or pvc[4]	a[2]	a	a	a
	no designation[5]+	na	a[1]	a[3]	a[3]
(a) Terraced house, or any other house, flat or other residential building, office or shop, all having a cubic capacity of more than 1500m^3. (b) Industrial or other non-residential of whatever size	AA, AB or AC	a	a	a	a
	BA, BB or BC	na	a	a	a
	AD+	na	a[1](X)	a	a
	BD, CA, CB, CC CD++ DA, DB, DC, DD	na	na	na	na
	thatch or wood shingles	na	na	na	na
	glass or pvc[4]	a[2]	a	a	a
	no designation[5]+	na	a[1]	a[3]	a[3]

a = acceptable, na = not acceptable, X means that the restriction in Note 1 below does not apply to a house.

\+ For rooflights having a lower surface of at least Class 3 surface spread of flame, see Table 21

\++ Rooflights with these designations, which have a lower surface of at least Class 3 surface spread of flame, are permitted subject to the limitations in Table 15.

1 The area of the part of the roof should not be greater than 3 m^2 and it should be at least 1.5 m from any similar part, with the roof between the parts covered with a material of limited combustibility , see Table 14.

2 Only for (i) a balcony, verandah, carport, covered way or detached swimming pool; or (ii) a garage, conservatory or outbuildings with a floor area no more than 40 m.

3 Twice the height of the building if this gives a greater distance.

4 Glass which cannot be designated and rigid pvc as described for suspended ceilings in Rule 10.

5 A covering which cannot be designated because of its low softening temperature.

6 It is expected that in the revision of B.S. 476: Part 3 from which this Table is taken that the letters will be changed: AA, AB, AC become P60 which means the specimen passed the preliminary test and fire penetration did not occur in less than 60 minutes; (30, 15, and 5 minutes in the following new designations): BA, BB, BC become P30; AD, BD, CA, CB, CC, CD become P15; no designation becomes P5.

EFFECTS OF FIRE ON MATERIALS

The periods of fire resistance for elements of structure are given in Table 12. The following list includes construction with some of the materials that are in regular use:

Brickwork. Common and facing bricks have a very high fire resistance due to them having been subjected to heat in course of manufacture, the maximum temperature varying from 850 to 1 100° C (Chap. I, Vol. II). According to Table 12 a 200 mm thick brick load-bearing wall has a fire resistance of 4 hr.

Stonework. It will be observed that walls built of stone masonry are not included in Table 12. Although their behaviour when subject to fire will vary according to the composition of the stone it may be accepted that their fire resistance will approximate to that of solid walls built with clay bricks.

When water from fire hoses is played on heated masonry a shattering effect is produced resulting in cracking and the spalling of fragments. As described in Chap. I, Vol. II, quicklime is produced when limestone is heated to a certain temperature; this calcination starts when the temperature has risen to 600° C or thereabouts and proceeds slowly until 700–800° C has been reached. Examination of limestone masonry damaged by fire showed that the degree of calcination was less than was expected, the depth being but a few millimetres. It is considered, therefore, that calcination of limestone is not likely to be a serious factor, especially in buildings with a low combustible content. Tests carried out on blocks of stone removed from buildings damaged by fire confirm that the strength in compression has been little affected and the load-bearing capacity is unimpaired, unless the blocks are cracked or have spalled.

Reinforced Concrete. The fire resistance of concrete is largely influenced by the nature of the coarse aggregate. Coarse aggregates which have been subjected to fire, such as broken brick, clinker, foamed slag and pumice (referred to as "Class I aggregates") have a high fire resistance and in this respect are superior to those of gravel and broken stone ("Class 2 aggregates") other than broken limestone which is included in Class 1. The fire resistance of solid reinforced concrete structures depend upon the coarse aggregate and the thickness of the concrete cover given to the reinforcement, but, as indicated in Table 12, it compares favourably with brickwork. The fire resistance of patent precast concrete beam floor units of the arch type depends upon the depth and the crown thickness of the beams, the thickness of the screed and the nature of the ceiling, if any; for example, standard fire test results on several floors composed of one patent precast floor illustrated at E, Fig. 28, show that a floor consisting of 150 mm deep units having a thickness of 32 mm at the crown, a 38 mm screed and without a ceiling has a ½ hr fire resistance. See also p. 91.

Building Boards. The many building boards on the market may be classified into (1) vegetable fibre building boards, (2) fibre-cement boards, (3) glass fibre cement boards, (4) resin-bonded boards, (5) plasterboards, and (6) plastic boards described under "Plastics" below. Some of these are referred to in Vol. III.

(1) *Vegetable Fibre Building Boards* (B.S. 1142) are of wood or other *vegetable* fibres (such as sugar cane), bonded under pressure, and of varying densities; they include insulating boards, hardboards, and wallboards (see also p. 208). All are combustible. Insulating boards (or soft boards) have a density not exceeding 368 to 400 kg/m^3, and the most commonly used thickness is 12.5 mm. The homogeneous quality serves as a base for plaster, and others have smooth surfaces which, if required, can be painted, etc., direct. These boards have a rapid flame spread (Class 4 – see p. 84) and construction with them has a fire resistance much less than the ½-hr grading. The rate of flame spread, however, can be much reduced if they are coated with plaster, or if chemically impregnated (with ammonium phosphate) or if surfaced on both sides with asbestos felt. In addition to the homogeneous kind, there are: laminated (not suitable for plastering), bitumen-bonded (for humid conditions), bitumen-impregnated (for expansion joints in concrete) and acoustic types.

Hardboards are formed under pressure in varying densities, there are four main types: medium, standard, super, and decorative.

Medium hardboard has a density from 480 to 770 kg m^3, thicknesses are 6.4, 9, 9.5, 10 mm, etc., up to 19 mm, it is a little harder than insulation board and used for similar purposes.

Standard hardboard has a density of not less than 800 kg/m^3, thicknesses are 2, 2.5, 3.2, 4.8 and 6.4 mm.

Super hardboard is the standard quality that has been very highly compressed and oil treated to increase hardness or resistance to water, or both, the density reaching 1 280 kg/m^3, most hardboards have a smooth surface finish. They are used for providing a suitable finish (panelling) to walls and ceilings, lining formwork (when a smooth surface to the concrete is required), furniture, etc.

The three types are rated as having a Class 3 flame spread, and construction with them has a fire resistance regarded as being less than the ½-hr grading.

Decorative hardboards include plastic and metal-faced types, perforated, enamelled, etc., their fire properties are similar to the above.

Wallboards, both homogeneous and laminated, are the originators of these materials; they are comparable, having similar uses, but are cheaper than insulating board and have corresponding fire properties.

(2) *Fibre-cement Boards.** These consist of special fibres and Portland cement in varying proportions, they are non-combustible and include: fibre-cement sheets, semi and fully compressed flat and decorated fibre-cement sheets, fibre millboard, fibre wallboard, which has a Class 0 surface spread of flame; the remainder are Class 1.

Fibre-cement sheets will shatter when exposed to fire. A steel-framed wall with a single skin asbestos-cement cladding is graded ½ hr.

Fibre-cement insulation board (6.4, 9.5 and 12.7 mm) offers a higher resistance than other sheets. It is used for suspended ceilings and as a fire-protecting casing to elements of structures. For example, a steel column covered with two layers of 9.5 mm thick material affords 2 hr fire resistance.

Fibre millboard and wallboard posses a high fibre content, the former is used for heat baffles and the latter as a lining medium.

Fibre-cement wood (4.8 to 12.7 mm) is used for fire-resistant linings and a 12.7 mm thickness will give 1 hr protection to a steel beam or column.

Fibre partition board, 3.2 mm thick, can be curved to a radius of 305 mm and has comparable uses to that of the standard hardboard (see above), over which it has the advantage of having a surface of very low flame spread (Class 1).

(3) *Glass-reinforced Cement Boards* do not incorporate asbestos; their uses are the same as fibre-cement boards but are more costly; thicknesses are 4.5, 6 and 9 mm.

(4) *Resin-bonded Boards* include plywood (see Vol. III), bonded paper sheets, and bonded wood waste boards.

Resin-bonded plywood is described in Vol. III. Resin-bonded paper sheets are made from paper pulp treated with resin. Resin-bonded wood waste boards are made from sawdust and shavings. These three types of board are combustible, they are rated as Class 2–3 for spread of flame according to their composition and density, and their fire resistance is less than the ½-hr grading.

The uses of these boards include the lining of walls, partitions and ceilings.

(5) *Plasterboards.* Plasterboard consists of a core of gypsum plaster enclosed between and bonded to two sheets of heavy paper, see Vol. III.

There are four types of plasterboard, the composition being the same in each case. They are fully described in Vol. III and briefly here:

Gypsum baseboard is used as a base to receive one or two coats of gypsum plaster. For this purpose it has a suitable paper surface to afford a good key for the applied plaster and normally the edges are square. The board width is 914 mm with lengths of 1 200, 1 219 and 1 372 mm; thickness is 9.5 mm. It can have a layer of polythene bonded to the reverse side as a vapour barrier.

Gypsum lath is somewhat similar to the above, but with rounded edges and of a narrower width in two thicknesses, 9.5 and 12.7 mm, the sizes being 406 mm wide by 1 200, 1 219 and 1 372 mm.

Gypsum wallboard is a dual-purpose board, one side being prepared as a base

* From information supplied by Eternit-TAC, Royston, Herts who make a wide range of products using cement reiforced with man-made fibres like alkali-resisting glass and polyvinyl alcohol which have replaced asbestos.

for plaster and the other for direct decoration. It is in two thicknesses 9.5 and 12.7 mm and several sizes, the most common being 2 438 mm by 1 200 mm, 1 829 by 900 mm and 1 219 by 914 mm.

Gypsum plank is a dual-purpose board 19 mm thick and 600 mm wide in lengths of 2 350, 2 400, 2 700 and 3 000 mm.

Insulating gypsum baseboard and wallboard are either baseboards or wallboards which have a covering of aluminium foil on one or both sides to increase their sound proofing and thermal insulation qualities.

Whilst plasterboard is combustible, owing to the papered surfaces, its rate of flame spread is very low (Class 1) and its fire resistance varies depending upon its thickness and whether or not it is given a coat of plaster. For example, a wall having a steel or timber frame, faced each side with 12.7 mm plasterboard, has a resistance of $\frac{1}{2}$ hr, unplastered; the addition of 12 mm gypsum plaster gives a 1-hr wall. By having two layers of 9.5 mm plasterboard both sides of a timber frame a 1-hr fire-resisting non load-bearing wall is produced.

Glass.* Windows and doors glazed with ordinary sheet or plate glass are very vulnerable, the glass cracking and collapsing at an early stage of a fire; the rate of fire growth is thereby increased as the gases of combustion escape and fresh air is admitted (p. 83). By using 6 mm wire reinforced glass in panes not exceeding 1.2 m^2 in area in a timber framed window where the frame members and dividing bars are not less than 56 mm deep and 44 mm wide, a minimum rebate depth of 13 mm and if glazing beads are used these are painted with intumescent paint a $\frac{1}{2}$-hr fire-resisting window is obtained. A metal framed window with the same glazing has a 1 hr fire resistance; so has glazing with hollow glass blocks.

Hollow Blocks. The fire resistance varies according to the material of which they are composed. The clay block, being a burnt product, has a good fire resistance value although it has been subjected to a lower kiln temperature than that for bricks to prevent distortion during manufacture. As classified in Table 12, the thickness of concrete blocks, especially if composed of Class 1 coarse aggregates, is very satisfactory at high temperatures.

Plaster surfaces give a Class O flame spread. Being non-combustible, plaster is fire-resistant and, as shown in Table 12, the thickness of walls of certain fire resistances can be slightly reduced when plastered with vermiculite-gypsum plaster; a ceiling of such plaster 7 mm thick improves a 90 mm R.C. slab from $\frac{1}{2}$ to 1 hr resistance. When exposed to fire, however, plaster tends to spall, leaving areas of exposed wall, etc., surfaces; if metal lathing is employed at ceilings and stud partitions this tendency to spall is much reduced, especially if deep meshed metal lathing, such as Hyrib (p. 79), is used, due to the reinforcement gripping the plaster key. Vermiculite-gypsum plaster (1-vol. of retarded hemi-hydrate plaster to $1\frac{1}{2}$-vol. of grade 2 vermiculite) has a good fire resistance. This mix, when applied to metallic lathing wrapped round a steel column, gives a resistance of 1 hr with 12 mm thick plaster and 2 hr with a 19 mm thick layer. In comparison with a concrete casing, this method gives a considerable weight reduction. Gypsum plaster and cement-lime plasters have comparable resistances being slightly less effective than vermiculite-gypsum plaster, a perlite-gypsum mix compares with the latter. Straight vermiculite or straight perlite mixes are slightly more effective and are of equal value.

Plastics* In present use, being of organic origin, are combustible. Some give rise to dense smoke, toxic fumes and burning droplets when subject to fire. They are made from widely differing formulations and their behaviour under fire must be found by using the spread of flame test (p. 84). Some, like glass reinforced plastics, may have Class 1 surfaces; such have additives to raise the Class to this level from Class 3, but it is possible additives may harm the weathering properties.

Among the common plastics used for building purposes are: *Acrylic and polyester* sheets for dome lights and roof sheeting. *Foamed polyurethane* sometimes used for filling cavity walls to improve thermal properties. *Polystyrene* used in slab form as an insulation board; it can be obtained in the *self-extinguishing* form which means that burning ceases once the flame has been removed. *Polythene* film sheet used as a d.p.c. membrane; polythene pipes (see p. 228). *Polyvinyl chloride* (p.v.c.) used as surfacing materials.

When plastics are used on external walls they fall under the heading of an unprotected area (see Rule 4, p. 92) and so their area may be controlled by the Building Regulations. Plastics may be allowed to cover a building completely if it is sufficiently far from the boundary, but it must be observed that the fire insurance premium is likely to be increased in such a case.

Plastic materials are increasingly used because they have attractive properties, such as wide variety of colours, ease of cleaning, etc. One satisfactory way of using them is as a surfacing for composite boards. Such can have a backing of asbestos insulation board or foamed cement.

Sprayed Limpet Mineral Fibre.† This is another effective fire-resisting material consisting of specially treated selected inorganic binders and mineral fibres which is applied with a very fine water spray from a gun to ceilings, walls, steel beams and pillars, etc., being plastic for about 2 hr after application, the surface can be given a smooth (by trowel pressing) or other textured finish. The coating can be applied in thicknesses up to 200 mm in one operation. Besides being effective in resisting fire, this material is efficient as a means of increasing thermal insulation and providing sound absorption, and when applied to steelwork it is claimed to afford complete protection against corrosion. The surface is durable but where physical damage is expected a very tough Limpet cement can be applied to it.

Steelwork. Mild steel, for structural members of a steel framed building has a very low fire resistance value if unprotected. The ultimate or breaking stress of mild steel is about 460×10^6 N/m^2 in tension and compression, and at the yield point, where a marked elongation occurs when a steel specimen is under test, the stress is approximately 262×10^6 N/m^2. At a temperature of slightly more than half of that of a normal building fire this yield stress is reduced by about two-thirds. Consequently, when subjected to a fire of great severity, *unprotected* steel beams and pillars become considerably distorted, the beams twist and sag

* See also p. 153.

* See Rule 10.
† This material is asbestos free and made by Eternit – TAC Ltd.

causing collapse of the superstructure, and any steel roofs, probably much misshapen, may take with them considerable areas of external walling as they overturn, causing further damage to lower floors, etc. It is most essential, therefore, that steel members shall be suitably protected – see below.

Protection of Steelwork. Table 12 specifies the minimum thickness of protecting cover to steel beams, steel pillars and steel reinforcement, with corresponding periods of fire resistance. Some of these requirements are illustrated in Fig. 34. It should be noted also that, in regard to floors, the fire resistance periods vary according to the thickness specified in Table 12.

The detail at A, Fig. 34, shows a section of part of a steel filler beam floor with the minimum thickness of concrete cover to the steel main beam.

B shows a portion of a hollow block floor in cross section with the minimum concrete cover to the reinforcement. The ceiling is plastered.

A longitudinal section through a hollow block floor is shown at C. Here the ceiling is of sprayed fibre-cement as is the protecting cover to the steel beam.

A detail of a typical reinforced concrete floor is shown at D. This is a T-beam – see p. 57. The concrete cover to the mild steel reinforcement which gives the beam 1- and 4-hr protection is stated.

Note in each of the above examples the protecting cover is thicker at the beams than at the flat soffits of the floors because these projecting members are more vulnerable to the action of fire.

E, F, G and H, Fig. 34, show the so-called "solid protection" referred to in Table 12. E is the plan of a detached steel pillar encased in concrete. F shows a plan of a pillar at an external wall. Detail G is that of a compound steel pillar with clay bricks laid on edge (or terra-cotta blocks) and concrete encasement. H is a plan of a similar pillar at an external wall partly encased with foamed slag blocks (see Chap. I, Vol. III). Note that the 62 mm thick foam slag blocks afford the same protection as the 75 mm clay brick casing.

J, K and L are examples of "hollow protection" – see Table 12. The casing to the steel pillar at J is of brickwork and that at K of foamed slag blocks. The steel pillar at L is encased with plasterboard, bound with nichrome wire and plastered. Hollow protection to columns must be effectively sealed at each floor level, *e.g.*, by a steel cover plate welded to the top of the pillar. M shows the steel pillar covered with sprayed fibre-cement.

N and O are typical examples of reinforced concrete columns. The common practice is to provide a concrete cover to the main bars of thickness equal to that of the diameter of the bars. Reinforced concrete details are described on pp. 57–65.

Strawboard, composed of compressed straw encased in stout paper (Chap. I, Vol. III), is combustible, has a flame spread rating of Class 3 (untreated) and Class 1 if treated with a fire retardant. A framed partition having 50 mm strawboard slabs on each face (with 75 by 12 mm cover strips to the joints) has a resistance of $\frac{1}{2}$ hr. If instead of the cover strips the strawboard was in timber frames and both sides plastered, a 1-hr wall would result. When the partition has additionally a 3 to 5 mm skim coat of plaster (omitting the cover strips but including a metal scrim at the stud positions), it has a 1-hr grading. It is also used for roof decking, see Fig. 64.

Timber. Practically all building timbers will burn when heated to 300° C. As a severe fire in a building may reach a temperature of 1 000° C it follows that wood elements of structure within it are liable to catch fire. Resistance of wood members to fire depends upon the scantlings, the larger they are the more resistant are they to burning and collapse; thus, large timber beams and posts have a satisfactory fire resistance partly because of the surfaces becoming charred shortly after ignition; carbon formation, being a bad conductor of heat, delaying and sometimes preventing further destruction of the timber.

Timber of density (see Vol. III) more than 400 kg/m^3 is Class 3, lighter species are Class 4. Impregnation of timber with certain solutions, such as ammonium phosphate, renders it less likely to become ignited and Class 1, although, when exposed to fire of sufficient length and intensity such timber is destroyed; this is called *flame-retardant timber* (see below).

Several wood joists and boarded floors which give a $\frac{1}{2}$-hr protection when plastered are listed in Table 12. As shown in Table 12 certain house floors can have the modified $\frac{1}{2}$-hr period of fire resistance. This applies to timber floors and examples are given in the table.

Vermiculite is a micaceous mineral* which, when heated, exfoliates (splits into scales) and forms a light-weight aggregate. This aggregate when used with cement produces a fire-resistant concrete used for partitions, as a protection to steel pillars (see Table 12), beams, etc., and for insulating floor and roof screeds†. When mixed with gypsum it forms a fire-resisting plaster.

Wood-wool Cement Slabs‡ to B.S. 1105, are made of Portland cement and wood shavings to which gypsum may be added (Chap. I, Vol. III), are non-combustible, they are of Class 1 flame spread rating, and their fire resistance is very satisfactory. A steel or timber framed wall faced each side with 51 mm wood-wool slabs and plaster has a resistance of 1 hr (2 hr for 75 mm slabs).

Flame-retardant Treatment. The fire resistance of some of the above materials and structures may be greatly increased if so-called fire retardants or other means of protection are afforded. For example:

As mentioned above, timber is less likely to become ignited if it is impregnated with ammonium phosphate, so are building boards if they are surfaced with fibre-cement materials. There are a number of fire retardants for protecting timber and building boards obtainable in powder form, to which water is added. When applied by spray or brush and exposed to fire, it swells (referred to as "intumescence") and forms an insulating covering which prevents the fire from spreading and retards the penetration of heat through the treated material; vegetable fibre insulating boards, for example, which are rated at Class 4, are raised after treatment to Class 1 for retardance of flame spread. The impregnation treatment is better than surface application.

* A type of mica having a foliated or laminated structure.
‡ See p. 174.

FIRE-FIGHTING EQUIPMENT

Access to Buildings for Firemen. It is important to provide reasonable access for fire-fighting purposes to all buildings and it should be possible to drive the fire appliances to within 18 m (36 m for domestic premises not exceeding three storeys) of the main entrance. Access roads should be at least 3.7 m wide and the internal radius of any corners at least 8.2 m, a minimum headroom of 3.5 m is needed. In addition adequate working space for firemen must be placed near the sides of the building.

Alongside all buildings other than small residential ones there should be an area of cleared ground the extent of which should be agreed with the fire authority. The surface of this area should be capable of carrying an axle load of 10 tonnes.

Note that the limit of fire hoses is 60 m up the building and that the maximum height for rescue by fireman's turntable ladder is 24 m. So it is particularly important that within a high building fire-fighting requirements are incorporated to enable the fire to be fought and rescues made from the interior.

Irrespective of the requirements in the building regulations it is advisable to restrict the size of compartments (Rule 2, p. 86) within a building to 7 000 m^3 For this is about the largest building capacity a fire brigade can handle, over this size the building should have sprinklers (see p. 105).

Fire fighting stairs should have a clear width of 1 m and be subdivided at ground level to prevent smoke from basement entering the stairway. Natural ventilation or, preferably, an air pressure system should be provided to keep smoke away. Two kinds of pressure systems are used: (1) A *single stage* one which operates in an emergency and (2) a *two stage* system where there is a low pressure all the time which is boosted if a fire starts, B.S. 5395 deals with these stairs.

Fire fighting lobby. This should have an area not less than 5 m^2 and not more than 20 m^2 with no main dimension less than 1.5 m or more than 8 m. It should have self-closing fire doors marked "Fire Fighting Lobby" and be ventilated as above, permanent openings should be avoided because, in a fire, wind can blow smoke into the lobby.

Fire lifts. These are provided in tall buildings for the use of firemen, when not required by the fire brigade they can be used by the occupants. Certain provisions for them are given in the Scottish building regulations, among them are the following:

A fire lift is required for any storey over 24 m above the ground, it must be in a protected shaft (see Rule 6, p. 94). The lift must have an independent electrical supply; a platform of area not less than 1.44 m^2 capable of carrying at least 544 kg; and a switch at ground floor level enabling firemen to summon the lift without interference from landing call points, the switch being placed in a glass fronted lock-fast box marked "Fire Switch".

See also pp. 118–122.

Water Supply for Fire-fighting. Fire mains should be put in buildings where any storey is higher than 10.6 m and in buildings and compartments exceeding 900 m^2 in floor area. They should be in a protected shaft or lobby (pp. 94, 113, 114 and below). C.P. 402, 101: *Hydrant Systems* is relevant.

Fire-fighting equipment for large public and industrial buildings includes internal water supply pipes, usually 100 mm dia., called *fire mains* or *rising mains* to enable the fire brigade (or privately trained staff) to deal more expeditiously with a fire. Otherwise much valuable time is lost in running out long lengths of hose from street hydrants, especially when an outbreak occurs in a high building. Such mains should be readily accessible with hose connections at each floor and at the roof, it being considered that any part of a building shall be reached by a jet from a 18 m long hose. Fires can be fought from within large buildings if each floor has a lobby* (5.5 m^2 min. area) which is free from fire risk and has windows. The lobby gives access to the fireman's lift and staircase, has a rising main and telephone and is separated from the rest of the floor by a 1-hr fire-resisting door. There are two kinds of rising mains: wet and dry. A *wet main* is connected to the public water supply and, being a branch from the street main, is fully charged with water under pressure, the pressure varying from 0.55 to 0.7 N/mm^2. A *dry main* is not connected to the public water supply but is continued to a convenient point in the public road at which the fire brigade can pump water into it from the street main or other source; in a dry main the water pressure can be regulated to that required, such a main is therefore effective for tall buildings and is preferred to the wet main type which latter may provide only an inadequate water pressure when dealing with fires on the upper storeys.

Occupants of a building can be of service also in coping with a fire at its early stage if 20 mm dia. *hose reels* connected to wet mains are available; these should be sufficient in number so that with 37 m of hose they can reach any point on the floor area and deliver a minimum of 23 litres per minute.

Detection and Warning. Early detection and warning of an outbreak are essential to prevent or reduce loss of life and if extensive damage or a complete burn-out are to be avoided. Measures to ensure early detection depend upon the size and height of the building, the value of the building and or its contents, the nature of the occupancy and fire load, etc. In the day-time when a fire occurs in an occupied building it is not unusual for it to be discovered at an early stage and dealt with successfully either by the occupants with the hand appliances, or by the public fire service. Such early detection by personal observation is unlikely, however, when at night the premises are unoccupied or the occupants are asleep; much time may have elapsed before discovery by a passer-by or an awakened occupant and meanwhile an extensive spread of fire may have occurred. Hence, for many types of buildings† *automatic electric fire alarm systems* are required to be installed. They consist of detectors linked together and fixed in suitable positions which are actuated by the effects of heat, smoke or combustion gas to operate an electric circuit to give the alarm by the ringing of bells inside and outside (usually at an entrance) the building. The signal is transmitted to the local fire brigade or, if a large establishment, to the private

* See also *lobby approach stairways*, pp. 113.

† Health and Safety at Work Act 1974 requires offices, shops and railway premises to have alarms.

fire brigade consisting of specially trained personnel. The system automatically warns the occupants, summons the fire brigade(s) and gives the exact location of the fire. Sprinkler systems (see below) serve both as fire extinguishers and alarms.

Detection and warning systems incorporate either detectors or "break-link" cables placed at ceiling level. There are three types of detector: (1) Heat sensitive detector. (2) Photo-electric cell smoke detector. (3) Combustion gas detector. These are briefly described below, BS 5839: Pt. 1. Fire Detection and Alarm Systems in Buildings is relevant.

1. *Heat sensitive detectors*. These comply with B.S. 3116: Part 1. They are of several types, one kind has a fusible link device which when subjected to heat will melt and thus interrupt a current flowing through it to allow a relay to operate the alarm circuit. Another kind is the more expensive infra-red detector which responds to heat in the form of radiated light. In effect it sees the flames of a fire so it operates instantaneously unlike the fusible link type which has to feel the heat before becoming operative.

2. *Photo-electric cell smoke detector*. This contains a photo-electric cell and a source of light. It operates when the first trace of smoke enters the detection chamber to activate the alarm circuit. It therefore operates more quickly than a detector which is inoperative until the heat from a fire has developed – this may be some time after the fire starts.

In another type of smoke detector a *laser beam* of light is used which traverses the area to be protected. The laser produces a narrow parallel beam of light over long distances and is used in conjunction with photo-electric cells and mirrors. Variation in the refractive index of air caused by combustion gases from a fire oscillates the laser beam; this movement is detected by the photo cells to give the warning.

3. *Combustion gas detector*. This detects combustion gases even before smoke is produced from a fire. It consists of an ionisation chamber containing a low strength radio active material which is capable of making the air round it slightly conductive when an electric current passes between two electrodes separated by an air gap (the ionised area). The strength of the current varies according to the constituents of the air and when combustion gases enter the ionised area the change in current operates the circuit.

The area protected by a single detector can vary from 20 to 100 m² depending on the type adopted; heat detectors need to be placed at a lower level and closer together than smoke detectors.

The alternative and cheaper system to the use of detectors is a heat sensitive installation using *break-link* cable or linear detector system. This consists of a flexible cable which is cut at 2 m intervals and the ends rejoined with low melting point solder. Heat from a fire will melt the solder thus breaking the current in the cable to operate the alarm. The cable runs parallel to the ceiling and 50 mm below it at 3 m intervals.

A similar type of linear detector has cables which consist of two high tensile wires encased in a heat sensitive thermoplastic which will melt from the heat of a fire allowing the wires to touch each other to complete an electric circuit and activate an alarm signal.

A detection system must have an alternative source of electrical supply which will operate in the event of a mains failure.

The following is another system sometimes adopted in large buildings in which there is a private fire service and where a night porter or fireman is employed. At strategic points on each floor at intervals not exceeding 30 m there are fire buttons behind glass panels. When a fire occurs, the nearest button is pressed and this signals the location of the call to the commissionaire's lodge. The commissionaire starts off the fire alarm bell and the fire service goes into action. There may be an automatic signal to the public fire station or a direct telephone line from the lodge to the station; this line is checked thrice daily and four times at night by ringing up the station. On each floor there are several hose reel points placed near the bell push buttons; at each point there are two connections for fire hoses (p. 104) and two buckets of sand; portable fire extinguishers (p. 107) are also available where there are special risks. The fireman makes four rounds nightly of all floors of the building; at several points he punches a time clock which he carries and these times and locations are recorded on the clock tape.

Automatic Sprinkler and Fire Alarm System. This is provided in a building for the purpose of extinguishing a fire at its earliest stage by the use of water, and for sounding an alarm automatically and simultaneously. Water is discharged instantly on to the seat of the outbreak and adjacent area when the fire causes a sufficient rise in temperature to bring the sprinklers into action.

Buildings exceeding 7 000 m³ capacity and those wherein the area of any one floor exceeds 900 m² should have sprinklers, C.P. 402, 201: *Sprinkler Systems* is relevant. Their value may be gauged by the recognition given by fire insurance companies which, for certain types of premises, allow from 50 to 60 per cent rebate on annual fire insurance premiums if sprinkler systems are fed by two independent water supplies.

The extinguishing equipment consists of a main water supply pipe, 100 to 150 mm in diameter, to which are connected range pipes, graded in size down to 25 mm dia., with the sprinklers (also referred to as sprinkler-heads or valves) screwed to them. The range pipes are suspended from the ceilings or roofs. If the wet system (see below) is employed the sprinklers are fixed, pendant fashion, below the range pipes; in the dry,* and the alternate wet and dry,* systems the sprinklers are fixed upright above the range pipes. A sprinkler must be placed so that its deflector (the plate opposite to the outlet) is not more than 300 mm below the traditional wood joisted and plastered type of ceiling and not more than 450 mm from a fire-resisting ceiling. Rules of the fire insurance companies state that there must be at least one sprinkler per 9 m² of floor area; if the ceilings are non-fire resisting the sprinklers must not be more than 3.35 m apart and not more than 1.8 m from walls, and if the ceilings are fire resisting the

* See p. 106.

sprinklers must be placed at centres not exceeding 3.7 m and not more than 1.8 m from walls.

The modern sprinkler, such as the Grinnel Quartzoid Sprinkler,† employs a small barrel-shaped bulb of tough, transparent material, as a strut to support a valve assembly, which forms a water-tight joint, and the deflector. This bulb contains a liquid which expands when heated; as the temperature increases, so does the internal pressure, until the bulb eventually fractures and shatters into small pieces, followed by an immediate discharge of water from the now open valve on to the deflector which produces an evenly-distributed spray over the area it protects. The temperature within buildings varies and may be abnormally high for some manufacturing processes; seven temperature ratings of sprinklers are made for operations ranging from 68 ° to 260 ° C. The operating temperature is marked on every sprinkler and the colours of the liquid filling of the bulbs vary to distinguish them. There is a reserve margin between the maximum atmospheric temperature where the sprinkler is located and that at which it will operate; for example, a bulb for general situations in this country and which operates at 68 ° C in the event of fire, would be used where the atmospheric temperature is 49 ° C.

In large premises especially, it is usual to divide the sprinkler equipment into separate groups or installations, each with its own fire alarm and control valves; the maximum number of sprinklers per group is 1 250 on the wet system and 750 on the dry or alternate system. By sub-division of the premises, control is thereby simplified as in a fire break-out only one installation is involved, leaving the others fully operative. When the main part of a building is protected so that the water in the pipes cannot freeze, this part can be on the wet system; sprinklers in a part of the building that is subject to frost would be on the dry system.

The water supply to a sprinkler system must be strictly confined to it and be adequate for the purpose at all times. To qualify for the highest rebate on annual fire insurance premiums allowed by insurance companies to owners of sprinklered premises, a system must have two independent water supplies to ensure that one will always be available if the other fails. One must be an unlimited supply, such as is afforded by a connection from the public water main, which must have a minimum running pressure of 0.17 N/mm² at the highest sprinkler. If the water pressure in the public main is inadequate it can be increased by employing an automatic centrifugal pump with its suction branch connected direct to the public main and its delivery pipe connected to the sprinkler main. The second source of supply may be that either from (1) a tank, having a 4-hr capacity fed from the main and supplied to the sprinkler installation by means of a pump, or (2) a cylindrical pressure tank, situated in a room which is heated in winter as a protection against frost, having a capacity of from 22 500 to 45 000 litres charged with water and with compressed air in suitable ratio and to the required pressure, or (3) an elevated rectangular tank, usually situated on a flat roof and of capacity according to conditions such as 23 000 litres if the base of the tank is 6 m above the highest sprinkler or 34 000 litres if its base is 4.6 m above the highest sprinkler, or (4) water from an adjacent canal, river, pond or static tank at ground level which is automatically pumped to the sprinkler main.

There are three types of sprinkler systems, *viz.*, (1) wet, (2) dry, and (3) alternate wet and dry.

(1) In the *wet system* the pipes are constantly full of water under pressure. It is always employed if there is no danger of damage by frost. If a fire occurs and the heat has risen to a temperature at which the sprinklers will operate (see above), the nearest one will function and discharge water on to the outbreak.

(2) In the *dry system*, the sprinkler pipes are charged with air at a moderate pressure and the water is held back by a valve out of frost range until a fire develops to bring into operation one or more sprinklers; air then escapes through the open sprinkler(s) causing a reduction in the air pressure in the pipes whereupon the valve opens to allow the water to enter the range pipes and discharge at the sprinkler(s). An accelerator can be fitted to reduce the time lag before the water reaches the sprinklers. This system is employed in buildings where the water is liable to freeze.

(3) The *alternate wet and dry system* is applied in buildings which may be subject to freezing during the winter months. The pipes are charged with water during the summer, but in the autumn, before there is any danger of frost, the water is drained out of the pipes, the control valves are reset and the pipework charged with compressed air; with the dry or alternate systems, the sprinkler pipes are given a slight fall towards a drain valve to facilitate draining.

In all three systems, if the water showered from the sprinkler nearest the fire is not at first sufficient to quench it, the heat will cause adjacent sprinklers to function in turn until the fire has been extinguished or held in check until the arrival of the fire brigade.

After a fire has been quenched, the water supply is cut off by means of a stop valve. The sprinklers which have operated are unscrewed and replaced by new ones; air or water is then admitted to the pipes, depending on which system is used, to bring it to the alert.

Control valves are concentrated to form a unit fixed to the rising main which embodies the stop and drain valves, the accelerator, and an automatic alarm mechanism actuated by the flow of water through the pipes and its escape from the sprinklers. When the flow starts, a valve at the control unit permits some of the water to pass up a small bore pipe to the alarm motor that sounds a gong; weekly proving tests of the alarm should be made by operating a small valve provided for the purpose.

Mulsifyre Sprinkler System. Developed by Mather & Platt Ltd., this is designed to deal with fires of the worst type, namely, those involving burning oil, paints, etc., and it is therefore employed for the protection of equipment, such as oil-filled electrical transformers and switchgear, oil-processing plant and that used in oil-fired boiler rooms and paint and varnish works.

† From information supplied by Mather & Platt Ltd., Manchester.

Whilst the use of water from a hose is futile in quenching burning oil, it is a fact that if the oil is emulsified in water, such emulsions will not burn. To form an oil-in-water emulsion, the constituents must be mechanically agitated to separate the oil into fine globules surrounded by the water. To produce this condition on a large scale, specially designed nozzles, called projectors, are employed. The projectors discharge water with considerable force into the surface of the oil and the impact creates the emulsion resulting in the fire being extinguished within a few seconds. This emulsion is but temporary; after the water has been turned off, separation of the water from the oil results with no detriment to the latter. The projectors are open nozzles and are fixed on pipework coupled to controls or valves which open automatically when fire occurs to allow water to flow. The installation may be on the dry or wet systems as circumstances require. Like the sprinkler system, a Mulsifyre installation should have two independent sources of water supply and automatic alarm equipment is provided.

Carbon Dioxide System. CO_2 is stored under pressure in steel cylinders from which pipes deliver it to discharge as a gas from nozzles operated by detectors. The CO_2 system is suitable for the same purposes as the halogen system below.

Halogenated Hydrocarbon System. Such compounds (known also as halogens) are vapourizing liquids which, when exposed, become gaseous to create an inert atmosphere to extinguish fire. Two compounds are available: bromochlorodifluoromethane and bromotrifluoromethane; they are held in containers having a discharge nozzle which can be operated by a detector. The compounds, are toxic and are a more expensive alternative to CO_2; systems of this kind are generally more suitable for the protection of small areas such as those containing archives, valuable collections, computers, electrical switchgear, etc. Halogens have a higher liquid density than CO_2 to the extent that they can be stored in vessels requiring about one-fifth of the capacity of those used in an equivalent CO_2 system.

Automatic Drenchers or Water Curtains. It is sometimes necessary to protect openings in separating and fire-division walls of large industrial premises. Fire would spread readily from one compartment to another if such openings were unprotected. One form of protection is the automatic drencher which consists of a row of sprinkler-heads above and extending the full width of the opening. It operates like an automatic sprinkler system (p. 105), the heat from a fire in the vicinity opens the heads liberating a continuous shower of water covering the opening. Fire protection is increased if automatic drenchers are provided to windows and glazed doors in which fire-resisting glass is employed (p. 102). The water supply to drenchers must be independent from any other source, including that which feeds the sprinkler system, otherwise, in the event of a fire, the volume of water being consumed may reduce the pressure to such an extent as to produce an inadequate flow at the drencher-heads.

Portable Fire Extinguishers. These are regarded as essential equipment for most buildings including those in which automatic sprinklers are installed; they are desirable for houses. If a fire occurs in a building which is occupied, the immediate application of this type of extinguisher by the occupants is often successful in putting it out, or at least reducing the damage and limiting the fire spread. There are several types, cylindrical in shape and in various sizes, that of 9 litre capacity being common. They should be adequate in number and be ready to hand, such as at the head of a staircase at each floor; they are usually hung on walls or accommodated in recesses. One used for general purposes is the *Water Gas* type; by striking a knob at the top a jet of water is discharged under high pressure by means of a cartridge of liquified carbon dioxide. Another general purpose type is the *Soda-Acid* extinguisher; it contains water, a strong solution of bicarbonate of soda and a quantity of sulphuric acid; when brought into use a gaseous effervescing liquid is projected on to the fire. A *Foam* type operates to blanket the fire with globules of CO_2 gas and is particularly effective for petrol, etc., fires; foam is not employed unless absolutely necessary as it causes a certain amount of damage. A CO_2 manually-operated appliance is especially suitable for dealing with small fires involving electrical wiring and apparatus, it discharges carbon dioxide in liquid form; it is also effective in dealing with fires in chemical, etc., laboratories; in some fires, such as those involving heavy oil, the CO_2 apparatus is applied, but whilst this may be effective in putting out the fire, it may burst into flames again and, therefore, after the CO_2 treatment the oil is covered with foam. If a fire occurs at electrical switchgear there may be an explosion which could blow out any adjacent window(s) through which the CO_2 would escape; this may cause the appliance to become ineffective. Halogens are also used in portable extinguishers.

One or two buckets of sand provided at each portable fire extinguishing point are useful in an emergency and may be sufficient to smother a small fire.

Fire blankets made of asbestos wool or glass fibre are also useful for smothering small local fires.

FIRE-RESISTING DOORS AND SHUTTERS

As has been mentioned in the Rules for fire precautions, doors in certain places must be fire resisting for a given period; for example, a door between a house and an attached garage must have a $\frac{1}{2}$-hr* rating. Several publications, issued

* *A $\frac{1}{2}$-hr fire-resisting timber door* should have 95 mm by 38 mm stiles and rails, and 165 mm middle rail forming the core. This is clad with 9.5 mm plasterboard set into rebates of the core members, to which 3.2 mm plywood is glued (metal fastenings are not permitted). The door is hung on one pair of hinges, it must fit closely to the frame which has a continuous stop 25 mm deep (instead of the normal 12.5 mm rebate).

A 1-hr timber door has a core as above but impregnated to a depth of 12 mm with mono-ammonium phosphate in water. In addition a 5 mm sheet of asbestos wallboard (not sheeting) is placed between the plywood covering and the plasterboard. The timber frame must be the same as for the $\frac{1}{2}$-hr door but $1\frac{1}{2}$ pairs of hinges are used for hanging it. Alternatively, a metal frame with 19 mm stop can be used.

A 2-hr door must be made of 6 mm steel plate as described in (1) above.

A 4-hr door consists of double steel doors.

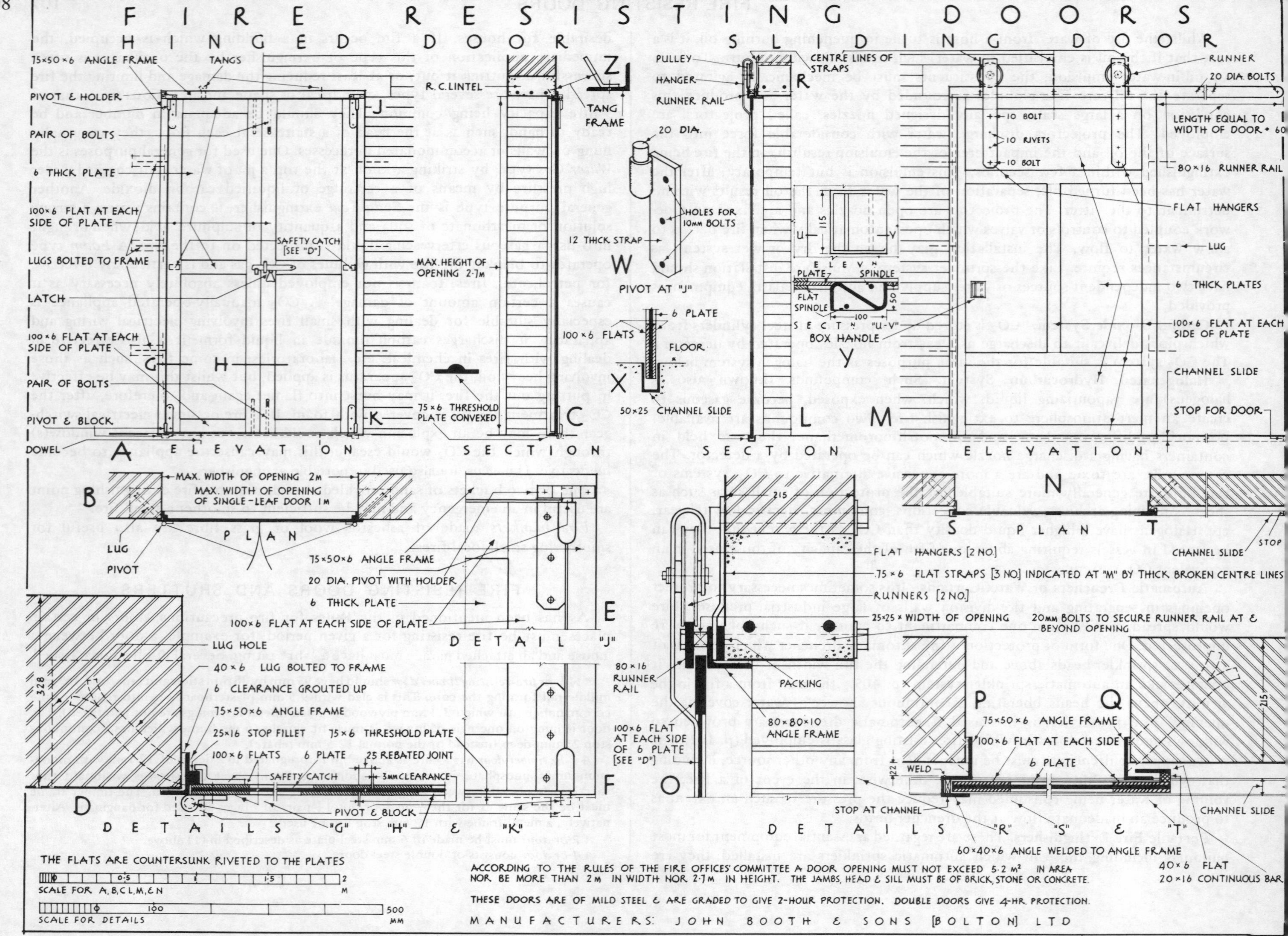
FIRE RESISTING DOORS
HINGED DOOR Z
75×50×6 ANGLE FRAME
TANGS
PIVOT & HOLDER
PAIR OF BOLTS
6 THICK PLATE
100×6 FLAT AT EACH SIDE OF PLATE
SAFETY CATCH [SEE "D"]
LUGS BOLTED TO FRAME
MAX. HEIGHT OF OPENING 2·7m
LATCH
100×6 FLAT AT EACH SIDE OF PLATE
PAIR OF BOLTS
PIVOT & BLOCK
DOWEL
R.C. LINTEL
TANG FRAME
75×6 THRESHOLD PLATE CONVEXED
A ELEVATION
C SECTION
B
MAX. WIDTH OF OPENING 2m
MAX. WIDTH OF OPENING OF SINGLE-LEAF DOOR 1m
PLAN
LUG
PIVOT
75×50×6 ANGLE FRAME
20 DIA. PIVOT WITH HOLDER
6 THICK PLATE
100×6 FLAT AT EACH SIDE OF PLATE
DETAIL "J"
E
LUG HOLE
40×6 LUG BOLTED TO FRAME
6 CLEARANCE GROUTED UP
75×50×6 ANGLE FRAME
25×16 STOP FILLET
75×6 THRESHOLD PLATE
100×6 FLATS
6 PLATE
25 REBATED JOINT
SAFETY CATCH
3mm CLEARANCE
PIVOT & BLOCK
328
D DETAILS "G" "H" & "K"
F
SLIDING DOOR
PULLEY
HANGER
RUNNER RAIL
20 DIA.
CENTRE LINES OF STRAPS
HOLES FOR 10mm BOLTS
12 THICK STRAP
W
PIVOT AT "J"
6 PLATE
100×6 FLATS
FLOOR
X
50×25 CHANNEL SLIDE
PLATE
SPINDLE
FLAT SPINDLE
BOX HANDLE
"U" "V"
SECTION
RUNNER
20 DIA BOLTS
10 BOLT
10 RIVETS
10 BOLT
LENGTH EQUAL TO WIDTH OF DOOR + 600
80×16 RUNNER RAIL
FLAT HANGERS
LUG
6 THICK PLATES
100×6 FLAT AT EACH SIDE OF PLATE
CHANNEL SLIDE
STOP FOR DOOR
L M
N
ELEVATION
S PLAN T
STOP
CHANNEL SLIDE
FLAT HANGERS [2 NO.]
75×6 FLAT STRAPS [3 NO.] INDICATED AT "M" BY THICK BROKEN CENTRE LINES
RUNNERS [2 NO.]
25×25×WIDTH OF OPENING
20mm BOLTS TO SECURE RUNNER RAIL AT & BEYOND OPENING
80×16 RUNNER RAIL
PACKING
80×80×10 ANGLE FRAME
100×6 FLAT AT EACH SIDE OF 6 PLATE [SEE "D"]
O
P
Q
75×50×6 ANGLE FRAME
100×6 FLAT AT EACH SIDE
WELD
6 PLATE
STOP AT CHANNEL
CHANNEL SLIDE
DETAILS "R" "S" & "T"
60×40×6 ANGLE WELDED TO ANGLE FRAME
40×6 FLAT
20×16 CONTINUOUS BAR
THE FLATS ARE COUNTERSUNK RIVETED TO THE PLATES
SCALE FOR A, B, C, L, M, & N
SCALE FOR DETAILS
ACCORDING TO THE RULES OF THE FIRE OFFICES' COMMITTEE A DOOR OPENING MUST NOT EXCEED 5·2 m² IN AREA NOR BE MORE THAN 2m IN WIDTH NOR 2·7m IN HEIGHT. THE JAMBS, HEAD & SILL MUST BE OF BRICK, STONE OR CONCRETE.
THESE DOORS ARE OF MILD STEEL & ARE GRADED TO GIVE 2-HOUR PROTECTION. DOUBLE DOORS GIVE 4-HR. PROTECTION.
MANUFACTURERS: JOHN BOOTH & SONS [BOLTON] LTD

FIGURE 35

by the Fire Protection Association and known as the "Rules of the Fire Offices' Committee (F.O.C.)", give complete specifications relative to the construction of these doors and shutters. If metal doors are required they must be made of either steel or wrought iron, not less than 6 mm thick; cast iron, because of its brittel characterisitcs, is not permitted.

(1) Hinged Folding Door. One type of steel door which complies with the F.O.C. Rules is illustrated in Fig. 35. It has a resistance of 2 hr.

This shows the door to be in two leaves, a necessary requirement if the opening exceeds 1 m in width. The opening must not exceed 5.2 m^2 in area, not be more than 2 m wide nor 2.7 m high; a single leaf door is used if the width of the opening does not exceed 1 m. The door and frame are of mild steel. An elevation, plan and vertical section are shown at A, B and C. The 75 mm by 50 mm by 6 mm angle frame is secured to the brickwork jambs by 40 mm by 6 mm steel lugs, three to each jamb, which are grouted into 215 mm by 215 mm by 75 mm holes formed in the brickwork; these lugs are fish-tailed, bent and turned up against the longer leg of the angle to which it is bolted – see D. The angle frame at the head is secured by means of two tangs which are grouted into the reinforced concrete lintel; as shown at Z, a tang is a bent 40 mm by 6 mm strip of steel which is bolted to the frame. The frame must be fitted closely to the jambs and lintel, any gaps being grouted up. The door is fitted flush with the surface of the wall and it should open outwards in the direction of escape, giving a swing of 180 degrees. The leaves consist of 6 mm thick steel plates divided into panels, as shown at A, by 100 mm by 6 mm steel flats (stiles and rails) on both faces, giving an overall thickness of 18 mm at the edges – see D; these flats are secured to the plates by countersunk rivets, not less than 8 mm dia. and spaced at not more than 150 mm apart. According to the F.O.C. Rules a rebated joint, not less than 12 mm wide, must be formed at the meeting stiles; as indicated at detail H, there is a 3 mm clearance between the adjacent plates and flats, the latter being staggered to give a 25 mm rebate. A steel threshold plate, convexed on top, is dowelled to the floor – see A and C. It is *recommended* that the threshold be raised 50 mm above the floor to check the flow of water (in the case of a fire) from one compartment to another, indicated by broken lines at B, Fig. 36 although this is often disregarded if the door is in constant use because of the risk of tripping.

Each leaf is hung on substantial metal pivots, one top and bottom. A sketch of a pivot, 20 mm in dia., is shown at W with details at D, E and F. The pivot is of forged steel and is secured to the plate by 10 mm dia. bolts. The top pivot engages in a metal holder (see E) which is bolted to the head of the frame, and the bottom pivot rotates in a metal block grouted into the floor (see F).

A continuous stop fillet is mounted on the sides and top of the frame and to this the door must fit tightly – the fillet at each side terminating 25 mm above the floor to permit the easy removal of refuse, see C and D. As an additional precaution against the passage of fire and smoke, a substantial lug or so-called "safety catch" is bolted to the middle rail of each leaf, these grip the leaves to the frame – see A and D.

As indicated at A, there is a shoot bolt provided at the top and bottom of each leaf. These are so arranged to enable the door to be opened from either side, thus, whilst the pair on the left leaf is operated from one side only, those on the right leaf can be worked from both sides. Panic bolts can be fitted where exit doors have to be kept closed when the premises, such as factories and public buildings, are occupied; such a fastening, which should be rustless, consists of two long bolts one engaging in a socket in the floor and the other in a socket in the head of the frame; these bolts are released from their sockets when a connecting horizontal bar, at about 1 m height is pressed down from inside or by a key from the outside.

The above type of door is known as a "single fire-resisting door" and has a graded resistance of 2 hr. A "double fire-resistance door" consists of two such doors fitted one on each side of the wall opening, the full thickness of the wall apart, provided there is at least a space of 175 mm between the inner faces of the doors; such doors give a 4-hr protection.

The hinged type is the cheapest of the steel fire-resisting doors.

(2) Sliding Door.* This type, which conforms to the above F.O.C. Rules, is illustrated in section, elevation and plan at L, M and N, Fig. 35. The sides of the frame, lugged to the wall, are of mild steel angle, and the angle at the head is 80 mm by 80 mm by 10 mm. Like the hinged folding type, this door is of 6 mm thick plate, with 100 mm by 6 mm steel flat stiles, rails and muntin at both sides. It slides to one side by means of two malleable iron ball bearing frictionless runners, pinned to hangers extending at least 380 mm down the door, to which it is bolted and countersunk riveted – see M; not less than three runners must be provided if the door exceeds 1.5 m in width. The runners travel on a runner rail securely bolted through the lintel and the wall, and additional support is provided over the opening by three flat straps shown at O and by broken centre lines at M. At the bottom, the door slides in a channel of mild steel let into the floor – see X for sectional detail. Alternatively, the channel guide can be omitted, providing the bottom of the door is reinforced by a steel angle. The length of the runner rail must, of course, be equal to the width of the door plus a margin (65 mm). The channel slide is slightly longer than the runner rail for, as indicated at M and P, it is extended at the left side (with a sloping bottom) to permit the ready removal of accumulated dirt. As shown at P, the edge of the door is housed for at least 32 mm into a recess formed by a steel angle welded to the angle frame. The opposite edge of the door is built up as shown at Q, the 40 mm by 6 mm steel flat engaging the recess between the wall and the leg of the angle frame which has a 22 mm clearance. To prevent damage to the door if closed violently a stop is provided (indicated at P) in the form of a metal saddle over the channel slide; a metal end to the channel forms a stop at the opposite end – see M and N.

When required by regulations, this door can be closed automatically in the event of a fire by provision of a *fusible link* (see p. 95). The runner rail is given a

* See p. 213 for ordinary timber sliding doors and partitions.

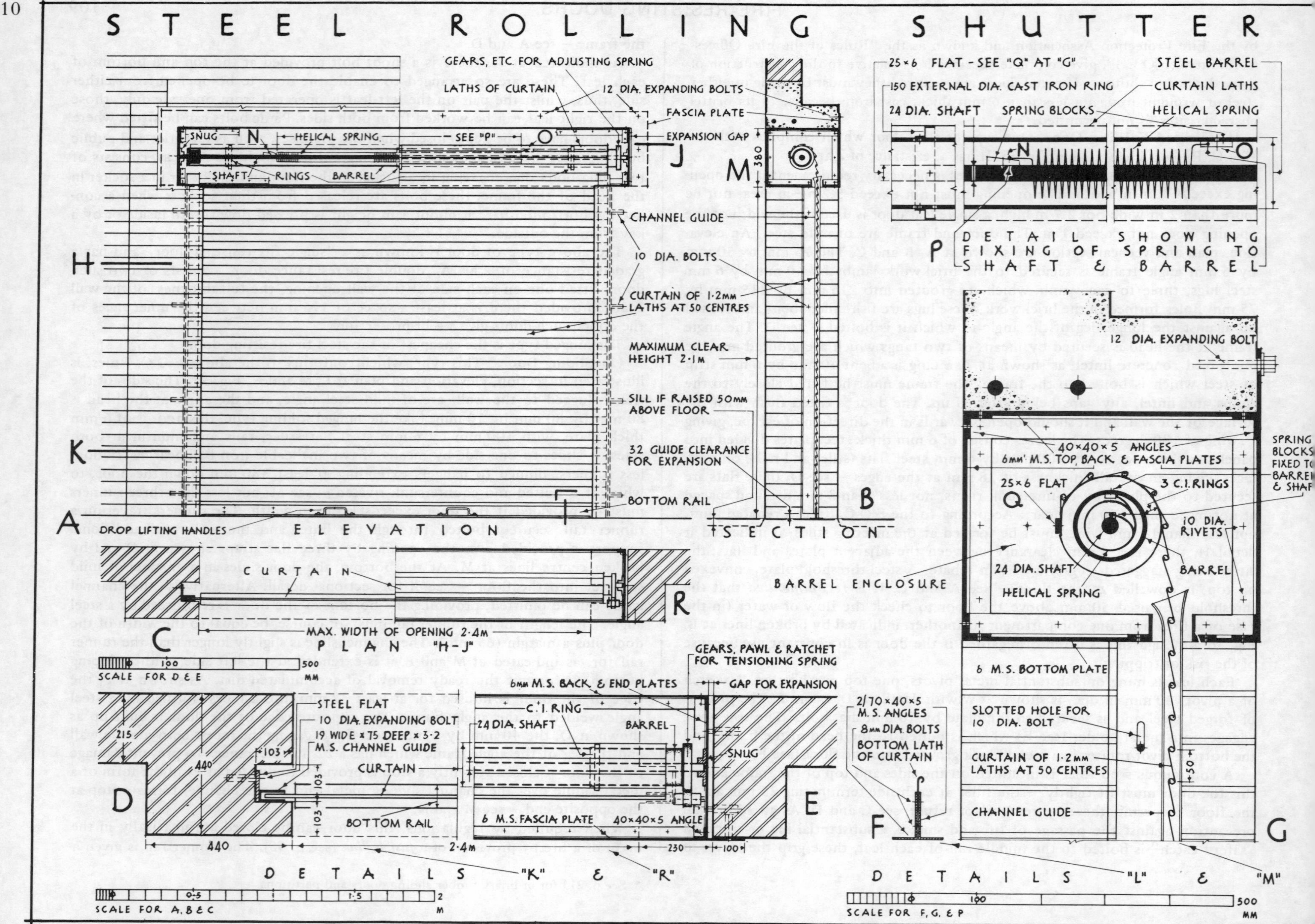
STEEL ROLLING SHUTTER
GEARS, ETC. FOR ADJUSTING SPRING
LATHS OF CURTAIN
12 DIA. EXPANDING BOLTS
FASCIA PLATE
EXPANSION GAP
SNUG
HELICAL SPRING
SEE "P"
SHAFT
RINGS
BARREL
CHANNEL GUIDE
10 DIA. BOLTS
CURTAIN OF 1·2MM LATHS AT 50 CENTRES
MAXIMUM CLEAR HEIGHT 2·1M
SILL IF RAISED 50MM ABOVE FLOOR
32 GUIDE CLEARANCE FOR EXPANSION
BOTTOM RAIL
DROP LIFTING HANDLES
ELEVATION
SECTION
25×6 FLAT - SEE "Q" AT "G"
150 EXTERNAL DIA. CAST IRON RING
24 DIA. SHAFT
SPRING BLOCKS
STEEL BARREL
CURTAIN LATHS
HELICAL SPRING
DETAIL SHOWING FIXING OF SPRING TO SHAFT & BARREL
12 DIA. EXPANDING BOLT
40×40×5 ANGLES
6MM M.S. TOP, BACK & FASCIA PLATES
SPRING BLOCKS FIXED TO BARREL & SHAFT
25×6 FLAT
3 C.I. RINGS
10 DIA. RIVETS
24 DIA. SHAFT
HELICAL SPRING
BARREL
BARREL ENCLOSURE
6 M.S. BOTTOM PLATE
SLOTTED HOLE FOR 10 DIA. BOLT
CURTAIN OF 1·2MM LATHS AT 50 CENTRES
CHANNEL GUIDE
CURTAIN
MAX. WIDTH OF OPENING 2·4M
PLAN "HJ"
SCALE FOR D, E
MM
STEEL FLAT
10 DIA. EXPANDING BOLT
19 WIDE × 75 DEEP × 3·2 M.S. CHANNEL GUIDE
CURTAIN
BOTTOM RAIL
GEARS, PAWL & RATCHET FOR TENSIONING SPRING
6MM M.S. BACK & END PLATES
GAP FOR EXPANSION
C.I. RING
24 DIA SHAFT
BARREL
2/70×40×5 M.S. ANGLES
8MM DIA. BOLTS
SNUG
BOTTOM LATH OF CURTAIN
6 M.S. FASCIA PLATE
40×40×5 ANGLE
DETAILS "K" & "R"
DETAILS "L" & "M"
SCALE FOR A, B & C
SCALE FOR F, G & P

FIGURE 36

slight rise from left to right. A fusible wire, attached to the top left corner of the door and passed over a pulley fixed to the right end of the runner rail carries suspended weights to counter-balance the weight of the door when open. If a fire occurs when the door is open, the heat (68 °C) fuses the wire, and the door, now relieved of the counter-balancing weight, slides back to cover the opening.

This door has a 2-hr fire resistance and a double door (one at each face of the opening) gives a 4-hr protection.

Sliding doors are more expensive than the hinged folding type, but, unlike the latter with leaves that swing outwards, a sliding door has the merit of occupying no additional space when being opened.

Rolling Shutter. According to the Rules of the F.O.C., the doorway must not be more than 2.4 m in width nor 2.1 m clear height plus space for the barrel enclosure. One type of rolling shutter is illustrated in Fig. 36. The *barrel enclosure*, rectangular in section, is made of 6 mm thick mild steel plates secured to angles (see G) by rivets. The fascia plate is fixed independently of the barrel enclosure and is secured at the top and sides by bolts, the bolt holes being slotted (like that shown at G, but with the bolts set centrally) – see A and G. The enclosure accommodates the shaft, spring, barrel, rings and, when open, the curtain. The wall is 440 mm thick (328 mm min.) to accommodate the enclosure and the latter extends 215 mm beyond one side of the opening, and 150 mm at the other.

The *curtain* consists of 1.2 mm steel laths or slats at 50 mm centres, each lath being curled on both edges to form an interlocking hinge. The bottom lath is bolted to two mild steel angles which form the bottom rail – see F. The top lath is secured to a flat steel bar (see Q at G) by 8 mm screws or bolts at not more than 300 mm centres; this bar is fixed to three rings (see below). The curtain moves in 19 mm wide by 75 mm deep by 3.2 mm mild steel channel guides. As shown at D, each guide is situated in a $\frac{1}{2}$ brick by $\frac{1}{2}$ brick recess formed in the brick jamb and is fixed to a flat plate which is bolted to the brickwork; these bolts are arranged as indicated at A, not more than 600 mm apart and, with exception of that at 150 mm from the top, must be in slotted holes so as to allow for expansion in a downward direction. It will be observed that a slotted hole with the normal position of the bolt, is indicated at G; this is for illustration only, for, as mentioned above, this top bolt is fixed and only the lower bolts are engaged in slotted holes. In order to minimize the passage of smoke at the guides an *end lock* is riveted or welded at each end of each lath; these locks conform to the shape of the laths and should fill the guides as closely as possible.

The *shaft* is of 24 mm dia. mild steel. It is securely fixed at each end in a bracket or so-called snug of malleable iron bolted through the end plate of the enclosure and into the brickwork. Note that the shaft is stationary – see below, except when turned during the initial setting of the counterbalancing springs.

The *barrel*, a mild steel tube, is mounted on ball bearings at each end of the shaft – see A and E. The barrel must not be less than 75 mm external dia. and not less than 3 mm thick. Note that the barrel rotates – see below.

The helical steel *spring* is situated centrally within the barrel – see A. These springs vary in size, that shown being 80 mm in dia. and 1.5 mm in length. One end of the spring is fixed to the shaft and the other to the barrel. Each end of the spring is fixed to a cast iron block. Before assembly, one of the blocks is fixed to the shaft, and a hole is drilled in the block which is to be fixed to the barrel. The shaft, with spring attached, is threaded through the barrel and when the hole in the barrel block coincides with one previously drilled in the barrel a set screw is inserted and tightened. Thus, one end of the spring is fixed to the shaft, which is stationary, and the other to the barrel, which rotates. The spring block fixed to the shaft is indicated in the detail P at N and the block secured to the barrel is shown at O; these fixings are also shown at G.

Three *rings*, at not more than 1 m centres (see A), are fixed to the rotating barrel. These are either of cast iron, gun metal or bronze, shaped as shown at P, and the overall diameter is 150 mm. As mentioned above, the curtain is fixed to the rings and, as the latter are secured to the barrel, any rotation of the barrel will raise or lower the curtain. The section at G shows the relative position of the laths and the rings (with flat bar Q attached) when the curtain is down.

Two lifting handles are fixed at each side of the bottom rail (see A) and fixed to let the rail contact the floor.

As indicated at E, at one end of the enclosure there is a ratchet device consisting of gears (toothed wheels which communicate motion to, or receive it from, each other), a pawl (a pivoted catch engaging in the toothed wheel to prevent recoil) and a ratchet (teeth on a wheel so set that the pawl working these allows rotation in one direction but checks it in reverse).

The helical spring counterbalances the weight of the curtain. Correct adjustment is obtained by means of a spanner applied to the ratchet mechanism. As emphasized above, one end of the spring is attached to a stationary object (the shaft) and the other end is fixed to a rotating barrel. Hence any movement of the gears when the spanner is applied will rotate the shaft, which in turn will increase (or reduce) the spring tension. The curtain is operated simply by lifting or lowering it by the handles and if the spring has been correctly adjusted the curtain will retain its position when application at the handles ceases. An opening with a 6 mm steel cover plate, is provided in the fascia plate for access when adjustment of the spring is needed.

In the event of a fire the heat may cause the shutter, fascia, etc., to expand and cause damage. This is prevented by making allowance for such movement by having a gap between one of the end plates of the barrel enclosure and the brickwork, the allowance being 12 mm per metre of length – see A and E. Movement is also provided for at the fascia, where the bolts are engaged in slotted holes; similar provision is made at the jamb flats to which the channel guides are attached (see D) and, as shown at B, these guides have a clearance at the bottom not exceeding 32 mm and not less than 20 mm from the floor.

From Rule 7, p. 95, there are requirements which insist on the provision of a fusible link mechanism which causes the automatic closing of the shutter in response to heat from a fire.

Whilst there is a recommendation in the F.O.C. Rules that the sill be raised 50 mm above the floor (as indicated at B) in order to prevent or reduce the flow of water from one room to another, it is often disregarded for the reason given on p. 109.

This is a single fire-resisting shutter and, like the hinged and sliding doors, gives a 2-hr protection. A double shutter gives a 4-hr protection. The construction of the latter is the above type in duplicate; the construction at each jamb consists of two 102.5 mm by 102.5 mm recesses to receive the channel guides, set back 102.5 mm from each face of the wall and with at least a 300 mm thickness of brickwork between each. The barrel enclosure is divided into two by a 6 mm thick plate, each compartment accommodating a shaft, barrel, etc.

The above doors and shutter are of mild steel. A cheaper and less efficient type of fire-resisting door consists of a timber core of t. and g. boards completely covered with 2 mm thick sheet steel. It is frameless, the door covering and overlapping the opening at the jambs and head, and having straps top and bottom engaged in pivots lugged at one face of the wall.

MEANS OF ESCAPE

The Building Regulations demand that there should be adequate means of escape in case of fire to a place of safety outside and that this is to be achieved by observing the HMSO publication Mandatory Rules for the Means of Escape in Case of Fire. This contains provisions for: (1) a house and flats of three or more storeys; (2) offices and (3) shops. This aspect should be considered for all buildings except that it is not normally needed for a 2 storey house.

The Fire Precautions Act, the Health and Safety at Work Act and the Factories Act also demand these facilities.

The essence of the requirements is that sufficient protected escape routes and exits are provided.

The provision of special means of escape in two storey houses is not mandatory, as the normal wood staircase is adequate for this purpose when the number of occupants is small. When designing other types of buildings, however, careful attention is paid to the means of escape of the occupants by providing corridors of adequate width leading directly to stairs which must be suitably located and be adequate in width, and lead to well-sited and distributed exits which, again, must be sufficient in number. Fire escape notices (sometimes specified as being in red block letters, not less than 75 mm in height and on a white background) indicating the direction of the exit should be fixed in conspicuous positions in public rooms and corridors. In addition along all corridors manual fire alarm buttons should be placed at 30 m intervals. Due to the vast difference in the construction, type, size and occupancy of buildings the length of an *escape route* or *travel distance* (see p. 82) will vary. Thus, whilst a 45 m travel distance (including a maximum of 30 m of corridor length) may be regarded as satisfactory for a workshop which has a low fire risk and whose occupants are well acquainted with the escape route and who may have undertaken regular fire drills, it may be deemed necessary to halve this distance in a building, such as an hotel, where the occupants may be in bed at the fire alarm and who may be unfamiliar with the route, and *especially if there is an absence of conspicuous indicators to escape routes.*

The materials of which corridor walls and partitions are constructed are an additional factor which should be taken into consideration; it is clear that the travel distance can be longer if these structures are of non-combustible materials compared with timber-studded corridor partitions or those constructed of the several contemporary combustible materials. Since corridors form escape routes they should be well protected. If corridor walls are load-bearing or form separating compartment walls they are elements of structure (p. 82) and so must have the minimum fire resistance given in Table 7. Other types of corridor wall, *e.g.*, of the non-load-bearing partition type, must have a minimum fire resistance of $\frac{1}{2}$ hr; additionally their surfaces and corridor ceilings must have a Class O surface (except small houses of not more than two storeys – see Table 19, note that in this Table "circulation space" includes a corridor). Stairs, lobbies and fire escape routes must be protected against smoke by natural ventilation.[1]

The above Mandatory Rules refer to B.S. 5588 giving fire precautions for certain dwelling houses, flats, shops and offices; they also refer to B.S. Code of Practice CP 3 in regard to fire precautions for flats and maisonettes (in blocks over 2 storeys. These are now described:

Means of Escape from Dwellings. These are included in B.S. 5588 Fire Precautions in the Design and Construction of Buildings Section 1.1 Code of Practice for Single Family Dwelling houses. It applies to a house of 3 or more storeys a single protected stair is adequate; if it is more than 7.5 m above ground level alternative means of escape such as a fire escape balcony (see p. 116) plus the single stair is needed. Such a balcony to be placed at the upper floors.

Means of Escape from Flats and Maisonettes. The requirements of the escape route from these dwellings depend on the plan of the building and the type of access to them. There are two basic means of access to each dwelling: via a balcony or via a corridor. B.S. Code of Practice, Chapter 4, Part 1 Flats and Maisonettes deals with these buildings over 2 storeys high.

In the balcony approach type escape is easily accomplished and two provisions are needed: (1) All parts of the building are to be within 60 m of the rising water main used for fire fighting; and (2) The walls of the dwellings facing the balcony should have a minimum $\frac{1}{2}$ hr fire resistance for at least 1 100 mm above balcony level and no glazing should be included in this height.

If the dwellings have a corridor approach and an alternative escape route (via a balcony or private stair down to another corridor) the corridor should extend to an external wall at one point if its length does not exceed 30 m. For greater lengths it should extend to the extremities at both ends. In both cases at the

1. Or by an air pressure system (B.S. 5588) creating airflow away from escape routes.

points of contact with the external wall there should be a balcony (from which rescue by the fire brigade can be made). If the escape route along the corridor leads in one direction only to a main stair the dwelling entrance door should be not more than 40 m from the stair. If it leads in two directions this distance can be increased to 50 m.

Dwellings with corridor approach and no alternative escape route can have their escape routes protected in two ways: (*a*) by smoke containment; or (*b*) by smoke dispersal. In the case of (*a*) the dwelling entrance must not be more than 4.5 m from the stair wall *or* from a $\frac{1}{2}$-hr fire-resisting door across the corridor between the entrance door and the stair. The main purpose of such a door in a corridor in this method is to limit the spread of smoke in the building. In addition if the entrance door is between two stairs it should not be more than 30 m from one of them; but if access is in one direction only this distance is 15 m.

In the smoke dispersal method (*b*) the corridors are cross ventilated[1] and touch an external wall at 60 m intervals. At these points of contact is an opening of 1.5 m² of which 0.5 m² is permanently open or controlled by smoke detectors and 1 m² is opened by hand. Also if the entrance door of the flat or maisonette leads in one direction only it should not be more than 15 m from the stair; if it leads in two directions the distance is 40 m.

Staircase provisions for these dwellings are given on p. 114.

Means of Escape from Offices. The maximum travel distance (distance along the escape route between the furthest point in an office and an exit door from the storey) when escape is possible in one direction only is 30 m for ground and first storeys – provided the offices have opening windows with cills not more than 3.8 m above ground level. In the absence of this proviso the maximum travel distance is 12 m. In all cases the escape route from an inner office should not pass through more than one other office and both offices should be of the same occupancy.

When escape is possible in alternative directions the maximum travel distance is 46 m. No point in an office should be more than 12 m from the office exit. The distance between any two exits from a storey should not exceed 60 m.

In multi-staircase buildings corridors should allow access to at least two stairs without the need to pass through the enclosure of one to reach the other. Where escape is possible in alternative directions along a corridor $\frac{1}{2}$-hr fire-resisting doors to contain smoke should be placed at 60 m intervals along the corridor. In such buildings the width of staircase doors should not be less than 765 mm for floor areas up to 230 m². For greater floor areas the door width is 1 070 mm up to 1 860 m² of floor area plus an extra 76 mm for each additional 140 m².

Stairs are best sited on external walls having openable windows at each floor. Between the stair and the offices there should be a protected and ventilated corridor or lobby (*a lobby approach stairway*) with a minimum $\frac{1}{2}$ hr fire resistance to the walls which should have a minimum openable window area of 1.4 m²; the minimum floor area of the lobby is 5.5 m² and it must contain hydrants and rising mains (see p. 104). A stair should not continue to a basement for this is more likely to become filled with smoke and heat than other floors. So it is preferable to have the basement entered directly from the open air but if this is not possible a basement stair should be adequately separated from upper levels.

Means of Escape from Shops. *Small Shops.* These are not more than 3 storeys high, of limited floor area (840 m² maximum) and for on occupancy; they require one $\frac{1}{2}$ hour fire protected stair. The maximum distance from a point on any floor is 30 m to the ground floor final exit. In many cases small ground floor shops will not need a secondary exit but if the accommodation extends through more than one storey such wil be required. Also in long narrow buildings where the ratio of length to width exceeds 4:1 and the travel distance exceeds 12 m a secondary exit is needed at the end of the building opposite the main entrance.

The discharge from a stair at ground level may be through the sales area if the distance from foot of stair to exit is not more than 15 m.

In *large shops*, those over 840 m², the travel distance is 12 m when escape is possible in one direction only and 30 m if in more than one direction. Two fire protected staircase are needed.

The lobby approach type of stair should be used in all shops more than one storey high and stairs are preferably placed on external walls.

The above mentioned B.S. 5588 Fire Precautions Part 2 Code of Practice for Shops is relevant.

Means of Escape from Hotels and Boarding Houses. Stringent precautions must be adopted for these premises because the occupants, in many cases, will not be familiar with the building or the escape routes from it.

In a room with only one exit no point in the room should be more than 9 m from the exit from the room; but 6 m in the case of high risk areas like kitchens. In a room with more than one exit, both or all of which lead to an escape route which leads to safety in one direction only the distance from any point in the room to the nearest exit should not exceed 9 m, or 6 m in rooms of high fire risk. In large rooms such as drawing rooms two exits are required each leading by a separate route to safety. The distance from any point in a large room should not exceed 18 m unless there are at least three exits when the distance is 30 m. Alternative exits should be distributed to permit escape in at least two separate directions from the room. The minimum width of exits from a room is 760 mm for up to 5 occupants and 1 m up to 100 occupants, when more than one exit is needed then with any one exit excluded the aggregate width of the remaining exits should be 760 mm for up to 100 persons, 1 060 for up to 200 persons and an additional 75 mm for each additional 15 persons.

The maximum travel distance from a room exit to a protected route (one which is separated from the rest of the building by fire-resisting doors and is of fire-resisting construction – *e.g.*, a stair wall) is 18 m for a room with one or more exits leading to alternative escape routes; 7.6 m if there is no alternative escape route.

Corridor walls should have the appropriate fire resistance as demanded by the

Building Regulations; often this will be of a $\frac{1}{2}$-hr period; surface finishes should be Class O. Fire-resisting doors are needed at 18 m intervals along corridors.

The lobby approach stair is the type to use; stair widths may be determined according to the number of occupants (see below).

Stairs.* Certain provisions for these are given in the building Regulations; see Rule 6, Protected Shafts (p. 94).

The width of stairs and corridors approaching them should be such that all occupants, in the case of fire, will evacuate the building in 2.5 minutes; it is assumed that a stair 500 mm wide allows 40 people per minute to escape; staircase widths are described below. Escape routes for 110 persons should be 926 mm wide, for 220 persons 1 100 mm wide and for 300 persons 1 400 mm wide.

The usual wood stair, such as those illustrated in Chap. II, Vol. III, although combustible, is adequate for houses, as in the event of fire, should it become ignited, it will usually remain intact for a sufficient time to enable the occupants to escape. In such a timber stair the treads and risers must be tongued and grooved together and the soffit covered with 16 mm plaster on metal lath or equivalent material.

For other types of buildings, however, a higher standard of fire resistance is required than that offered by the normal timber stair. A staircase includes a stair and the part of the building enclosing it. It is a vertical shaft which, in an outbreak, could readily transmit fire from one storey to another if it did not comply with Rule 6 – Protected shafts. It is therefore essential that, in addition to the stair (such as the R.C. fire-resisting stair shown in Fig. 50, Vol. II), its enclosing walls should be of fire-resisting construction. The fact that staircases provide a convenient means of access for firemen is an additional reason why such structures should be able to withstand fire as long as possible.

In the case of buildings over 24 m high, it will often be necessary for firemen to fight the fire from the building itself due to the limitation on the height of firemen's ladders. Access will thus be gained by the staircases, which should have a vestibule (or lobby) separating the stair from the main floor area (*a lobby approach stair*, see p. 104 and below).

For flats and maisonettes the minimum tread width for a stair is 240 mm with risers a maximum of 190 mm; for offices and shops these two figures are 254 mm and 190 mm. In all buildings there should not be more than 16 risers per flight and not less than 3 (other than flats and maisonettes when the minimum number is 2).

The width of the final exit from a building should not be less than the min. stair width and if this exit is a revolving door a side hung door(s) must be placed adjacent to it and opening out. If, for security or other reasons, exit doors have to be kept locked they should be provided with panic bolts or panic latches (which open the door automatically when subject to pressure) or have a key attached to a chain in a glazed box.

An exit notice must be provided in a staircase enclosure at the level of the discharge to the final exit.

Corridors and staircases should be provided with good artificial lighting served by a secondary source of supply which lights up automatically on the failure of the normal mains supply. They should have clear indication of the direction to exits and have notices as to the action to be taken in the event of fire, *e.g.*, (1) Raise alarm; (2) Call fire brigade (tel. No.); (3) Attempt to extinguish fire.

Staircase widths. Stairs for flats and maisonettes should have a minimum width of 1 m measured between walls or 900 mm between a wall and inside of opposite handrail. If such buildings house more than 200 persons the stair width may be found by consulting the Table below.

The above mentioned B.S. 5588 in regard to shops gives particulars for stair widths which are applicable to offices and public buildings; two tables are given and extracts from them are shown here:

Table A gives stair widths and the number of people who can escape for the *total* evacuation of the building. Table B is based on the evacuation of 2 floors only when the building is compartmented to restrict the fire to fewer floors; it gives stair widths for premises of unlimited height. Stairs should be approached by a fire resistant lobby.

In estimating the number of people in an area the following guide gives the space in m² occupied by one person (it excludes the space taken up by stairs, lift and lavatories): (1) in shops other than (2) and (3), 7; (2) in supermarkets, 2; (3) in department stores, 2-7; (4) in open plan offices, 5; (5) in other offices, 7; in car park, 30.

WIDTHS OF STAIRCASES

A. Stair widths for total evacuation of a building						B. Stair widths for limited evacuation	
No. of floors served	Max. no. of persons on one stair of width (mm) 1 000 mm	1 2000	1 4000	1 600	1 800	Max. no. of persons per storey	
1	150	240	280	320	360	100	1 000
2	190	285	335	385	435	120	1 100
4	270	375	445	515	585	140	1 300
10	510	645	775	905	1 035	190	1 800

Lobby Approach Stairways. The Scottish Building Regulations require the provision, in certain circumstances, of a *lobby approach stairway* (this is a stairway to which access is obtained only by a lobby).

The lobby must have: a minimum floor area of 5.5 m²; one of its walls an external wall adjacent to an area of cleared ground; a permanent opening to the external air of 0.05 m² plus 1.4 m² of openable window; fire-resisting walls; rising water mains and access to it by a fire-resisting door.

Smoke spreads quickly during a conflagration and is one of the main hazards to firemen and those escaping; to reduce its spread, fire doors should be placed in corridors and near the head of staircase landings.

Lifts. When lifts are provided in a building one of them should be classed as a fireman's lift which, although it can be used by others at normal times, can be

* Other Building Regulation requirements for stairs are given in Volume III.

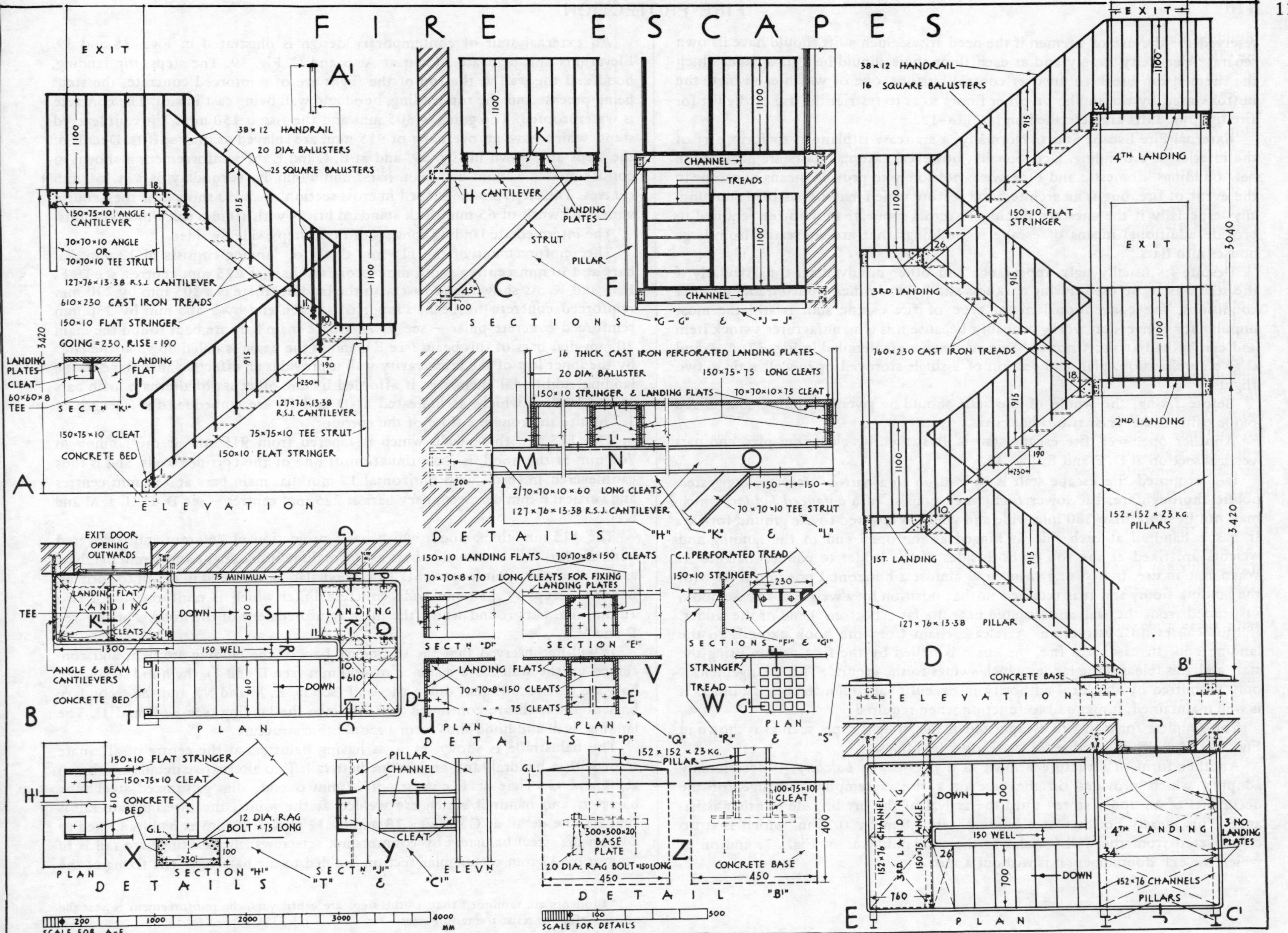

FIRE ESCAPES
EXIT
A'
38×12 HANDRAIL
20 DIA. BALUSTERS
25 SQUARE BALUSTERS
1100
915
150×75×10 ANGLE CANTILEVER
70×70×10 ANGLE OR 70×70×10 TEE STRUT
127×76×13·38 R.S.J. CANTILEVER
610×230 CAST IRON TREADS
150×10 FLAT STRINGER
GOING = 230, RISE = 190
3420
LANDING PLATES
CLEAT
60×60×8 TEE
LANDING FLAT
SECTN "K"
J'
127×76×13·38 R.S.J. CANTILEVER
75×75×10 TEE STRUT
150×75×10 CLEAT
CONCRETE BED
150×10 FLAT STRINGER
A
ELEVATION
K
H
CANTILEVER
LANDING PLATES
STRUT
PILLAR
45°
100
C
SECTIONS
38×12 HANDRAIL
16 SQUARE BALUSTERS
CHANNEL
TREADS
CHANNEL
F
"G-G" & "J-J"
4TH LANDING
150×10 FLAT STRINGER
EXIT
3040
3RD LANDING
760×230 CAST IRON TREADS
2ND LANDING
1ST LANDING
127×76×13·38 PILLAR
152×152×23 KG PILLARS
3420
D
B'
CONCRETE BASE
ELEVATION
16 THICK CAST IRON PERFORATED LANDING PLATES
20 DIA. BALUSTER
150×75×75 LONG CLEATS
150×10 STRINGER & LANDING FLATS
70×70×10×75 CLEAT
L'
M
N
O
2/70×70×10×60 LONG CLEATS
127×76×13·38 R.S.J. CANTILEVER
"H"
"K" & "L"
70×70×10 TEE STRUT
DETAILS
EXIT DOOR OPENING OUTWARDS
75 MINIMUM
LANDING FLAT
LANDING
K
TEE
DOWN
S
CLEATS
1300
150 WELL
ANGLE & BEAM CANTILEVERS
CONCRETE BED
DOWN
B
T
PLAN
150×10 LANDING FLATS
70×70×8×150 CLEATS
70×70×8×70 LONG CLEATS FOR FIXING LANDING PLATES
SECTN "D"
SECTION "E"
LANDING FLATS
70×70×8×150 CLEATS
75 CLEATS
E'
V
D'
U
PLAN
DETAILS "P" "Q" "R" & "S"
C.I. PERFORATED TREAD
150×10 STRINGER
230
SECTIONS "F" & "G"
STRINGER
TREAD
W
G'
PLAN
150×10 FLAT STRINGER
150×75×10 CLEAT
H'
CONCRETE BED
12 DIA. RAG BOLT×75 LONG
G.L.
X
PLAN
SECTION "H"
DETAILS
PILLAR
CHANNEL
CLEAT
Y
SECTN "J" & ELEVN "C"
"T"
152×152×23 KG. PILLAR
300×300×20 BASE PLATE
20 DIA. RAG BOLT×150 LONG
450
100×75×10 CLEAT
Z
CONCRETE BASE
450
DETAIL "B"
DOWN
150 WELL
4TH LANDING
3 NO. LANDING PLATES
152×76 CHANNEL
3RD LANDING
DOWN
152×76 CHANNELS
PILLARS
760
E
PLAN
C'
SCALE FOR A-F
SCALE FOR DETAILS

FIGURE 37

reserved for the use of firemen if the need arises. Such a lift should have its own separate electricity supply and at each floor there should be a glass panel which the firemen can break to uncover control buttons, one of which can isolate the buttons used by the public on other floors so as to restrict the use of the lift for fire-fighting. Lifts are described on pp. 118–122.

External Fire Escape Stairs. Normally, a staircase is planned to form part of the interior of a building. Occasionally, however, external stairs are provided in new buildings, domestic and otherwise, not solely to provide means of escape in the event of fire, but as an architectural feature which may be justified functionally, especially if the sites are sloping. External stairs are more often required to provide additional means of escape in buildings that are converted from large houses into flats.

Despite its usually ugly appearance and other disadvantages, particularly if the stair has to be used during darkness and icy and other unfavourable weather conditions, the conventional metal type of fire escape stair is still the most popular for conversion work, probably because it is a manufacturer's stock item and can be had at short notice. Two such stairs are detailed in Fig. 37. A, B and C give an elevation, plan and section of a single-storeyed open-well stair in two flights.

Before fixing, the whole of the stair should be given a priming coat of red oxide paint and at least two other coats.

Another open-well fire escape stair is illustrated by elevation, plan and part vertical section at D, E and F, Fig. 37.

If a proposed fire escape stair is to lead on to a narrow street or congested public thoroughfare, the lower flight may consist of a *balanced ladder*, which may not be more than 380 mm wide and which is lowered to the ground for use. It has a handrail at each side, is hinged at the open end of the landing and weights are fixed at the top on both sides of the ladder to counter-balance it. When not in use, it is swung to occupy almost a horizontal position level with the landing floor, and it is retained in that position by a weighted release hook, suspended from the wall and situated near the far ("bottom") end of the ladder. It thus causes no obstruction. A release chain from the hook extends to the landing end. In case of a fire, the chain is pulled by the first person using the stair and this releases the ladder which swings to the ground. This arrangement is only permitted by the local authority in exceptional circumstances, as, unless it is well maintained, it may fail to function when required.

The simplest form of fire escape stair is the straight type, such as is shown in Fig. 38 and which is suitable for two-storey buildings.

Another form of structure known as a *fire escape balcony*, is occasionally adopted which provides, in the case of a fire, a temporary refuge for the occupants of an upper storey until the arrival of the fire brigade or other assistance. This merely consists of a landing, say 1.8 m by 0.76 m, which is strut-cantilevered from the wall (similar to the top landing at A, Fig. 37) and on to which the exit doors open; it is without a stair.

An external stair of contemporary design is illustrated in Figs. 38 and 39. Elevations and plan are shown at A, B and C, Fig. 39. The steps, top landing, hood and the wall at the top of the flight are of reinforced concrete, the steps being precast and the top landing, hood and wall being cast in-situ. The concrete is waterproofed. The going is 305 mm and the rise is 150 mm. The cantilevered steps, which have an overhang of 915 mm, are splayed at their soffits. Details of the steps are shown in Fig. 39, and at B, C and E the reinforcement is shown to consist of two 12 mm dia. main bars* and 6 mm dia. secondary bars at 150 mm centres. The steps are tee-shaped in cross-section. C and D show how they course with brickwork of 65 mm thick standard bricks with 10 mm thick mortar joints.

The intermediate landing consists of three steps, side by side.

The reinforcement of the 115 mm thick top landing consists of 12 mm dia. bars at 150 mm centres and 6 mm secondary bars at 225 mm centres, see D, E, H, J and K. As shown, and cast with the landing, there is a 305 mm by 230 mm reinforced concrete tie beam supported at each end by a 305 mm by 230 mm reinforced concrete pillar – see V. Alternate main bars are bent round the main 20 mm dia. bars of this beam (see K), and as the beam is tailed down at the ends by the inner leaf of the brick cavity wall it provides an effective anchorage to the landing; additional anchorage is afforded by the other set of alternate main bars of the landing which, as indicated at D and H, are embedded for a length of 1.2 m into the concrete floor of the corridor.

The 115 mm thick wall, which is tapered from 915 mm at the landing to 760 mm at the hood, is a continuation of one of the corridor walls, and is thus cantilevered in form, with horizontal 12 mm dia. main bars at 150 mm centres and vertical 6 mm dia. secondary bars at 225 mm centres – see D, E, H, J, M and N.

The 115 mm thick hood, which has a projection of 760 mm and is covered with copper, has 10 mm dia. bars as the main reinforcement and 6 mm dia. bars as the secondary reinforcement. This hood slab is increased in depth to form an 215 mm deep by 280 mm wide concrete lintel which is reinforced with two 16 mm dia. bars round which the main reinforcement of the hood is bent – see D and M.

It will be observed that the secondary bars of the landing are bent and continued up the wall for a distance of 460 mm (see D and J), the hood secondary bars are carried 305 mm down the wall (see D, E, M and N), and the secondary bars of the wall are continued 305 mm into the landing (see E, H and J). The landing, wall and hood thus form a monolithic structure.

The balustrade is shown at A as having balusters at the centre of alternate steps with a handrail and an intermediate rail. Two alternative details are shown at F and G. That at F consists of 27 mm outside dia. galvanized steel tube balusters and handrail which are welded at the joints; the intermediate rail is similar. The detail at G shows a 38 mm by 12 mm steel convex handrail fixed to 24 mm dia. steel balusters by countersunk setscrews; the intermediate rail is of 38 mm by 12 mm rectangular section, welded to the balusters. The fixing of the

* Students are reminded that, as the steps are cantilevers, the reinforcement is near the upper surface to resist the tensile stress.

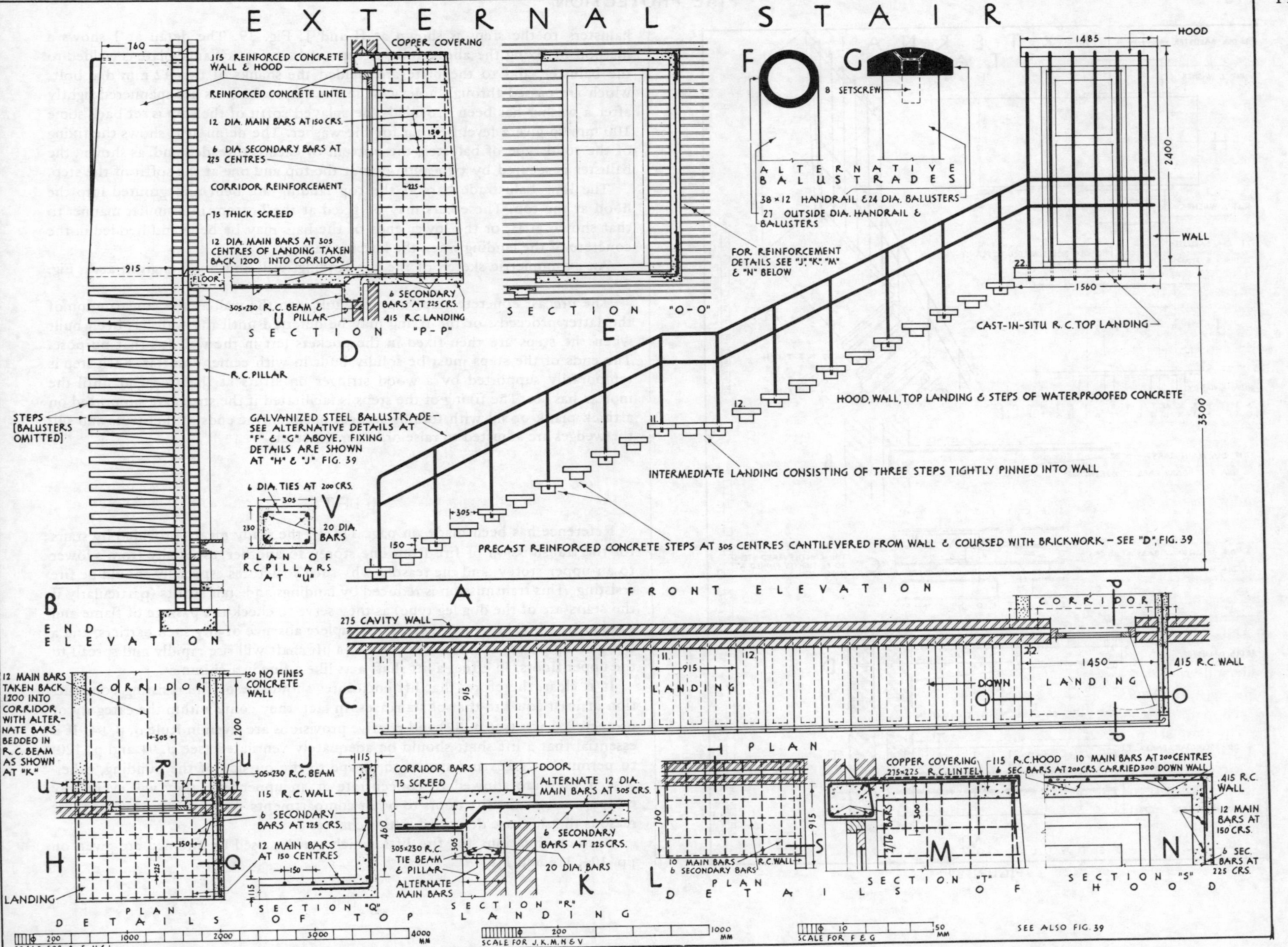

EXTERNAL STAIR
760
COPPER COVERING
115 REINFORCED CONCRETE WALL & HOOD
REINFORCED CONCRETE LINTEL
12 DIA. MAIN BARS AT 150 CRS.
150
6 DIA SECONDARY BARS AT 225 CENTRES
225
CORRIDOR REINFORCEMENT
75 THICK SCREED
12 DIA. MAIN BARS AT 305 CENTRES OF LANDING TAKEN BACK 1200 INTO CORRIDOR
915
FLOOR
6 SECONDARY BARS AT 225 CRS.
305×230 R.C. BEAM & PILLAR
415 R.C. LANDING
SECTION "P-P"
U
D
R.C. PILLAR
STEPS [BALUSTERS OMITTED]
GALVANIZED STEEL BALUSTRADE SEE ALTERNATIVE DETAILS AT "F" & "G" ABOVE. FIXING DETAILS ARE SHOWN AT "H" & "J" FIG. 39
6 DIA. TIES AT 200 CRS.
305
230
20 DIA BARS
PLAN OF R.C. PILLARS AT "U"
V
B
END ELEVATION
SECTION "O-O"
F
G
8 SETSCREW
ALTERNATIVE BALUSTRADES
38×12 HANDRAIL & 24 DIA. BALUSTERS
27 OUTSIDE DIA. HANDRAIL & BALUSTERS
FOR REINFORCEMENT DETAILS SEE "J", "K", "M" & "N" BELOW
HOOD
1485
2400
WALL
22
1560
CAST-IN-SITU R.C. TOP LANDING
E
HOOD, WALL, TOP LANDING & STEPS OF WATERPROOFED CONCRETE
12
11
3300
INTERMEDIATE LANDING CONSISTING OF THREE STEPS TIGHTLY PINNED INTO WALL
305
150
PRECAST REINFORCED CONCRETE STEPS AT 305 CENTRES CANTILEVERED FROM WALL & COURSED WITH BRICKWORK – SEE "D", FIG. 39
A
FRONT ELEVATION
275 CAVITY WALL
CORRIDOR
11
12
915
LANDING
22
1450
DOWN
LANDING
415 R.C. WALL
C
O
O
PLAN
12 MAIN BARS TAKEN BACK 1200 INTO CORRIDOR WITH ALTERNATE BARS BEDDED IN R.C. BEAM AS SHOWN AT "K"
CORRIDOR
150 NO FINES CONCRETE WALL
1200
305
U
R
U
J
115
305×230 R.C. BEAM
115 R.C. WALL
6 SECONDARY BARS AT 225 CRS.
150
225
12 MAIN BARS AT 150 CENTRES
H
Q
LANDING
PLAN
DETAILS OF TOP LANDING
115
150
SECTION "Q"
CORRIDOR BARS
75 SCREED
DOOR
ALTERNATE 12 DIA. MAIN BARS AT 305 CRS.
460
6 SECONDARY BARS AT 225 CRS.
305
305×230 R.C. TIE BEAM & PILLAR
ALTERNATE MAIN BARS
20 DIA. BARS
SECTION "R"
K
760
915
10 MAIN BARS
6 SECONDARY BARS
R.C. WALL
PLAN
L
S
COPPER COVERING 275×275
115 R.C. HOOD
R.C. LINTEL
6 SEC. BARS AT 200 CRS. CARRIED 300 DOWN WALL
10 MAIN BARS AT 200 CENTRES
300
BARS
M
SECTION "T"
DETAILS OF HOOD
415 R.C. WALL
12 MAIN BARS AT 150 CRS.
6 SEC. BARS AT 225 CRS.
N
SECTION "S"
0 200 1000 2000 3000 4000 MM
SCALE FOR A-E, H & L
0 200 1000 MM
SCALE FOR J, K, M, N & V
0 10 50 MM
SCALE FOR F & G
SEE ALSO FIG. 39

FIGURE 38

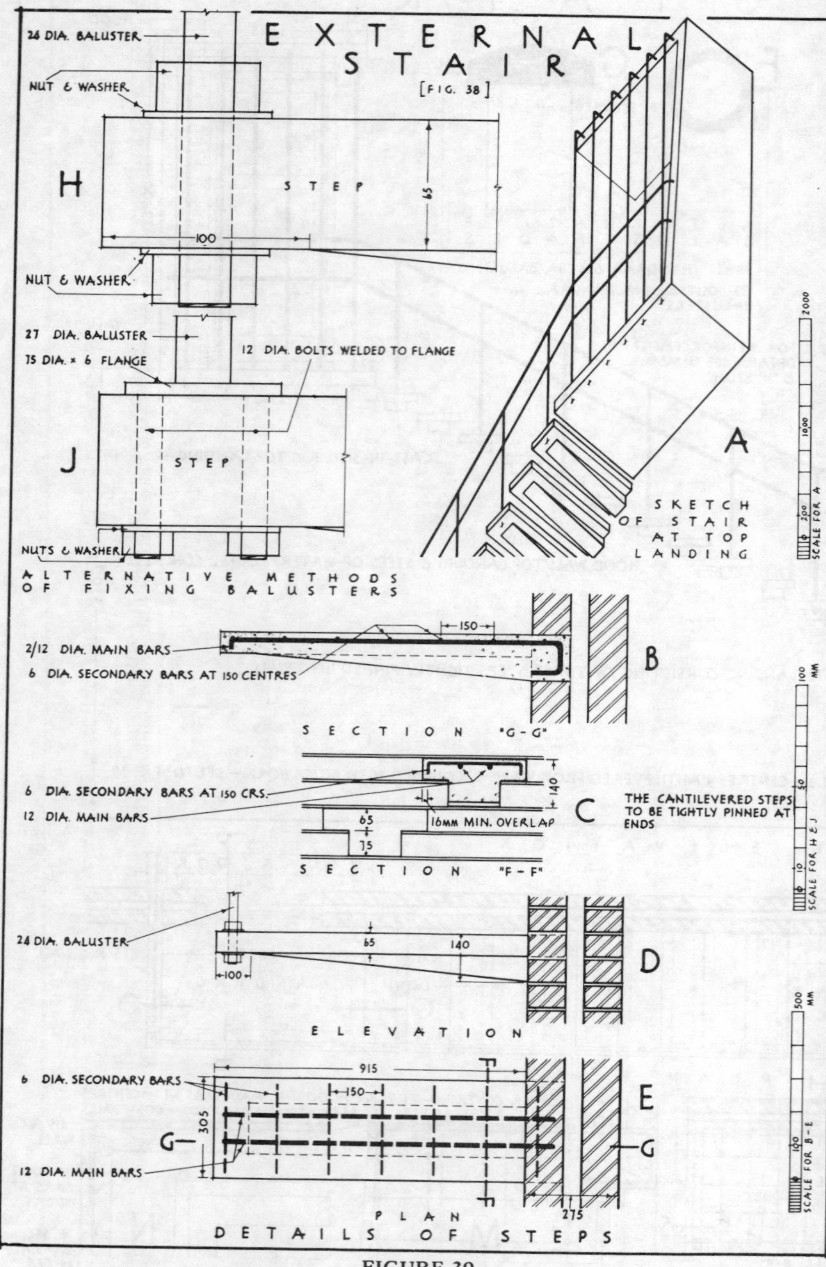

FIGURE 39

balusters to the steps is shown at H and J, Fig. 39. The detail at J shows a method of fixing the above tubular type of baluster; a flange plate is welded to the baluster, and to the plate are welded the shanks of two 12 mm dia. bolts which are passed through holes cast in the steps; the nuts are spannered tightly after a washer has been provided; the splayed soffit of the step is set back some 100 mm to give a level bearing for the washer. The detail at H shows the fixing of the solid type of baluster; the bottom of each is threaded and, as shown, the baluster is secured by two nuts, one at the top and one at the soffit of the step.

The long balustrade bars at the top landing are bent and grouted into the hood at the top. These bars may be fixed at the bottom in a similar manner to that shown at H, or the lower ends of the bars may be bent and bedded in the concrete of the landing when the latter is cast.

An axonometric sketch of the top landing, wall and hood is given at A, Fig. 39.

The precast concrete steps may be built into the wall as the construction of the latter proceeds, or the fixing may be deferred until the wall has been built when the steps are then fixed in the pockets left in the wall for that purpose. The ends of the steps must be solidly built in with cement mortar. Each step is temporarily supported by a wood stringer on struts at the free end until the mortar has set. The fixing of the steps is facilitated if the struts are supported on a thick plank or sill with folding wedges between the ends of the struts and sill; the wedges are adjusted to raise or lower the strut.

LIFTS

Reference has been made on page 114 to the ready means provided by stairs for the transmission of fire from one storey to another, especially from a lower to an upper storey, and the reasons why such structures especially should be fire resisting. This transmission is reduced by landings and stair soffits (particularly if the stairs are of the dog-leg type) as they serve to check the passage of flame and smoke. In a lift, however, there is a complete absence of any such barriers, and a fire gaining access at a lower section of a lift shaft will rise rapidly and spread to the upper floors. In effect a lift shaft acts like a flue in a chimney.

It is clear, therefore, that lift enclosures should be of fire-resisting construction at least equal to that of staircases. In fact, they come within the category of protected shafts (see p. 82) and relative provisions are given in Rule 6, p. 94. It is essential that a lift shaft should be adequately ventilated (see p. 94 and p. 120) to permit hot gases and smoke to escape to the outside of the building, otherwise if they are allowed to concentrate at an upper level they will eventually escape through the lift doors to other compartments – see p. 120. It is for these reasons that lifts are described in this chapter.

Recommendations for fire lifts which can be used by firemen are given on pp. 104, 114 and 116.

LIFTS

Lift shafts should be fire resisting but should not be used for escape purposes; for the reasons given, the effects of fire have to be considered in their design. The appropriate provisions are given below, but first it is desirable to give a description of several types of lifts, preceded by a glossary.

Glossary. Some of the terms are illustrated in Fig. 40.

Automatic Control. A form of control by which the car is automatically set in motion and caused to stop at any required landing by pressing a button.

Bottom Clearance. The distance, including buffer compression, the platform could travel below the bottom landing until the full weight of the car, when loaded, rests on the buffer.

Buffers, of the oil or spring type, are fixed at the bottom of the pit, one immediately in line with the centre of the car, the other in line with the counterweight, their purpose being to reduce or absorb the impact of the car or counterweight at the extreme lower limit of travel.

Car or Cage. The unit which carries the passengers and/or materials; it has a steel frame or sling which supports the floor or platform, in addition to side and top bodywork and to which the safety gear, guide shoes and suspension ropes are fixed; it is provided with a door.

Controller. A group of devices, mounted on a panel, which governs the motion, direction of travel, speed and stopping.

Counterweight or *Balance-Weight*. A unit, consisting of steel weights, which counterbalances the weight of the car and a portion of the load, and to which the suspension ropes are attached.

Diverting Pulley. A wheel, sometimes referred to as an *idler pulley*, situated at the top of the shaft and below the driving sheave, which serves to bring the suspension ropes directly over the counterweight.

Door Closer. A device which closes a door automatically.

Driving Sheave. A wheel, with vee-shaped grooves on its face, over and in which pass the suspension ropes (see p. 121) to which power from the lift machine is transmitted.

Electro-Mechanical Lock. This is fitted to a landing door or gate to prevent the lift being operated if any door is open and to prevent any door being opened unless the car is opposite a landing.

Enclosure. The walled structure which encloses the lift. The walls should be highly fire resistant; those shown in Fig. 40 are of 215 mm brickwork, with exception of the external wall at A and B, which is 328 mm thick. It is a protected shaft, see p. 82.

Guide Rails. These, fixed truly vertical in the shaft, are of steel and serve to guide the movement of both car and counterweight. *Guide-rail shoes*, fixed to the car and counterweight, engage in and traverse the guide rails during movement.

Landing Call Push. A push button provided at a landing for actuating the call indicator.

Lift. An appliance by which persons and goods are moved vertically from one level to another; its component parts consist of the winding machine, car, counterweight, guides, suspension ropes, control gear with safety devices. A *passenger lift*, as implied, is designed to carry persons. A *goods lift* or *hoist* serves primarily to transport materials, but may carry an attendant or people. A *service lift* (or dumb waiter) is small and used exclusively to carry goods or food (as from a hotel kitchen to the dining room) with the serving level usually above the floor; it is generally hand-powered. A *platform lift* is used for transporting materials on a platform or floor; unlike a car, it has neither sides nor door.

Machine Room. This is usually located at the top of the shaft and accommodates the winding machine, etc.

Overspeed Governor. A device, located at the top of the shaft, which brings the car

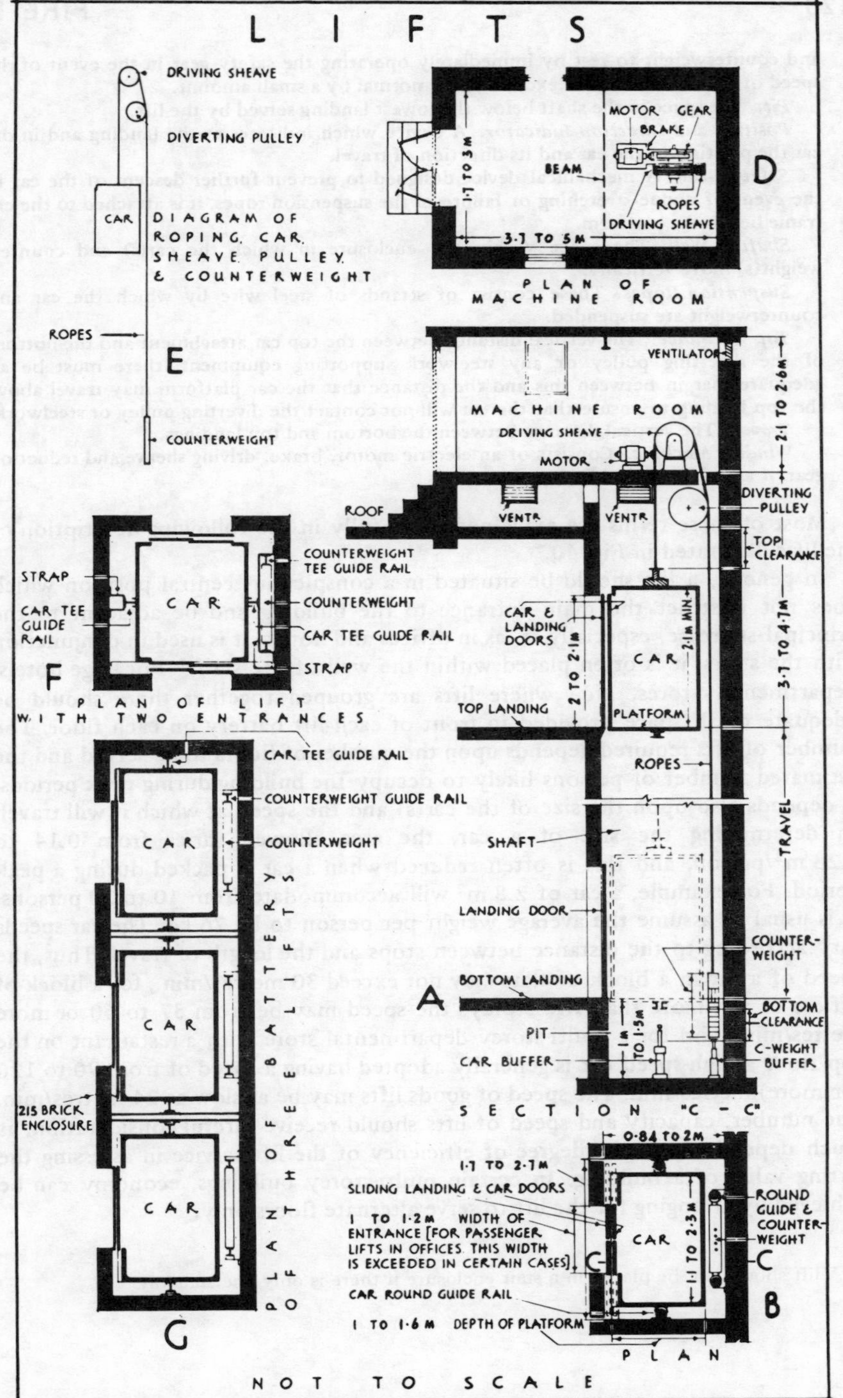

FIGURE 40

and counterweight to rest by immediately operating the safety gear in the event of the speed of the descending car exceeding the normal by a small amount.

Pit. The space in the shaft below the lowest landing served by the lift.

Position and Direction Indicator. A device which indicates at the landing and in the car the position of the car and its direction of travel.

Safety Gear. A mechanical device designed to prevent further descent of the car in the event of undue stretching or failure of the suspension ropes, it is attached to the car frame below the platform.

Shaft or *Well.* The space within the enclosure in which the car(s) and counterweight(s) move vertically.

Suspension Ropes. These consist of strands of steel wire by which the car and counterweight are suspended.

Top Clearance. The vertical distance between the top car attachment and the bottom of the diverting pulley or any steelwork supporting equipment; there must be an adequate margin between this and the distance that the car platform may travel above the top landing to ensure that the car will not contact the diverting pulley or steelwork.

Travel. The vertical distance between the bottom and top landings.

Winding Machine. Consists of an electric motor, brake, driving sheave and reduction gear, if any – see A and D, Fig. 40.

Most of these terms are explained more fully in the following description of the lifts illustrated in Fig. 40.

In general, a lift should be situated in a conspicuous central position which does not obstruct the main entrance to the building and be adjacent to the principal staircase, especially if, as in offices and hotels, it is used in conjunction with the stairs; it is often placed within the well of the stair.* For large hotels, departmental stores, etc., where lifts are grouped together there should be adequate crush space provided in front of each lift battery on each floor. The number of lifts required depends upon the number of floors to be served and the estimated number of persons likely to occupy the building during peak periods; it depends also upon the size of the car(s) and the speed at which it will travel. In determining the size of a car, the area allowed varies from 0.14 to 0.28 m^2/person, and this is often reduced when a car is packed during a peak period. For example, a car of 2.8 m^2 will accommodate from 10 to 20 persons. It is usual to assume the average weight per person to be 76 kg. The car speeds vary according to the distance between stops and the length of travel. Thus, the speed of a car in a block of flats may not exceed 30 metres/min., for a block of offices of not more than five storeys the speed may be from 37 to 60 or more metres/min., and for a multi-storey departmental store with a restaurant on the top floor a high-speed car is generally adopted having a speed of from 90 to 120 (or more) metres/min. The speed of goods lifts may be as slow as 24 metres/min. The number, capacity and speed of lifts should receive careful consideration, as much depends upon the degree of efficiency of the lift service in assessing the letting value of a building. In certain multi-storey buildings, economy can be achieved by arranging for the lift to serve alternate floors only.

* A lift should not be placed in a stair enclosure if there is only one stairway.

A vertical section through a lift enclosure and the machine room is shown at A, Fig. 40, and B and D show plans of the enclosure and machine room respectively. Some sizes are figured on the drawing; these vary in accordance with the size of the car to be installed. In this example the dimensions are related to the type of car usually employed in small- and medium-sized commercial buildings, hotels, shops, etc.

A diagram showing the usual arrangement of roping whereby a car is raised and lowered is provided at E. As defined above, the diverting pulley is to enable the counterweight to travel freely within the space between the car and enclosure wall. Such a pulley may not be necessary for a small narrow car and when the driving sheave is sufficiently large to ensure that the suspension ropes are suspended vertically to give sufficient clearance for the counterweight. As shown at A, the driving sheave is situated in the machine room and the diverting pulley is at the head of the shaft just below the floor of the machine room.

The machine room, as shown at A and D, is usually located at the top of the shaft and accessible from the flat roof, it accommodates the winding gear, etc. A steel beam should span the room, built in just below the ceiling, from which slings can be suspended for lifting heavy pieces of machinery. The room should be adequately lighted and ventilated. Very occasionally, the machine room is situated in the basement, as in a hotel where exception may be taken to the noise from the machinery by those occupying the top floor bedrooms if the room were at the top of the shaft. A machine room can be effectively sound-insulated by providing a thick cork (or rubber) mat upon which the machine bed is seated to insulate it from the floor.

The lift enclosure, of brickwork, is in accordance with the requirements already stated in respect to fire resistance, length of travel, top and bottom clearances, and ventilation. The importance of adequately venting the shaft cannot be over-emphasized; it has been suggested that the area of the smoke ventilators should be a minimum of one-third the cross-sectional area of the shaft. The Greater London Council requires that the smoke outlet shall not be less than 0.186 m^2 in area (see also Rule 6, p. 94, which stipulates 0.1 m^2 of permanently opened vent per lift). As shown at A, there are two ventilators which would allow smoke to escape outside above the roof; to satisfy the above recommendation, additional ventilators would have to be provided in the opposite wall.

The designs for the car, guides, safety gear, etc., adopted by specialist firms vary considerably in detail. Essentially, a car consists of an external frame, sling or cradle which supports the platform, bodywork and certain safety gear. The frame usually consists of steel channels, two extending from side to side in the centre at the bottom to which the platform is fixed, two at the centre of each side (called the stiles) and two across the top, called the suspension channels, and to which the suspension ropes are fixed; these members are securely riveted or bolted together. Rigidity is increased by the provision of inclined steel rods fixed at the top at each of the ends of the suspended channels and at the bottom to the corners of the platform. The frame of a goods lift to carry heavy loads is well gusseted at the corners to increase rigidity. The bodywork, which is fixed to the frame, depends upon the type of lift; if a passenger lift, the sides and top may be hardwood panelled, either framed with solid panels, or given a flush plywood finish; the plywood, or laminboard, may be surfaced with a rich wood veneer or a metal alloy of bronze, etc. Angles at the platform should be splayed to facilitate cleaning. The car should be provided with a ventilator and an emergency exit in the top. There are various types of car door, either of wood or metal, the latter may be a collapsible grille and referred to as a gate; the metal flush sliding type (about 32 mm thick), in one or two leaves (depending upon the width of opening), is now general – at the top of each leaf there is a pair of wheels which run on a steel rail and the bottom is engaged in a metal groove in the platform. An electric door operator should be provided which opens and closes the door automatically. The minimum height of the door is 2.1 m, slightly more than that of the landing opening.

The steel guide rails up and down which the car traverses are either of tee or round section – the former is indicated at F and G and the latter at B. These rails, which must be truly vertical, are screwed to plates or palms which are rag-bolted to the enclosure walls (or secured to steelwork). Guide shoes, of phosphor-bronze or gunmetal, are self-acting and spring-loaded and are fitted centrally at the top and bottom of both sides of the car; these shoes fit the smooth-surfaced rails to ensure that the car does not "jump" the rails when in motion.

The counterweight consists of thick top and bottom steel plates with vertical side steel channels between the flanges of which are fitted steel weights; these weights are connected together by two bolts which pass down and through the bottom plate. The counterweight balances the weight of the car (including frame, safety gear, etc.) together with 40 to 50 per cent of the live load (passengers) at 367 kg/m^2 of car floor area. The counterweight can be adjusted as required to ensure a well-balanced car. Like the car, the counterweight traverses two guide rails, fixed dead plumb, of tee or round section, the self-acting guide shoes (two at each side) being bolted to the top and bottom weights. The suspension ropes are fixed to the top plate through which they pass, the plate being some distance above the top weight to allow for the insertion of any additional weight which may be found necessary subsequently. It is usual for the counterweight to be at the back of the car, as shown at B and G – see below.

Suspension wire ropes must have a high factor of safety, namely, the ratio of the breaking strength of the rope to the total load carried. The recommended minimum factor is 12, and for ropes on high-speed cars, because of the greater strain to which they are subjected by frequent acceleration and deceleration, this minimum should be increased to 20. Ropes should be kept well oiled and frequently inspected.

The driving sheave or traction drive is mounted and connected to the motor. V-shaped grooves are formed on the face of the sheave and the suspension ropes from the car pass over the sheave in these grooves to the counterweight after they have been offset by the diverting pulley. For medium and large-sized cars, the latter pulley is provided, as shown at A and E, to bring the ropes from the sheave centrally over the counterweight to ensure that there is ample clearance between the car and counterweight when the lift is in motion.

Buffers are provided in the pit symmetrically underneath both car and counterweight to absorb or reduce the impact of both at the extreme bottom limit of travel. There are two types, the spring buffer being used with lifts having a speed not exceeding 90 metres/min. and the oil buffer with faster lifts.

The motive power is electricity. The *winding machine* is indicated in the machine room at A and D, and consists of the motor, brake(s), reduction gear (if any) and sheave, mounted on a rigid base. There are several types, including the worm-geared machine (in which the electric power is transmitted from the motor to the sheave through worm reduction gearing) and the gearless machine (in which the power is transmitted direct). The machine is equipped with a brake, the function of which is to arrest the motor when the controller is in the "off" position.

The *controller*, an ingenious piece of equipment, is placed adjacent to the winding machine and has the function of starting the motor in the required direction and with the necessary acceleration and deceleration. There are four methods of control, *i.e.*, (1) full automatic control by push button, (2) car switch control, (3) dual control, and (4) semi-automatic control.

(1) Full Automatic Control. At each landing, in a conspicuous position near a door jamb, there is a call-push which, when pressed, will bring the car from any position in the shaft to the landing where the intending passenger is standing and releases the doors to permit access. Inside the car, attached to one of the sides, is a panel with a push button for each floor. On entering the car, the passenger pushes the button indicating the floor to be reached. An electrical impulse is thereby received by the controller which operates mechanism to close the doors and start the car, followed by a quick acceleration to top speed and a gradual reduction in speed as the required floor is approached, when the car stops (with the platform level with the landing) and the doors open automatically. Both car and landing doors must be closed to establish electrical contact with the controller and enable it to answer the next call.

(2) Car Switch Control. In this method the movement of the car is directly under the control of an attendant by means of a car switch. The various operations described above are performed by the controller as the switch handle is rotated.

(3) Dual Control. This combines both the above automatic and car switch methods by the operation of a conversion switch which changes the control from one method to the other. This requires an attendant to be on duty only during the peak periods; before going off duty, he removes the switch handle, whereupon the controller functions automatically, as described in (1) above, when a passenger wishes to use the lift.

(4) Semi-Automatic Control. The car has three push buttons marked "up", "down" and "stop". Pressure on a button causes the car to start and continue on its travel in the required direction until it (*a*) reaches the top or bottom floor, when it is stopped by limit switches fixed in the shaft, or (*b*) approaches an intermediate floor at which it is stopped by pressing the "stop" button. This method is used chiefly for goods lifts.

Safety Gear. Every passenger and goods lift must be provided with an emergency stop switch, a press button alarm and automatic safety gear on the car which, in the event of rope failure, will stop and sustain the fully-loaded car in the guides. Such gear is fitted below the platform and between the car guide rails. For slow-speed lifts (up to 60 metres/min.) the gears should be quick acting, and for high-speed lifts they must be more gradual in action. Details differ, but essentially the guide rails are gripped by the mechanism sufficiently to stop the car during its descent. It is brought into action as described below.

Overspeed Governor. This is a form of safety gear which operates when a descending car exceeds the predetermined maximum speed. It must be fitted to every lift having a travel exceeding 6 metres and is situated near the top of the shaft. A steel or phosphor-bronze rope, connected to the safety gear described above, is passed over the pulley of the governor, continued down the shaft and passed under a pulley fixed in the pit, and up to the car to which it is attached. If the car during its descent exceeds the maximum speed, the governor comes into operation to lock the rope and thereby bring into operation the safety gear.

Other electrical equipment includes a *position and direction indicator* (a device which indicates at the landing and in the car the position of the car and its direction of travel), and an *electro-mechanical lock* (fitted to a landing door or gate to prevent the lift being operated if any door is open and to prevent any door being opened unless the car is opposite a landing).

For departmental stores, hotels and buildings in which large numbers of passengers have to be moved, several cars in the one lift enclosure are provided; such is known as a lift battery. A battery of three lifts is shown at G, and this number is often increased to six or more, sometimes arranged back-to-back. Whilst most of these are used as passenger lifts, one per battery at least may be reserved for goods. Emergency exit doors, opening *inwards*, or panels are sometimes provided in the sides of the cars to enable passengers to pass from one car to another.

The lifts shown at B and G show the usual arrangement of the counterweights being at the back and with the car guide rails at the sides; they also show each car with one entrance only. In some cases, however, two entrances to the car are necessary, such as a goods lift which receives goods at street level and conveys them to the several floors through doors on the opposite side. A plan of such a lift is shown at F. Because of the two openings front and back, the counterweight is at one side, and the car guides are also at the sides. To effect this, these guide rails are secured to stout straps rag-bolted to the walls, as indicated, sufficient space being allowed between the strap on the right and the wall to permit of the free movement of the counterweight. In lieu of the strap shown on the left, the guide rail can be secured to a cast iron distance piece which is bolted to the wall.

All lifts should be properly maintained. According to the Factories Act, every lift in the factory type of building shall be thoroughly examined by a competent person at least every six months and a report of such examination must be entered in a register which is inspected by the factory inspector on his visits. Every lift in a factory shall have a conspicuously marked notice giving the maximum safe working load, this must not be exceeded.

CHAPTER FOUR

WALLS

Syllabus. Definitions. Non-calculated and calculated brick walls. Weights of materials, loadings. Further cavity wall details. Cross-wall construction. Stone and brick niches. Masonry columns, pediments and entablatures. Masonry walls attached to steel framework. Maintenance of stonework. Reconstructed stone and terra-cotta walls attached to steel framework.
Curtain wall construction; infilling panels and glass. Industrialized building system using large precast R.C. panels.

The following are definitions of some of the terms used in this chapter.

Dead load is the weight of walls, floors, roofs and partitions. The weights of various building materials are given in Table 32, p. 129.

Imposed loads or *superimposed loads* are all loads other than dead loads. A list of minimum imposed loads supported by floors and roofs of various types of buildings is given in Table 31, p. 128.

Load-bearing wall is one which supports load.

Framed structure, often a multi-storey building, consists of a series of frames composed of pillars (or columns or stanchions) connected together by beams at the floor and roof levels. These pillars and beams are of steel or reinforced concrete – see Chap. II. The walling within these frames is supported by the beams and are called *panel walls* or *infillings*. Therefore, the walling or panel which a beam supports is that between adjacent pillars and the beam above it, and, consequently, no matter how tall a building may be, the height of wall carried by any one beam is the storey height only, the wall load is relatively light and the panels are comparatively thin. In external panels, the thickness must be sufficient to prevent rain transmission, be strong enough to resist wind pressure and be adequately insulated to reduce heat losses and the transmission of sound. As mentioned on p. 134, certain solid block walls and some cavity walls satisfy these essentials. Although internal walls are not subject to weather conditions, these should be of cavity construction or, if solid, sufficiently thick to ensure adequate sound insulation; this requirement is especially important in respect to party walls and those of buildings such as offices, schools, etc.

Industrialized building systems are those consisting mostly of storey height load-bearing R.C. precast wall panels and large slab flooring units.

Light-framed structures are usually one storey in height and may consist of steel or wood pillars with cladding panels – see p. 152.

Cladding is the term applied to relatively thin sheets or slabs used to enclose framework. Examples are asbestos-cement, aluminium and copper sheets, tiles, concrete slabs, glass, wood boarding and proprietary panels (see p. 152); cladding details are illustrated in Figs. 17 and 52 to 54.

The following are definitions of two of the terms used in the section below dealing with the Rules contained in the Building Regulations for determining the thickness of non-calculated walls.

Separating wall is one which is common to two adjoining buildings (formerly known as *party wall*).

Buttressing wall is one, including a return wall, which affords lateral support and is bonded to any other wall (hereinafter called "the supported wall") and which:

(*a*) has a length measured from the centre of the supported wall to the centre of the buttressing wall not less at any level than one sixth of the height of the supported wall from that level to the top of the supported wall; (*b*) if it is not a wall to which Rules 1, 2, 3 and 4 (see Table 27) relates has a thickness not less than the greater of:—(i) half the thickness given in Rule 1 less 5 mm; or (ii) 75 mm if it is part of a house and the supported wall does not exceed 6 m in height and 10 m in length; (iii) 90 mm in any other case; (*c*) has no opening (other than one not exceeding 0.6 m^2 in area) nearer to its junction with the supported wall than 550 mm.

Pier. A pier must extend for the full wall height and (*a*) project from the supported wall at least twice the latter's thickness; (*b*) be at least 190 mm wide; (*c*) have a plan area (excluding that part of the supported wall to which it is bonded) of not less than that of a pier having a projection and width equal to twice the required wall thickness.

NON-CALCULATED AND CALCULATED BRICKWORK

Prior to the introduction of framed structures, loads from floors and roofs were supported directly by load-bearing walls. Before considering the provisions of the Building Regulations in respect to non-calculated and calculated load-bearing walls it is desirable to recapitulate that the strength of brickwork is influenced by (1) the strength of the bricks and mortars, (2) the bond, and (3) the quality of the workmanship.

(1) Bricks and Mortar. Table 28 (p. 126) shows how the basic compressive stresses on masonry (including brickwork) increase in accordance with the strength of the bricks and the composition of the mortars. Thus, the maximum stress allowed on brickwork constructed of bricks having a crushing strength of 27.5 MN/m² and cement mortar (1 : 3) is 2.05 MN/m² and this is reduced to 0.42 MN/m² for brickwork composed of bricks which have a crushing strength of 7 MN/m² and lime mortar (1 : 3). Table 24 gives typical compressive strengths of various types of bricks.

TABLE 24 TYPICAL COMPRESSIVE STRENGTHS OF BRICKS

Type of Brick	Strength (N/mm² = MN/m²)
Commons:	
London stocks	3.45–10.34
Flettons	13.79–31
Wirecuts	13.79–41.37
Facings:	
Handmade	6.89–58.6
Machine made	3.45–103.4
Machine made London Stocks	3.45–17.24
Machine made Flettons	13.79–31
Engineering:	
B.S. Grade A	68.9–137.9
B.S. Grade B	48.26–68.9

(2) **Bonding.** Doubts are sometimes raised as to the need for bonding brickwork and in some quarters it has been contended that bond can be dispensed with altogether. That this is a fallacy may be proved by the comparative results of tests,* given in Table 25, showing failing loads and the difference in strength between bonded and unbonded brickwork. In each case the pier was 440 mm square and 2.4 mm high, and was built of selected common bricks.†

TABLE 25 STRENGTH OF BONDED AND UNBONDED BRICK PIERS

English Bonded (loads in MN)	Unbonded (loads in MN)	Mortar	Remarks
1.99	1.02	1 cement : 3 sand	First crack appeared
0.707	0.448	1 cement : 2 lime : 9 sand	First crack appeared

* These tests were carried out on a 2.5 MN compression machine in the Structural Laboratory of the Department of Building and Structural Engineering in the University of Manchester Institute of Science and Technology.

† Twelve bricks were tested in accordance with C.P. 111 and the mean failing stress in compression was 38.9 MN/m².

These results show that bonded piers were approximately from 58 to 94 per cent stronger than those which were unbonded.

(3) **Workmanship.** Tests on specimens of brickwork prepared under ideal conditions in the laboratory, where care is taken to ensure sound workmanship and correct mixes of mortars, may produce results which cannot generally be equalled for brickwork constructed on the site. The human element is an important influence. For example, indifferent workmanship resulting in partially filled mortar joints is capable of producing a specimen of brickwork much weaker than that built to comply with a specification requiring that "the joints shall be properly filled and flushed with mortar". Also, there is a big reduction in strength of brickwork constructed of dry porous bricks compared with that built of similar bricks which had been given an adequate pre-soaking.

In the former case the dry bricks absorb water from the mortar, thus impairing the chemical setting action of the cement (or lime) and sand giving a low mortar strength. The following results (Table 26) of compression tests* carried out on 440 mm square piers, 2.4 mm high, built of common bricks in English bond with lime-cement mortar (composed of 1 part cement, 2 parts lime and 9 parts sand) show the importance of adequately wetting absorbent bricks.

TABLE 26 EFFECT OF PRE-SOAKING OF BRICKS

Condition of Bricks	Load (MN)	Remarks
Dry	0.707	First crack appeared
Wetted	1.35	First crack appeared

In addition to the above factors, the strength of a brick wall or pier is dependent upon its slenderness ratio (p. 127) and lateral pressure due to wind. The strength of a wall is influenced also by the distance apart of return walls, cross-division walls, etc.

The Building Regulations require that the structure of a building above the foundations shall safely sustain and transmit to the foundations the dead and imposed loads without such deflection or deformation as will impair the stability of, or cause damage to, the building. The thickness of a load-bearing wall may be determined by either (*a*) relating the thickness to the height and length by using Table 27, *i.e.*, a *non-calculated wall*; or (*b*) basing the construction on C.P. 111; Structural Recommendations for Load-bearing Walls, *i.e.*, *a calculated wall*.

NON-CALCULATED WALLS

Before describing the Building Regulations for load-bearing walls it is emphasized that, as stated on p. 123 modern multi-storey buildings are usually of the framed structure type having thin panelled walls which do not support roof and

TABLE 27 RULES FOR DETERMINING THE THICKNESS OF BRICK AND BLOCK WALLS (NON-CALCULATED WALLS)

The following Rules apply to non-calculated walls which:– (*a*) do not support floor members having a span exceeding 6 m; (*b*) do not transmit a load exceeding 70 kN/m at the base; (*c*) are part of a building of not more than 3 storeys; (*d*) carry an imposed load not exceeding 2 kN/m^2 distributed or 1.8 kN concentrated on floors above the ground storey, 0.25 kN/m^2 distributed and 0.9 kN concentrated (or alternatively 720 N/m^2 distributed) on any ceiling and 0.75 kN/m^2 distributed or 0.9 kN concentrated on any roof. Buildings covered by the Rules must:– (i) not have any part higher than 15 m above ground level; (ii) have a width at least half the height; (iii) have the area of each storey or, if it is divided by buttressing walls the area of each sub-division not exceeding 70 m^2. At each side of an opening in a wall there must be a length of wall at least one-sixth of the opening width; a wall between two openings must be at least as long as one-sixth of the combined opening widths; the aggregate width of all openings in a wall must not exceed two-thirds of the wall length.

Rule Number	Type of Wall	Height of Wall	Length of Wall	Minimum Thickness of Wall (*t*)
1	External walls, compartment walls & separating walls built as *solid* walls & provided with roof lateral support* and, if they are longer than 3 m, floor lateral support* at the top of each storey *Note.* In addition to the minimum thickness (*t*) given alongside, *t* in any storey must be not less than one-sixteenth part of that storey height.	Not exceeding 3.5 m	Not exceeding 12 m	190 mm for the whole height
		Exceeding 3.5 m but not exceeding 9 m	Not exceeding 9 m	190 mm for the whole height
			Exceeding 9 m but not exceeding 12 m	290 mm from the base for the height of *one* storey, and 190 mm for rest of height
		Exceeding 9 m but not exceeding 12 m	Not exceeding 9 m	290 mm from the base for the height of *one* storey, and 190 mm for rest of height
			Exceeding 9 m but not exceeding 12 m	290 mm from the base for the height of *two* storeys, and 190 mm for rest of height
2	External, compartment or separating *cavity* walls provided with roof lateral support* and, if they are longer than 3 m, floor lateral support* at the top of each storey. Each leaf of wall not less than 90 mm thick with ties not less than 900 mm apart horizontally & 450 mm vertically (300 mm vertically at jambs). Cavity width not less than 50 mm nor more than: (i) 100 mm if wire ties are placed not more than 750 mm apart horizontally and 450 mm vertically; (ii) 75 mm in any other case			The sum of the thickness of the two leaves and 10 mm must not be less than the thickness required by Rule 1
3	Internal *solid* load bearing walls (not being compartment or separating walls) having roof lateral support* or floor lateral support* at the top of each storey			(i) If the wall is other than one in (ii) below the sum of its thickness & 5 mm must not be less than half the thicknesses in Rule 1. (ii) If it is the lowest wall of a 3 storey building the thickness must not be less than the greater of (i) above or 140 mm
4	External *solid* walls of one storey non-residential buildings having a roof span not greater than 9 m and wall heights not exceeding 3 m. This also applies to a garage, store, outbuilding etc. having walls not higher than 3 m being part of a house			Not less than 90 mm
5	Parapet walls			Thickness not less than the greater of: (i) one-quarter of its height; (ii) if it is a solid wall, not less than the thickness of the wall on which it rests or 190 mm whichever is the less; (iii) if it is a cavity wall, the thickness of the wall on which it rests or the least thickness required by Rule 2

* *Floor lateral support & roof lateral support mean support afforded to a wall so as to restrict its movement in either direction at right angles to its length. They must be adequate to transfer lateral forces to buttressing walls, piers or chimneys and hold or restrain the supported wall by connections given on p. 125A or by other equally adequate means.*

Specification of connections (see bottom of p.125)

Description of floor	Description of roof	Specification of connection between floor or roof and supported wall	Circumstances to which reference is made in previous column
1. Concrete floor	*1. Concrete roof*	*1. Irrespective of the direction of span of the floor or roof, a bearing onto the supported wall of not less than 90 mm (a) throughout the wall length; or (b) if the circumstances described in next column are relevant, throughout the length of each portion of the wall on either side of the opening*	*The circumstances to which reference is made in previous column are (a) part of the supported wall is adjacent to an opening in a floor or roof for a stairway or other purpose; (b) the opening extends for a distance not exceeding 3 m parallel to the wall; and (c) there is no other interruption of the lateral support*
2. Concrete or timber floor	*2. Concrete or timber roof*	*2. Mild steel anchors which have a minimum cross-section of 30 mm × 5 mm and are provided so as to anchor the floor or roof to the supported wall (a) at intervals of not more than 2 m (b) if the circumstances described in next column are relevant, at such intervals on either side of the opening as will result in the provision of as many anchors as would be provided if there were no opening*	
3. Floor which (a) forms part of a house having not more than two storeys; and (b) has timber members spanning so as to penetrate into the supported wall at intervals of not more than 1.2 m	*3. Roof which (a) has a pitch of 15° or more; (b) is tiled or slated; (c) is of a type known by local experience to be resistant to damage by wind gusts; (d) has timber members spanning onto the supported wall at intervals of not more than 1.2 m*	*3. Bearing by each timber member of not less than 90 mm (if bearing is directly on supported wall) or 75 mm (if bearing on a timber wall plate) (a) throughout the length of the wall; or (b) if the circumstances described in next column are relevant, throughout the length of each portion of the wall which is situated on either side of the opening*	
4. Concrete or timber floor	*4. Concrete or timber roof*	*4. Continuous contact (or contact at 2 m max. intervals) between each side of the supported wall and a floor or roof, such contact being provided on each side (a) either (i) throughout wall length; or (ii) if the circumstances given in next column are relevant, for the length of each part of the wall on either side of the opening; and (b) at or about the same level and (if intermittent contact is given on both sides of the wall) at or about the same positions on plan.*	

wall loads. The thickness of high walls should be calculated as described in the section "Calculated Walls" (pp. 127–133).

Non-calculated walls are designed by following the Rules given in Table 19. The rules apply to walls of brickwork, blockwork and stonework which (except for a wall in Rule 7 less than 2.5 m high and long) has at each end either a pier, buttress, buttressing wall or chimney. They do not apply to basement walls (see Vol. II).

There are also regulations for the strength of bricks which may be used and for measuring the height and length of walls:

Bricks. The solid content of bricks must be not less than 50 per cent of the total volume. Both solid and hollow bricks may be used. A solid brick is defined as one having not less than 75 per cent solid material within its overall volume; a hollow brick is one having less than 75 per cent solids.

Bricks in walls of a one or two-storey house (or flat) must have a resistance to crushing of not less than 5 N/mm^2 if the storey height does not exceed 2.7 m; for greater heights or in the case of other buildings the bricks must have a resistance of 7 N/mm^2.

The height of a ground storey is measured from the base of the wall and of an upper storey from the level of the underside of the floor of that storey, in each case to the level of the underside of the floor next above it, or, if there is no such floor, then to the top of the wall, or, in the case of a storey comprising a gable, to half the height of the gable. Wall heights are measured in the same way

TABLE 28 BASIC COMPRESSIVE STRESSES FOR BRICKWORK AND BLOCKWORK MEMBERS (AT AND AFTER THE STATED TIMES)

Description of Mortar	Mix (parts by volume)			Hardening Time After Completion of Work†	Basic Stress in MN/m^2 Corresponding to Units whose Crushing Strength (in MN/m^2)‡ is:								
	Cement	Lime	Sand		2.8	7.0	10.5	20.5	27.5	34.5	52.0	69.0	96.5 or greater
				days									
Cement	1	0–¼*	3	7	0.28	0.70	1.05	1.65	2.05	2.50	3.50	4.55	5.85
	1	½	4½	14	0.28	0.70	0.95	1.45	1.70	2.05	2.80	3.60	4.50
Cement-lime Cement with plasticizers§ Masonry cement‖	1 1 —	1 — —	6 6 —	14	0.28	0.70	0.95	1.30	1.60	1.85	2.50	3.10	3.80
Cement-lime Cement with plasticizers§ Masonry cement‖	1 1 —	2 — —	9 8 —	14	0.28	0.55	0.85	1.15	1.45	1.65	2.05	2.50	3.10
Cement-lime	1	3	12	14	0.21	0.49	0.70	0.95	1.15	1.40	1.70	2.05	2.40
Hydraulic lime	—	1	2	14	0.21	0.49	0.70	0.95	1.15	1.40	1.70	2.05	2.40
Non-hydraulic	—	1	3	28¶	0.21	0.42	0.55	0.70	0.75	0.85	1.05	1.15	1.40

* The inclusion of lime in cement mortars is optional.
† These periods should be increased by the full amount of any time during which the air temperature remains below 4.4°C plus half the amount of any time during which the temperature is between 4.4°C and 10°C.
‡ Linear interpolation is permissible for units whose crushing strengths are intermediate between those given in the table. Note than MN/m^2 = N/mm^2.
§ Plasticizers must be used according to manufacturers' instructions.
‖ Masonry cement mortars must be used according to manufacturers' instructions, and mix proportions of masonry cement to sand should be such as to give comparable mortar crushing strengths with the cement : lime : sand mix of the grade.
¶ A longer period should ensue where hardening conditions are not very favourable.

except in the case of a separating wall which is also a gable, in this case the height is measured from the base of the wall to the base of the gable.

The length measurements of a wall are made from the centre of any buttressing wall, buttress, pier or chimney; provided these features comply with the following: (*a*) buttressing wall satisfying the definition on p. 123. (*b*) A pier or buttress at least 200 mm wide which extends from the base of the wall to within a distance from its top of not less than three times the least thickness of the wall; and at any level projects from the wall not less than twice the wall thickness at that level; and has a width and projection of at least twice the wall thickness at that level or forms a projecting area of equivalent amount. (*c*) A chimney which has a plan area (excluding any fireplace opening or flue) of not less than the area required for a pier or buttress and an overall thickness of not less than twice that of the wall it is deemed to divide.

CALCULATED WALLS

Calculated walls are designed by following the provisions of C.P. 111. *This provides a more economical method of design, particularly for high buildings, than is obtained by using the non-calculated method given in Table 27 as the walls are designed in accordance with the bricks and mortars adopted, the given imposed floor loads and slenderness ratios, etc.*

As previously explained, although most multi-storey buildings are best designed with a frame, there have been many instances (*e.g.*, for three and four-storey blocks of flats) where designers have incurred the expense of a frame when this has not been justified. The adoption of a frame *plus* relatively heavy non-load-bearing infilling panel walls is seldom justified.

The Code relates to load-bearing walls of brickwork, blockwork, masonry and concrete.

It defines a load-bearing wall as one designed to carry a superimposed (or imposed) load, imposed loads are given in Table 31; it also specifies how the permissible stress in a masonry wall or column is obtained. According to the Code the:

Effective height of a wall which is laterally* supported should be taken as follows: (*a*) $\frac{3}{4}$ of the height between centres of lateral supports where (i) the wall carries a floor or roof spanning at right angles to it and (ii) where concrete floors bear on it irrespective of the direction of span. (*b*) The height between centres of lateral supports when these are provided by floors of roofs having a direction of span parallel to the wall and do not bear on it. (*c*) $1\frac{1}{2}$ times the height above the bottom support of a wall which has no lateral support at the top.

Effective length of a wall is the measurement between properly bonded adjacent piers, buttresses or intersecting walls.

Effective thickness of (*a*) walls not stiffened by intersecting walls or piers is for a *solid wall* its actual thickness; and for a *cavity wall* $\frac{2}{3}$ the sum of the actual thickness of the two leaves (*e.g.*, in a 280 mm cavity wall the effective thickness is $\frac{2}{3}(102.5 + 102.5) = 137$ mm). (*b*) Where the wall is stiffened by piers the effective thicknesses given above should be multiplied by the appropriate stiffening coefficient† given in Table 29.

TABLE 29 STIFFENING COEFFICIENT FOR WALLS STIFFENED BY PIERS

Ratio: Pier spacing (centre to centre) / Pier width	Ratio: Pier thickness / Effective wall thickness		
	1	2	3
6	1.0	1.4	2.0
10	1.0	1.2	1.4
20	1.0	1.0	1.0

Slenderness ratio of a solid wall =

$$\frac{\text{Effective height (or effective length – if this be less)}}{\text{Effective thickness}}$$

The slenderness ratio of a wall should not exceed:

(1) 13 for unreinforced brick or block walls set in hydraulic lime: sand mortar (no Portland cement) except in the case of buildings of not more than two storeys when it should not exceed 20.

(2) 27 for brick or block walls set in other than hydraulic lime: sand mortar; except in the case of walls less than 90 mm thick in buildings of not more than two storeys when it should not exceed 20.

Permissible compressive stresses. The permissible stresses uniformly distributed in a masonry wall or column depend upon (1) the crushing strength of the

* A wall is adequately supported laterally if the construction providing the support is capable of resisting the sum of the following assumed lateral forces: (i) The simple static reactions to the total applied horizontal forces at the point of lateral support; and (ii) $2\frac{1}{2}$ per cent of the total vertical load that the wall is designed to carry at the point of lateral support.

Concrete floors and roofs will satisfy (i) and (ii) above when they have a 90 mm minimum bearing on the wall. Where concrete slabs do not bear on the wall they should be tied to the wall with 380 mm long x 30 mm x 5 mm metal bars bedded 380 mm into the slab and placed at 1.8 m maximum intervals for one or two-storey buildings and 1.2 m for other buildings. Timber floors and roofs should be anchored similarly to the wall whether or not they bear on it.

† For a solid wall stiffened by intersecting walls the coefficient may be found from the Table on the assumption that the intersecting walls are equivalent to piers of width equal to the thickness of the intersecting wall and of thickness equal to 3 times the thickness of the stiffened wall.

For a cavity wall where one or both leaves are stiffened by piers a modified leaf thickness for use in (*a*) above may be found from the Table by treating each leaf as an independent wall.

brick, etc., units, (2) the grade of mortar used, and (3) the slenderness ratio of the wall or column. The permissible stress in an axial loaded member should not exceed the product of the *basic stress* (obtained from Table 28) and the reduction factor given in Table 30.

The basic stresses given in Table 20 are suitable when the units are of the standard brick format. A modified basic stress is used in the case of *solid* concrete blocks laid with a mortar not weaker than 1 : 2 : 9 having: (1) a crushing strength *not* greater than 35 MN/m²; and (2) a crushing strength greater than 35 MN/m². In case (1) the *modified basic stress* is the Table 28 basic stress multiplied by a factor dependent on the ratio: block height ÷ block thickness. For the ratios 0.75, 1.0, 1.5 and 2.0–3.0 the respective factors are 1.0, 1.2, 1.6 and 2.0. In case (2) the permissible stress is the modified one as obtained under (1) or the Table 20 basic stress, whichever is the greater.

For unfilled *hollow* concrete blocks and all other types, using the 1 : 2 : 9 mortar, having: (*a*) a crushing strength not greater than 5.5 MN/m² the modified basic stress is as obtained under case (1) above; (*b*) a crushing strength between 5.5 and 21 MN/m² the appropriate stress is obtained by linear interpolation between the modified basic stress for a unit of crushing strength of 5.5 MN/m²

TABLE 30 STRESS REDUCTION FACTORS FOR SLENDERNESS AND ECCENTRICITY

Slenderness Ratio	Stress Reduction Factor*			
	Axially Loaded	Eccentricity of Vertical Loading as a Proportion of the Thickness of the Member		
		1/6	1/4	1/3†
6	1.00	1.00	1.00	1.00
8	0.95	0.93	0.92	0.91
10	0.89	0.85	0.83	0.81
12	0.84	0.78	0.75	0.72
14	0.78	0.70	0.66	0.62
16	0.73	0.63	0.58	0.53
18	0.67	0.55	0.49	0.43
20	0.62	0.48	0.41	0.34
22	0.56	0.40	0.32	0.24
24	0.51	0.33	0.24	—
26	0.45	0.25	—	—
27	0.43	0.22	—	—

* Linear interpolation between values is permitted.

† Where in special cases the eccentricity of loading lies between 1/3 and 1/2 of the thickness of the member, the stress reduction factor should vary linearly between unity and 0.20 for slenderness ratios of 6 and 20 respectively.

and the Table 28 basic stress for a block of crushing strength 21 MN/m² or the basic stress, whichever is the greater; (*c*) a crushing strength greater than 21 MN/m² the basic stress is as given in Table 28.

The permissible stresses given in Table 28 may be increased by not more than 25 per cent where additional stresses occur due to eccentricity of loading.

WEIGHTS OF MATERIALS, LOADING

For the purpose of calculating the dead load of a building the Building Regulations require that the weights of the materials shall be those specified in B.S. 648 *Schedule of unit weights of building materials*. Some of the weights are listed in Table 32.

TABLE 31 MINIMUM IMPOSED FLOOR LOADS

Building	Intensity of Distributed Load kN/m²	Concentrated Load, Unless Otherwise Stated, to be Taken over a Square with a 300 mm side (kN)
Houses and flats	1.5	1.4
Offices		
Offices for general use	2.5	2.7
Offices with computing equipment	3.5	To be determined
Filing offices and storage	5	To be determined
Hotels		
Bedrooms	2	1.8
Bars and vestibules	5	—
Lounges, dining rooms	2	2.7
Colleges and schools		
Assembly areas with fixed seating	4	—
Bedrooms	1.5	1.8
Classrooms	3	2.7
Gymnasia	5	3.6
Factories	5 to 10	To be determined
Warehouses and storage buildings	To be determined but not less than 2.4 for each metre of storage height	To be determined

TABLE 32 DENSITY OF BUILDING MATERIALS

Material	Nominal Thickness or Size (mm)	Density kg	per
Asphalt, as laid	per 25 mm	42	m^2
For 12 mm macadam finish, add		35	m^2
Battens, roofing			
38 mm x 19 mm			
At 100 mm gauge		3.4	m^2
Blockwork, walling	per 25 mm		
Clay			
Hollow	per 25 mm	25.5	m^2
50% perforated, medium density	per 25 mm	27.9	m^2
Concrete			
Stone aggregate			
Solid	per 25 mm	53.9	m^2
Cellular	per 25 mm	40	m^2
Aerated	per 25 mm	14.4	m^2
Boarding			
Softwood, rough sawn	19	9.8	m^2
Softwood, rough sawn	25	12.3	m^2
Softwood, rough sawn	32	14.7	m^2
Boards			
Hardboard	6.4	6.5	m^2
Insulating	13	3.67	m^2
Plasterboard	9.5	9.8	m^2
For setting coat add		4.9	m^2
Brickwork			
Common and sand-lime		2 000	m^3
Engineering, dense		2 400	m^3
Glazed		2 080	m^3
Pressed		2 240	m^3
Concrete			
Brick aggregate		1 840	m^3
Clinker aggregate		1 520	m^3
Foamed slag aggregate		1 280	m^3
Gravel or stone aggregate (plain)		2 310	m^3
Gravel or stone aggregate (reinforced)		2 500	m^3
Copper roofing sheet			
As laid	0.6	6.5	m^2
Cork insulation slabs	per 25 mm	4.9	m^2
Felt, roofing	see Table 15		
For 12 mm asphalt finish, add		20	m^2
Fibre-cement			
Rectangular slating	6	12.2	m^2
Corrugated sheeting	6	16.6	m^2
Flat sheeting	6	12.2	m^2
Flooring			
Compressed cork	25	9.8	m^2
Granolithic	25	61	m^2
Rubber	6	13.2	m^2
Floors, structural			
Hollow, clay blocks, including, reinforcement and mortar jointing between blocks	100	147	m^2
	125	171	m^2
	150	191	m^2
	175	225	m^2
	200	260	m^2
Hollow clay blocks, including reinforcement and concrete ribs between blocks	100	122	m^2
	115	132	m^2
	125	142	m^2
	140	152	m^2
	150	162	m^2
	175	181	m^2
	200	200	m^2
For each 25 mm of thickness concrete topping, add		61	m^2
Hollow clay blocks, including reinforcement, concrete ribs between blocks and constructional concrete topping			
75 mm block, 25 mm topping	100	152	m^2
90 mm block, 38 mm topping	125	196	m^2
115 mm block, 38 mm topping	150	220	m^2
140 mm block, 38 mm topping	175	240	m^2
150 mm block, 50 mm topping	200	279	m^2
Hollow concrete units, including constructional concrete topping	100	171	m^2
	125	196	m^2
	150	220	m^2
	175	244	m^2
	200	269	m^2
	225	318	m^2
Floors, wood			
Hardwood	22	16.2	m^2
	28	21.1	m^2
Softwood	22	11.3	m^2
	28	13.7	m^2
Mastic for block flooring		1.47	m^2
Glazed roof lights (as C, Fig. 66)	58	122	m^2
Glazed roofing			
With lead-covered steel bars at 610 mm centres			
spans up to 1.8 m	6	26.2	m^2
spans 1.8 m to 3.4 m	6	29.4	m^2
With aluminium alloy bars			
spans up to 3.4 m	6	19.6	m^2
Iron, cast		7 210	m^3
Iron, wrought		7 690	m^3
Lead		11 330	m^3
Lead sheet (No. 6 grade)	2.5	29.4	m^2
Plaster			
Acoustic	12	9.8	m^2
Barium sulphate	12	36.7	m^2
Fibrous	16	14.7	m^2
Gypsum or lime	12	24.4	m^2
Hydraulic lime or Portland cement	12	29.4	m^2
For wood or metal lathing, add		6.1	m^2
Plasterboards	9.5	9.8	m^2
For setting coat, add		4.9	m^2
Plywood	per mm	0.69	m^2
Screeding			
Portland cement (1:3)	25	61	m^2
Shingle, cedar		7.5	m^2
Slag wool		272	m^3
Slate, slab	per 25 mm	75	m^2
Slating			
Cornish, thin		29.4	m^2
medium		36.7	m^2
Welsh, thin		29.4	m^2
thick		56.3	m^2
Westmorland, thin		44	m^2
thick		56.3	m^2
Steel, mild		7 850	m^3
Tiling, plain roof		71	m^2

NOTE

The above density values are in kg/m^3 or kg/m^2 for given thicknesses. The unit of force is the newton (N) and 1 N = 1 kg x 1 m/second^2 = 1 unit of mass x 1 unit of acceleration. As the earth's gravitational acceleration is 9.806 65 m/s^2 then the force exerted by the earth's gravity on a mass of 1 kg = 1 kg x 9.806 65 m/s^2 = 9.806 65 N. The units used in structural calculations are newtons so the values in the Table should be multiplied by 9.806 65 to give the value in N; for practical purposes and because the values in the Table are average ones the multiplying factor can be taken as 10.

The *minimum* imposed loads which must be taken into account when designing floors, columns and load-bearing walls are given in B.S. 6399 Design Loading for Buildings: *Dead and Imposed Loads*, and shown in Table 31.

In a multi-storeyed building it is improbable that all floors will be subjected to maximum loading at the same time and allowance is therefore made when computing the imposed loads in respect to certain buildings. B.S. 6399 states that when designing walls, piers or columns, their supports and foundations, the total imposed floor loads may be reduced by the percentage specified in Table 33; a roof may be regarded as a floor. For factories and workshops designed for 5 kN/m² or more the reductions in Table 33 apply, provided that the loading on all floors is taken as not less than 5 kN/m² with no reductions. Reductions are not allowed for: (1) plant or machinery; (2) for storage buildings, warehouses or garages; or (3) office areas used for storage and filing.

TABLE 33 REDUCTION IN IMPOSED FLOOR LOADS

Number of Floors incl. the Roof Carried by the Member under Consideration	Reduction (%) in Total Distributed Imposed Load on all Floors Carried by the Member under Consideration
1	0
2	10
3	20
4	30
5 to 10	40
over 10	50

Roof Loading. On flat roofs and sloping roofs up to and including 10°, where roof access (in addition to that necessary for cleaning and repair) is provided, the vertical imposed load, including snow, is 1.5 kN/m² measured on plan; or a load of 1.8 kN concentrated on a square with a 300 mm side, whichever produces the greater stress.

On flat roofs and sloping roofs up to and including 10°, where no access is provided (other than that necessary for cleaning and repair), the imposed vertical load, including snow, is 0.75 kN/m² measured on plan, or load of 0.9 kN concentrated on a square with a 300 mm side.

On roofs sloping more than 10°, with no access (other than that necessary for cleaning and repair), the following are the vertical imposed loads, including snow: (1) For a roof slope of 30° or less: 0.75 kN/m² measured on plan or 0.9 kN concentrated on a square with a 300 mm side whichever produces the greater stress; (2) For a roof slope of 75° or more: no allowance necessary.

For roof slopes between 30° and 75°, the imposed load is obtained by linear interpolation between 0.75 kN/m² for a 30° roof slope and nil for a 75° roof slope.

To provide for loads incidental to maintenance, all roof coverings (other than glazing) at a slope of less than 45° should be capable of carrying a load of 0.9 kN concentrated on any square with a 125 mm side.

Wind Loading. The Building Regulations require that wind loads on a building shall be calculated in accordance with B.S. 6399 Design Loading for Buildings. The B.S. sets out an involved method for determining wind load which is unpopular among designers because: (1) it assumes an accuracy incompatible with the fickle nature of wind; and (2) is unjustifiably lengthy. It is not considered here. An earlier edition of the Code adopted wind pressures according to the wind speed at the site and the shape of the building. For example a 15 m high building exposed to a wind speed of 100 km/hour would endure a wind pressure of 68 kgf/m².

In a brick building resistance to wind force is provided by cross walls and floors and there are usually sufficient of these to provide stability. It is considered that wind pressure may be ignored in buildings of solid wall construction if the height does not exceed twice the width. In framed buildings with panel walls the effects of wind pressure are more crucial.

Application of the Calculated Method for Finding Wall Thicknesses.

Example 1 (B, Fig. 41). Find the wall thickness at each storey of a seven-storey hotel. The wall has lateral support by properly bonded cross division walls in addition to the support from the roof and floors. For simplicity it is assumed that it is an end external wall without windows. The roof and floors are continued to the outer leaf to distribute the load (Fig. 42).

Assume the following:

Span of roof and floors, 6 m.

Each storey height, 3 m.

Imposed load on flat roof, 0.75 kN/m².

Imposed load on each floor, 2 kN/m² (Table 31).

Dead load on roof (reinforced concrete, asphalt, insulation and plaster), 3.35 kN/m².

Dead load on each floor (hollow blocks, reinforcement, topping, insulation, battens, wood flooring, plaster boards), 2.87 kN/m².

Weight of brickwork,

2 000 kg/m³ = 2 000 x 0.025 = 50 kg/m² per 25 mm thickness

$$= \frac{50 \times 9.806}{10^3} = 0.49 \text{ kN/m}^2 \text{ per 25 mm thickness}$$ (see p. 129)

Mortar composed of 1 cement : 2 lime : 9 sand.

Crushing strength of bricks, 27.5 MN/m².*

Procedure. The following is the procedure adopted to determine the thickness of the wall at each storey.

1. Commencing at the top storey, assume the thickness of the wall which, in addition to being of sufficient strength, must prevent the admission of rain into and undue heat loss from the room.

* This value is conservative, it being less than the average crushing strength of good quality commons – see p. 124. Normally, especially for a wall of this height, better class bricks of greater strength would be employed.

2. Obtain the slenderness ratio.

3. Obtain the corresponding reduction factor from Table 30. The second column of this table gives the factor for axially loaded walls (which is the case in this example). If the wall were eccentrically loaded the appropriate factor would be selected from one of the last three columns. For example, if the load in a 215 mm thick wall were applied 72 mm off centre the eccentricity would be $\frac{72}{215} = \frac{1}{3}$ and the reduction factor would be found from column 5 in the table.

4. Obtain the basic stress from Table 28 and multiply this by the reduction factor to find the permissible stress.

5. Obtain the *actual* stress. If this does not exceed the allowable stress the assumed thickness of the wall is adequate; if the allowable stress is exceeded, the assumed thickness must be increased and the above sequence of operations repeated to check that the revised thickness is sufficient.

6. The wall at each storey is designed in this manner, working downwards to the bottom floor.

In this example assume the thickness of the wall at each storey is 328 mm.†

Therefore:

Effective height = $\frac{3}{4}$ storey height (p. 127).

$$\text{Slenderness ratio} = \frac{\text{effective height}}{\text{effective thickness}} = \frac{\frac{3}{4} \times 3 \text{ m}}{0.328 \text{ m}} = 7 \text{ approx.}$$

Therefore reduction factor (Table 30) = 0.975.

According to Table 28, the basic stress on the brickwork is 1.45 MN/m² for the brick and mortar strengths given.

Therefore permissible stress = 1.45 × 0.975 = 1.41 MN/m².

$$\text{Actual stress} = \frac{\text{total load}}{\text{area}} = \frac{31.6}{0.328} = 96.3 \text{ kN/m}^2 \text{ at the foot of the sixth storey}$$

which is well below the permitted value of 1.41 MN/m².

The various details are given in tabular form in the following schedule.

The total load is the sum of the (1) imposed load on the roof or floor, (2) the dead weight of the roof or floor, and (3) the weight of the wall. The load or weight of each item appears in the schedule in column 3 and the total load in column 4.

This is the type of building where the reduction in imposed loads (Table 33) applies; this load reduction at each storey is tabulated in column 5 and the reduced total load in column 6.

The area of the wall per metre length is figured in column 7 and the actual stress in column 8. Thus, for each of the 6th and 5th storeys, the actual stress (column 8) = $\frac{\text{total load in column 4}}{\text{area in column 7}}$; for the remaining storeys, the actual stress = $\frac{\text{reduced total load in column 6}}{\text{area in column 7}}$.

† See adjacent footnote.

1 Storey	2 Details of Loading (per metre run of wall)	3 Load on Each Floor (kN/m²)	4 Total Load (kN)	5 Imposed Load Reduction (kN)	6 Reduced Total Load (kN)	7 Area (m²)	8 Actual Stress (kN/m²)
Roof 6th storey	Imposed, 3 × 1 × 0.75 kN Dead, 3 × 1 × 3.35 kN Wall, $3 \times 1 \times 0.49 \times \frac{0.328}{0.025}$ kN†	2.25 10.05 19.3 —— 31.6	31.6	(† See p. 128)		1 × 0.328 = 0.328	96.3
Floor 5th storey	Imposed, 3 × 1 × 2 kN Dead, 3 × 1 × 2.87 kN Wall, as before	6 8.61 19.3 —— 33.91	65.51			0.328	200
Floor 4th storey	As before Less 10% of 2 × 6 kN	—— 33.91	99.42	1.2	98.22	0.328	299
Floor 3rd storey	As before Less 20% of 3 × 6 kN	33.91	133.33	3.6	129.73	0.328	396
Floor 2nd storey	As before Less 30% of 4 × 6 kN	33.91	167.24	7.2	160.04	0.328	488
Floor 1st storey	As before Less 40% of 5 × 6 kN	33.91	201.15	12	189.15	0.328	577
Floor G. F. storey	As before Less 40% of 6 × 6 kN	33.91	235.06	14.4	220.66	0.328	673 = 0.673 MN/m²

The actual stress of 0.673 MN/m² (note that in the tabulated calculations the actual stress is given in kN/m² and that here this is divided by 10^3 to give MN/m² which are the values given in Table 28) to which the bottom storey is subjected is less than half of that of the allowable stress (1.41 MN/m²). Therefore, a 328 mm* thick wall as shown at B, Fig. 41 would be adequate for the whole height of the wall.

It should be observed that only 27.5 MN/m² has been assumed to be the crushing strength of the bricks; if faced brickwork were used this value would be increased – see p. 124. It should be noted also that, in order to take a simple case, it was assumed that the wall was without door and window openings; the provision of such openings results in concentrated loads – and consequently an increase in the "actual stress" – on the brickwork between the voids; this case is dealt with in Example 3.

Example 2. If, instead of solid construction, wall B, Fig. 41 was a cavity wall as shown at C, the following would be the thickness at each storey, assuming the same roof and floor loading, brickwork strength, etc., as in the last example. The roof and floors are continued to the outer leaf of the wall in order to distribute the loads over both leaves – see p. 134.

* This wall would be sufficiently strong to withstand the maximum actual stress if it were only 215 mm thick, as the allowable stress would be 1.27 MN/m² and the actual stress at ground floor storey would be lower than 0.673 MN/m² because a less heavy wall is used. It should, however, be pointed out that, besides having a low insulating value, a solid 215 mm thick external wall is not sufficient to ensure the non-transmission of rain, especially if it is highly exposed.

Assume the thickness of the wall at each storey is 275 mm.

For determining the slenderness ratio, the effective thickness = $^2/_3(2 \times 102.5)$ = 136.7 mm (see p. 125).

$$\text{Therefore slenderness ratio} = \frac{\text{effective height}}{\text{effective thickness}} = \frac{\frac{3}{4} \times 3 \text{ m}}{0.137 \text{ m}} = 16.4$$

Reduction factor = 0.72. The basic stress is the same as in Example 1, *i.e.*, 1.45 MN/m². Hence the permissible stress = 1.45 x 0.72 = 1.04 MN/m².

1 Storey	2 Details of Loading (per metre run of wall)	3 Load on Each Floor (kN/m²)	4 Total Load (kN)	5 Imposed Load Reduction (kN)	6 Reduced Total Load (kN)	7 Area (m²)	8 Actual Stress (kN/m²)
Roof	Imposed, 3 x 1 x 0.75 kN Dead, 3 x 1 x 3.35 kN	2.25 10.05					
6th storey	Wall, 3 x 1 x 0.49 x $\frac{0.205}{0.025}$ kN	12.06 24.36	24.36			1 x 0.205 = 0.205	119
Floor	Imposed, 3 x 1 x 2 kN Dead, 3 x 1 x 2.87 kN	6 8.61					
5th storey	Wall, as before	12.06 26.67	51.03			0.205	249
Floor 4th storey	As before Less 10% of 2 x 6 kN	26.67	77.7	1.2	76.5	0.205	373
Floor 3rd storey	As before Less 20% of 3 x 6 kN	26.67	104.37	3.6	100.77	0.205	492
Floor 2nd storey	As before Less 30% of 4 x 6 kN	26.67	131.04	7.2	123.8	0.205	604
Floor 1st storey	As before Less 40% of 5 x 6 kN	26.67	157.7	12	145.7	0.205	710
Floor G. F. storey	As before Less 40% of 6 x 6 kN	26.67	184.4	14.4	170	0.205	829 = 0.829 MN/m²

Here again, as shown in the schedule above, the lower portion of this wall is understressed and 275 mm cavity wall construction suffices from top to bottom.

Example 3 (E, Fig. 41). In the above two examples it was assumed that the walls were without voids. In the following one, windows are provided of width equal to the maximum allowed, *e.g.*, three-quarters the length of the wall units. Unlike the previous cases, where the loads were considered to be uniformly distributed, there is concentrated loading on the portions of the wall between the windows, the greatest stresses occurring at sill levels X–X; it will be obvious that a big increase in the actual stress occurs here resulting in a greater thickness of wall unless stronger bricks and mortars are employed.

Assume the thickness of this solid wall at the upper storeys is 328 mm and the loading, etc., is as in Example 1.

Allowable stress for 328 mm thick wall = 1.41 MN/m² (p. 131).

1 Storey	2 Details of Loading (per 5 m run of wall)	3 Load on Each Floor (kN)	4 Total Load (kN)	5 Imposed Load Reduction (kN)	6 Reduced Total Load (kN)	7 Area (m²)	8 Actual Stress (kN/m²)
Roof	Imposed, 5 x 3 x 0.75 kN Dead, 5 x 3 x 3.35 kN Wall, 5 x 0.6 x 0.49 x $\frac{0.328}{0.025}$ kN	11.25 50.25 19.29					
6th storey at X–X	Wall, 1.25 x 1.5 x 0.49 x $\frac{0.328}{0.025}$ kN	12.05 92.84	92.84			1.25 x 0.328 = 0.41	227
Floor	Imposed, 5 x 3 x 2 Dead, 5 x 3 x 2.87 Wall, 5 x 1.5 x 0.49 x $\frac{0.328}{0.025}$ kN	30 43.1 48.2					
5th storey at X–X	Wall, as before	12.05 133.35	226.2			0.41	552
Floor 4th storey at X–X	As before Less 10% of 2 x 30 kN	133.35	359.6	6	353.6	0.41	862
Floor 3rd storey at X–X	As before Less 20% of 3 x 30 kN	133.35	493	18	475	0.41	1 159
Floor 2nd storey at X–X	As before Less 30% of 4 x 30 kN	133.35	626.4	36	590.4	0.41	1 440
The actual stress of 1.44 MN/m² is greater than the permitted value of 1.41 MN/m², so the thickness of the wall at the 2nd storey must be increased to 440 mm. Hence slenderness ratio now = $\frac{\frac{3}{4} \times 3}{0.440}$ = 5.1 Therefore reduction factor = 1 so permissible stress is now 1.45 x 1 = 1.45 MN/m²							
Floor	Imposed, 5 x 2.9* x 2 kN Dead, 5 x 2.9 x 2.87 kN Wall, 5 x 1.5 x 0.49 x $\frac{0.440}{0.025}$ kN Wall, 1.25 x 1.5 x 0.49 x $\frac{0.440}{0.025}$ kN	29 41.6 64.7 16.2 151.5	644.5	* Because of increased wall thickness the floor span is now 6 – 2(0.440 – 0.328) = 5.776 m, so half span = 5.776 ÷ 2 = 2.9 m.			
2nd storey at X–X	Less 30% of (3 x 30) + (1 x 29) kN			35.7	608.8	1.25 x 0.440 = 0.55	1 107
Floor 1st storey at X–X	As above Less 40% of (3 x 30 + 2 x 29) kN	151.5	796	59.2	736.8	0.55	1 340
Floor G. F. storey at X–X	As above Less 40% of (3 x 30 + 3 x 29) kN	151.5	947.5	70.8	876.7	0.55	1 594 = 1.594 MN/m²

Here again the wall is overstressed and needs to be thickened to 542 mm which will be found to be satisfactory.

Example 4 (F, Fig. 41). The following is the designed thickness of wall E, Fig. 41, if stronger bricks and mortar are employed. It is assumed that the bricks selected have a crushing strength of 52 (instead of 27.5 MN/m²) and the mortar is composed of 1 cement: 2 lime: 9 sand.

Assuming the thickness of the upper storeys (328 mm) and the loading, etc., as before, the slenderness ratio = 7 approx. (p. 131).

Reduction factor = 0.975 (p. 131). Basic stress = 2.05 MN/m² (Table 28).

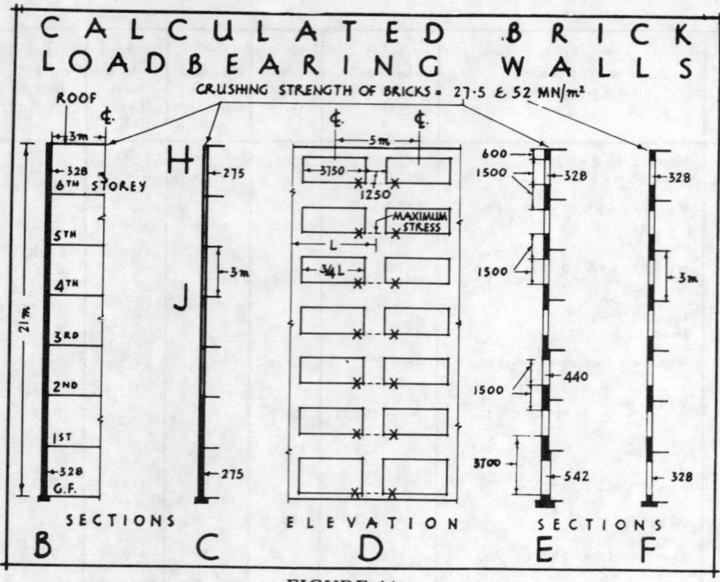

FIGURE 41

Therefore allowable stress = 2.05 x 0.975 = 2 MN/m^2.
In the schedule in Example 3 the actual stress at X–X 2nd storey is 1.44 MN/m^2.

Hence the assumed thickness of the wall of 328 mm at this level is adequate.

Proceeding:

1 Storey	2 Details of Loading (per 5 m run of wall)	3 Load on Each Floor (kN)	4 Total Load (kN)	5 Imposed Load Reduction (kN)	6 Reduced Total Load (kN)	7 Area (m^2)	8 Actual Stress (kN/m^2)
		Brought forward from Example 3	626.4				
Floor 1st storey	As before	133.35	759.8				
at X–X	Less 40% of 5 x 30 kN			60	699.8	0.41	1 707
Floor G. F. storey	As before	133.35	893.2				
at X–X	Less 40% of 6 x 30 kN			72	821.2	0.41	2 002 = 2.002 MN/m^2

The 328 mm wall is therefore slightly overstressed at the ground floor storey; so improve the mortar to a 1:1:6 mix for this storey. The permissible stress is consequently increased to 2.5 x 0.975 = 2.44 MN/m^2, which is greater than the actual stress.

The thickness of the wall is therefore 328 mm throughout. This is shown at F, Fig. 41, and can be compared with the calculated wall at E, constructed of weaker bricks.

Example 5. Most multi-storey buildings of the factory type have a structural frame and it is most unlikely that they would be constructed with non-calculated solid brick load-bearing walls. However, it is not unusual for such buildings to be designed with calculated walls, and the following example is provided to show how the walls are designed in accordance with C.P. 111.

In this example it is assumed that the wall is an end wall (without windows) of a factory, the floors of which support heavy loads (Table 31). Further assumptions are:

Span (between external wall and opposite internal wall) of roof and floors, 7.3 m.
Each storey height, 4.8 m.
Imposed load on flat roof, 1.5 kN/m^2 (p. 130).
Imposed load on each floor, 10 kN/m^2 (Table 31).
Dead weight of roof and each floor, 3.35 kN/m^2.
Weight of brickwork, 0.49 kN/m^2 per 25 mm thickness.
Mortar composed of 1 cement: 2 lime: 9 sand.
Crushing strength of bricks, 52 MN/m^2.
Note: It is assumed that the reduction in imposed floor loads (Table 33) does not apply to this class of building.
Assume the thickness of the wall is 328 mm.

Slenderness ratio = $\dfrac{\frac{3}{4} \times 4.8}{0.328} = 11$.

Reduction factor (Table 30) = 0.865.
Basic stress = 2.05 MN/m^2 (Table 28).
So permissible stress = 2.05 x 0.865 = 1.77 MN/m^2.

1 Storey	2 Details of Loading (per metre run of wall)	3 Load on Each Floor (kN/m^2)	4 Total Load (kN)	5 Area (m^2)	6 Actual Stress (kN/m^2)
Roof 4th storey	Imposed, 3.65 x 1 x 1.5 kN Dead, 3.65 x 1 x 3.35 kN Wall, 4.8 x 1 x 0.49 x $\dfrac{0.328}{0.025}$ kN	5.47 12.23 30.9 48.6	48.6	1 x 0.328 = 0.328	148
Floor 3rd storey	Imposed, 3.65 x 1 x 10 kN Dead, as before Wall, as before	36.5 12.23 30.9 79.63	128.2	0.328	391
Floor 2nd storey	As above	79.63	207.8	0.328	634
Floor 1st storey	As above	79.63	287.4	0.328	876
Floor G. F. storey	As above	79.63	367	0.328	1 119 = 1 119 MN/m^2

The maximum actual stress is approximately 63 per cent of the allowable stress. Therefore, this wall constructed of brickwork and supporting the loads assumed would be 328 mm through its height, as shown at F, Fig. 41.

Framed Structures. Multi-storey buildings especially are now generally framed structures, namely, those having (*a*) frames of steel or reinforced concrete pillars and beams (Chap. II), and (*b*) relatively thin brick, etc., wall panels or infillings; the floors, roofs and wall panels are supported by the beams which transmit the loads direct to the pillars and these, in turn, conduct the weights to the foundations. Thus, the portion of wall supported by a beam is the panel between it and the beam immediately above it, *i.e.*, that of storey height. Consequently, the wall load is comparatively light and the panel thin; if external panels are of brickwork they need be only sufficiently thick to exclude rain, be resistant to wind pressure and be adequately insulated.

As mentioned on p. 123, light-framed structures, usually single-storeyed and of a wide span, may consist of pillars of steel (sometimes of the light-gauge type – see p. 43) or wood with cladded panels. This *cladding* may be of asbestos-cement or metal sheeting, thin concrete slabs, wood boarding, etc.

As an alternative to the use of a structural frame an industrialized building system may be used where the loads are carried on large precast R.C. wall panels – see p. 154.

CAVITY WALL DETAILS

Cavity wall construction is introduced in Vol. I and considered in more detail in Vol. II. If the roof is pitched it is advisable to distribute its weight over both leaves of the wall, as shown at A and B, Fig. 13, Vol. II, in preference to the construction at P where the roof is supported solely by the inner leaf. Normally, for two or three-storey domestic buildings the floors are supported by the inner leaves (see P).

Whilst cross walls, floors and roof have a stiffening effect on the inner leaf, such support is absent from the outer leaf and hence the need for properly distributed wall ties to connect both leaves, otherwise a high outer leaf would tend to buckle. The object of the ties is to increase the stability of the wall. They are not regarded as a means of transferring some of the load from the inner to the outer leaf. Obviously, wall ties especially some of the light-gauge butterfly type (F and H, Fig. 13, Vol. II) are ineffective for this purpose.

If certain precautions are taken, the loading from the floors, in addition to that from the roof, can be distributed uniformly over both leaves. In order to spread the floor loads over the maximum area of cavity walling, and as mentioned on p. 131, it is assumed that the roofs and floors of the multi-storey buildings illustrated in Fig. 41 (this volume) are supported on both skins by continuing them to the outer leaf. Alternative details showing this construction are given in Fig. 42.

In order to prevent the cracking of external brick walls which can be caused by thermal movement, their size should be restricted to 16 m long by 7 m high; for parapet walls the length should be reduced to 9 m. Thus the wall may have to be subdivided and a horizontal break could be as shown at G′, Fig. 42, a vertical break would have to be a straight joint (associated with a strengthening pilaster) leaving a 12 mm gap similar to O, Fig. 25.

Treatment at Roofs. Detail A shows the eaves of a reinforced concrete flat roof covered with 20 mm thick asphalt. This may be continued down the edge of the flat to form an apron finished with a drip, as indicated, or it may stop at the edge as shown at C. Alternatively, the apron may be of copper or aluminium (as shown at D) or lead with the asphalt dressed over it.

The heat transmitted in summer time through a roof may be so intense as to cause not only an uncomfortably high temperature within the building but also serious damage to the structure, especially if the roof is a reinforced concrete flat. Unless precautions* are taken, excessive expansion, followed by contraction, may result in the development of cracks in the concrete, and in an extreme case the absorbed heat may cause the concrete roof to expand to such an extent as to crack the external walls and thrust out parapets. The temperature rise in the concrete will be lessened if the radiation of the sun (solar radiation) is reflected. White surfaces are effective reflectors and, therefore, if the black asphaltic surface of a roof is given a light-coloured treatment the amount of absorbed heat will be reduced. The most effective, as it is the most permanent, treatment takes the form of washed fine white grit or chippings which are lightly rolled into the surface of the asphalt, as shown at C, Fig. 42. If the flat at A is likely to be exposed to the rays of the sun it should be treated in this manner.

The transmission of heat to the concrete roof and interior of the building from the hot asphalt is further reduced if, as shown at A, an insulated layer is provided; this also reduces the heat losses from the building in winter and eliminates condensation on the ceiling. The insulation may take the form of compressed wood-wool slabs, cork boards, vermiculite screeds, etc. (see also p. 57).

It is now a common practice, before the asphalt is applied, to cover the structure with either building paper or felt, called sarking felt or sheathing felt – see A. This is especially necessary if there is to be no insulation, as at C, and the asphalt would otherwise be laid direct on the concrete. This membrane or underlay is laid loosely and renders the asphalt independent of any expansion and contraction to which the concrete may be subject.

Blistering of the asphalt sometimes occurs. This defect, which takes the form of blisters which may develop in size to a diameter of 100 mm or more, is liable to arise in a roof which is exposed to intense sunshine. A blister contains beads of moisture. This moisture, through defects in a parapet for example, may have gained access between the asphalt and concrete when the bond is defective, and this entrapped moisture when heated by the sun vaporizes with the result that the internal pressure exerted causes the characteristic swelling. It is considered

* See Chap. XII.

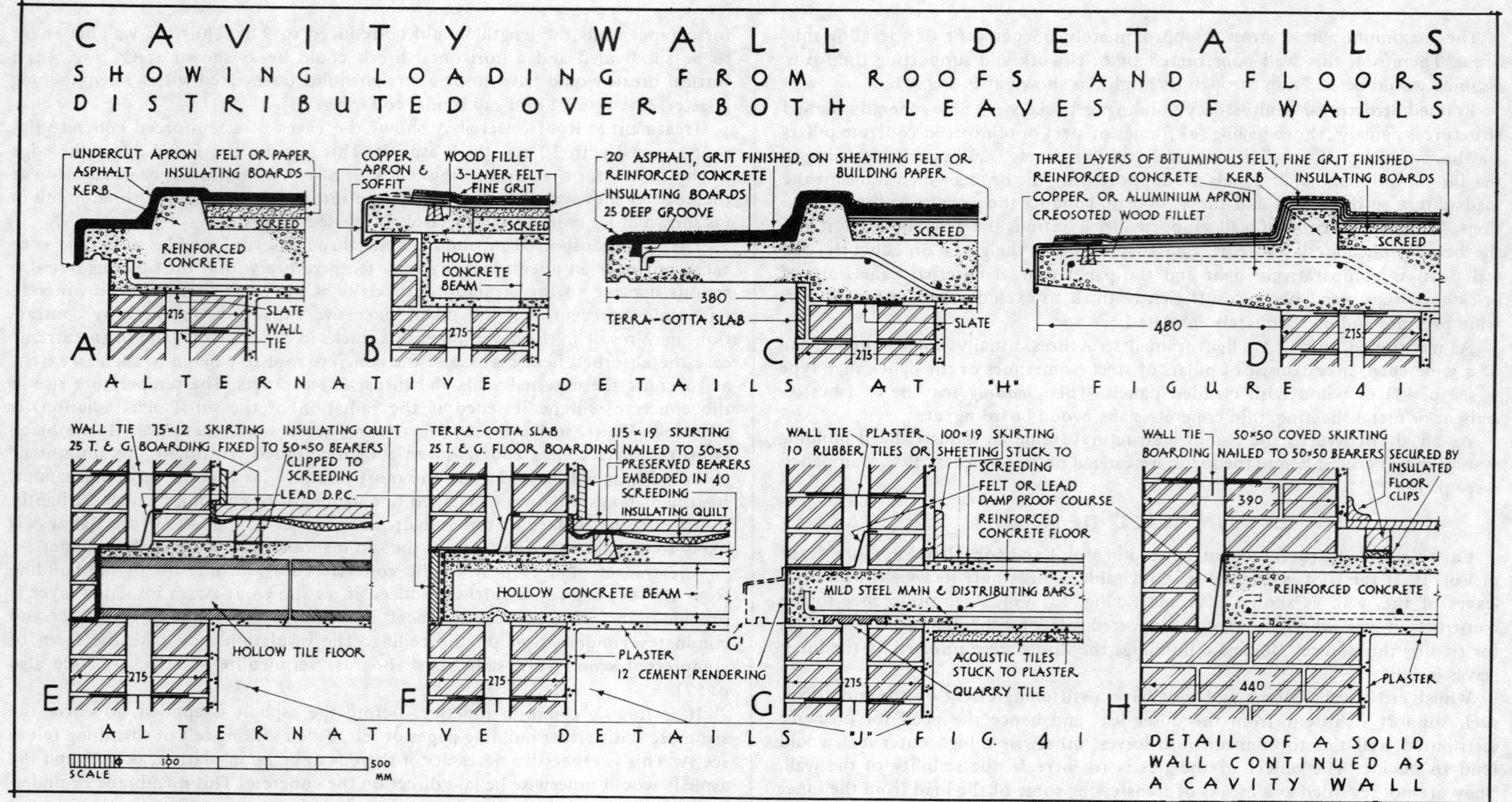

FIGURE 42

also that absorption of condensation on the underside of the roof may be a likely cause of blister-formation. The provision of building paper or felt, an insulated layer, and a vapour barrier (see p. 257) prevent the occurrence of this defect, provided parapets, etc., are soundly constructed.

Normally, roofs should be free of standing water, and therefore the screeds should be laid with a minimum fall, towards suitably placed outlets, of 13 mm per metre. Sometimes the screeding is formed above the insulated layer and below the building paper or sheathing felt.

The cavity should be closed by a layer of slates (see A) or tiles (see G) before the concrete is laid. If the building is to be in an exposed position the concrete at the eaves should be dense and preferably waterproofed as a precaution against rain penetration. A satisfactory surface can be provided to the exposed concrete, especially if the formwork is lined with hardboard; otherwise the concrete may be cement rendered, as shown at G.

The alternative detail at B shows a covering consisting of three layers of bituminous felt, laid breaking joint, and bonded together with a bituminous compound, the whole being sometimes referred to as a "built-up-system". As explained above, the top layer after being given an application of liquid bitumen, is covered with fine grit. A copper apron and soffit are shown, the former being secured at 100 to 150 mm centres to a creosoted splayed wood fillet embedded in the concrete; alternatively, this finish could be in aluminium, the apron or flashing being laid over the first layer of felt (as shown at D) and screwed to the fillet. The felt could be dressed over the apron, as indicated by broken lines. If, as is usual, the hollow concrete beams are open-ended and not solid, as shown, they should be partially filled with waterproofed concrete before the two courses of brick bats are laid. A groove formed in each beam, as shown at F, would be an additional precaution against the transmission to the inner leaf of any rain which may have penetrated at the eaves. An alternative finish at the eaves could take the form of a terra-cotta or reconstructed stone fascia, as shown at F, or the beams could be given a larger bearing on the outer leaf with their open ends partially filled with waterproofed dense concrete and cement rendered on face – see G.

The detail at C, to which much of the above description applies, shows the concrete roof, suitably reinforced, projecting 380 mm.

A reinforced concrete flat, having a larger overhang than the above and finished with a triple-layered bituminous felted and gritted covering, is shown at D.

Treatment at Floors. Four alternative details showing the construction when the floors are extended to give a bearing on the outer leaves of 275 mm (or 380 mm) cavity walls are provided at E, F and G. As explained in Chap. 1, Vol. II, the heads of door and window openings must be protected by suitable damp-proof courses to prevent the transmission of rain. It is equally important that, when the cavity is bridged by floors, a similar safeguard is provided. At E the damp-proof course of asphalt felt (or lead or copper) extends the full length of the wall, lapped 75 mm at joints, and passes over the end of the hollow tiled floor to the external face. The d.p.c. at F may be extended to pass over the ends of the concrete floor beams, as shown by broken lines, that at G finishes at the outer face of the wall and that at the alternative G′ is extended over the projecting floor. Detail H shows the construction when a solid wall is continued as a cavity wall.

It will be observed that each floor is insulated. At E and F the insulation is in the form of a flexible quilt or blanket (such as Cabot's Quilt, fibreglass quilt or slagwool blanket) passed over the floor bearers; to provide discontinuity the material should be packed between the walls and the edges of the floor boards. The ceiling of the rubber surfaced floor at G is covered with acoustic tiles which are readily stuck to the plastered ceiling by an adhesive applied to the back of each tile before being slid-pressed into position. The floor clip of the type shown at H has a 12 mm thick insulated pad riveted to two separate metal portions of the clip. These are effective in reducing the transmission of impact sound from the floor to the room(s) below. Additional insulation could take the form of that shown at E and F and/or insulating board at the ceiling nailed to grounds let into or plugged to the soffit of the concrete floor.

CROSS-WALL CONSTRUCTION

The term "cross-wall construction" is applied to buildings in which the walls at right angles to the principal axis are designed to carry the loads from the floors and roof, the lateral front and rear external walls being non-load-bearing. This principle is by no means new, it being the usual practice in traditional building to arrange timber joists in the direction of the shortest span and this has often resulted in the joists being supported on cross walls and partitions, not on the external and other lateral walls; but, although the latter external walls were non-load-bearing, there was no resulting economy in materials, as they were relatively thick (328 mm brickwork or 400 mm masonry if solid, or 275 mm cavity) in order to prevent rain transmission; in contemporary cross-wall construction, however, the external walls are of relatively light-cladded construction which is resistant to rain-transmission and is adequately insulated.

Cross-wall construction now being adopted for certain types of building is illustrated in its simplest form at A, Fig. 43; internal partitions (some of which may be load-bearing) have been omitted. It is thus a box-framed structure, the open ends of the "boxes" being the cladded main external walls. The cross walls of a multi-storey building are designed as explained on pp. 127–134 . One form of cladding is shown at C. This is an expensive form and consists of 102.5 mm common brickwork faced with terra-cotta slabs (see p. 145) with an inner skin of hollow clay blocks or alternatively, concrete blocks as shown at D, F and G. The L-beams shown of the reinforced floor would be supported on reinforced concrete pillars at the ends of the cross walls and the pillars could be faced with terra-cotta blocks, a similar treatment to that shown at D. In lieu of the common brickwork with the terra-cotta facing, the cladding may be of facing bricks; the reinforced concrete beams at the floor levels may be left exposed with a plain or textured finish and they may project to give horizontal emphasis. More economical and lighter forms of cladding than that shown at C are illustrated in Figs. 17 and 18.

Maximum economy is obtained if the cross walls are planned to be the same distance apart throughout the length of the building; certain elements can thereby be standardized, such as reinforced concrete floors having the same imposed loading (which, because of the span being common, are of uniform thickness with the same amount of tensional reinforcement) and panels of lightweight cladding; work in the design office is thereby reduced, setting-out on the site is facilitated, floor formwork can be used over and over again without modification, and, if the cladding is prefabricated, erection is expedited.

The types of building for which this form of construction is most suited include blocks (up to five storeys high) of maisonettes and flats, the spacing of the cross walls varying from 3 to 5.5 m centres. It is not suitable for the office

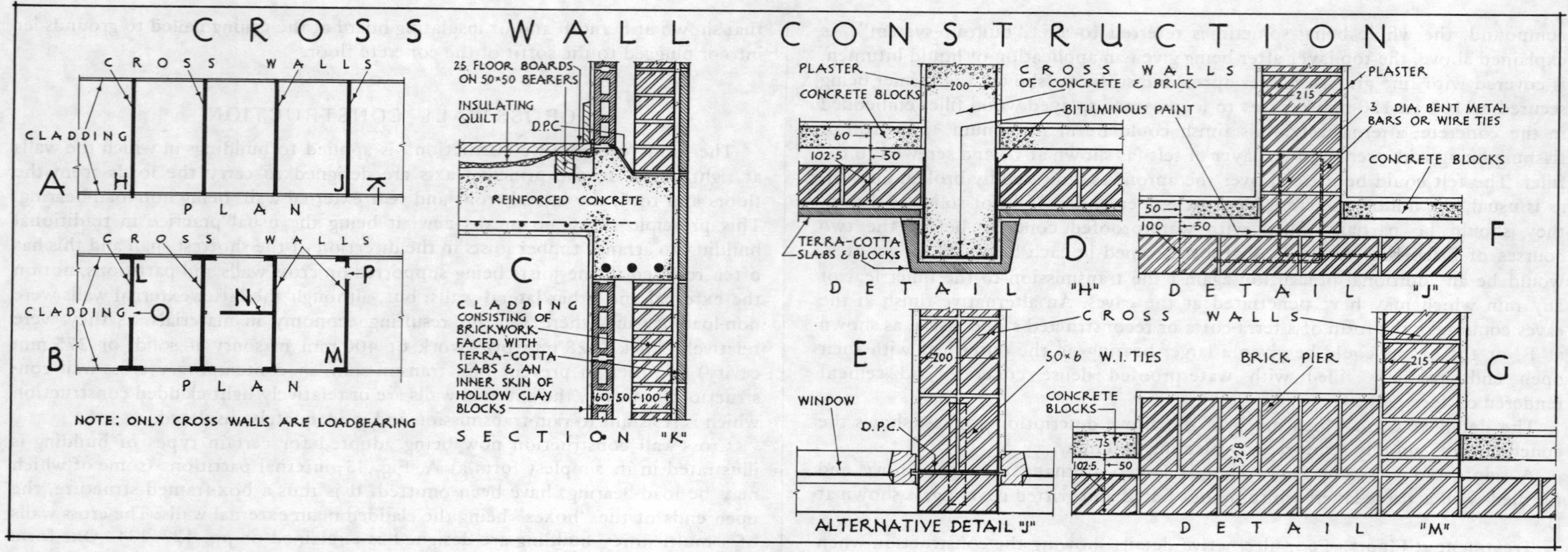

FIGURE 43

type of building where the floor space must be open and adaptable to meet the requirements of tenants and which often are not known until after the building (without dividing partitions) has been completed.

Care must be taken to ensure that the ends of the cross walls are sealed to prevent the admission of rain. One method is shown at E, Fig. 43, the end of the 215 mm brick cross-wall being faced with brick with a fibrous asphalt felt or other d.p.c. built in as the work proceeds and with the edges engaged in grooves in the window frames. An alternative treatment is shown at D. Like C, the cladding is of terra-cotta faced brickwork, but concrete blocks (which may be of the solid or hollow type – see Figs. 12 and 13, Vol. III) constitute the inner skin. The cross-wall is of concrete, which may be plain or reinforced according to the loading, and the projecting end is covered with terra-cotta blocks. To prevent the admission of rain through any defective joints in the terra-cotta facing, the end of the wall may be given two good coats of bituminous paint or similar water repellant emulsion. Slabs and blocks of reconstructed stone (see Fig. 48) may be adopted instead of terra-cotta, or, alternatively, such slab facing may be omitted if the cladding consists of facing bricks or selected commons. F shows a third method, the outer skin of the brick cladding being bonded to the cross-wall (after the end surface has been painted with two coats of bituminous emulsion) by means of 3 mm dia. metal bars, bent as shown, or wire ties at every third course. See Figs. 17 and 52 for alternative methods of cladding.

The merits claimed for cross-wall construction are: (1) As mentioned above, structural and non-structural elements can be standardized and some can be prefabricated, resulting in a speeding up of erection; (2) the width of windows is not restricted (see p. 125) and therefore greater freedom is permitted in respect to fenestration, etc., and (3) the cross walls are designed as explained on pp. 127–134 (resulting in an economy of labour, materials and space), but unlike the calculated external walls considered on these pages, where the computed thickness may have to be increased to prevent damp penetration, the cross walls, being internal (with exception of the end of gable walls), are not affected by the weather. Provided the designed thickness affords a reasonable standard of sound insulation (namely, 215 mm if of brickwork and 175 mm if of concrete), no additional thickness is called for, as the problem of rain penetration does not rise.

The demerits of the cross-wall system include: (1) The limitations of planning which result when the cross walls are maintained at maximum intervals of about 5.5 m from the foundations through each floor to the roof. (2) It is clear that a building would be structurally unsound if it consisted of a number of detached cross walls extending through several storeys without lateral or longitudinal ties or supports, especially if the cladding is of the lightweight type. Care must therefore be taken to ensure overall stability. Reinforced concrete floors are effective in producing a measure of lateral stability, especially if some of the reinforcement at the ends of the floor slabs is bent and turned into the concrete or brick cross walls. Relatively heavy cladding, such as the examples shown in Fig. 43, effect a restraining influence. Solid dividing walls or partitions parallel to the main axis serve to buttress cross walls, such as N, Fig. 43, which is a 215 mm brick wall. Staircases at right angles to the cross walls assist as buttresses. A stiffening effect is also produced if the cross walls are "T" ended, as at L shown in the key plan B, or "L" ended, as at M and detailed at G, the 215 mm brick cross-wall being bonded to a 328 mm brick pier. Such brick panels in the external walls can provide an effective feature.

Any openings in a cross-wall should preferably be within the middle third, as at O in the key plan, rather than near the ends, as indicated at P.

Another example of cross-wall construction is described on pp. 154 and 156 and in Fig. 54 where the large precast R.C. floor slabs are supported by precast R.C. wall panels.

NICHES

A niche is an arched recess in a wall, still occasionally employed as an interesting decorative feature, and which may accommodate a piece of sculpture.

It may take several forms, satisfactory types being illustrated in the two examples in Fig. 44. These are quarter-spherical niches, each being semi-circular in plan with a semi-domical head or *hood*. Other forms include those which are semi-elliptical in plan and semi-circular in elevation, or semi-elliptical in both plan and elevation.

The niche at A, B and C is in ashlar. The elevation B shows a stepped extradosed head, plain jointed on the left and, as an alternative, channel jointed on the right. The radiating bed joints are curtailed near the centre of the hood by the provision of an *eye* or *boss*; this conical-shaped stone thus avoids fine feather-edged blocks at the centre. The hood on the right comprises single voussoirs, and the alternative on the left shows smaller units with end joints *cd*, *rt*, etc.

The sketch at D indicates more clearly the shape of the hood stones with their radiating bed joints.

Plan C shows, on the left, the joints in the hood. These are developed as follows: At the elevation drop vertical projectors from the intersections between the voussoir radiating joints and the semicircle to the plan, giving "face" points 1, 2, 3, 4 and 5; similarly, project the "eye" points on to the plan. Next, develop on the plan the end joints; starting with *a* in the elevation, drop a projector until it intersects the curve on plan at *a*; points *b*, *c*, *d*, *e* and *f* on plan are at the intersections between vertical projectors from the elevation and a horizontal line from *a* on plan; to develop the end joints *rt*, etc. (elevation) continue curve *rt* to point *u* on the springing line, vertically project to *v* on the plan and the bed joints on plan are at the intersections between projectors from the elevation and a horizontal line from *v*. The bed joints on plan are now drawn, fair curves being obtained if one or two intermediate points are projected on to the plan. The joints can now be developed on the section; obtain the "face" and "eye" points by horizontally projecting from the elevation; the vertical end joints *ab*, *rt*, etc., are then developed from the plan and elevation as shown; projections from intermediate points will assist in producing fair curves at the section of the hood.

An example of a brick quarter-spherical niche is given at E, F and G. The faced brickwork consists of 50 mm bricks laid in Flemish bond with 10 mm flush joints. When deciding upon the diameter of the niche and the surmounting arch, consideration should be given to the bond, size of the bricks, and thickness of the joints to be employed, so as to ensure that after careful setting out, the joints are balanced and the normal face appearance of the bond above the niche is maintained (Chap. I, Vol. II).

The boss or eye obviates fine edges at the centre, and extremely fine feather edges are avoided, especially when the hood is built of 50 mm (out of) bricks, if alternate radiating bed joints only terminate at the eye as shown. The eye would appear too conspicuous and out of scale if it were in one unit, and it should consist therefore of thin bricks or tiles (as shown on the left); if, as shown on the right and in the section at F, it is formed of one rubber block the same effect will be obtained if two false horizontal joints (grooves filled with mortar) are formed.

In the elevation on the left, the hood is shown constructed of purpose-made bricks with normal thicknessed joints to harmonize with the adjacent brickwork. Alternatively, as indicated at J, it can be formed of rubbers with fine joints.

Rubbers (Chap. I, Vol. II) are obtainable in various sizes, up to about 380 mm long. Briefly, if rubbers are to be used for both the body and the hood of the niche, they are shaped in the following manner: A full size plan of the niche is set out (showing the bond and thickness of the joints). From this plan the bed moulds (thin wood templets) are shaped to that of the headers and stretchers which are to form the body; each mould is thus tapered and has a curved edge. Two wood cutting boxes are now made, each having a base and two sides, the sides of one being shaped to that of the header bed mould and those of the other are made to conform to the size and shape of the stretcher bed mould; a box is generally large enough to take two bricks at a time and the sides are usually protected with strips of metal. The bricks having been rubbed on bed are placed in pairs in a box, wedged and sawn by means of a bow saw, to the curve and tapered sides; the curved faces at least are then smoothed with a file or carborundum stick. Finally, these shaped rubbers are brought to the required uniform thickness in a reducing cutting box having rectangular sides of depth equal to course thickness; the rubbers, placed on bed in the box are sawn along the top, level with the sides.

The rubbers for the arch of the hood are shaped as follows: All the bricks are rubbed and squared, *i.e.*, the bed is rubbed to a smooth, level surface on the rubbing stone (a hard grit sandstone or carborundum), followed by one face rubbed until it is straight and square with the bed, as tested by the try square. From the full-size drawing of the elevation a face mould or templet is prepared to the shape of the key bricks and on which the extrados, cross joint, commencement of soffit or concave part, etc., are marked. Only one face mould is needed, as the voussoirs are tapered alike. The outer voussoirs, not forming part of the soffit of the hood, are placed in pairs in a cutting box and sawn at the cross joint and extrados; the slight curves of the cross joint and extrados being

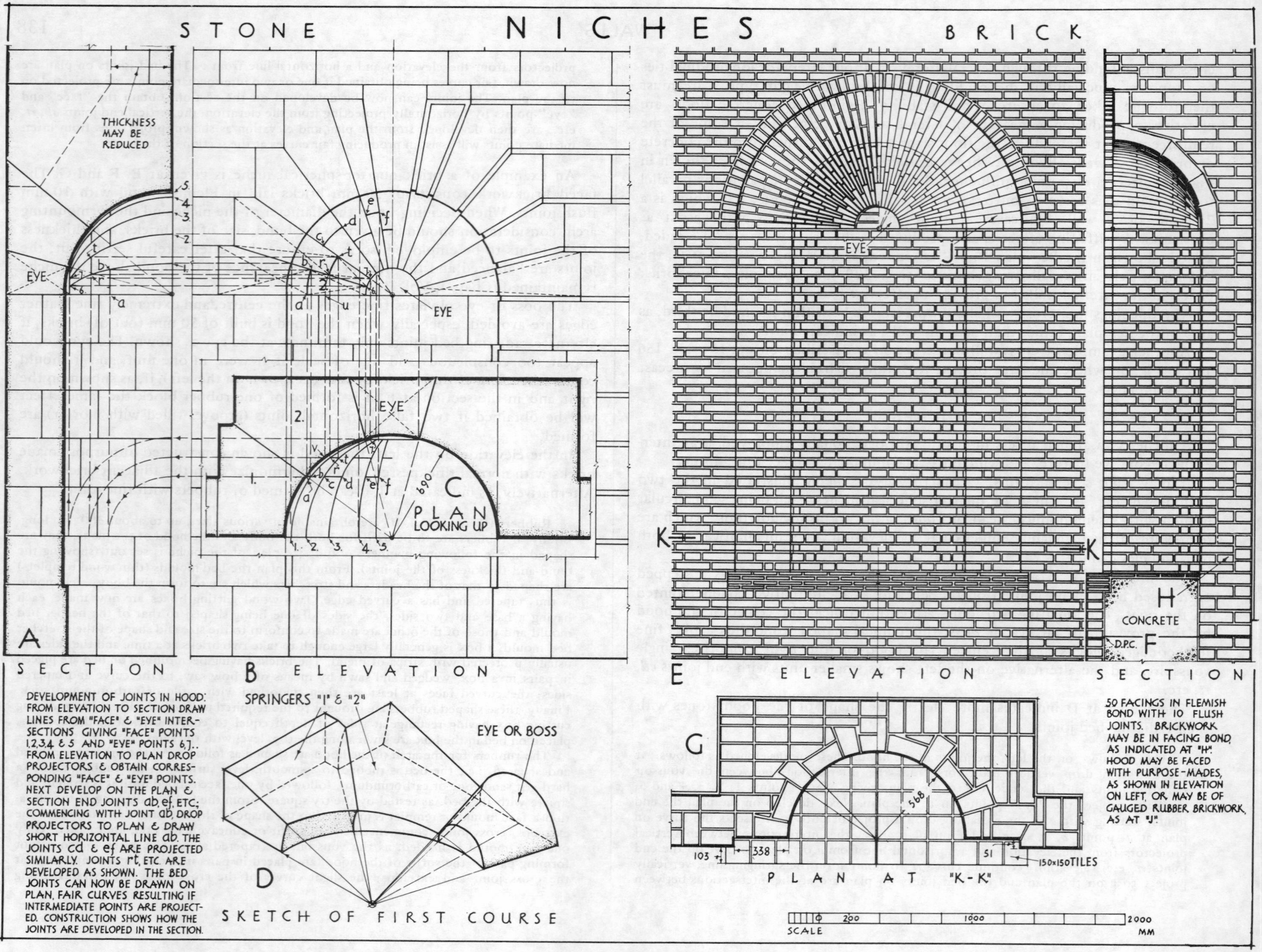

STONE NICHES BRICK

THICKNESS MAY BE REDUCED

EYE

EYE

EYE

PLAN LOOKING UP

A SECTION

B ELEVATION

C

D SKETCH OF FIRST COURSE

SPRINGERS "1" & "2"

EYE OR BOSS

DEVELOPMENT OF JOINTS IN HOOD. FROM ELEVATION TO SECTION DRAW LINES FROM "FACE" & "EYE" INTERSECTIONS GIVING "FACE" POINTS 1,2,3,4 & 5 AND "EYE" POINTS 6,7. FROM ELEVATION TO PLAN DROP PROJECTORS & OBTAIN CORRESPONDING "FACE" & "EYE" POINTS. NEXT DEVELOP ON THE PLAN & SECTION END JOINTS ad, ef ETC. COMMENCING WITH JOINT ad DROP PROJECTORS TO PLAN & DRAW SHORT HORIZONTAL LINE ad. THE JOINTS cd & ef ARE PROJECTED SIMILARLY. JOINTS r't, ETC. ARE DEVELOPED AS SHOWN. THE BED JOINTS CAN NOW BE DRAWN ON PLAN, FAIR CURVES RESULTING IF INTERMEDIATE POINTS ARE PROJECTED. CONSTRUCTION SHOWS HOW THE JOINTS ARE DEVELOPED IN THE SECTION.

EYE

J

K K

H

CONCRETE

D.P.C.

E ELEVATION

F SECTION

G

568

103 338 51

150×150 TILES

PLAN AT "K-K"

50 FACINGS IN FLEMISH BOND WITH 10 FLUSH JOINTS. BRICKWORK MAY BE IN FACING BOND, AS INDICATED AT "H". HOOD MAY BE FACED WITH PURPOSE-MADES, AS SHOWN IN ELEVATION ON LEFT, OR, MAY BE OF GAUGED RUBBER BRICKWORK, AS AT "J".

SCALE 0 200 1000 2000 MM

FIGURE 44

scraped to shape by means of stiff metal shaped blades. The inner voussoirs forming part of the soffit have their cross joints and face curves cut in purpose made boxes having sides shaped to that required, the slight concavity of the soffited portion being scraped. The cutting boxes for the rest of the bricks forming the soffit have sides shaped to the face curve and tapered end joints which serve as guides for the saw. After the bricks of one course have been shaped in this manner they are tapered in a reducing box. The latter consists of a wood base sufficiently large to take one-half of the bricks of a course, including the arch rubbers and two sides which are the same size and taper-shape of the face mould. A quarter-circle is described on the base of the reducing box (with the springing line parallel to an open edge of the base and the centre line at right angles to it) and the prepared rubbers are carefully placed round the curve. After being securely wedged in position the bricks are bow-sawn level with the tapered sides and they thus resemble in shape that of the half course of masonry shown at D, Fig. 44. After the second half of the course has been taper-shaped in this manner, the two halves are placed together on one side and numbered. Each course of rubbers is shaped as described, numbered and stacked ready for the bricklayer.

The body of the niche is built, a true curve being maintained by means of the trammel (Vol. II, Fig. 29 and Chap. I). The head is, of course, constructed on a centre.

The niche is shown finished at the base with a tile creasing. A suitable alternative finish would be a 50 mm stone course.

The plan G shows the Flemish bonded facings backed by brickwork in English bond, plastered.

Facing bond (Chap. I, Vol. II) is shown in the section at H. The concrete base on which the top course of tiles is bedded is an alternative to solid brickwork.

MASONRY COLUMNS, PEDIMENTS AND ENTABLATURES

Construction adopting these features has been repeated over the ages in many styles, it is recognized as producing one of the finest forms of architecture and this is why examples of it are to be seen in almost every capital city in the world. This alone is sufficient reason for devoting two drawings (Figs. 45 and 46) to the subject in a book concerned mainly with new construction. Many of the existing buildings featuring these traditional motifs are scheduled for preservation. This is a further important cause for the brief reference here, for the maintenance* of these buildings is a task requiring knowledge of the method and particularly the jointing of the masonry. The skill with which these old buildings have been proportioned, detailed and enriched are a lesson in design worthy of study, albeit short, by those concerned with building.

The system is Greek in origin, being based on a particular type of column. The rows of columns are connected at the top by a horizontal band of stonework known as an *entablature*, which at the gable is surmounted by a triangular shaped *pediment*. The Greeks developed what are now known as the first three of the five "Orders of Architecture": Doric, Ionic, and Corinthian, the other two being: Tuscan (a modified Doric), and Composite (a modified Corinthian). Each of the "Orders" is recognized mainly by the design of the upper portion of the column known as the *capital*, thus a Doric capital and an Ionic one are shown at H and B respectively in Fig. 46.

Probably the best known example of the Doric order is the Parthenon, Athens, erected in 447 B.C., renowned for its unique beauty, noble proportions and simplicity of construction.

In all the orders of architecture, the height and spacing of the columns, the dimensions of the base and capital and the size of the various parts of the entablature are all proportionally related to the diameter of the column base; this is one of the distinctive features of the arrangement.

Compared with the fussy appearance of many Victorian buildings, twentieth-century work is severe. In searching for new forms whilst taking advantage of new materials and techniques, it frequently lacks the disciplined grace provided by the "Orders". It is considered that, in many cases, the extreme functionalism, plain appearance with obvious rectangularity, lack of relieving ornamentation, and hence beauty, are serious demerits. This is not to suggest that good examples of modern architecture cannot be found, but rather that much of it is lacking in quality. Nor is it advocated that the styles of the past should be repeated; the reasons for including a brief reference here to classical work are given above.

Examples such as that given in Fig. 45 are to be seen in many places; the entrances to a large number of public buildings erected as recently as the first quarter of the twentieth century, and later, follow this type. If they are properly maintained (see p. 143), these buildings have many years of useful life. This Figure shows the Doric order applied to a typical *portico* (porch or covered entrance) with columns and pedimented entablature. The diameter (D) of bottom of the column shaft is 914 mm and the column spacing is $2 \times 1\frac{1}{4} \times D$ (2 285 mm) for the outer ones, and $3 \times 1\frac{1}{4} \times D$ (3 428 mm) at the centre as shown at the plan E; this reduced spacing at the corners increases the appearance of solidity at these weaker positions. Two types of base are shown, the one on the left of the elevation being more elaborate, both are $\frac{1}{2}D$ (457 mm) in height, note that the base stone includes the bottom part of the column; these are Renaissance in origin, the original Doric order not having a column base. The column shaft may be plain or fluted (with segmental or half-round flutes as at K, Fig. 46) as shown and is made up of five stones with a central bronze dowel at the joints; alternatively, a central steel pillar may be used as at G, Fig. 46. Columns have a slight longitudinal curvature known as an *entasis*, this is a refinement to counteract the illusion of concavity that would appear in a series of closely spaced tall vertical members; the method of obtaining the correct entasis is given at B′, Fig. 45. A moulded capital is placed at the top of the column of the same depth as the base, the top stone incorporates the necking and upper portion of the shaft. The plan at E shows *pilasters* (rectangular on plan) on the main wall behind the outer columns only, these have the same appearance as the

* Recent figures have shown that, of the total annual expenditure on building work, more than one-third of it was for maintenance.

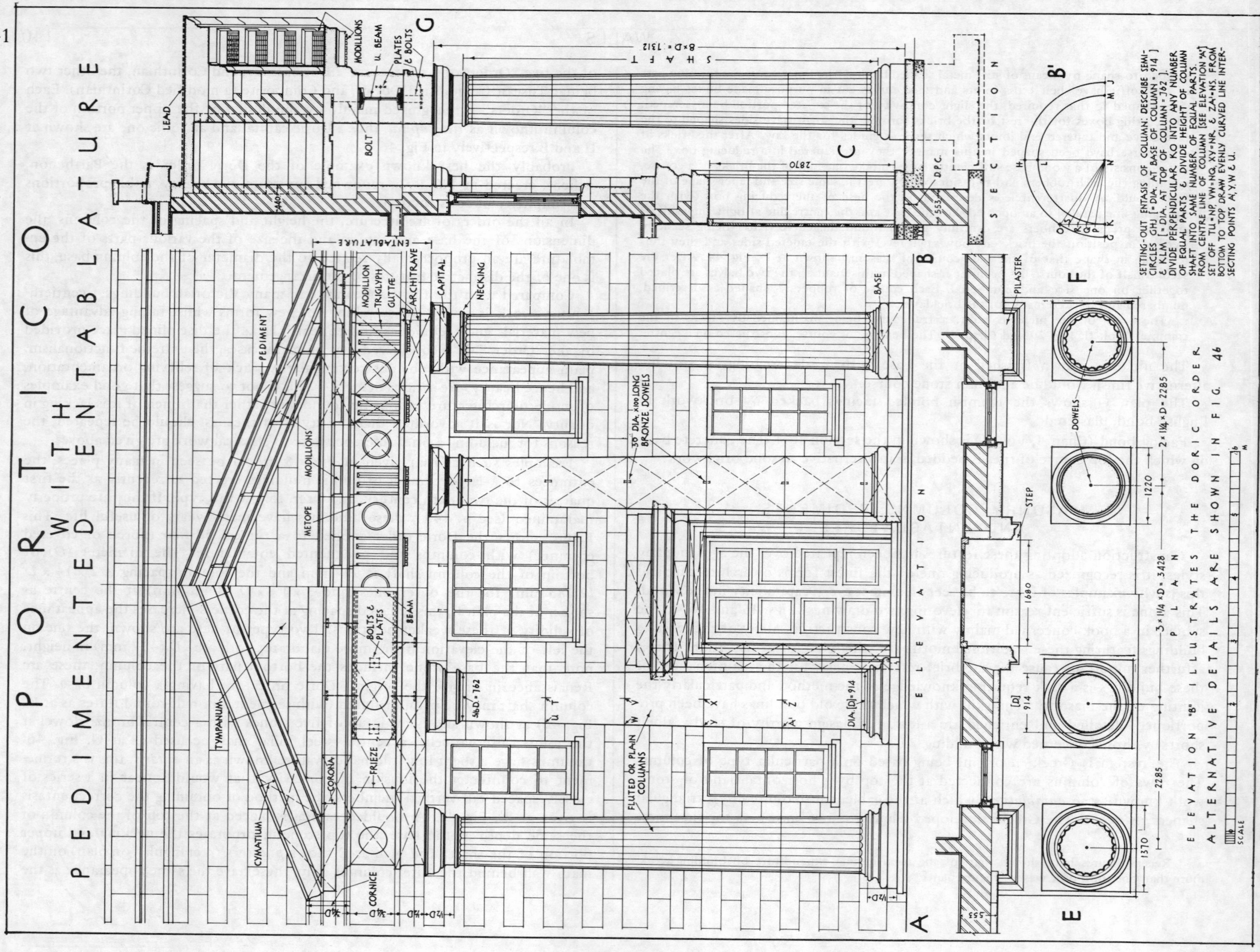

PORTICO WITH PEDIMENTED ENTABLATURE

TYMPANUM
CYMATIUM
PEDIMENT
METOPE
MODILLIONS
CORONA
CORNICE
FRIEZE
BOLTS & PLATES
BEAM
MODILLION
TRIGLYPH
GUTTÆ
ARCHITRAVE
ENTABLATURE
CAPITAL
NECKING
BASE
¾D
¾D
½D
½D
½D
5/6D = 762
U T
W V
Y X
A' Z
DIA. [D] = 914
FLUTED OR PLAIN COLUMNS
30 DIA. ×100 LONG BRONZE DOWELS

LEAD
440
MODILLIONS
BOLT
U. BEAM
PLATES & BOLTS
G
SHAFT 8×D = 7312
2870
C
553
D.P.C.

A ELEVATION B

SECTION

553
[D] 914
1680
STEP
PILASTER
DOWELS
E
F
B'
H L O S R Q P G K N M J
1370
2285
3 × 1¼ × D = 3428
1220
2 × 1¼ × D = 2285

PLAN

ELEVATION "B" ILLUSTRATES THE DORIC ORDER
ALTERNATIVE DETAILS ARE SHOWN IN FIG. 46

SCALE 0 1 2 3 4 5 6 M

SETTING-OUT ENTASIS OF COLUMN: DESCRIBE SEMI-CIRCLES GHJ [= DIA. AT BASE OF COLUMN = 914] & KLM [= DIA. AT TOP OF COLUMN = 762]. DIVIDE PERPENDICULAR KO INTO ANY NUMBER OF EQUAL PARTS & DIVIDE HEIGHT OF COLUMN SHAFT INTO SAME NUMBER OF EQUAL PARTS. FROM CENTRE LINE OF COLUMN [SEE ELEVATION "A"] SET OFF TU = NP, VW = NQ, XY = NR, & ZA' = NS. FROM BOTTOM TO TOP DRAW EVENLY CURVED LINE INTERSECTING POINTS A', Y, W & U.

FIGURE 45

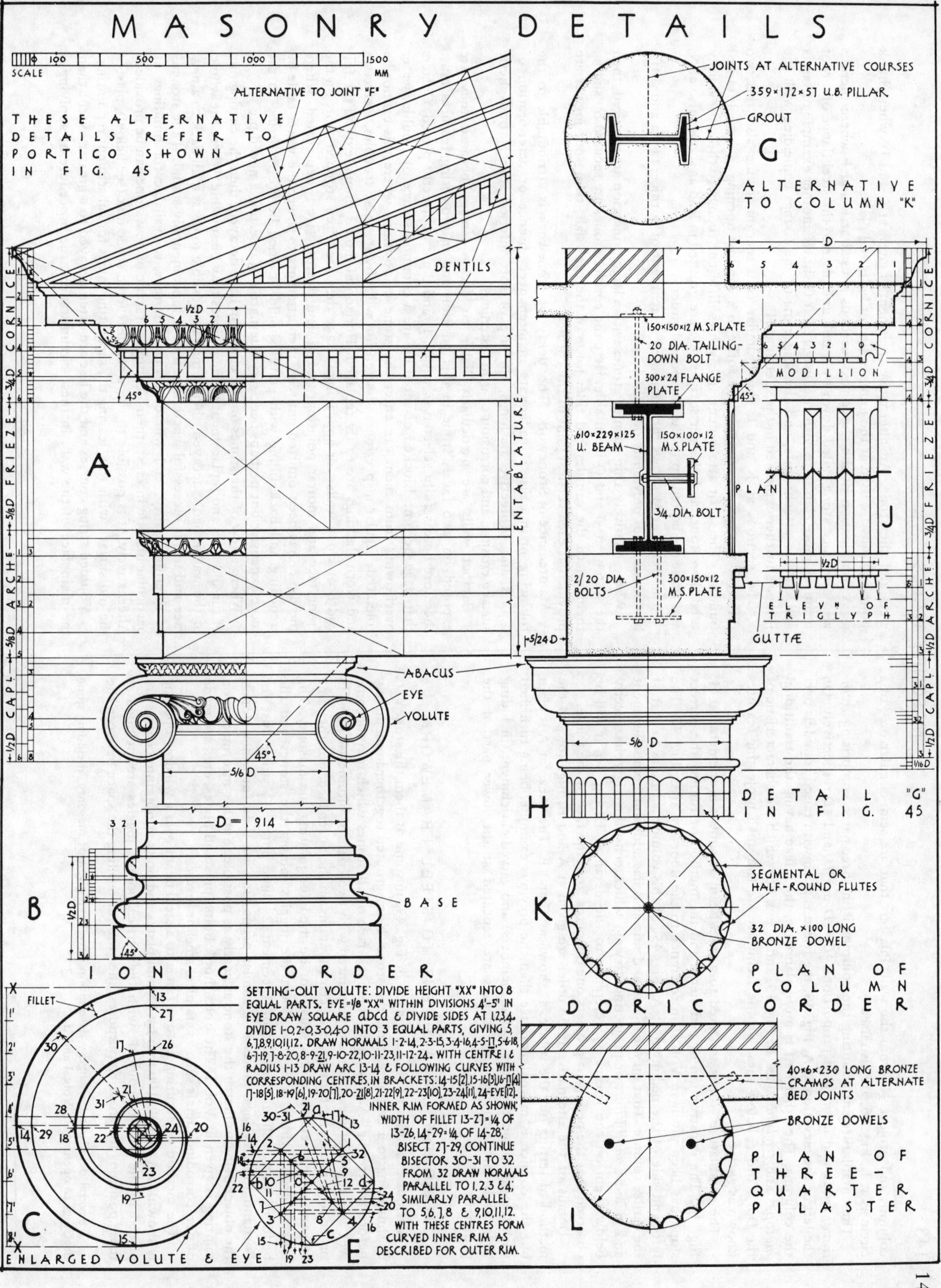

MASONRY DETAILS
SCALE
100
500
1000
1500
MM
ALTERNATIVE TO JOINT "F"
THESE ALTERNATIVE DETAILS REFER TO PORTICO SHOWN IN FIG. 45
JOINTS AT ALTERNATIVE COURSES
359×172×57 U.B. PILLAR
GROUT
G
ALTERNATIVE TO COLUMN "K"
DENTILS
CORNICE
FRIEZE
ARCHE
CAPL
ENTABLATURE
A
150×150×12 M.S. PLATE
20 DIA. TAILING-DOWN BOLT
300×24 FLANGE PLATE
610×229×125 U. BEAM
150×100×12 M.S. PLATE
3/4 DIA. BOLT
2/20 DIA. BOLTS
300×150×12 M.S. PLATE
MODILLION
PLAN
J
ELEVN OF TRIGLYPH
GUTTÆ
ABACUS
EYE
VOLUTE
D = 914
BASE
B
H
DETAIL "G" IN FIG. 45
SEGMENTAL OR HALF-ROUND FLUTES
32 DIA. ×100 LONG BRONZE DOWEL
K
PLAN OF COLUMN
IONIC ORDER
DORIC ORDER
SETTING-OUT VOLUTE: DIVIDE HEIGHT "XX" INTO 8 EQUAL PARTS. EYE=1/8 "XX" WITHIN DIVISIONS 4'-5" IN EYE DRAW SQUARE abcd & DIVIDE SIDES AT 1,2,3,4. DIVIDE 1-0,2-0,3-0,4-0 INTO 3 EQUAL PARTS, GIVING 5, 6,7,8,9,10,11,12. DRAW NORMALS 1-2-14, 2-3-15, 3-4-16, 4-5-17, 5-6-18, 6-7-19, 7-8-20, 8-9-21, 9-10-22, 10-11-23, 11-12-24. WITH CENTRE 1 & RADIUS 1-13 DRAW ARC 13-14 & FOLLOWING CURVES WITH CORRESPONDING CENTRES, IN BRACKETS: 14-15[2], 15-16[3], 16-17[4], 17-18[5], 18-19[6], 19-20[7], 20-21[8], 21-22[9], 22-23[10], 23-24[11], 24-EYE[12]. INNER RIM FORMED AS SHOWN; WIDTH OF FILLET 13-27 = 1/4 OF 13-26, 14-29 = 1/4 OF 14-28; BISECT 27-29, CONTINUE BISECTOR 30-31 TO 32. FROM 32 DRAW NORMALS PARALLEL TO 1,2,3 & 4; SIMILARLY PARALLEL TO 5,6,7,8 & 9,10,11,12. WITH THESE CENTRES FORM CURVED INNER RIM AS DESCRIBED FOR OUTER RIM.
FILLET
40×6×230 LONG BRONZE CRAMPS AT ALTERNATE BED JOINTS
BRONZE DOWELS
PLAN OF THREE-QUARTER PILASTER
C
ENLARGED VOLUTE & EYE
E
L

FIGURE 46

columns and project $\frac{1}{6}D$ from the wall. Pilasters that are semi-circular or $\frac{3}{4}$ of a circle as at L, Fig. 46, are also used.

The entablature surmounting the columns is in three parts, comprising *architrave*, *frieze* and *cornice* of proportions $\frac{1}{2}D$, $\frac{5}{8}D$ or $\frac{3}{4}D$, and $\frac{3}{4}D$ respectively. On the left of the elevation at A, Fig. 45, the frieze is plain with raised roundels over the columns. The other half is more elaborate, the frieze having the traditional *metopes* and *triglyphs* (see B, Fig. 45, and J, Fig. 46) which are characteristic of the Doric order, below these on the architrave are the small projecting features known as *guttae*.

The entablature stones are fixed to a steel beam as shown in the detail at H, Fig. 46. The construction of pediments and the method of finding the correct slope has been given in Vol. II in reference to the doorway at C, Fig. 42. The left-hand side of the pediment at A, Fig. 45, of this volume is similar to that of the earlier volume. That on the right-hand side at B has additional embellishment and includes *modillions* or projecting carvings which echo the triglyphs directly below them on the frieze. By reference to the detail at H, Fig. 46, it will be observed that the pediment projects one diameter from the face of the frieze.

Details of the alternative Ionic order are given at A and B, Fig. 46, and the method of setting out the volutes is shown at C and E. The frieze at A is plain but the cornice is more decorative than the previous example, being furnished with dentils (projecting rectangular members) and carved enrichment (including "egg and dart" carving), the details are repeated at the lower part of the pediment.

MASONRY* ATTACHMENT TO STEEL FRAMEWORK

Various examples of this are given in Fig. 47, in some of them the stone acts as shuttering to a certain extent, the stones being grouted together immediately before concreting. Accordingly, the back face of all stones which may become wet as a result of weather must be painted with two coats of bitumastic paint in order to prevent the formation of cement stains on the outer face. For the same reason, strong cement mixes must not be used for jointing the masonry. The mortar grout which is poured down the joggles joining the stones and the bedding mortar should consist of 1 cement : $2\frac{1}{2}$ lime putty : $3\frac{1}{2}$ stone dust for Portland stone facings. Mixes of a similar proportion are used for other stones, the object being to match the stone as nearly as possible. Further information on jointing is given in Vol. I. The bolts, hook bolts, pins and plates, etc., are made of non-corroding metals such as stainless steel or bronze.

The method of securing a stone fascia to a steel beam over a window opening is shown at A and B. 100 mm by 75 mm plates and bolts at 600 mm centres are placed in the web to coincide with the vertical joints, joggles are included at these positions for grouting purposes, the grout also filling the space between the steel and the stone. An alternative treatment is given at C and D, where hook bolts and pins are used at the joints in lieu of bolts and plates.

A combination of the above two methods is used at E and F where there is also a cornice stone tailed down by a bolt and plate to the steel flange of a roof beam. A more elaborate cornice illustrated at G shows another example of fascia and cornice attachments, and the staggering of the fixings coinciding with the joints is further explained in the sketch at H.

The sections at K and L show similar construction, giving also the two different ways of securing a stone soffit to a window opening in a steel-framed building. The soffit attachment at L shows different fixings to those previously used; here four rag bolts per soffit stone are grouted in lead as shown also at N, and these are bolted up to the compound girder.

The detail at M shows the combined attachment of cornice, fascia and soffit by the methods previously described.

Where relatively thin cornice stones with a large projection are required, then the system at O and Q is suitable. Here the cornice stones are secured by sliding them on to the cantilevered filler joists of the roof slab, two grout joggles are provided at each vertical joint of the cornice.

Maintenance of Stonework. The decay of stonework is attributable to the following main causes: inadequate maintenance, absence or deterioration of d.p.c.s and protective flashings, the use of soft inferior stone, atmospheric surface erosion, and corrosion of iron fastenings.

Parapet walls are particularly liable to decay damage because they are exposed on two faces, stone in this position and in projecting features must therefore be carefully selected (see Vol. I) and d.p.c.s correctly placed. Gutters that have become blocked or silted up are a common source of trouble, water overflowing from them can enter the stone in positions where this cannot be tolerated; regular inspection and attention will obviate these troubles. Defective and worn flashings are easily replaced. Horizontal d.p.c.s should extend the full width of stone walls; for appearance's sake they are often stopped short on the front face and mortar pointing used in lieu, this practice is deprecated. Where the d.p.c. has been omitted entirely, then attempts to lower the water table by trenching and back filling with gravel should be tried before resorting to the more expensive but perhaps necessary alternative of inserting a new d.p.c.

Where a few of the stones on the elevation have decayed, then the cutting out of the old ones and replacement by new pieces may be suitable. Where the whole of the wall is badly decayed, then it may be possible to dress it all back to a new face and this is successful where the stone is fundamentally sound. If the stone is of inferior quality, and where sufficient money is available for buildings of particular historic interest, then a complete façade of new stone can be provided. Alternatively, it is possible to use a reconstructed stone mix (see below), plaster the old surface with this, leaving the separating joints for subsequent repointing.

Moulded string courses and the like are often decayed to a greater extent than the main face of the wall. In these circumstances, the procedure of applying a

* Several details and a lengthy description have been given of masonry, including stone dressings to openings in Vols. I and II.

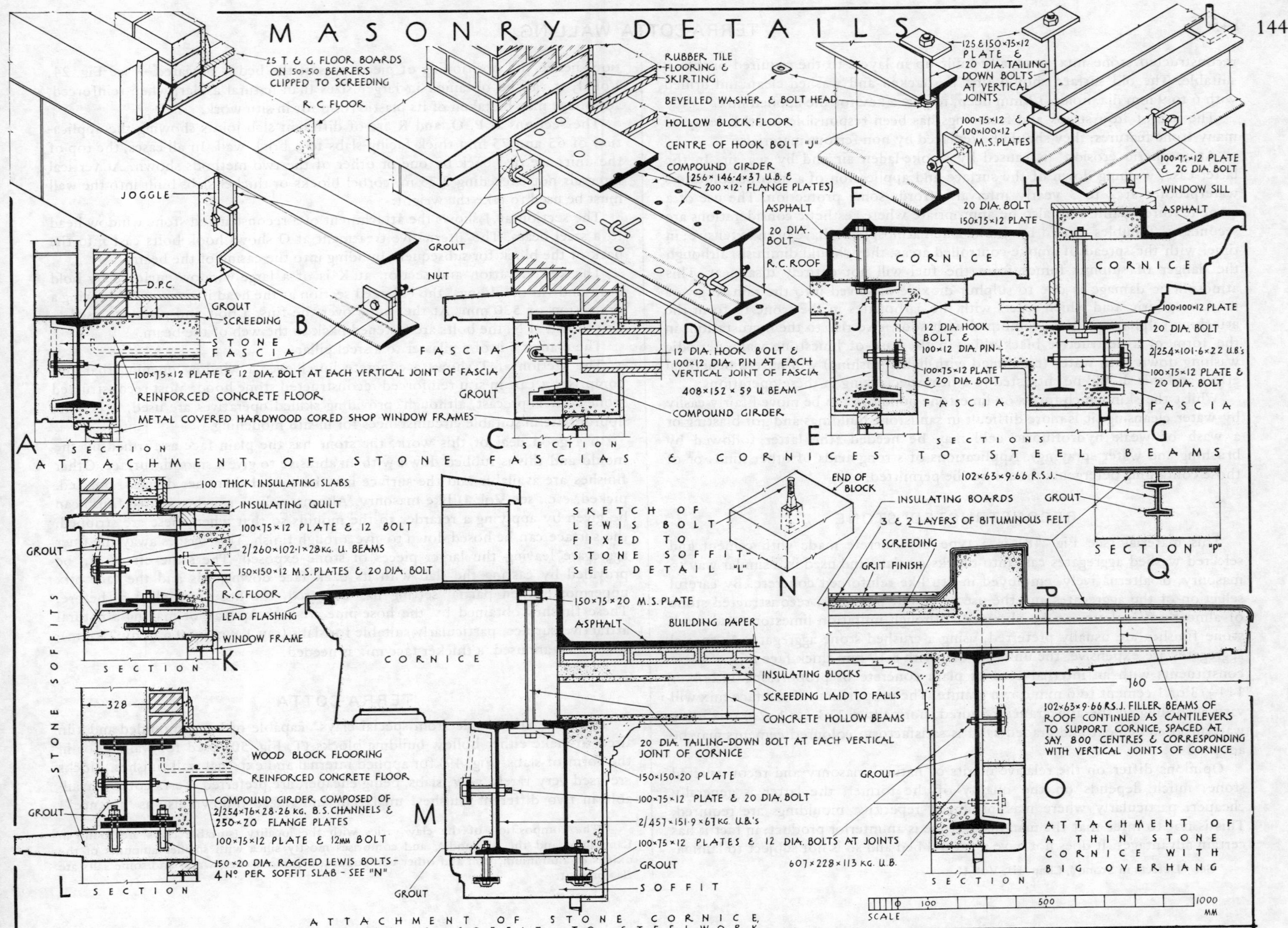
MASONRY DETAILS
25 T. & G. FLOOR BOARDS ON 50×50 BEARERS CLIPPED TO SCREEDING
R.C. FLOOR
JOGGLE
D.P.C.
GROUT
SCREEDING
B
NUT
GROUT
STONE FASCIA
100×75×12 PLATE & 12 DIA. BOLT AT EACH VERTICAL JOINT OF FASCIA
REINFORCED CONCRETE FLOOR
METAL COVERED HARDWOOD CORED SHOP WINDOW FRAMES
FASCIA
GROUT
A
C
SECTION
SECTIONS
ATTACHMENT OF STONE FASCIAS
RUBBER TILE FLOORING & SKIRTING
BEVELLED WASHER & BOLT HEAD
HOLLOW BLOCK FLOOR
CENTRE OF HOOK BOLT "J"
COMPOUND GIRDER [256×146·4×37 U.B. & 200×12 FLANGE PLATES]
ASPHALT
20 DIA. BOLT
R.C. ROOF
CORNICE
D
12 DIA. HOOK BOLT & 100×12 DIA. PIN AT EACH VERTICAL JOINT OF FASCIA
408×152×59 U BEAM
COMPOUND GIRDER
F
J
12 DIA. HOOK BOLT &
100×12 DIA. PIN
100×75×12 PLATE & 20 DIA. BOLT
FASCIA
E
125 & 150×75×12 PLATE & 20 DIA. TAILING DOWN BOLTS AT VERTICAL JOINTS
100×75×12 & 100×100×12 M.S. PLATES
H
100×75×12 PLATE & 20 DIA. BOLT
WINDOW SILL
ASPHALT
20 DIA. BOLT
150×75×12 PLATE
CORNICE
100×100×12 PLATE
20 DIA. BOLT
2/254×101·6×22 U.B's
100×75×12 PLATE & 20 DIA. BOLT
FASCIA
G
SECTIONS
CORNICES TO STEEL BEAMS
100 THICK INSULATING SLABS
INSULATING QUILT
100×75×12 PLATE & 12 BOLT
2/260×102·1×28 KG. U BEAMS
GROUT
150×150×12 M.S. PLATES & 20 DIA. BOLT
R.C. FLOOR
LEAD FLASHING
WINDOW FRAME
SECTION
K
STONE SOFFITS
SKETCH OF LEWIS BOLT FIXED TO STONE SOFFIT SEE DETAIL "L"
150×75×20 M.S. PLATE
ASPHALT
BUILDING PAPER
CORNICE
328
WOOD BLOCK FLOORING
REINFORCED CONCRETE FLOOR
COMPOUND GIRDER COMPOSED OF 2/254×76×28·26 KG. B.S. CHANNELS & 250×20 FLANGE PLATES
100×75×12 PLATE & 12mm BOLT
150×20 DIA. RAGGED LEWIS BOLTS - 4 Nº PER SOFFIT SLAB - SEE "N"
GROUT
SECTION
L
M
GROUT
20 DIA. TAILING-DOWN BOLT AT EACH VERTICAL JOINT OF CORNICE
150×150×20 PLATE
100×75×12 PLATE & 20 DIA. BOLT
2/457×151·9×67 KG. U.B's
100×75×12 PLATES & 12 DIA. BOLTS AT JOINTS
GROUT
SOFFIT
ATTACHMENT OF STONE CORNICE, FASCIA & SOFFIT TO STEELWORK
END OF BLOCK
INSULATING BOARDS
3 & 2 LAYERS OF BITUMINOUS FELT
SCREEDING
GRIT FINISH
N
P
102×63×9·66 R.S.J.
GROUT
SECTION "P"
Q
INSULATING BLOCKS
SCREEDING LAID TO FALLS
CONCRETE HOLLOW BEAMS
607×228×113 KG. U.B.
GROUT
760
102×63×9·66 R.S.J. FILLER BEAMS OF ROOF CONTINUED AS CANTILEVERS TO SUPPORT CORNICE, SPACED AT SAY 800 CENTRES & CORRESPONDING WITH VERTICAL JOINTS OF CORNICE
O
ATTACHMENT OF A THIN STONE CORNICE WITH BIG OVERHANG
SECTION
0 100 500 1000 MM
SCALE

FIGURE 47

reconstructed stone mix, gradually built up in layers to the required profile is suitable. The old surface should first be hacked and washed clean and drilled with 6 to 9 mm dia. holes, 12 mm deep, to give a key for the applied mix.

The use of iron straps and fastenings has been responsible for the decay of many stone features; they should be replaced by non-ferrous materials.

Atmospheric erosion* is caused by smoke-laden air and by sea air. In the latter case, washing down of the surface and application of a silicone colourless waterproofer at 2 to 3 yearly intervals affords some protection. The use of a stone-textured paint may also be appropriate where aesthetic considerations are secondary. Troubles caused by smoke-laden atmospheres have been extensive; in time, with the spread of smoke-controlled areas, they should diminish, although the danger of sulphur fumes from the fuel will not entirely disappear. This atmospheric damage is due to sulphur dioxide dissolved into the rain to give a weak sulphuric acid which reacts with the carbonates in the stone to form the attacking sulphates. These, combined with soot, give rise to the incrustations in the form of a destructive black skin. In the case of limestone walls periodic washing down with water (combined with light brushing) will have a beneficial effect and this should be entrusted to a firm specializing in these operations.

Whilst the skin which forms on limestone buildings can be moved fairly easily by water cleansing, it is more difficult in sandstone buildings and grit-blasting or a wash of weak hydrofluoric acid may be needed (the latter followed by brushing and water spraying). Applications of strong acids of other kinds or of those containing detergents should not be permitted.

RECONSTRUCTED STONE

This material (see Fig. 48) is a type of concrete made with cement and selected washed aggregates cast into blocks or slabs and used in a similar way to masonry, or alternatively, employed in-situ like reinforced concrete. By careful selection of the aggregates and the use of colour pigments, reconstructed stone of almost any colour can be obtained, although imitation limestone and sandstone finishes are usually preferred, using a crushed stone aggregate. As special aggregates are expensive, the units are cast with a 19 mm thick face mix of these constituents with an internal core of plain concrete of proportions $1:2:4$ or $1:1\frac{1}{2}:3$ or 1 cement to 6 mm down granite. The proportions of the face mix will vary according to the appearance required, normally a $1:3$ (or $1:2\frac{1}{2}$) mix using waterproofed cement and graded sand is satisfactory; coloured cements may be adopted.

Opinions differ on the relative merits of natural masonry and reconstructed stone; much depends on the quality of the former, the latter is generally cheaper, particularly where mass-produced repetitive mouldings are required. This is not to infer that the man-made stone is an inferior product; in fact it has certain advantages. It does not have a natural bed and so is not subject to lamination, hence the positioning of pieces to suit the bed is obviated — see Fig. 24, Vol. I; it can be obtained in larger sizes than natural ashlar; when reinforced, advantage may be taken of its plastic form for in-situ work.

* See "Defects in Stone", Chap. III, Vol. II.

The sections at P, Q, and R are of different slab joints showing the application of 65 and 75 mm thick facing slabs to a brick wall. In all cases, the top of the units are tied back by one or other of the two methods shown. At vertical intervals not exceeding 2.75 m, corbel blocks or thicker slabs built into the wall must be used to take the weight.

The section at J shows the attachment of a reconstructed stone window head to a steel beam. The alternative treatment at O shows hook bolts cast into the back of the block for subsequent building into the casing of the beam.

The key elevation and section at K is of a large window enclosed by bold head and fin mouldings, the enlarged section at the head is given at M showing a projection of 530 mm. At the joints over the fins, a bolt and plate are used as also shown at N, the bolts are fastened back to the web of the beam.

The plan at S is of a pilaster to a steel pillar.

The section at T shows a concrete lintel over a window opening that also comprises a cast in-situ reinforced reconstructed stone hood. Most reconstructed stonework is precast, although, providing skilled operatives are used, it is quite appropriate in suitable circumstances for in-situ modelling.

In a good deal of this work, the stone has the plain face as formed by the mould and this is rubbed down with an abrasive to give a smooth surface. Other finishes are available and the surface may be tooled (hammer dressed, boasted, picked, etc., see Vol. I) like masonry. Alternatively, a rough-textured finish can be given by applying a retarder to the moulds so that when these are stripped, the surface can be hosed down to give a rough finish. This washes away the finer aggregate leaving the larger pieces of stone exposed. The same effect can be provided by casting the slab with its back face downwards and the face mix uppermost; when partial setting has occurred, the hose is applied as before. These finishes obtained by the hose-pipe are a cheap way of making a natural attractive surface, particularly suitable for slabs (say 1.8 m by 0.6 m by 75 mm); when they are used, a thicker face mix is needed.

TERRA-COTTA

This material is made from special clays* capable of being moulded and kiln fired to make either hollow building blocks (T, Fig. 50) used for walling; or in the form of slabs (Fig. 49) for applied internal and external wall finishes. Blocks are used very rarely now; slabs, being cheaper, are preferred. Terra-cotta is available in two different finishes: unglazed, and glazed (known also as "faience")

* The composition of the clay varies with the locality (suitable clays are found in Lancashire and the Midlands), and comprises mostly silica with smaller amounts of the oxides of aluminium, iron and other compounds; organic matter, water and some salts are also present.

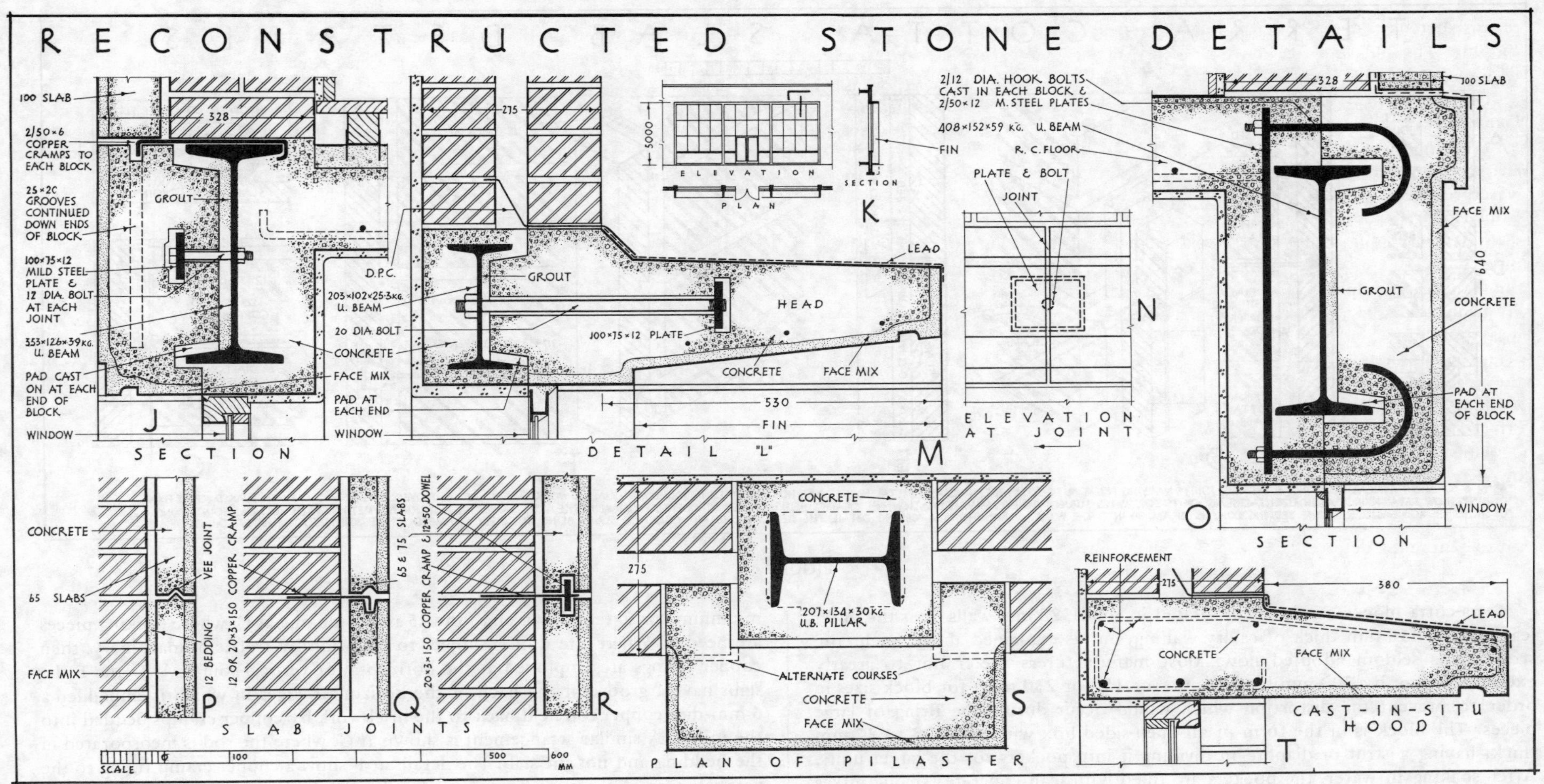

FIGURE 48

which has a smoother, more polished surface than the unglazed variety and which is recommended externally in areas of atmospheric pollution; the use of the unglazed type should be restricted to internal application. Its natural self colour varies from buff to red, grey is also available; faience can be made in any colour.

The material is known to have been used during the early Egyptian dynasties and was introduced from Italy (hence the name origin "burnt-clay" or earth) to Britain about the sixteenth century. The manufacture requires much skill and careful control of the various processes; these technicalities are now fully understood and the failures associated with the product at the end of the nineteenth century have been overcome in the development of a first-class building material. Although it may not have the same aesthetic appeal as stone, terra-cotta can be moulded into any shape and it has good weatherproofing and fire-resisting properties, it is dense and very durable. It is normally cheaper than stone over which it has the advantage of having a non-porous surface that can be readily cleaned with soap and water.

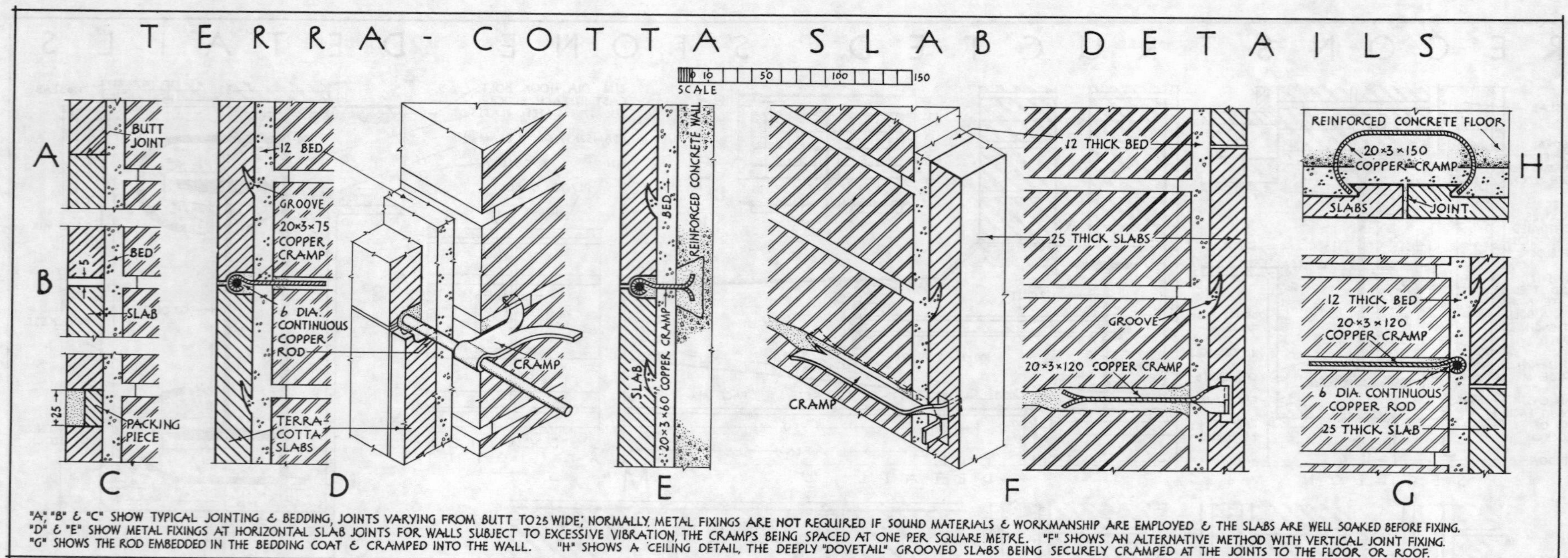

FIGURE 49

Terra-cotta blocks can be incorporated in solid 328 mm walls or as the outer leaf 100 to 150 mm thick of cavity walling; but as explained above, such construction is seldom adopted now. Most manufacturers prefer not to greatly exceed 450 mm by 300 mm by 100 mm (or 150 or 230 mm) for block sizes in order to prevent the distortion which would occur during the firing of large pieces. The block is in the form of an open-sided box with walls 28 to 32 mm thick, having a strut or diaphragm dividing it into pockets for the larger units. After soaking in water, the pockets are filled with lean concrete (strong mixes should not be used) of the proportion 1 : 3 : 6.

Slabs are made approximately 25 mm thick up to 600 mm by 300 mm.

Application and Fixing Details. The finished pieces must not be chipped or cut during transportation or fixing, they must be carefully stacked on site and precautions taken to prevent damage. They have to be soaked in water before the blocks are filled with concrete and again before they are placed in position. This is particularly important in the case of slabs so that the water is not absorbed from the mortar backing. The mortar mix for slabs is 1 : 3, with 1 : 4 for blocks.

Some typical slab fixings are shown in Fig. 49, the joint thicknesses vary from the tight butt joint at A (which is undesirable) to the one 5 mm thick at B (the minimum for external work), to the 25 mm wide one at C, where packing pieces are needed. Where the wall is subject to vibration by traffic or machinery, then copper fixings are employed at the horizontal or vertical joints. At D and E the slabs have a groove at the back of the horizontal edges in which is embedded a 6 mm dia. copper rod held back to the brickwork by copper cramps bedded into the joints. A similar arrangement is shown at G, where the rod is incorporated in the bedding and not the slab. The details at F show a copper cramp fixing to the vertical sides of the slab. The soffit detail at H shows one way of fixing ceiling slabs by means of copper cramps, the backs of the slabs being deeply dovetailed. A further method for soffits is to cast dovetailed channels in the concrete, and use short dovetailed copper cramps which engage in the channel and the slab.

Some typical elevational treatments using slabs are given at C, E, F, G, K to M, and W, Fig. 50; rebated* and moulded slabs are shown at X and Y, Fig. 51; also in this Figure at S, 25 mm thick slabs are used as a facing to a reinforced concrete column. The elevations at L and M, Fig. 50 show different fenestration treatment with various arrangements of slab facing to a three-storey building. The left-hand half L makes a feature of the columns which are expressed on the

* Used to give horizontal or vertical emphasis to the wall.

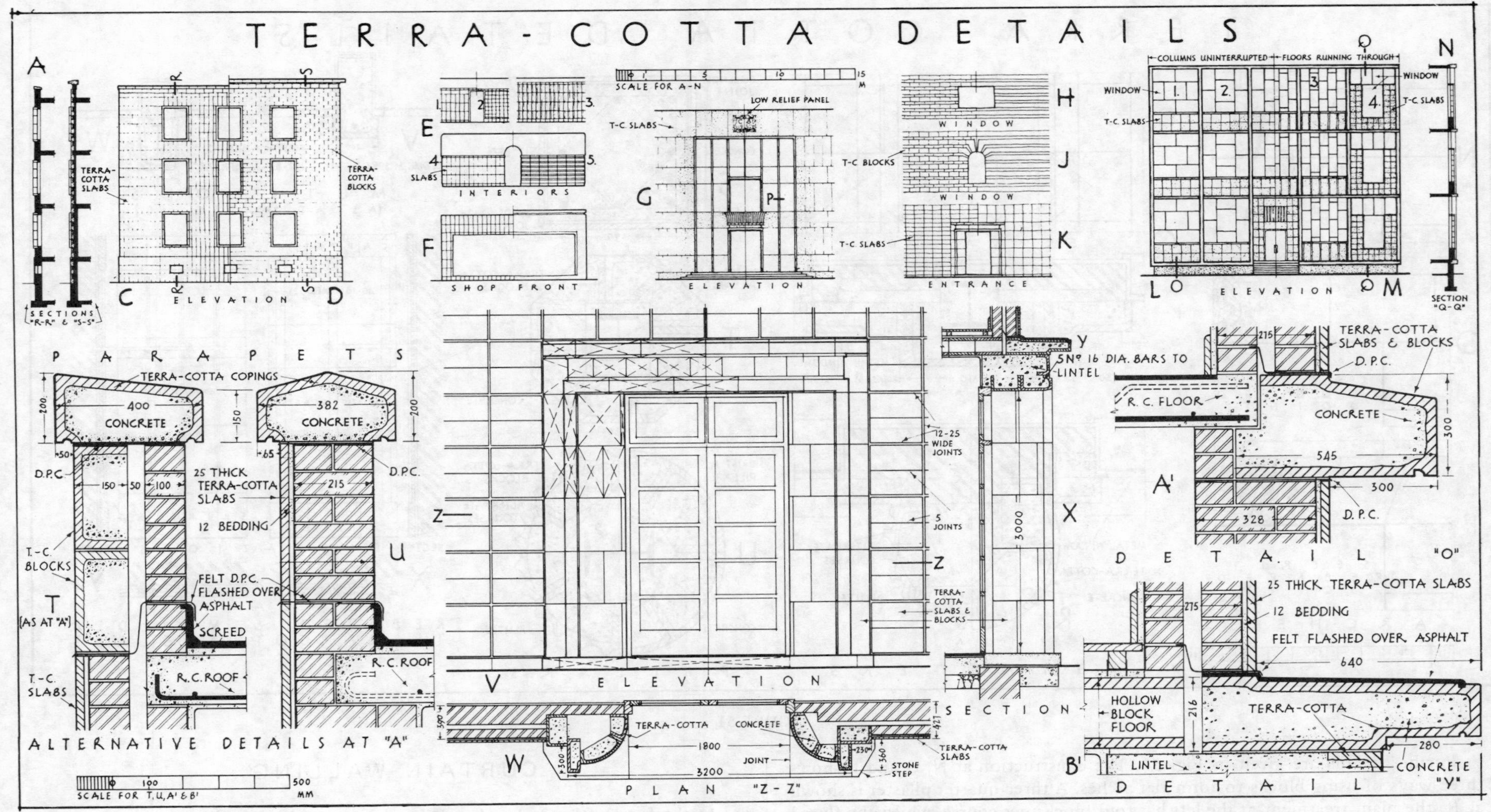

FIGURE 50

façade and which could be of the type shown at W, Fig. 51. The verticality is not so pronounced at the right-hand half at M because the edges of the floor slabs are carried through, these could be emphasized by using blocks of the sill type shown at A′, Fig. 50.

The details at T and U, Fig. 50, show terra-cotta copings with blocks and with slabs applied to a brick backing.

The details at V, W and X show an opening in a slab-faced wall with moulded blocks as a surround to the door, the canopy Y is detailed at B′; notice that the soffit blocks and the course below the canopy at Y are laid dry, cast integrally with the lintel and incorporate the reinforcing bars. Another entrance detail is given at G, this is mostly in glass, with a specially moulded central panel and mullions P detailed at V or W, Fig. 51.

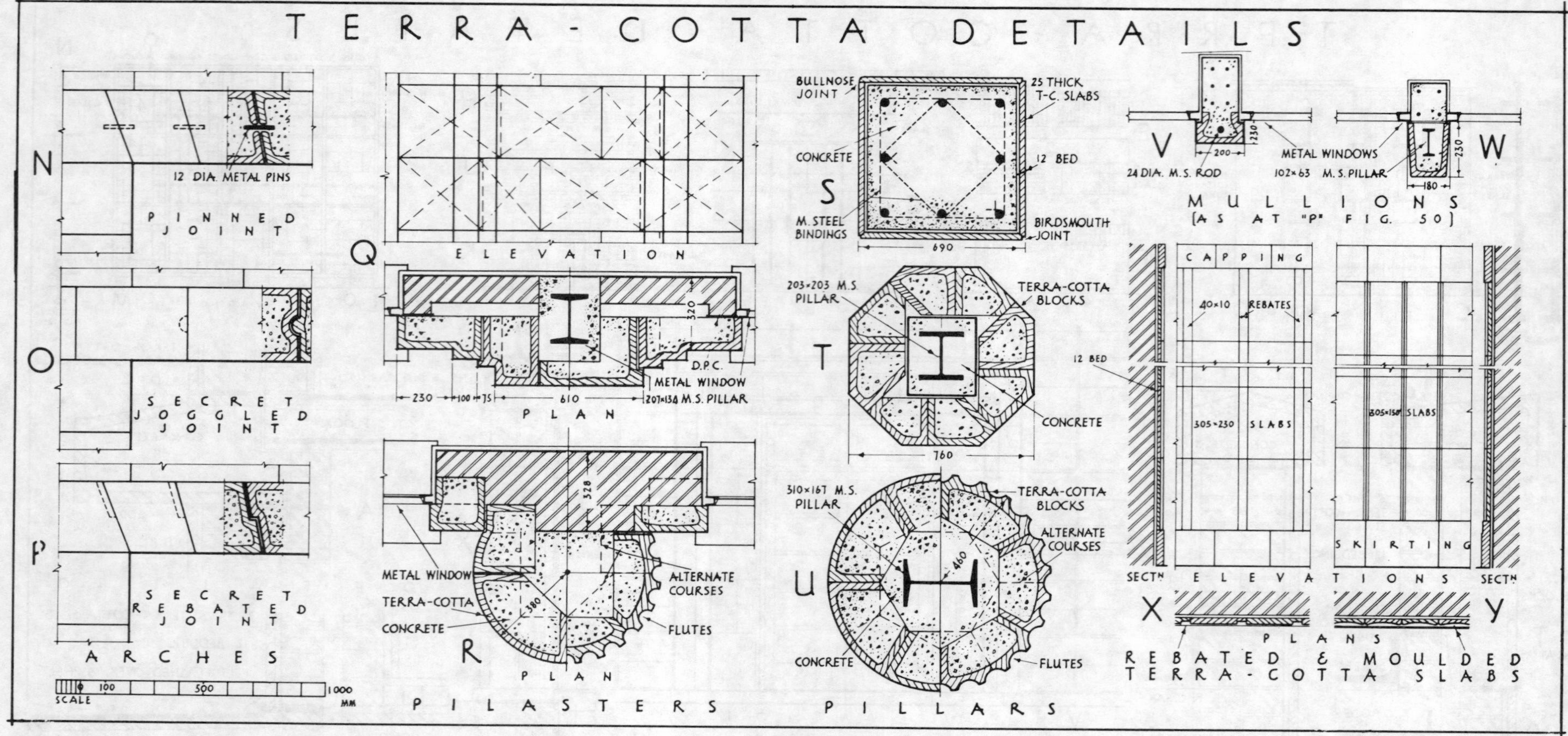

FIGURE 51

Further details are given in Fig. 51. The construction at N, O and P shows three ways of using blocks to form flat arches. A three-quarter pilaster is shown at R, the plain treatment at the left has four blocks per course, whilst the fluted finish at the right has three.

Slab facing to a square column is shown at S, the bird's-mouth and the bullnose joints being given, the former is not suitable for external work as it is inclined to admit water.

The details at T and U show block facings to an octagonal and a round column, it is generally advisable to cast the column casing first rather than attempting to use the blocks as shuttering.

More faience details are given in Fig. 109.

CURTAIN WALLING

In the form of large glazed and sheeted areas, curtain walling (or envelope to the structural frame) has been in use for many years. More recently, special systems have been introduced comprising standard framing components for modern light-weight infilling panels. Prior to the advent of these newer methods, both patent glazing (see Chap. IX) and fibre-cement and other sheeting were the most common light-weight materials for external cladding; these were, and still are, used instead of the heavier traditional walling for factories and similar buildings. A curtain wall is non-load-bearing and, basically, its parts are the vertical members (mullions) with connecting horizontal members (transoms) and the infilling panels of glass and other materials all supported by the building framework.

The advantages of curtain wall construction are: being very light in weight dead loads are minimized, giving full economy in the size of the building structure; as it is relatively thin, it gives a greater floor area than the heavier materials; being factory produced, ready for quick assembly, site erection times may be 50 per cent less than the more traditional methods; it allows greater architectural freedom because the curtain need not be related to the stanchion spacing and the components can be combined into imaginative designs by varying form, colour and texture. Of the few disadvantages, only three have any substance: being light in weight, the wall offers less resistance to fire than does heavier construction; to appear at its best, the wall needs regular cleansing and provision should be made for this at the outset by arranging for the suspension of cleaner's cradles from the roof, or possibly by open-out casements on extended hinges, or pivoted windows with open-in portions can be arranged to give access to the exterior face; thirdly, whilst this type of façade is eminently suitable for many tall buildings, it must be remembered that, during prolonged rainfall, a considerable amount of water passes over surfaces which are often entirely non-absorbent, and, due to wind turbulence, this rapid flow is not always downwards – weakness of joint design have been revealed by this effect in early examples. The joint then is of critical importance (see p. 152) and this aspect demands careful attention. In regard to fire resistance, a curtain wall must, of course, comply with the Building Regulations like every type of external wall. The relevant requirements are given in Rules 3 and 4 in Chap. III, and the period of fire resistance which has to be provided is given in Table 10. Any cladding which has less fire resistance than that of the wall of which it forms a part comes into the category of an unprotected opening (see p. 82), hence its area is controlled, being largely dependent on the distance of the wall from the boundary.

The substantial advantages of curtain wall construction make it a logical solution for many types of building, particularly tall blocks of offices where rentable floor space is expensive.

The building must be well insulated to prevent heat loss and the admission of street noises, but these principles are now well established no matter what kind of construction is used. The extra capital charge of providing effective double glazing and other thermal improvements (see Chap. IX) is soon recouped in greater comfort and lower heating costs.

In choosing a type of curtain wall for a job, four aspects must be considered in addition to that of weatherproofing: (1) The joints in the framework of the wall and its panelled areas must allow for expansion and contraction due to temperature changes; this is overcome if the sizes of individual panels, and the length of mullions and transoms are kept within reasonable limits and special spigots are used in the frame joints. (2) The connection between the wall and the structure must allow for the differential thermal movement of these two parts; this is usually accomplished by having the fixing bolts in slotted holes. (3) The wall must be sufficiently strong to withstand wind pressures; compliance with the manufacturers' instructions, which take into account the height and exposure of the building, will satisfy this requirement. (4) Due to the relative thinness of the wall, precautions are required to avoid the danger of condensation forming on inner surfaces; this is overcome by having either a ventilated cavity behind the panel with condensation outlets, or by a sealed cavity with a vapour barrier (see Chap. XII) within the panel near the warm side.

CURTAIN WALL SYSTEMS

The simplest type consists of lightweight sheeting fixed back to the structural members, many industrial buildings are of this type. Fibre-cement and aluminium alloy sheeting are commonly used, backed by a block wall below the window sill and perhaps fibre board at the sides of and over the windows. Associated with these materials are steel and aluminium alloy windows, or more cheaply, patent glazing; examples of the latter as vertical lighting are given at J and K, Fig. 98.

Another type of curtain wall consists of the heavier traditional materials of concrete, terra-cotta, stone, slate, marble or mosaic panels. These can be made into slabs and slung from supporting angles, hooked back to stanchions or made to rest on the floor slab. Similar methods can be adopted with the other materials as described earlier in this chapter.

The main methods, with which this section is concerned, are the proprietary systems incorporating light curtain wall framing (frequently of aluminium alloy), lightweight infilling panels (see p. 152) and glass. These are light in weight, take up little space, are rapidly erected and specially designed for the task of enclosing the structural frame.

Timber can be used as a framing for the wall, but is more appropriate for heights up to two storeys; most commonly used for multi-storey work are galvanized steel, stainless steel, aluminium, bronze and reinforced concrete. An example of a patent curtain wall system showing components available from stock is shown in Fig. 52. *This shows the key elevation for only two storeys – this is because of space limitations; in fact, it can be adopted for much taller buildings.* A description of lightweight infilling panels used in curtain walling is given on p. 152. Glass, of course, is widely used as an infilling medium and a description of various kinds appears on pp. 153–154.

A typical curtain wall system made by Crittall-Hope Ltd, is shown in Fig. 52. It consists of hollow aluminium alloy transoms and split mullions; the latter allow for thermal movement of the framing members.

The plan detail at G shows the split mullion to which glazing is fixed on one side with a side-hung opening light having p.v.c. weatherstripping on the other side. The two halves of the mullion are bedded together with sealing compound. The spacing of mullions depends on their length and varies from 1.2 m for 3.7 m long mullions to 1.8 m for those 3 m long. The mullions are tied back to the structure as shown at H and J and described below.

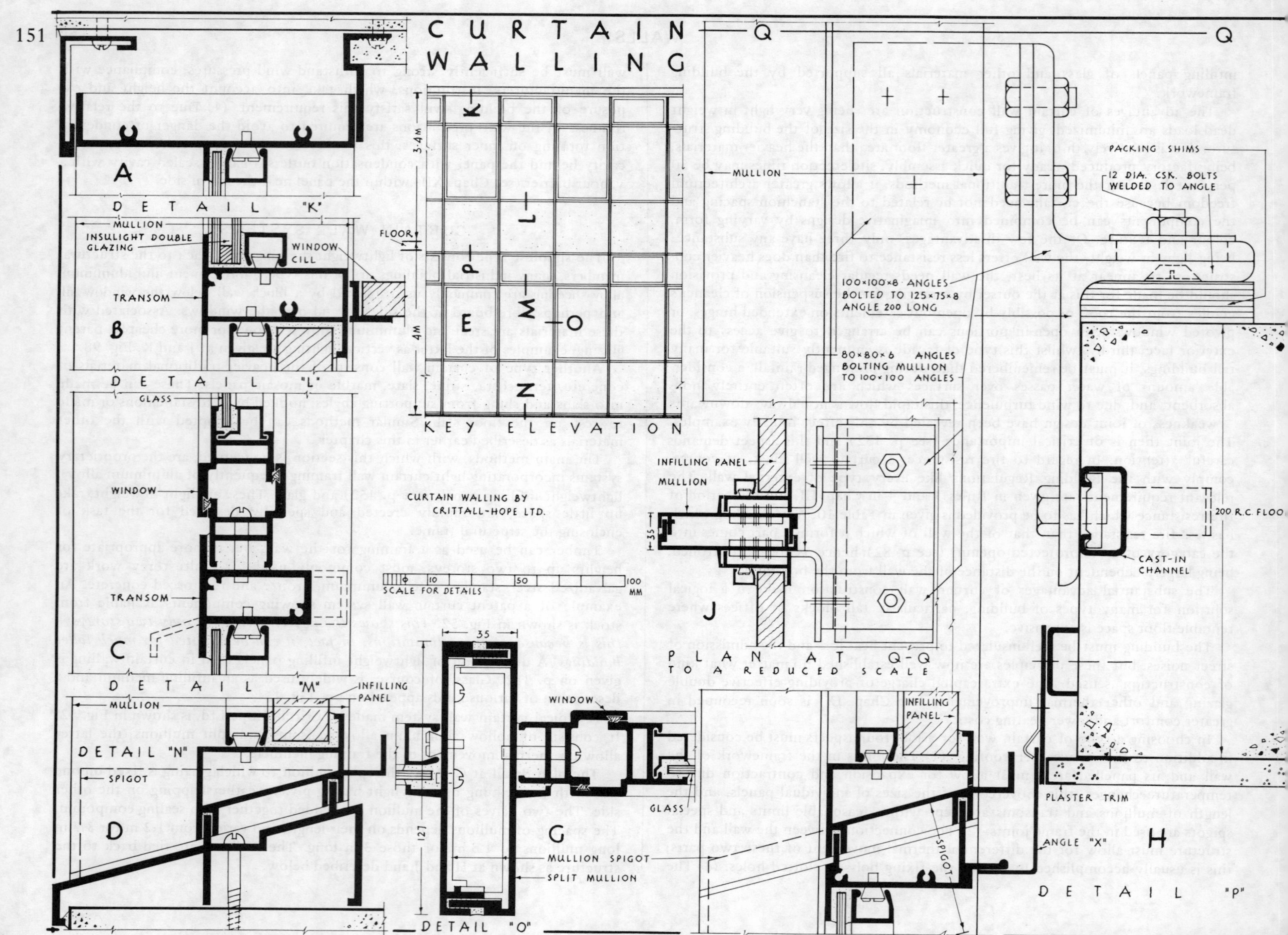
CURTAIN WALLING
A
DETAIL "K"
MULLION
INSULIGHT DOUBLE GLAZING
WINDOW CILL
TRANSOM
B
DETAIL "L"
GLASS
WINDOW
TRANSOM
C
DETAIL "M"
MULLION
INFILLING PANEL
DETAIL "N"
SPIGOT
D
K
3·4M
FLOOR
P
L
E
M
O
4M
N
KEY ELEVATION
CURTAIN WALLING BY CRITTALL-HOPE LTD.
10
50
100 MM
SCALE FOR DETAILS
35
WINDOW
127
GLASS
G
MULLION SPIGOT
SPLIT MULLION
DETAIL "O"
Q
Q
MULLION
PACKING SHIMS
12 DIA. CSK. BOLTS WELDED TO ANGLE
100×100×8 ANGLES BOLTED TO 125×75×8 ANGLE 200 LONG
80×80×6 ANGLES BOLTING MULLION TO 100×100 ANGLES
INFILLING PANEL
MULLION
35
J
200 R.C. FLOOR
CAST-IN CHANNEL
PLAN AT QQ TO A REDUCED SCALE
INFILLING PANEL
PLASTER TRIM
SPIGOT
ANGLE "X"
H
DETAIL "P"

FIGURE 52

The detail at B is of a transom with Insulight double glazing (see p. 154) at the top and an infilling panel below. Panels from 3 to 38 mm thickness may be used. Another transom is shown at C, its size can be increased to that shown by the broken line. The bottom rail of a side-hung window is included.

The base of the curtain wall is given at D, it comprises a cill plate screwed to the floor over which a secondary cill member with condensation grove is fitted. The foot of the mullion is fitted over a mullion spigot (in two halves see G), which is attached to the main cill section.

The section at H and plan at J show how a mullion is fastened back to the structure by means of a steel angle, which is bolted to a channel inset into the edge of the floor slab. To this angle are bolted two 100 mm by 100 mm angles 50 mm long having their vertical legs bolted to the two halves of the split mullion as indicated at J. The detail at H also shows the joint between mullion lengths with a spigot between each length. The spigot, seen also in plan at G, is in two parts which are screwed inside the lower mullion length and project about 12 mm into the bottom of the upper mullion. A sealing compound is used to bed the parts together and the upper mullion, not being screwed to the spigot, can move vertically with temperature changes. The transom in the section at H is in two halves, one riding on the other; this permits thermal movement between adjacent parts of the curtain wall. Thermal expansion and contraction between the wall and the structure is also possible; it will be noted that the gap between these two is closed by an angle X screwed to the split-transom at ceiling level, the vertical leg of this small closure angle slides against an aluminium plate, which is screwed to a small channel bolted to the edge of the floor slab.

Curtain Wall with Thermal Break. In countries where the extremes of temperature are greater than those experienced in Great Britain, the effect of heat loss through mullions and transoms assumes some importance. One way of overcoming this loss, used at Dorval Airport, Montreal, is shown in Fig. 53, where the aluminium mullion is in two halves comprising an inner main portion and an outer cover mould. The two are connected by bolts at 450 mm centres, using nylon nuts and bushes to form a thermal break. The outer cover mould is fixed with stainless steel screws to a front plate which is bolted to the main member, plastic seatings are used with a pointing of polysulphide elastomer between the fixed members.

INFILLING PANELS

Reference has already been made to the importance of making a good joint between the cladding frame and the panel. Jointing has to be of a high standard to exclude weather and resist the strains developed in the continual expansion and contraction of the frame and panel. One of the most effective joints is the mechanical one such as is provided in patent glazing (see Fig. 97), other methods employ non-hardening sealants and patent bedding strips (gaskets). Jointing failures have occurred with sealing compounds because the early ones were inadequate in terms of adhesion, elasticity, and long life; troubles still arise

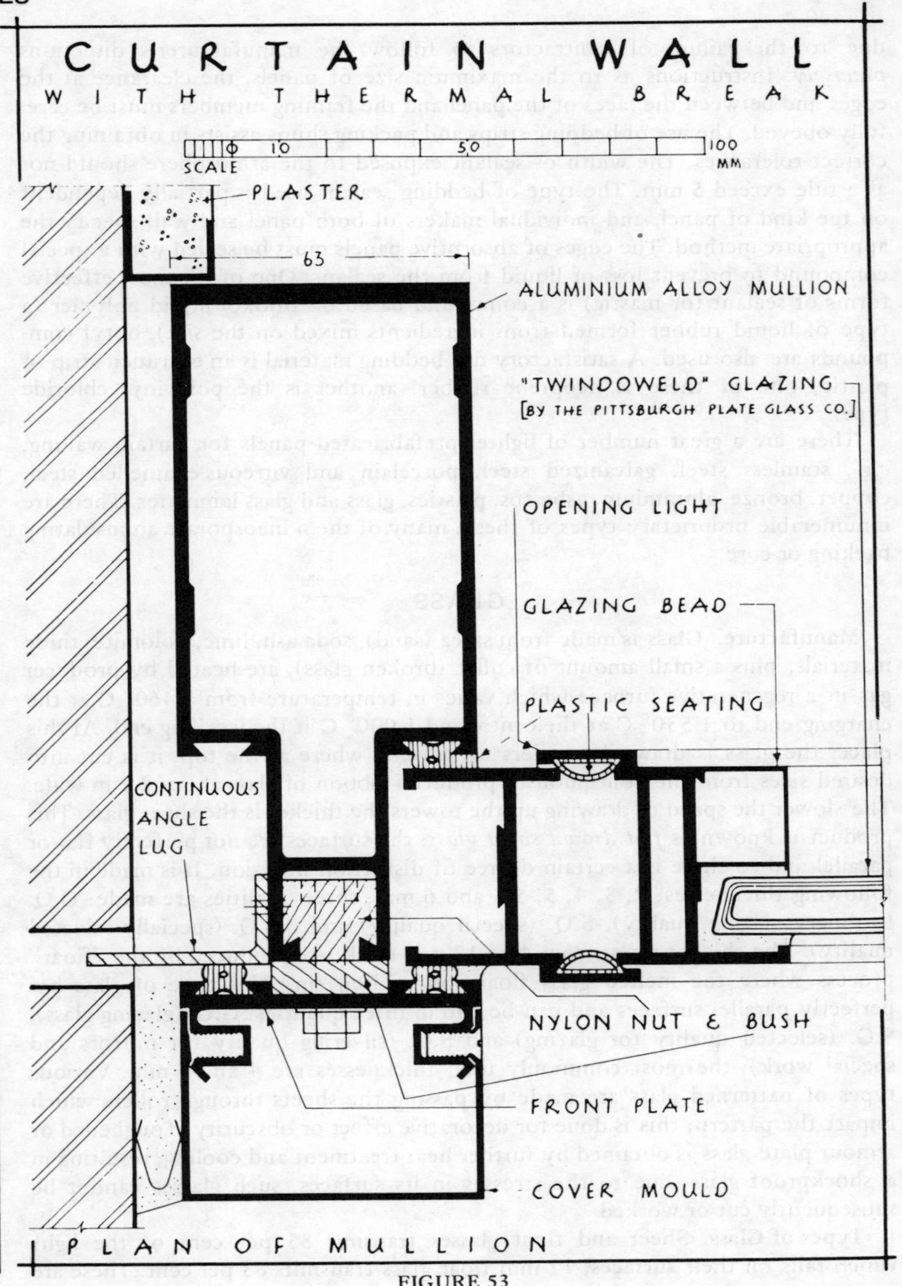

FIGURE 53

due to the failure of contractors to follow the manufacturer's directions *precisely*. Instructions as to the maximum size of panels, the clearance at the edges and between the faces of the panel and the framing members must be carefully obeyed. The use of bedding strips and packing shims assists in obtaining the correct tolerances. The width of sealant exposed to the atmosphere should not as a rule exceed 5 mm. The type of bedding sealant used is partially dependent on the kind of panel, and individual makers of both panel and wall specify the appropriate method. The edges of absorptive panels must be sealed with a special compound to prevent loss of liquid from the sealant. One of the most effective forms of sealant (or mastic) is a compound based on thiokol liquid polymer (a type of liquid rubber formed from ingredients mixed on the site), butyl compounds are also used. A satisfactory dry bedding material is an extruded strip of plastic; one of these is neoprene rubber, another is the polyvinyl chloride type.

There are a great number of lighter prefabricated panels for curtain walling, *e.g.*, stainless steel, galvanized steel, porcelain and vitreous-enamelled steel, copper, bronze, aluminium, asbestos, plastics, glass and glass laminates. There are innumerable proprietary types of these; many of them incorporate an insulating backing or core.

GLASS

Manufacture. Glass is made from silica (sand), soda ash, lime, dolomite; these materials, plus a small amount of cullet (broken glass), are heated by producer gas in a regenerative furnace which varies in temperature from 1 460° C at the charging end to 1 530° C at the centre and 1 000° C at the working end. At this place, the glass is drawn by rollers up towers, where at the top, it is cut into desired sizes from the continuously produced ribbon of glass about 2.7 m wide. The slower the speed of drawing up the towers the thicker is the sheet glass. This product is known as *flat drawn sheet glass*; the surfaces are not perfectly flat or parallel and so there is a certain degree of distortion in vision. It is made in the following thicknesses: 2, 3, 4, 5, 5.5 and 6 mm; three qualities are made: O.Q. (ordinary glazing quality), S.Q. (special quality) and S.S.Q. (specially selected quality). The thicker sizes, from 4 to 12 mm thick, are produced by the "float" process where the melted glass floats on molten tin. This type of glass has perfectly parallel surfaces and can be had in three qualities: G.G. (glazing glass), S.G. (selected quality for glazing) and S.Q. (silvering quality for mirrors and special work); the most commonly used thicknesses are 4 and 6 mm. Various types of patterned glass are made by passing the sheets through rollers which impart the pattern; this is done for decorative effect or obscurity. Toughened or armour-plate glass is obtained by further heat treatment and cooling, resulting in a shockproof glass; due to the stresses in its surfaces, such glasses cannot be subsequently cut or worked.

Types of Glass. Sheet and float glasses transmit 85 per cent of the light which falls on their surfaces; 12 mm float glass transmits 83 per cent. These are figures for diffuse light such as that from the sky falling on to the window. Other types of glass are given below for convenience, although not all may be appropriate for curtain walling.

(a) Cathedral, Rough Cast, Reeded, Fluted, Hammered, and Rolled. Are all types of patterned glass with different degrees of obscurity and decorative effect. Light transmission varies from 70 to 75 per cent.

(b) Wired. A rolled glass which is reinforced with steel wire mesh in a square pattern (Georgian) or hexagonal, available in transparent or translucent qualities. It is considered to have a $\frac{1}{2}$-hr fire resistance and is frequently specified for use with patent glazing. In the event of a breakage, the wires prevent the glass from falling.

(c) Prismatic. A rolled glass having the inner surface corrugated in the form of parallel prisms, used to direct the light in certain directions. When light falls on ordinary plain glass it emerges on the inside in a direction parallel to the incident rays falling on the outside. When the incident angle is steep (as it is when the window is overshadowed by tall buildings), prismatic glass can be used to bend the light rays (refraction) to that part of the room away from the window, hence improving the daylight penetration. Where clerestory windows are used on a wall opposite to the main windows, prismatic glass in the former can be used to deflect the daylight downwards where it is needed most. Conversely, this glass can be used to reduce the glare in rooms with large windows, the glass selected being that from which the rays emerge horizontally. The amount of refraction varies with different types from 35° to 45°, light transmission is 65 per cent.

(d) Heat-absorbing. "Calorex"* is one type having a greenish-blue tint which in the case of the 5 mm thickness, for example, rejects 52 per cent of the solar radiant heat whilst still transmitting 55 per cent of the visible light.

"Antisun"* is another type which rejects 30 per cent of the solar radiant heat whilst transmitting 80 per cent of the visible light. The glass is tinted green to an extent hardly noticeable; it can be used for observation windows and car windscreens.

"Solarshield"* is another heat-rejecting glass in gold and bronze colours consisting of two sheets of glass between which is deposited a thin metallic film; the sheets are laminated together.

These heat-rejecting glasses improve comfort standards inside the building and reduce air-conditioning costs.

(e) Toughened Glass. This is specially strengthened polished plate glass, not generally required in curtain walling. "Armourplate"* glass is one type used for doors (12 mm thick), shop fronts, shelves, table tops, etc.; when broken it disintegrates into small pieces lacking the sharp arrises of ordinary glass.

"Armourclad"* is another such type with a colour pigment fused to one face; it is suitable for curtain walling panels, in many colours 6 to 10 mm thick.

(f) Special Glasses. A cladding type of glass is "Vitrolite"* which is opaque in a wide range of inherent colours.

One-way-vision glass is tinted so that under suitable lighting conditions (darker on the viewer's side) vision is from one side only.

Anti-fly glass is amber tinted and deters flies; it is 3 mm thick and used for food stores and shops.

Hollow glass blocks for walling or panel infilling are made in various sizes of up to 240 mm square by 80 mm thick. They are non-load-bearing but carry their own weight; panel areas should not exceed 11 m². Above this size the panels need intermediate supports; mortar mix is 1 cement : 1 lime putty : 4 sand. The top and sides of panels must be 12 mm clear of the structure, the space being filled with a non-hardening sealer. The *U*-value is 2.5 W/m² ° C; light transmission is approximately 75 per cent of that through

* Manufacturer: Pilkington Brothers Ltd.

two thicknesses of glass spaced as the two faces of the block. A 2.4 m square glass block panel has a fire grading of $\frac{1}{2}$ hr.

(g) Double Glazing. (see also p. 218). Used to minimize heat losses, condensation and sound transmission. It can be of two types: two or more panes of glass bonded together with cavities of dried air between, or two or more separately glazed lights in the same opening. "Insulight"* is one of the former type where pieces of glass with a cavity of dehydrated air between are sealed together to form a single glazing unit. Such a piece has a *U*-value of 3.52 W/m^2 ° C when the cavity is 5 mm and 2.96 W/m^2 ° C when the cavity is 12 mm. These values are almost a 50 per cent improvement on a single sheet of glass, where the *U*-value is 5.7 W/m^2 ° C. Insulight panels can be made in any size up to about 3 m by 1.8 m. A similar type, Insulight Glastoglas,* has the two sheets of glass fused together at the edges with dried air in the cavity (like in Fig. 53); this unit is made in standard sizes to suit standard metal and timber windows. As with all these patent units, the manufacturer's fixing instructions must be very rigidly enforced. This type of glazing has practically no effect on the sound transmission when compared with a single sheet of glass. The thicker the glass, the greater is the resistance to transmission. Sound insulation is impaired if the windows are badly fitting, weather stripping devices, as at C and G, Fig. 52, make a useful contribution in sealing air gaps round windows. The following examples give the approximate sound insulation in decibels of various windows: (i) An ordinary closed openable window – 19 dB. (ii) A closed window with edge seals and 3 mm glass – 23 dB. (iii) as (ii) but 6 mm float glass – 27 dB. The successive improvements are small but often worth attaining in certain places; they illustrate the advantages of heavier glass and sealed lights. There is little to be gained by using thick glass if the edge seal is inadequate.

The other method of double glazing is to have separately glazed windows with an air space between, each one being hinged for cleaning. If the space between such windows is increased from 19 mm the effect on the *U*-value is insignificant; the improvement in sound resistance is more marked: this is partially because the sides of the space can be lined with absorbents. For example, with such a lining, a 100 mm space and 3 mm glass in both windows (closed), the improvement is roughly 11 dB over an ordinary opening light; this is raised to 14 dB if the air space is 200 mm. To make full use of the linings, the ventilating air should be admitted at the top of the outer frame (via a top-hung outward opening light) and at the bottom of the inner frame (through an inward opening bottom hung light). Examples of double glazed windows are shown in Fig. 95, Chap. IX.

INDUSTRIALIZED BUILDING SYSTEM

About 1950 there began to be developed building systems which used large precast R.C. wall, floor and roof elements in the form of panels. The systems were introduced for two purposes: to hasten construction and reduce site work in the building of high rise flat blocks. A constructional frame, in the conventional sense, is not used; instead a cross-wall method is adopted (see p. 136) with the shorter cross walls being load-bearing. The use of heavy precast units became possible as a result of the development of the tower crane which can lift to heights and over distances beyond the capacity of former crane equipment.

The panels, being factory made, are of high quality and accurate in shape. They incorporate glazed windows and electrical conduit set in place where required. The walls are ready for direct decoration and floor slabs for thermoplastic tiling. The site work consists of making the joints watertight, of a small amount of concrete filling to joints and plumbing, joinery and electrical work. Buildings of this kind can be erected four or five times faster than is possible by any other means.

One system of this kind by Concrete Ltd. is given in Fig. 54.

The sketch at C shows part of an upper flow of a high rise block of flats showing a gable on the left with the main longitudinal wall on the right. The system has been used for blocks up to twenty-three storeys high. The wall panels are storey height; the floor panels span longitudinally from gable wall to interior wall to interior wall, etc.

The internal elevation of an external non-load-bearing wall panel is given at A with the adjacent elevation showing the side view. It is a sandwich panel 210 mm thick for a longitudinal wall comprising an inner 102 mm thick R.C. leaf, a 25 mm thick internal slab of expanded polystyrene and an outer 83 mm R.C. leaf. The load-bearing gable wall panel is similarly constructed but the inner leaf is increased to 152 mm thick to give an overall panel thickness of 83 + 25 + 152 = 260 mm. Stainless-steel wire ties (X) couple both leaves together to make a composite panel with a timber window, ready glazed, inset. Recesses (Z) 20 mm deep are formed in the perimeter of the internal leaf to which the subsequently placed site concrete is bonded; additionally the vertical edges of the inner leaf have projecting stirrups (Y) which encircle the vertical joint rod (R) shown at D. The vertical edges of the outer leaf are grooved for placing of the neoprene baffle strip (see D). Two pockets (P) shown at A and B on the bottom inner edge, each have a short steel angle which is holed to receive one of the vertical rods (Q) which is cast into and projects above the top edge of the inner leaf. Rods Q serve four purposes: (1) They connect the top of one unit to the bottom of the one above; (2) Looped bars from the floor panel encircle them (see B); (3) They form lifting points for the crane; (4) They serve as fixing points for the stays used in erection (see below). The bottom edge of the panel is rebated on the inner leaf to form part of a groove in which cables for the power points are located behind the skirting (see B).

The internal 150 mm thick cross-wall panels are similarly constructed but, of course, do not have the thermal insulation; their vertical edges have projecting looped reinforcing bars which, as drawn at D, encircle the above mentioned in-situ rod R.

The R.C. precast slab floor is similar to that at E, Fig. 28, but in wider units and with the hollows filled with plastic foam; it has concrete nibs at the bearing edges, which rest on the supporting walls, and projecting steel loops which encircle the rods *Q*. The floor is of sandwich construction with a expanded polystyrene sound insulating quilt and screed topping over the structural slab.

Erection Procedure. The external wall panels followed by the internal panels are erected and plumbed. To do this each panel has two temporary tubular steel raking stays which connect to the rods *Q* and to a plate bolted to the floor slab. The joints are then made as described below followed by the next floor slabs.

* Manufacturer: Pilkington Brothers Ltd.

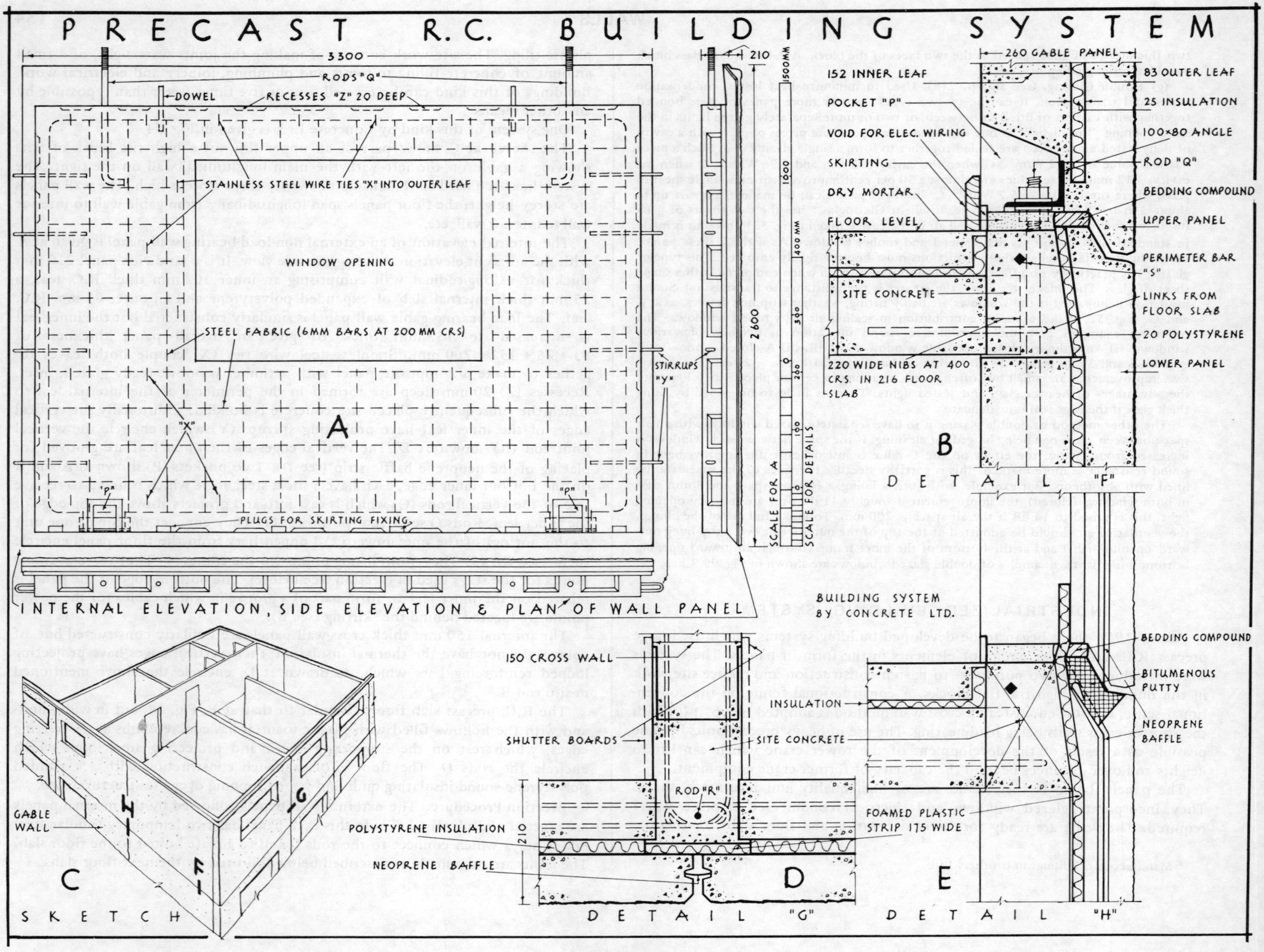

PRECAST R.C. BUILDING SYSTEM

3300
RODS "Q"
DOWEL
RECESSES "Z" 20 DEEP
STAINLESS STEEL WIRE TIES "X" INTO OUTER LEAF
WINDOW OPENING
A
STEEL FABRIC (6MM BARS AT 200MM CRS)
"P"
"P"
PLUGS FOR SKIRTING FIXING
INTERNAL ELEVATION, SIDE ELEVATION & PLAN OF WALL PANEL

210
1500MM
2600
400 MM
260
280
STIRRUPS "Y"
SCALE FOR A
SCALE FOR DETAILS

152 INNER LEAF
POCKET "P"
VOID FOR ELEC WIRING
SKIRTING
DRY MORTAR
FLOOR LEVEL
SITE CONCRETE
220 WIDE NIBS AT 400 CRS IN 216 FLOOR SLAB
260 GABLE PANEL
83 OUTER LEAF
25 INSULATION
100×80 ANGLE
ROD "Q"
BEDDING COMPOUND
UPPER PANEL
PERIMETER BAR "S"
LINKS FROM FLOOR SLAB
20 POLYSTYRENE
LOWER PANEL
B
DETAIL "F"

BUILDING SYSTEM BY CONCRETE LTD.

150 CROSS WALL
GABLE WALL
POLYSTYRENE INSULATION
210
NEOPRENE BAFFLE
SHUTTER BOARDS
INSULATION
SITE CONCRETE
ROD "R"
FOAMED PLASTIC STRIP 175 WIDE
BEDDING COMPOUND
BITUMENOUS PUTTY
NEOPRENE BAFFLE
C
G
H
D
E
SKETCH
DETAIL "G"
DETAIL "H"

FIGURE 54

Joints. The section at B at an intermediate floor is taken on a line through one of the pockets P in the bottom edge of a gable wall panel. It shows the rod Q projecting from the lower panel; if the section were at ground level this rod would have been cast in the ground floor slab. A lower nut and washer are placed on the rod at the correct level to receive the bottom flange of the steel angle which is embedded at its ends into the upper panel. The upper nut and washer are then added followed by 32 mm thick semi-dry concrete filling beneath the panel edge. The waterproofing of the joint is described below in the description of the two remaining joints. The detail at B also shows the floor slab with its projecting nibs and also the looped steel floor reinforcement which encircles the rods Q. In addition there is the steel bar S which is embedded in the concrete filling and goes right round the perimeter of the building.

The detail at D is a plan at the junction of two external panels and an internal wall. After these parts have been erected the neoprene baffle is sprung into the grooves in the outer leaves of the wall panels from the outside. At the back of the outer leaves and over the joint a 175 mm wide strip of waterproofed foamed plastic is bonded with adhesive. The vertical panel height rod R is placed within the projecting steel reinforcement from the three units; shutter boards shown in broken line are applied and the site concrete is poured and consolidated at the junction.

The detail at E is the section at an intermediate floor level taken on a vertical line at the centre of the joint. It shows the lower length of neoprene baffle in the groove with its top end turned over. The 175 mm wide vertical strip of foamed plastic mentioned above is bonded with adhesive to the back of the outer nibs. The horizontal strip of bituminous bedding compound is bonded along the top edge of the lower wall panel and is notched to pass the lower length of 175 mm strip of foamed plastic, the latter being bonded to the corresponding upper length. Beneath the horizontal bedding compound for a height of about 120 mm bituminous putty is placed across the joint under the upper length of neoprene baffle. This putty serves to secure the lower baffle, as a platform for the upper baffle and a seal. The upper panel is placed so that it compresses the horizontal bedding compound.

CHAPTER FIVE

TIMBER ROOFS

Syllabus. **Mansard, built-up, glued laminated, and open roofs. Hyperbolic paraboloid shell roof.**

MANSARD ROOF

This roof, named after a French architect who first adopted it in the mid-seventeenth century at the time when the height of external walls was restricted, provides bedroom, etc., accommodation within it. It is the most economic way of providing living space within the volume of a house.

It is illustrated in Fig. 55. It has two pitches, the lower varying from 60 to 70° and the upper from 30 to 40°, depending upon the roof covering. Two methods of setting out the roof are shown. In that at B, the ceiling line is drawn at the required height above the floor which is at eaves level; a line is drawn from each eaves to the higher ceiling line at the desired rake and from the intersection at each side the upper spar lines are drawn at the required inclination, meeting at the apex. In the method at C a semicircle is drawn on base 1–6 (floor) which is equal to the span and is divided into five equal parts; lines 1–2 and 5–6 are drawn, giving the pitch of the lower slope, and lines from 2 and 5 to the apex giving the pitch of the upper portion.

As shown at A, the floor joists are supported on cavity walls, the wall on the right having two skins of brickwork and the alternative on the left having an inner leaf of concrete blocks; an intermediate $\frac{1}{2}$ brick wall is shown. These joists extend to the outer faces of the external walls and are nailed to 50 or 75 mm thick wall plates. The 100 mm by 50 mm spars of the lower pitch are bird's-mouthed to 100 mm by 50 mm plates nailed (at the eaves) to the floor joists and to the purlins. The latter support the ceiling joists and the bird's-mouthed upper spars, the triangulated top portion of the roof conforming to normal construction. The size of the purlins varies, of course, with the span, weight of the covering material and the quality of the timber. Stoothed partitions are provided, the lower ends of the studs being fixed to 100 mm by 50 mm sills nailed to the flooring, as shown, and the upper ends are nailed to the purlins. Any of the alternative partitions described in Vol. III can be used in lieu of the wood stoothings. The space between these partitions and the spars provides useful storage accommodation.

Thermal insulation, to which attention must be paid, is obtained by insulating quilts or mats laid over the ceiling joists and nailed to the studs – see A and E.

Natural lighting to the upper room(s) is by means of windows in the gable wall(s), these are indicated by broken lines at A, and/or by dormer window(s). A dormer is detailed in Fig. 96.

In this example plain tiles are used as the roof covering, hence the adoption of a minimum pitch of 40° for the upper portion of the roof. The construction, including the tiling, is detailed at E. If slates are employed, the pitch of this top part of the roof need only be 30°. Two alternative finishes at the eaves are shown at F and G.

To offer increased fire resistance, it is advisable to have the ceiling joists and studs impregnated with fire-retardant solution, such as ammonium phosphate – see p. 103.

Whilst this type of roof provides an economy in space and cost, it is not often adopted, chiefly because of its somewhat ungainly appearance. It does, however, provide an interesting contrast if it is used on an occasional block of domestic buildings when, for example, most of the houses in a large building project are of the normal single pitched type of roof. Formerly, mansard roofs with trusses resembling the now obsolete queen post truss were employed in tall buildings in comparatively narrow streets where the designer was confronted with problems related to right of light. Such construction has now been superseded by the flat roof, etc.

BUILT-UP ROOF TRUSS

This type of timber roof, suitable for a 9 m span, is shown in Fig. 19, Vol. III, and two forms of connectors which give a high degree of efficiency at the joints are shown at Fig. 20. Another example is given in Fig. 39, Vol. I.

A similar truss with effective span of 14.1 m is illustrated here in Fig. 56. As shown at A and D, the roof has a one-quarter pitch ($26\frac{1}{2}°$) and the centre-line principle has been observed in setting it out, each top chord being divided into five equal parts and the bottom chord being divided into nine equal parts. The sizes of the various members depend upon the species and quality of the timber, the span, the distance apart of the trusses, the weight of the roof covering and

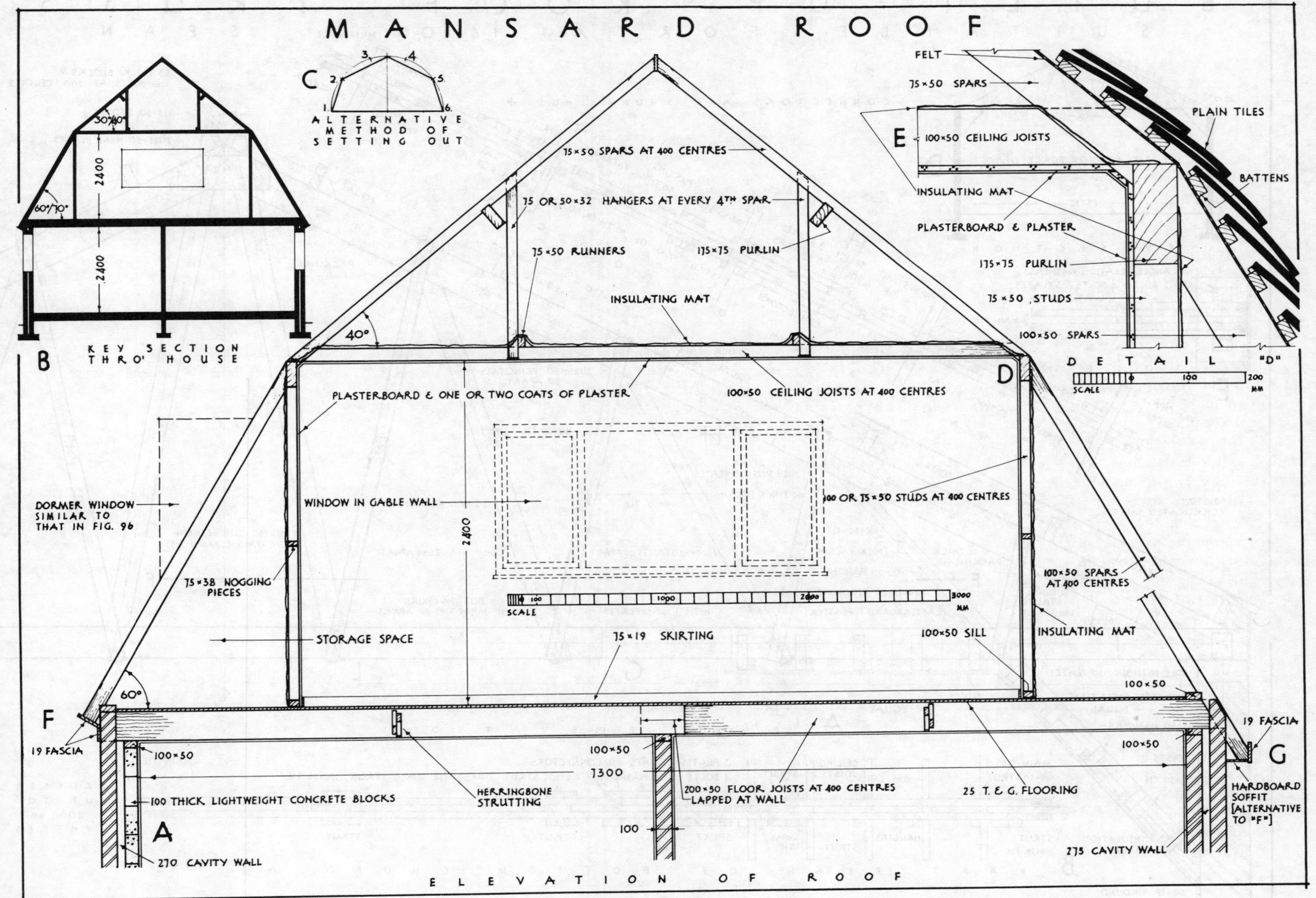
MANSARD ROOF
C
ALTERNATIVE METHOD OF SETTING OUT
1. 2. 3. 4. 5. 6.
30°/40°
2400
60°/70°
2400
B
KEY SECTION THRO' HOUSE
75×50 SPARS AT 400 CENTRES
75 OR 50×32 HANGERS AT EVERY 4TH SPAR
75×50 RUNNERS
175×75 PURLIN
INSULATING MAT
40°
PLASTERBOARD & ONE OR TWO COATS OF PLASTER
100×50 CEILING JOISTS AT 400 CENTRES
D
DORMER WINDOW SIMILAR TO THAT IN FIG. 96
WINDOW IN GABLE WALL
2400
100 OR 75×50 STUDS AT 400 CENTRES
75×38 NOGGING PIECES
SCALE 100 1000 2000 3000 MM
100×50 SPARS AT 400 CENTRES
INSULATING MAT
STORAGE SPACE
75×19 SKIRTING
100×50 SILL
60°
100×50
F
19 FASCIA
100×50
19 FASCIA
G
100×50
100×50
7300
200×50 FLOOR JOISTS AT 400 CENTRES LAPPED AT WALL
HERRINGBONE STRUTTING
25 T. & G. FLOORING
100 THICK LIGHTWEIGHT CONCRETE BLOCKS
HARDBOARD SOFFIT [ALTERNATIVE TO "F"]
A
100
270 CAVITY WALL
275 CAVITY WALL
ELEVATION OF ROOF
FELT
75×50 SPARS
PLAIN TILES
E
100×50 CEILING JOISTS
BATTENS
INSULATING MAT
PLASTERBOARD & PLASTER
175×75 PURLIN
75×50 STUDS
100×50 SPARS
DETAIL "D"
SCALE 100 200 MM

FIGURE 55

BUILT-UP ROOF TRUSS

SUITABLE FOR A 14100 MILLIMETRE SPAN

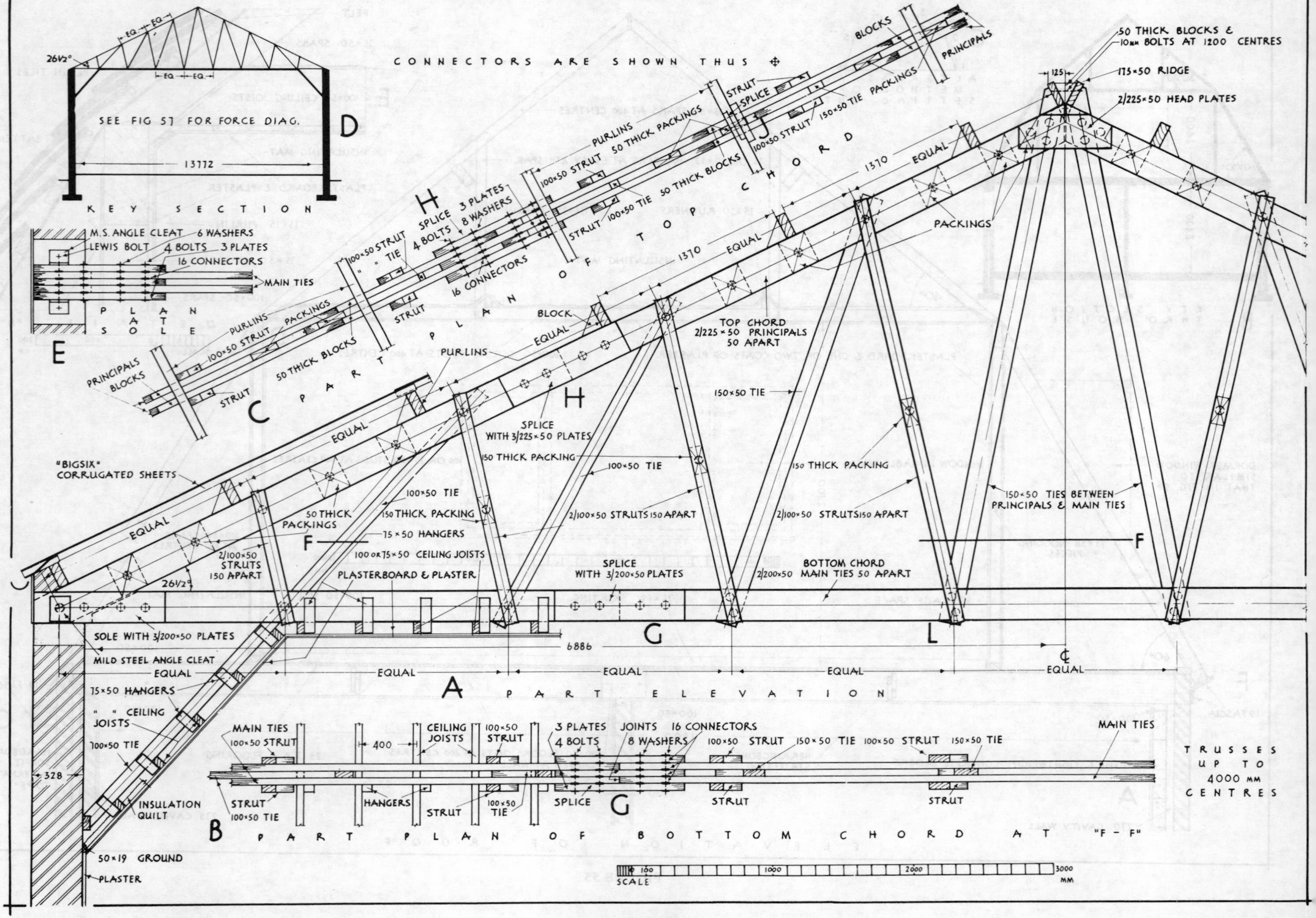

FIGURE 56

the weight of the ceiling, if such is to be provided. The size of the member comprising the top chord depends also upon the nature of the load which it supports; normally the purlins are placed at the intersections (panel points) of the top chord, struts and ties, resulting in primary stresses only in the top chord. This is not always possible and the purlins may be near to mid way between the panel points causing secondary bending stresses in the top chord (see p. 163). In this example, the covering consists of fibre-cement corrugated sheets; the spacing of the purlins depends upon the recommended maximum unsupported length of the sheets, which, in the case of the "Bigsix" type shown, is 1 372 mm and therefore the purlins do not coincidewith the intersections and the top chord is subjected to a bending stress. Hence, the projecting ends of the struts providing a secure means of fixing, as shown at A, Fig. 19, Vol. III, cannot be used to support the purlins, and triangular blocks, 50 mm thick, securely nailed to the principals are therefore provided to which the purlins are well spiked; two blocks are placed at each crossing – see C. Any splicing or half lapping of the purlins should occur at the trusses (see J at C, which includes a cover plate). If instead of "Bigsix" sheets, "Doublesix" corrugated sheets were employed, the purlins could be placed at the intersections as the purlin spacing can be up to 2 m centres for the stronger sheeting.

The thickness of the members comprising the principal rafters, struts and ties is 50 mm. The inclined ties are placed between the pair of 225 mm by 50 mm principal rafters which form each top chord and between the two 200 mm by 50 mm main ties at the bottom chord, and therefore the distance between these principals and main ties is 50 mm. Each strut consists of two members and, as they are placed on the outside of the top and bottom chords, the distance between the members of a double strut is 150 mm.

The bottom chord, consisting of two 200 mm by 50 mm main ties, is in three lengths, spliced together as shown at G at A and B with three 50 mm thick plates, (alternatively, steel cover plates could be used). Each end of the bottom chord is provided with three 200 mm by 50 mm sole plates – see A and E. Each top chord, which consists of a pair of principals, is spliced at mid-length with three 225 mm by 50 mm plates – see H at A and C.

The truss is secured at both ends by means of a mild steel angle cleat at each side which is lewis bolted to the stone pad – see A and E. The upper ends of the chords are head-plated together as shown at A.

As described in Vol. III, a connector is required at each interface. In the example shown here it is assumed that the connectors are 64 mm in diameter of the split ring type – see B and C, Fig. 20, Vol. III. Thus, at each splice there are sixteen connectors, four 12 mm dia. bolts and eight 50 mm by 50 mm by 3 or 5 mm thick washers. The number of connectors, bolts and washers required at each sole is indicated at E (see also B, Fig. 19, Vol. III). The sets of connectors needed at the top and bottom chords between the struts and ties are shown at A.

The members of the top and bottom chords are stiffened by means of packings of thickness equal to the distance between adjacent members – see A and C. These should be nailed securely or, as shown, 64 mm dia. connectors may be used.

The top chords are secured at the apex by a 50 mm thick head plate at each side. The 50 mm thick ridge purlins are spiked to the projecting ends of the ties, and, as shown, shaped blocks are bolted to the ridge purlins at 1.2 m centres to prevent tilting of the latter. Observe that the centre lines of the ties intersect those of the top chord at 125 mm from the centre line of the truss to permit the above construction.

The bottom chord should be slightly cambered by an amount equal to about 4 mm per metre of span. This is to ensure that there will be no appearance of sagging when the roof covering and ceiling (if any) are fixed.

If a plastered ceiling is required, the joists may be nailed to hangers which are well spiked to the bottom chord – see A and B. Alternatively, a fillet may be nailed along the lower edge and at each side of the bottom chord to which the notched ends of the ceiling joists are nailed. A further alternative is to support the ceiling joists on top of the bottom chord and encase the exposed chord with plywood or plasterboard, etc. The ceiling at A is given a finish of plasterboard and one or two coats of gypsum plaster. If it is desired to block out the top

TABLE 34 DRY STRESSES AND MODULI OF ELASTICITY FOR MACHINE STRESS-GRADED SOFTWOODS

Property	Grade	Standard Name				
		Western Hemlock (commercial)	Redwood and Whitewood	Douglas Fir (home-grown)	Scots Pine (home-grown)	Sitka Spruce (home-grown)
		N/mm^2	N/mm^2	N/mm^2	N/mm^2	N/mm^2
Bending	MSS MGS	7.3 5.1	7.3 5.1	9.0 6.3	7.6 5.3	5.2 3.6
Tension	MSS MGS	5.1 3.5	5.1 3.5	6.3 4.4	5.3 3.7	3.6 2.5
Compression parallel to grain	MSS MGS	7.9 5.5	8.0 5.6	9.0 6.3	8.0 5.6	5.0 3.5
Compression perpendicular to grain	MSS MGS	1.55 1.38	1.55(1) 1.38(1)	1.93 1.72	1.93 1.72	1.24 1.10
Shear parallel to grain	MSS MGS	0.80 0.80	0.86 0.86	0.87 0.87	0.86 0.86	0.66 0.66
Mean modulus of elasticity	MSS MGS	10 800 9 800	10 200 8 800	10 800 9 500	11 200 10 200	8 200 7 200
Minimum modulus of elasticity	MSS MGS	7 200 6 500	6 400 5 400	7 200 6 500	7 500 6 800	5 100 4 500

Notes: **These stresses apply to timber having a moisture content not exceeding 18%.**
(1) Where redwood is used separately these stresses may be increased by a factor of 1.1.
(2) MSS = Machine special structural grade timber.
(3) MGS = Machine general structural grade timber.

corners of the room as shown at D, the end 100 mm by 50 mm ties are extended to the walls where the ends are bird's-mouthed and nailed to short lengths of vall plate, the bottom edge of the plasterboard being nailed to 50 mm by 19 mm grounds plugged to the walls – see A.

Design of Built-up Roof Truss. The truss has a span of 14.1 m from centre to centre of bearings; trusses are at 3.66 m centres, made with machine special structural (MSS) grade Western hemlock timber, and designed in accordance with B.S. 5268: Part 2, The Structural Use of Timber in Buildings.

Table 34 giving permissible basic timber stresses is given on p. 160; Table 35 gives modification factors K_{18}, which are described below.

TABLE 35 MODIFICATION FACTOR K_{18} FOR SLENDERNESS RATIO AND DURATION OF LOADING ON COMPRESSION MEMBERS OF 40 GRADE AND 50 GRADE SOFTWOOD

Slenderness Ratio		Values of K_{18}		
l/r	*l/b*	Long-term Loads	Medium-term Loads	Short-term Loads
Less than 5	1.4	1.00	1.25	1.50
5	1.4	0.99	1.24	1.49
10	2.9	0.98	1.23	1.47
20	5.8	0.96	1.20	1.44
30	8.7	0.94	1.17	1.40
40	11.5	0.91	1.13	1.34
50	14.4	0.87	1.08	1.27
60	17.3	0.83	1.00	1.16
70	20.2	0.77	0.90	1.01
80	23.0	0.70	0.79	0.86
90	26.0	0.61	0.68	0.72
100	28.8	0.53	0.58	0.60
120	34.6	0.40	0.42	0.44
140	40.4	0.31	0.32	0.33
160	46.2	0.24	0.25	0.25
180	52.0	0.20	0.20	0.20
200	57.7	0.16	0.16	0.17
220	63.5	0.13	0.14	0.14
240	69.2	0.11	0.12	0.12
250	72.2	0.10	0.11	0.11

The *permissible* bending and tension stresses f_{ppar} and t_{ppar}, are 7.3 N/mm^2 and 5.1 N/mm^2 respectively. These are *basic* stresses for permanent loading and where they are caused by temporary loading such as superimposed and snow loads in addition to dead load, they may be increased by 25 per cent. Therefore in this case f_{ppar} = 9.125 N/mm^2 and t_{ppar} = 6.375 N/mm^2. The symbols used for *actual* bending stress and actual tensile stress are f_{apar} and t_{apar} respectively. The permissible and actual compressive stress symbols for compression parallel to the grain are c_{ppar} and c_{apar}; for MSS grade Western hemlock timber c_{ppar} = 7.9 N/mm^2, this grade stress has to be multiplied by a factor (K_{18}, obtainable from Table 27) which depends on the slenderness ratio* and duration of loading.

The dead load on the roof slope is 0.252 kN/m^2 (asbestos sheets 0.145 kN/m^2, purlins 0.107 kN/m^2) excluding the truss weight and 0.32 kN/m^2 including the truss weight of 0.068 kN/m^2; the imposed loading on it is 0.75 kN/m^2† on the *plan* of the roof. The dead load on the ceiling is 0.574 kN/m^2. Forces in the truss members caused by wind suction pressures on both windward and leeward slopes have been checked by drawing a wind force diagram but they have been neglected in the design and the wind force diagram has not been reproduced. The effects of wind in this example are *small* and *opposite* in action to the forces caused by dead loading.

The top chord of the truss is divided into five equal panels and the distance between each panel point is 1.575 m along the slope of the roof which corresponds to an "on plan dimension" of 1.4 m. The trusses are at 3.6 m centres.

* The slenderness ratio $= \frac{l}{r} = \frac{\text{effective length of column}}{\text{least radius of gyration of column}}$.

There are three properties which affect the strength of a column. Firstly, its length, for the longer a column, the greater is the tendency for it to buckle under load. Secondly, its stiffness which is measured by the radius of gyration (r) where

$$r = \sqrt{\frac{\text{moment of inertia (M.I.) of the section}}{\text{area of the section}}}.$$

The M.I. of a section is a value giving a measure of its cross sectional size and shape. For a rectangular section of breadth b and depth d, the M.I. about the neutral axis is $\frac{bd^3}{12}$. The third property affecting column strength is the nature of its end fixings, for as the stability of the end fixings improves so does the efficiency of the column. The latter property can be reflected in the slenderness ratio by multiplying the column length by a modification factor ranging from 0.7 to 2 for various types of end fixing as described in the B.S. This product of length times factor gives the *effective* length and for struts in a roof truss the factor, obtainable from B.S. 5626: Part 2, is usually taken as 0.8. Table 35 gives a modification factor K_{18} for various l/r values according to the duration of the compressive load. The value of c_{ppar} for the particular column and its l/r value is then obtained by multiplying the factor by the permissible basic stress of 7.9 N/mm^2 (Table 34).

† This includes an allowance for snow.

			kN
Roof panel: dead load	$= 1.575 \times 3.6 \times 0.32$	=	1.82
imposed load	$= 1.4 \times 3.6 \times 0.75$	=	3.78
Total roof panel load		=	5.6
Ceiling panel dead load	$= 1.575 \times 3.6 \times 0.574$	=	3.25
Upward reaction due to: roof load	$= 5 \times 5.6$	=	28
ceiling load	$= 4 \times 3.25$	=	13
Total reaction		=	41 kN

Design of purlin

Dead load on purlin	$= 1.575 \times 3.6 \times 0.252$	=	1.43
Imposed load on purlin	$= 1.4 \times 3.6 \times 0.75$	=	3.78
Total purlin load		=	5.21 kN

$$\text{B.M.} = \frac{WL}{8} = \frac{5.21 \times 3.6 \times 10^3 \times 10^3}{8} = 2.34 \times 10^6 \text{ N mm}$$

Assume the purlin is 75 mm wide and d mm deep.

$$Z = \frac{bd^2}{6} = \frac{75d^2}{6}$$

$$\text{B.M.} = Z \times f_{ppar} \text{ and } f_{ppar} = 9.125 \text{ N/mm}^2.$$

$$\text{Therefore } 2.34 \times 10^6 = \frac{75d^2}{6} \times 9.125, \text{ therefore } d = 144 \text{ mm}$$

therefore use 150 mm × 75 mm purlins.

Force Diagram (Fig. 57). In order to discover the magnitude of the forces in the members of the truss the force diagram must be drawn. The first step is to draw to scale an outline of the truss known as the truss or line diagram (see X), the roof panel point loads (2.8 kN, 5.6 kN, etc.) are added as well as the ceiling point loads (3.25 kN), and the reactions of 41 kN. The spaces between the loads are lettered (A, B, C, etc.) and the spaces between the truss members are numbered (1 to 9 to 1′). The members of the truss can thus be described, for example, A1, B2, 23, etc.

The force diagram* shown at Y is drawn to scale (*e.g.*, 20 mm to 1 kN) by measuring the roof and ceiling loads down line LL′, starting with the loads at the left-hand side of the truss and travelling (LA = 2.8 kN, AB = 5.6 kN, etc.) up the left-hand roof slope and down the right-hand slope (E′D′ = 5.6 kN to A′L′ = 2.8 kN). L′K′ is the upward reaction and the distance from L′ to K′ is 41 kN on the force diagram, down again with K′J′ = 3.25 kN to JK = 3.25 kN down. Finally, up with KL = 41 kN and back to the starting point at L.

The force lines are then plotted for each panel point starting with LA down, A1 parallel to the rafter back. The line from K to 1 will be horizontal and

* As the truss and its loadings are symmetrical, only half of the force diagram is shown, it is obvious that the force in member A1 is the same in A′1′.

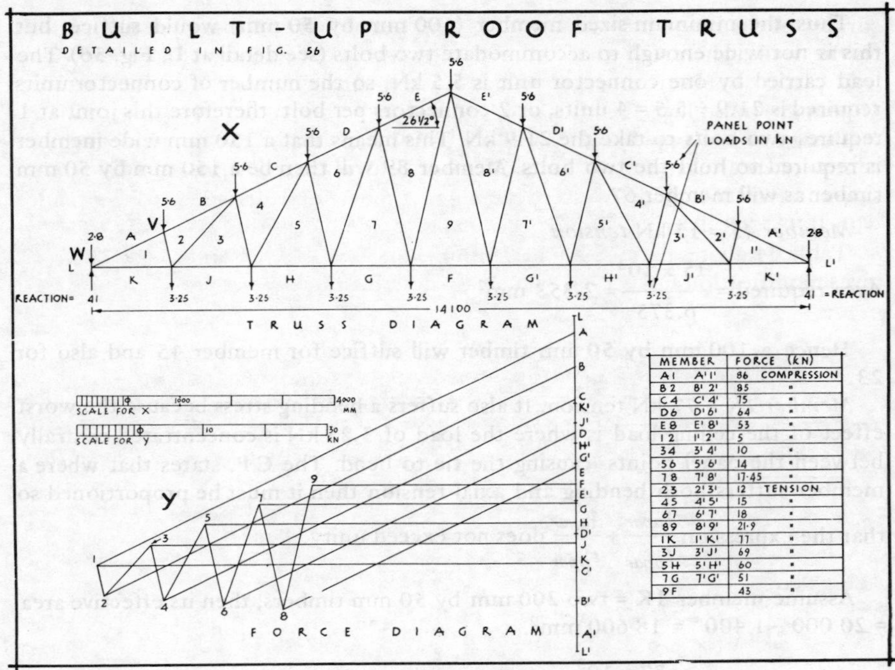

MEMBER		FORCE (kN)	
A1	A′1′	86	COMPRESSION
B2	B′2′	85	"
C4	C′4′	75	"
D6	D′6′	64	"
E8	E′8′	53	"
12	1′2′	5	"
34	3′4′	10	"
56	5′6′	14	"
78	7′8′	17·45	"
23	2′3′	12	TENSION
45	4′5′	15	"
67	6′7′	18	"
89	8′9′	21·9	"
1K	1′K′	77	"
3J	3′J′	69	"
5H	5′H′	60	"
7G	7′G′	51	"
9F		43	"

FIGURE 57

parallel to the main tie. The magnitude of the forces in A1 and 1K is found by measuring along the lines in the force diagram. Whether the force in the member is compressive or tensile is decided at each panel point by considering the direction in which the force diagram is drawn. Thus in the force diagram LA is down, A1 is down and to the left giving pressure on point W, showing that A1 is in compression. Moving from point 1 to K on the force diagram shows that 1K is in tension pulling away from W. Starting now at the next panel point AB down, draw B2 parallel to the rafter back then 21 parallel to 12 in the truss diagram. The nature of the forces in these members is found in the same way; B2 is down and to the left, giving pressure at V and so B2 is in compression. Moving up from 2 to 1 in the force diagram shows that this member is in compression giving pressure on V. The force diagram can now be completed to the appropriate scale and by measuring the force lines one can determine the forces in the members and tabulate them as in the figure.

Design of tension members (using $t_{ppar} = 6.375$ kN/mm^2 (see p. 161)):

Member 89 = 21.9 kN

$$\text{Net area of member required} = \frac{21.9 \times 10^3}{6.375} = 3\,435 \text{ mm}^2$$

Thus the minimum-sized member (100 mm by 50 mm) would suffice; but this is not wide enough to accommodate two bolts (see detail at L, Fig. 56). The load carried by one connector unit is 5.5 kN, so the number of connector units required is 21.9 ÷ 5.5 = 4 units, or 2 connectors per bolt; therefore this joint at L requires two bolts to take the 21.9 kN. This means that a 150 mm wide member is required to hold the two bolts. Member 89 will then be a 150 mm by 50 mm timber as will member 67.

Member 45 = 15 kN *tension*

$$\text{Area required} = \frac{15 \times 10^3}{6.375} = 2\,353\ \text{mm}^2$$

Hence a 100 mm by 50 mm timber will suffice for member 45 and also for 23.

Member 1K = 77 kN tension. It also suffers a bending stress because the worst effect of the ceiling load is where the load of 3.25 kN is concentrated centrally between the panel points, causing the tie to bend. The C.P. states that where a member suffers both bending and axial tension then it must be proportioned so that the expression $\frac{f_{apar}}{f_{ppar}} + \frac{t_{apar}}{t_{ppar}}$ does not exceed unity.

Assume member 1K = two 200 mm by 50 mm timbers, then its effective area = 20 000 − 1 400* = 18 600 mm².

$$\text{Tensile stress } t_{apar} = \frac{77 \times 10^3}{18\,600} = 4.14\ \text{N/mm}^2.$$

B.M. due to ceiling load of 3.25 kN placed centrally between the panel points = 1.63 × 1.575 ÷ 2 = 1.284 kN m = 1.284 × 10⁶ N mm.

$$Z = \frac{bd^2}{6} = \frac{100 \times 200^2}{6} = 66.6 \times 10^4\ \text{mm}^3. \quad \text{B.M.} = Zf_{apar}$$

$$\text{therefore} \quad f_{apar} = \frac{1.284 \times 10^6}{66.6 \times 10^4} = 1.93\ \text{N/mm}^2\dagger$$

$$\text{so} \quad \frac{f_{apar}}{f_{ppar}} + \frac{t_{apar}}{t_{ppar}} = \frac{1.93}{9.125} + \frac{4.14}{6.375} = 0.86$$

as this is less than unity, two 200 mm by 50 mm timbers are satisfactory.

* This deduction of 1 400 mm² allows for the *reduction* in cross-sectional area due to the 14 mm dia. bolt hole and the split ring connector.

† Actually this figure should be slightly greater because in the value of *Z* no allowance has been made for the reduction mentioned in the above footnote, but this would not materially affect the example.

Design of compression members: Member 78. This carries 17.45 kN and is 2.87 m long. Try two 100 mm by 50 mm timbers 150 mm apart. Moment of

$$\text{inertia about X–X axis} = \frac{100 \times 100^3}{12} = 8.33 \times 100^3\ \text{mm}^4.$$

$$\text{Therefore radius of gyration } (r) = \sqrt{\frac{8.33 \times 100^3\ \text{mm}^4}{2 \times 100 \times 50}} = 28.8\ \text{mm}$$

so $\frac{l}{r} = \frac{0.8 \times 2\,870}{28.8} = 80$. From Table 27 the modification factor (medium-term load) for this basic stress = 0.79. So $c_{ppar} = 0.79 \times 7.9 = 6.24$ N/mm².

$$\text{Hence area of member required} = \frac{17.45 \times 10^3}{6.24} = 2\,796\ \text{mm}^2.$$

Therefore two 100 mm by 50 mm timbers are considered satisfactory for member 78 and the same sizes will be adequate for members 12, 34 and 56.

Member A1 = 86 kN direct compression plus a bending* stress caused by the same load should the purlins be placed mid-way between the panel points. In such a case the C.P. states that the expression $\frac{f_{apar}}{f_{ppar}} + \frac{c_{apar}}{c_{ppar}}$ must not exceed unity for slenderness ratios not exceeding 20 and 0.9 for ratios exceeding 20. B.M. due to purlin load of 5.6 kN placed centrally between the panel points = 5.6 ÷ 2 × 1.575 ÷ 2 = 2.2 kNm.

Assume member A1 consists of two 225 mm by 50 mm timbers 50 mm apart, it is 1.575 m long.

$$Z = \frac{bd^2}{6} = \frac{100 \times 225^2}{6} = 843.8 \times 10^3\ \text{mm}^3. \quad \text{B.M.} = Zf_{apar}$$

$$\text{therefore } f_{apar} = \frac{2.2 \times 10^3 \times 10^3}{843.8 \times 10^3} = 2.6\ \text{N/mm}^2$$

$$c_{apar} = \frac{86 \times 10^3}{2 \times 225 \times 50} = 3.82\ \text{N/mm}^2.$$

The least moment of inertia in this case is about the Y–Y axis and equals

$$\frac{225 \times 150^3}{12} - \frac{225 \times 50^3}{12} = \frac{225}{12}(325 \times 10^4)\ \text{mm}^4. \quad r = \sqrt{\frac{\text{M.I.}}{\text{area}}},\ \text{so}$$

* As previously explained, it is more economical to arrange for the purlins to coincide with the panel points, but this cannot always be managed and the example here is included to show this worst case. In fact two 150 mm by 50 mm timbers would suffice for this member if there were no secondary bending stresses.

$$r = \sqrt{\frac{\frac{225}{12} \times 325 \times 10^4}{2 \times 225 \times 50}} = 52 \text{ mm}$$

The effective length of rafter backs in roof trusses is usually taken as 0.9 x the length of the member,

$$\text{therefore } \frac{l}{r} = \frac{0.9 \times 1\,575}{52} = 27.2$$

So from Table 27 the modification factor (medium-term load) is 1.18.

Therefore $c_{ppar} = 1.18 \times 7.9 = 9.32 \text{ N/mm}^2$

$$\text{Hence } \frac{f_{apar}}{f_{ppar}} + \frac{c_{apar}}{c_{ppar}} = \frac{2.6}{9.125} + \frac{3.82}{9.32} = 0.285 + 0.484$$

$= 0.769.$

As this is below the 0.9 limiting value for slenderness ratios exceeding 20 the two 225 mm by 50 mm sections chosen for this member A1 are satisfactory.

OPEN TIMBER ROOFS*

The most notable example of this type of roof in this country is that of the historic London building, the Westminster Hall. This hammer-beam trussed roof of oak was found to be in an advanced state of disrepair due to the ravages of the death watch beetle and dry rot. and extensive restoration work on it was carried out immediately after the First World War, the new timbers being reinforced with steelwork.

The traditional open roof is still used sometimes for small churches, college libraries, refectories, etc. It is expensive, as hardwood is usually specified, the timbers are wrought and, for the sake of appearance, the scantlings are large, being in excess of the sizes sufficient to withstand the stresses incurred. For example, whilst 100 mm by 50 mm softwood spars may be adequate for the purpose, if these rafters are to be exposed, as they usually are in an open roof, they may be 100 mm by 100 mm if a mean appearance is to be avoided. The most popular of the hardwoods adopted is oak, but if the roof members are to be of softwood, pitch pine is the usual selection, partly because it can be obtained in large sizes.

A traditional example of an open timber roof is on Fig. 58. The key section at C shows the clear span to be 9 m and the height from the floor to the underside of the collar beam of the truss is the same; the trusses are usually spaced at from 3.6 to 4.2 m centres, the section at B shows this distance to be 4 m.

The upper portion of the truss is in the form of a king-post truss – see brief description in Chap. I, Vol. III. Below this, each of the two inclined members (braces) is morticed and tenoned to the collar beam and the vertical wall post, which is let into and supported by the stone corbel (built into the wall) and tenoned into the short horizontal member, the sole. The latter receives the principal rafter, is supported on a stone pad at one end and its other end is tenoned and pinned into the brace. As shown at A, G and H, a curved gusset piece, tenoned into the adjacent members, is provided at the intersection between the collar beam and brace.

For aesthetic reasons, as mentioned above, the members are of large size, the thickness being 200 mm. The purlins are 200 mm by 200 mm. The spars, which are also exposed, are unduly large, being 125 mm by 100 mm laid flat (*i.e.*, measuring 125 mm on soffit); as shown at B, these spars are spaced uniformly 311 mm apart. The collar beam and braces have chamfered edges – see A, H and the enlarged section at J. The struts are shown slightly curved, although these may be of the conventional straight type, in which case the size would be reduced to 200 mm by 200 mm.

As indicated, the mortice and tenon joints are secured with hardwood pegs or dowels which, if tradition is followed, may be left projecting. In addition, the truss structure is strengthened by the provision of straps and/or bolts.

As shown at A, B and C, external buttresses are provided to assist in counteracting the thrust from the roof. Although not always necessary, these are sometimes adopted as an architectural feature. The intervening walling is shown of 440 mm thickness, and whilst this has been exceeded (even in recent examples) it is usually necessary to economize in such walling by adopting cavity construction.

Another traditional example of an open roof is on Fig. 59. The upper portion is of king-post construction and the collar beam, ribs and lower ends of the wall posts are shaped to conform to a semicircle of 3.58 m radius. Much of the above description is applicable, but the principal rafters, king post, struts, purlins and spars are smaller, and the thickness of the collar beam and wall posts is less. The collar beam and ribs, however, are out of wide stuff and must be specially selected if they are shaped out of solid timber; alternatively glued laminated construction can be adopted (see below). It will be observed that the curved portion of the truss is in five pieces, the four joints being morticed, tenoned and pegged. Each joint is twice bolted and the collar beam and principal rafters are

* In a general sense the term "open roof" may be applied to all roofs which are not enclosed with plaster, etc., and where the members are therefore exposed. Here it is restricted to those roofs where dressed timber is employed chiefly as an internal architectural feature and not solely for utilitarian purposes. In the examples shown of the traditional roof trusses, relatively large timbers are used and although the construction is still adopted for new buildings it has largely given way to glued laminated structures (see Vol. III and p. 167) in the U.K. In countries abroad where a plentiful supply of large baulk timber is freely available, the open roof with such timbers is used in preference to the more laborious built-up laminated work.

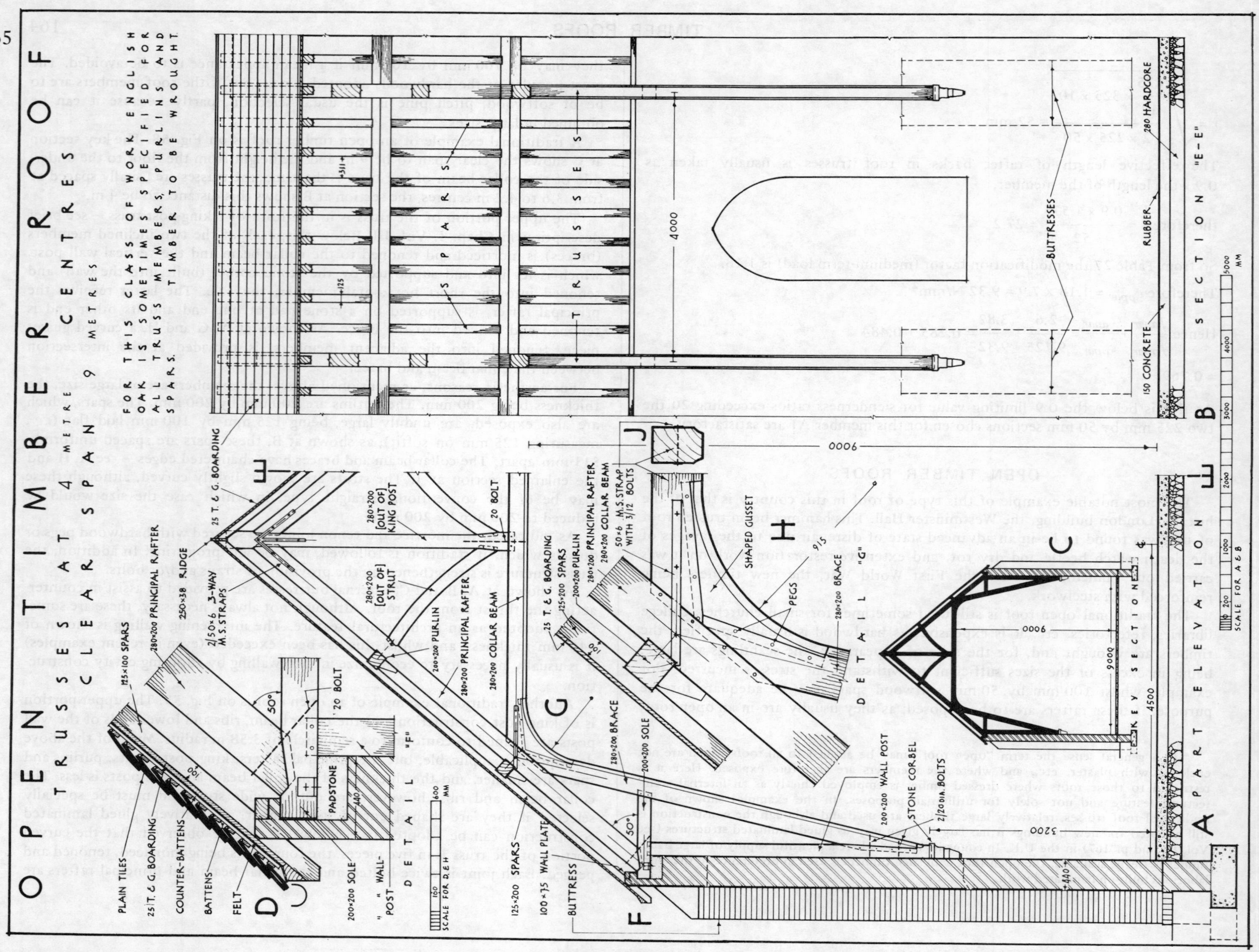

OPEN TIMBER ROOF

TRUSSES AT 4 METRE CENTRES
CLEAR SPAN 9 METRES

FOR THIS CLASS OF WORK ENGLISH OAK IS SOMETIMES SPECIFIED FOR ALL TRUSS MEMBERS, PURLINS AND SPARS. TIMBER TO BE WROUGHT.

PLAIN TILES
25 T. & G. BOARDING
COUNTER-BATTENS
BATTENS
FELT
125×100 SPARS
280×200 PRINCIPAL RAFTER
100
50°
PADSTONE
20 BOLT
200×200 SOLE
440
" " WALL-POST
DETAIL "F"
D

SCALE FOR D, E, H 100 600 MM

250×38 RIDGE
2/50×6 3-WAY M.S. STRAPS
25 T. & G. BOARDING
E
280×200 [OUT OF] STRUT
280×200 [OUT OF] KING POST
200×200 PURLIN
280×200 PRINCIPAL RAFTER
280×200 COLLAR BEAM
20 BOLT
125×200 SPARS
100×75 WALL PLATE
BUTTRESS
G
280×200 BRACE
50°
200×200 SOLE
F

25 T. & G. BOARDING
125×200 SPARS
200×200 PURLIN
280×200 PRINCIPAL RAFTER
280×200 COLLAR BEAM
50×6 M.S. STRAP WITH 3/12 BOLTS
100
J
SHAPED GUSSET
PEGS
915
H
280×200 BRACE
DETAIL "G"

200×200 WALL POST
STONE CORBEL
2/20 DIA. BOLTS
3200
440
9000
KEY SECTION
C
9000
4500
A PART ELEVATION

125
311
SPARS
TRUSSES
4000
9000
BUTTRESSES
150 CONCRETE
RUBBER
280 HARDCORE
B SECTION "E-E"

SCALE FOR A & B 200 1000 2000 3000 4000 5000 MM

FIGURE 58

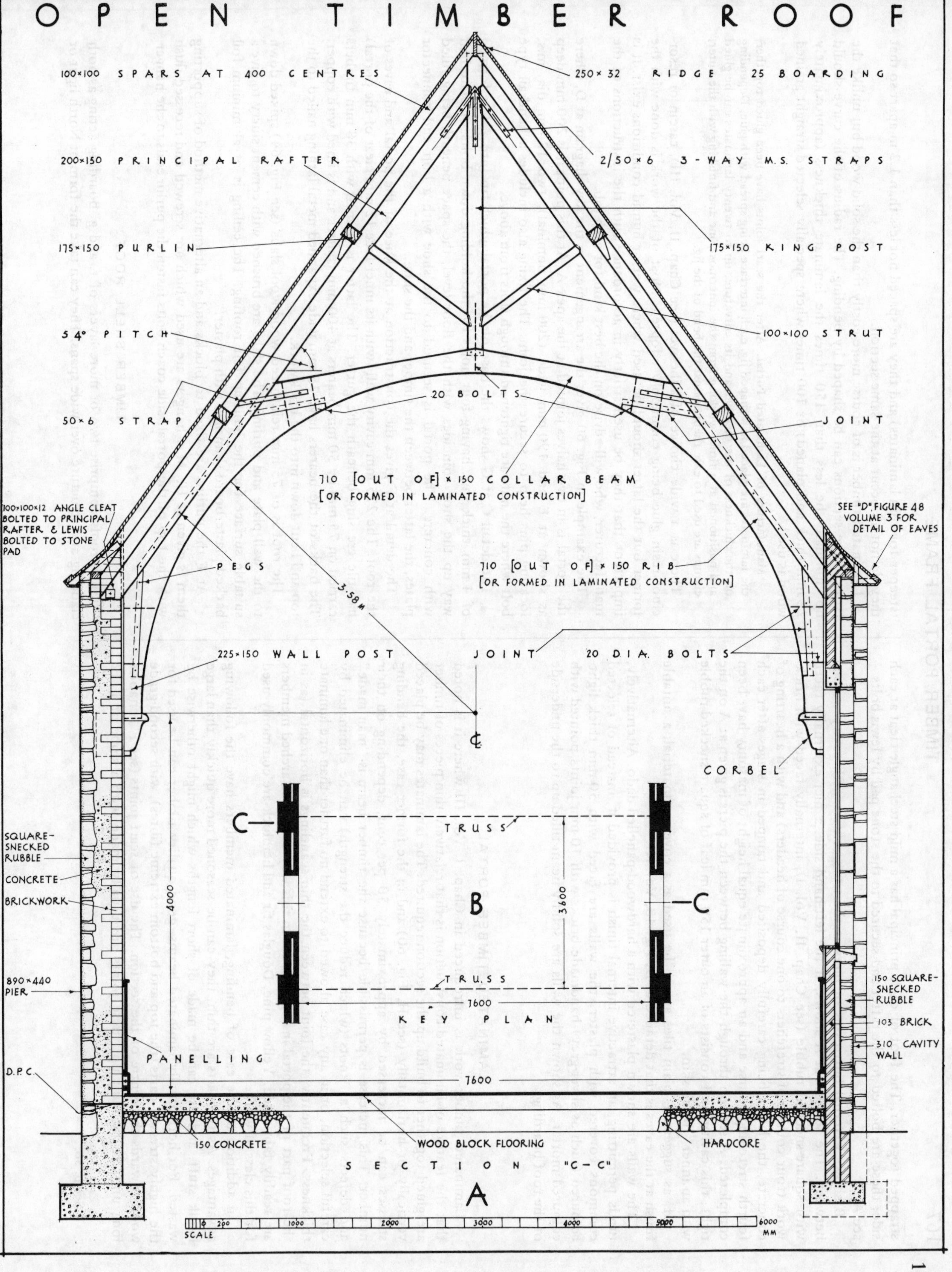
OPEN TIMBER ROOF
100×100 SPARS AT 400 CENTRES
250×32 RIDGE 25 BOARDING
200×150 PRINCIPAL RAFTER
2/50×6 3-WAY M.S. STRAPS
175×150 PURLIN
175×150 KING POST
100×100 STRUT
54° PITCH
20 BOLTS
50×6 STRAP
JOINT
710 [OUT OF] × 150 COLLAR BEAM
[OR FORMED IN LAMINATED CONSTRUCTION]
100×100×12 ANGLE CLEAT BOLTED TO PRINCIPAL RAFTER & LEWIS BOLTED TO STONE PAD
SEE "D" FIGURE 48 VOLUME 3 FOR DETAIL OF EAVES
PEGS
710 [OUT OF] × 150 RIB
[OR FORMED IN LAMINATED CONSTRUCTION]
3.58 M
225×150 WALL POST
JOINT
20 DIA. BOLTS
℄
CORBEL
C—
TRUSS
SQUARE-SNECKED RUBBLE
CONCRETE
BRICKWORK
4000
B
3600
—C
890×440 PIER
TRUSS
7600
KEY PLAN
150 SQUARE-SNECKED RUBBLE
103 BRICK
310 CAVITY WALL
PANELLING
D.P.C.
7600
150 CONCRETE
WOOD BLOCK FLOORING
HARDCORE
SECTION "C–C"
A
SCALE
0
200
1000
2000
3000
4000
5000
6000 MM

FIGURE 59

strapped together. The foot of each principal has a mild steel angle cleat at each side; these are bolted to the rafter and secured to the stone pad by lewis bolts — see A.

B shows external buttresses or piers at the truss centres with cavity walling between. The section at A shows, at the left-hand side, a pier externally faced with square-snecked rubble (see Chap. II, Vol. I), internally faced with brickwork (four courses of stretchers to one course of headers) and with a hearting of concrete, the latter being carefully deposited and tamped in stages after each fourth stretching course and an approximate equal height of masonry have been completed. A section through the walling between the piers is given at A on the right; this cavity wall consists of an outer 150 mm leaf of square-snecked rubble with an inner $\frac{1}{2}$ brick skin.

If, as suggested, plain tiles are to be used as a covering material, a suitable finish at the eaves is that detailed at D, Fig. 48, Vol. III.

The walls are shown plastered with a hardwood-panelled dado. Alternatively, funds permitting, an attractive internal finish is provided if, instead of selected commons covered with plaster, the walls are faced with 50 mm thick light-coloured (such as silver-grey) handmade bricks with 10 mm joints pointed with coloured mortar. As shown the walls are solidly beam-filled up to the underside of the roof boarding.

LAMINATED TIMBER PORTAL*

Laminated timber-work is introduced in Chap. I, Vol. III where it is noted that the feature of laminated construction is that relatively thin pieces of timber are glued together to build up the section required. The laminates may be placed vertically or horizontally (see H, Fig. 60) and in the former case, the bending stresses can be increased by approximately 50 per cent, depending on their number. This increase is permissible because the timber beam is "man made" and defects such as knots (which reduce the strength) can be eliminated by careful selection, or in any case allowed to extend no further than one laminate thickness. Frequently, the joint between the thin scantlings is horizontal (as in the roof part of the portal in Fig. 60), for in this way curved or arched members are readily fabricated. Yellow pine, Douglas fir and hemlock are commonly used for this class of work.

In addition to the ease of bending, laminated members have the following advantages. As the parts are thin, they can be seasoned more quickly than large baulk stuff, and use can be made of short lengths which might otherwise be wasted. For horizontally laminated beams, good quality timber can be used for the highly stressed parts (the top and bottom extreme fibres), with second-grade wood towards the centre of the section. The use of scarf joints (see F′) enables long units to be built up; these joints are usually made with a slope of 1 : 12 (steeper for thin laminates) and they are spaced not less than 1.2 m apart so that they do not all occur at the same section.

Laminated timber is of course more costly than the solid wood but unlike the latter, large sections can be shaped by bending. The radius of the curve should not normally be less than 150 times the laminate thickness (approximately 22 mm thick and planed) or 100 times where specially selected straight grained wood is used.

Manufacture of Laminated Portal. After the scarf joints have been glued together, the laminates are placed in a shaped jig, each interface being spread with glue. Depending on the thickness of the member and its curvature, up to twenty laminates can be glued and positioned at a time, working from the innermost one and finishing with the outer; clamps are used to ease them against the bend of the jig.

There is a wide choice of adhesives (see Chap. II, Vol. III), casein or resorcinol resin glue being commonly adopted. Most of the work is done with the former but the latter should be used where wet or humid conditions exist. It is important that they be used strictly in accordance with the instructions of the manufacturer, who will advise on the best kind for each job.

The example in Fig. 60 gives the arrangement in the key diagram at D, where the portal is in two halves jointed at the apex A. At this point it is 200 mm deep as shown at E and 190 mm wide (200 mm nominal); two 12 mm dia. m.s. locating pins help to secure the joint. The fixing also includes a handrail type bolt where the nuts are tightened through slots from above.

The detail C at G shows the base of the portal which fits into a shoe formed of 4 mm thick m.s. having four holes for the holding down bolts. A plate half way up the shoe coincides with the floor level, the space beneath being filled with concrete. The portal is secured to the shoe with a bolt and connector plates, the latter between the timber and the shoe.

The detail at F gives the construction at the knee of the portal and eaves of the roof. The 275 mm cavity wall (with its inner face 12 mm clear of the portal) has tile creasing beneath the gutter. The latter is framed with 38 mm timbers carried on 75 mm by 50 mm bearers at 400 mm centres and is lined with copper. The backs of the bearers have 75 mm wide expanded metal lathing nailed to the top and bent down into the brickwork.

The roof is of 75 mm reinforced wood-wool slabs (see Fig. 64) spiked down to the wall plate and purlins. The slabs are brushed with cement slurry to give a suitable surface for the built-up felt roofing. The ceiling is of aluminium foil backed plasterboard skimmed with plaster.

At F the purlins are fixed to blocks and an alternative method of supporting them is given at H. M.s. hangers are used which are screwed and recessed flush with the top of the portal, side coach bolts fasten the purlin ends to the hanger.

TIMBER SHELL ROOF

Such roofs comprise two or more layers of t. and g. boarding acting as both cladding and structure over wide spans. They can take the form of North light or

* See p. 36.

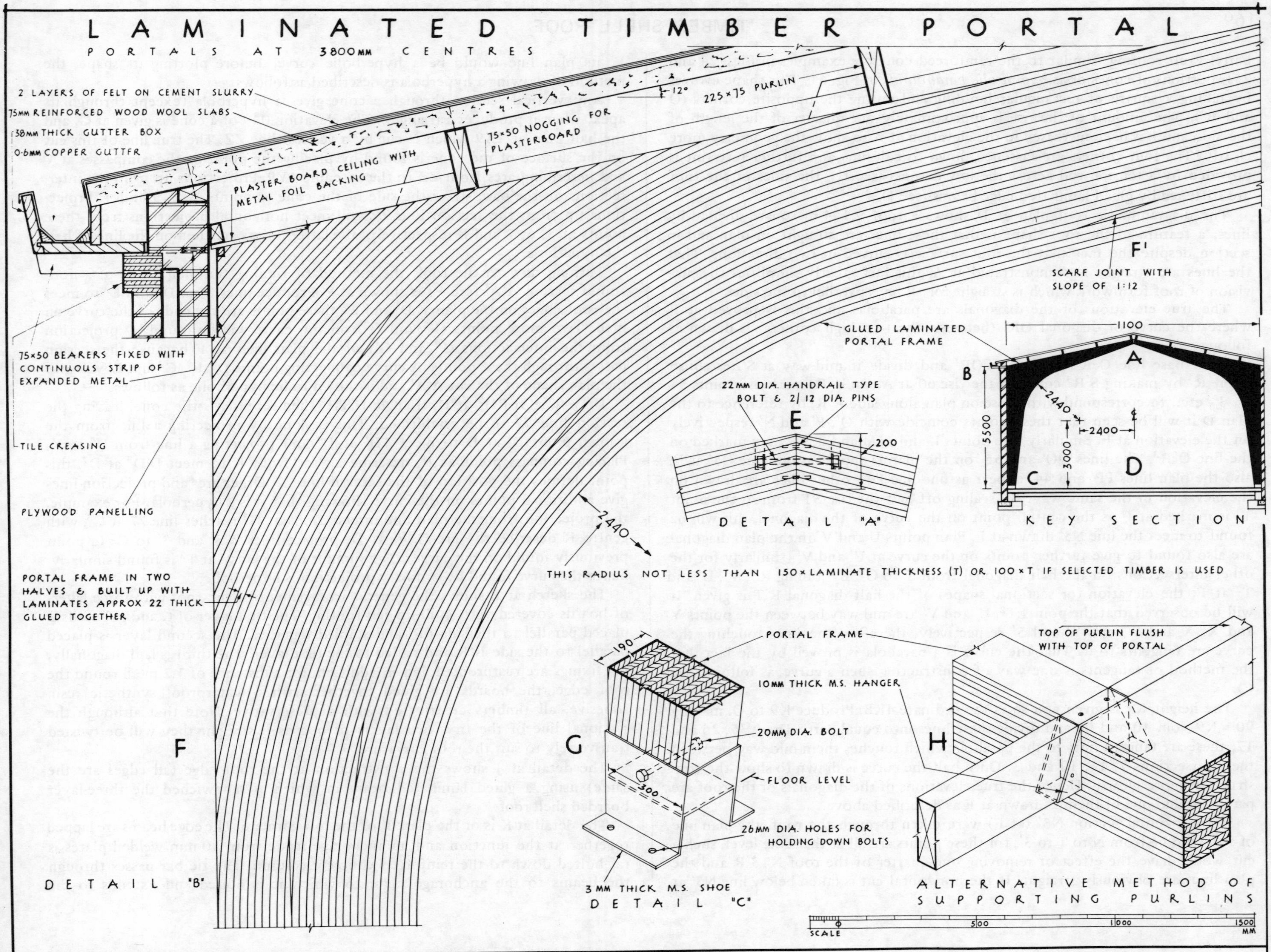

LAMINATED TIMBER PORTAL

PORTALS AT 3800MM CENTRES

2 LAYERS OF FELT ON CEMENT SLURRY
75MM REINFORCED WOOD WOOL SLABS
38MM THICK GUTTER BOX
0·6MM COPPER GUTTER
PLASTER BOARD CEILING WITH METAL FOIL BACKING
75×50 NOGGING FOR PLASTERBOARD
12°
225×75 PURLIN
75×50 BEARERS FIXED WITH CONTINUOUS STRIP OF EXPANDED METAL
TILE CREASING
PLYWOOD PANELLING
PORTAL FRAME IN TWO HALVES & BUILT UP WITH LAMINATES APPROX 22 THICK GLUED TOGETHER
2440
THIS RADIUS NOT LESS THAN 150× LAMINATE THICKNESS (T) OR 100×T IF SELECTED TIMBER IS USED
F
DETAIL "B"

F'
SCARF JOINT WITH SLOPE OF 1:12
GLUED LAMINATED PORTAL FRAME
1100
A
B
2440
3500
2400
2000
D
C
KEY SECTION

22MM DIA. HANDRAIL TYPE BOLT & 2/12 DIA PINS
E
200
DETAIL "A"

PORTAL FRAME
190
G
20MM DIA. BOLT
300
FLOOR LEVEL
26MM DIA HOLES FOR HOLDING DOWN BOLTS
3 MM THICK M.S. SHOE
DETAIL "C"

TOP OF PURLIN FLUSH WITH TOP OF PORTAL
10MM THICK M.S. HANGER
H
ALTERNATIVE METHOD OF SUPPORTING PURLINS

SCALE 0 500 1000 1500 MM

FIGURE 60

barrel vault roofing (similar to the reinforced concrete examples in Figs. 24 and 25), portions of cones or as *hyperbolic paraboloids* in Fig. 61. This shape evolves by taking a square or rectangular building and raising the opposite corners (O and R′). The amount of the rise is approximately one-quarter of the length of the side and has been increased in the elevation at A to show the geometry more clearly. The four corners are fastened down to columns and further restraint is provided by a tension rod across the low corners (see H), the sides of the roof are stiffened by glued laminated edge beams (see J).

The diagrammatic roof plan at D shows a roof 9.144 m square divided by lines, a feature of the roof shape is that these lines are straight on plan and in section despite the fact that the roof surface is curved in two directions. That the lines are straight is demonstrated at A, this fact greatly simplifies the provision of roof formwork which is straight for all lines parallel to the sides.

The true elevations of the diagonals are parabolas and this is proved at F where the curve of diagonal OR′ (between the two high corners) is drawn as follows.

Draw base line O^2R^2 parallel to OR′ and divide it mid-way at S′, establish point R^3 by making $S'R^3$ equal to the rise 60 at A. On R^2R^3 mark off points 5′, 4′, 3′, etc., to correspond with those on plan along side R′R; by reference to the plan D it will be seen that these points coincide with Q′, P′ and N′ respectively on the elevation at F. Similarly, the points L and 1, M and 2, etc., are marked on the line O^2R^3. The lines QQ′ and 55′ on the plan D appear as one line Q5′ at F; also the plan lines PP′ and 44′ appear as one line P4′, other lines are drawn on the elevation in the same way. By scaling off half the rise ST from A, the point T^2 is marked at F as the central point on the curve of the diagonal, this will be found to meet the line N3′ drawn at F. Plan points U and V on the plan diagonal are also found to give further points on the curve at U′ and V′ (similarly for the other intersections on the half diagonal from T to O). By joining R^2, V′, U′ and T^2 at F, the elevation (or sectional shape) of the half diagonal R′T is given. It will be observed that the points T^2, U′ and V′ are mid-way between the points Y and X, X and W, and W and 5′ respectively, therefore the lines touching the curve are tangents to it. That the curve is a parabola is proved by the fact that the method of tangents is one way of constructing such a curve, as follows (see C).

The height K9 is given and so is the ordinate 4K8. Produce K9 to O, making 90 = K9, join 40 and 08 and divide these lines into equal parts. Draw 35, 26 and 17, these are tangent lines to the parabola which touches them mid-way between the intersections 7, 11, 10 and 3. Only half the curve is drawn to show the construction more clearly. Hence the true elevations of the diagonals of the roof are parabolas and one of them is drawn at F as described above.

If a horizontal section N3′ (at F) were taken through the roof, the plan line of it would be from N to T to 3′, for these points are all at the same level; such a cut would have the effect of removing one-quarter of the roof NT3′R and the plan lines are obviously straight. If the horizontal cut is taken below line N3′ at F, its plan line would be a hyperbolic curve. Before plotting its shape, the method of drawing a hyperbola is described as follows.

Any vertical section through a cone gives a hyperbola (except through its apex, when it produces a triangle). The elevation 049 of a cone is given at G, and the half plan at 4K9 which is cut by a vertical line ZZ. The true line of this cut on the surface of the cone is found by placing the point of the compasses at Y and describing arcs from ZZ to the base line 4Y9. Projections up from the intersections on the base strike the side of the cone at points 1, 2, 3 and 4. Projections up from the section line ZZ will meet horizontal projections from these points at 5, 6, 7 and 8 respectively, the latter points are then on the line of half the hyperbola.

Turning now to the roof, the method of finding the plan shape of a horizontal section A′A′ (see F) is shown at E. Produce lines from D^3 and E^3 to meet the roof edges on the plan at D′ and E′, these points are the ends of the curve on plan. Two more points (F^2 and G^2) on the curve will be found by projection from the intersections (F′ and G′) of the plan lines at F because the section passes through these points. A curve connecting points D′, F^2, G^2 and E′ will give the plan shape of the cut A′A′ and is shown to be hyperbolic as follows.

Draw line $H'RH^2$ at D, triangle $H'TH^2$ then represents the cone, leaving the section line 77 to be established. This is done by projecting a line from the known point D′ at D to meet TH′ at D^4 and projecting a line from D^4 to K. Placing compass point at R, describe an arc from K to meet $D'D^3$ at D^2, this point defines the position of the section line 77. Other arcs and projection lines give additional points on the curve showing that it is a hyperbola. For example, the projection from the plan line intersections at G^2 reaches line 77 at G^3, with centre R describe the arc G^3W' at D, project lines W′3′ and 3′ to G^2 (a point previously found on the curve). The summit of the curve at T^3 is found similarly, hence the curve found by ordinary projection is hyperbolic.

The sketch at B shows the general arrangement of the roof with three layers of boards covered with built-up felt roofing. The first layer of t. and g. boards is placed parallel to the side 6R′ and stapled together. The second layer is placed parallel to the side R′R and nailed to the first layer. The third is laid diagonally. All fixings are rustproofed and in addition, for a distance of 1.2 m all round the roof edge, the boards are glued together with a waterproof synthetic resin adhesive; all timbers are treated with a preservative. Note that although the sectional line of the first two layers of boards is straight they will be twisted transversely to suit the roof curvature.

The detail at J shows the construction at the roof edge (all edges are the same) using a glued laminated beam in which is sandwiched the three-layer boarded shell roof.

The detail at K is of the plan B′ of the low corner 6. The edge beams are lapped together at the junction and an anchorage made from 10 mm welded plates is rag-bolted down to the reinforced concrete column. The tie bar passes through the beams to the anchorage plate to which it is bolted and extends to the

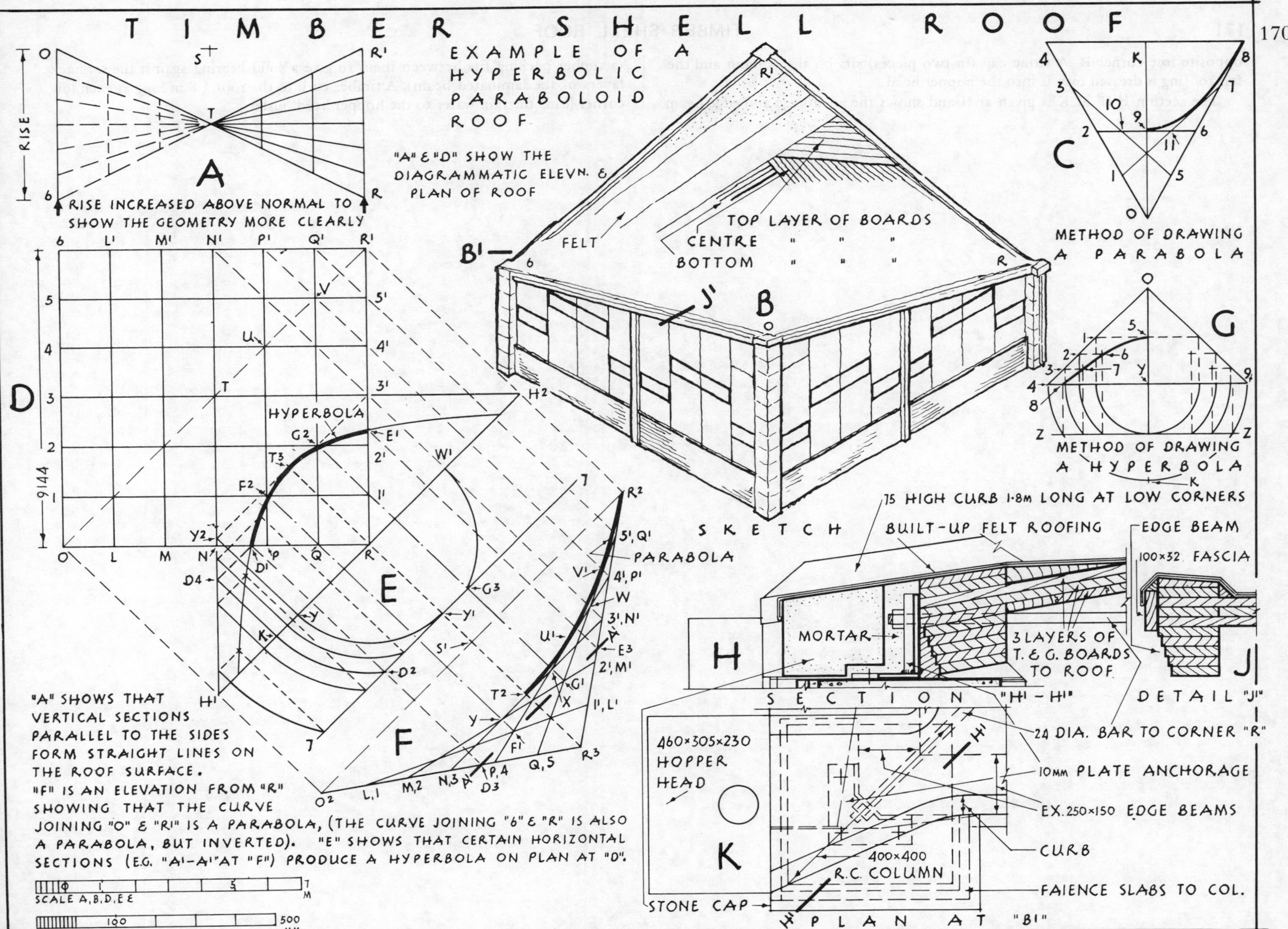
TIMBER SHELL ROOF
EXAMPLE OF A HYPERBOLIC PARABOLOID ROOF
"A" & "D" SHOW THE DIAGRAMMATIC ELEVN. & PLAN OF ROOF
RISE INCREASED ABOVE NORMAL TO SHOW THE GEOMETRY MORE CLEARLY
TOP LAYER OF BOARDS
CENTRE " " "
BOTTOM " " "
FELT
SKETCH
METHOD OF DRAWING A PARABOLA
METHOD OF DRAWING A HYPERBOLA
HYPERBOLA
PARABOLA
75 HIGH CURB 1·8M LONG AT LOW CORNERS
BUILT-UP FELT ROOFING
EDGE BEAM
100×32 FASCIA
MORTAR
3 LAYERS OF T. & G. BOARDS TO ROOF
SECTION "H1-H1"
DETAIL "J"
24 DIA. BAR TO CORNER "R"
460×305×230 HOPPER HEAD
10MM PLATE ANCHORAGE
EX. 250×150 EDGE BEAMS
CURB
400×400 R.C. COLUMN
FAIENCE SLABS TO COL.
STONE CAP
PLAN AT "B1"
"A" SHOWS THAT VERTICAL SECTIONS PARALLEL TO THE SIDES FORM STRAIGHT LINES ON THE ROOF SURFACE.
"F" IS AN ELEVATION FROM "R" SHOWING THAT THE CURVE JOINING "O" & "R1" IS A PARABOLA, (THE CURVE JOINING "6" & "R" IS ALSO A PARABOLA, BUT INVERTED). "E" SHOWS THAT CERTAIN HORIZONTAL SECTIONS (E.G. "A1-A1" AT "F") PRODUCE A HYPERBOLA ON PLAN AT "D".
SCALE A, B, D, E, E
SCALE FOR H, J & K
9144
RISE

FIGURE 61

opposite low corner R. A stone cap (in two pieces) sits on the column and the felt roofing is dressed over it into the hopper head.

The section H'H' at K is given at H and shows the anchorage and edge beam (a timber packing fits between them to give a solid bearing against the set-back layers of the laminated beam). A timber curb to the roof 1.8 m long at each low corner leads the rain water to the hopper-head outlet.

CHAPTER SIX

LIGHT-WEIGHT ROOFING MATERIALS

Syllabus. Aluminium sheets. Wood-wool, strawboard, aluminium and steel decking covered with built-up felt roofing. Ventilators. Roof lights.

For the roofing of domestic buildings, there is still a strong preference for the traditional tiles* and slates, but as the minimum pitch for the former is 24° and for the latter 21°, it would be uneconomic to use them on large-span structures because of the additional framing members required to support these fairly heavy materials over such pitches. For wide span structures, such as industrial buildings and the like, it is desirable to reduce the weight of the roof covering and the cubic content of the roof space as much as possible; this economizes in heating costs as well as structural framing.

The light-weight roofing materials are of two types: sheeting and decking, and because of their larger size, are laid more quickly than the traditional materials. The former are aluminium or fibre-cement sheets† which constitute both covering and waterproofing – they are laid on sloping roofs. Decking consists of wood-wool, strawboard, aluminium and steel units – all are used as the covering and require a waterproof layer of asphalt or roofing felt, the latter in one or up to three layers; decking is intended mainly for flat roofs‡ but is also used for sloping roofs.

The use and application of all these proprietary materials as roof sheeting and decking is now described; reference should be made to pp. 253–257 concerning roof insulation and vapour barriers – important provisions.

* The heavier roof coverings of slate and plain tiling are described in Vol. I, together with lead and built-up felt roofing. In Vol. III, further plain tiling and pan, Italian and Spanish tiling details in clay and concrete are given. In the same volume, stone slating, shingling and thatching are given, also copper and zinc coverings, fibre-cement slates and corrugated sheeting.

† Fibre-cement sheeting is described in Vol. III.

‡ It is important to remember that the flatter the roof pitch, the greater the suction due to wind on it. Positive wind pressure is only assumed to act on pitches exceeding 30°; for flatter pitches, suction is usually the most dangerous effect and may exceed the superimposed loading. It is therefore important to ensure that roof coverings and their supports are well fastened down, and this is particularly so with low pitches. In addition to carrying wind forces the roof must withstand superimposed loading including snow, according to its slope and usage (see p. 130).

The designation of different kinds of roof coverings for fire resistance purposes (see pp. 83, 99, 100) is given in Table 22.

Aluminium Roof Sheeting (Fig. 62). Aluminium alloyed with a small percentage of manganese for strength, is the lightest of all roof coverings. It is impervious to weather and does not corrode like steel; after a while, a thin film of oxide forms on the surface which protects the metal in the core, thereafter, subsequent oxidation is negligible. Aluminium must not be allowed to come in contact with other metals, concrete or brickwork because of danger of electrolytic action. Aluminium that is used adjacent to these materials should be protected by painting with bituminous, red oxide or zinc chromate paint. Where the roof sheeting is placed on steel frames it is sufficient in most cases to paint the frame with a leadless paint, or an aluminium or bituminous paint. However, in marine conditions or where humidity is high or if corrosive fumes are present then the aluminium sheeting must be insulated from the steel frame by covering the latter with self-adhesive p.v.c. tape or felt strips. If these precautions are not taken, corrosion of the aluminium would occur. Aluminium has a high coefficient of expansion (about twice that of steel) and so when it is used in large areas, adequate provision for movement must be made at the fixings. Aluminium alloy sheeting is corrugated or troughed to different depths according to the span and load; it is available in several widths and lengths.

B.S. 4868: *Profiled Aluminium Sheet* for Building describes three types of sheet for roofing and side cladding: *Type S* which is the one at A, Fig. 62; *Type A* shown at C; *Type B* is similar to *Type A* but the depth of the trough is 44.5 mm.

Aluminium roof sheeting has a *U*-value of 4.54 W/m^2 °C and the surface finish can be plain, embossed or baked paint.

At A,* the cross section of 76.2 mm pitch corrugated sheeting is given. It is made in lengths up to 12.04 m, 914 mm wide and obtainable in 0.55, 0.7 and 0.9 mm thicknesses. The fixing is similar to fibre-cement sheeting as described in Vol. III; at the purlins a hook bolt is required at every third corrugation, with inter-

* Manufactured by the British Aluminium Co. Ltd.

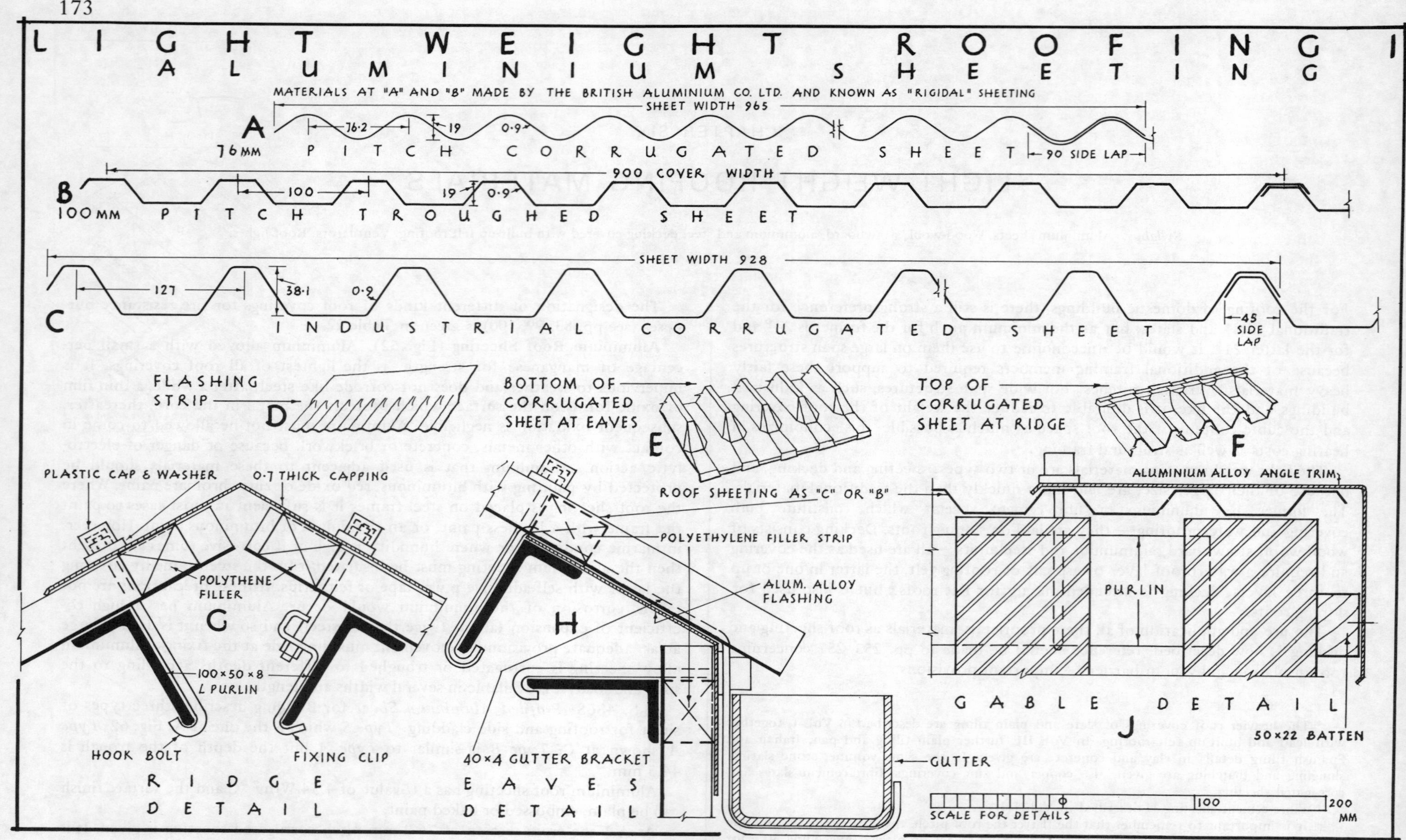

FIGURE 62

mediate seam bolts at end laps (150 mm) and at 300 mm centres down the side laps (these may be 1½ to 2 corrugations). The sheeting is also used for vertical surfaces and can be had in curved lengths, plastic or glass fibre sheeting for roof lights is available of the same section. Aluminium eaves filler pieces and ridge cappings are used similar to those for fibre-cement construction. Using the 0.9 mm sheet the maximum purlin spacing is 1.35 m.

The troughed section at B* is made in the same thicknesses as A, up to 4.98 m long and 900 mm wide; fixing and purlin spacing is like that for A.

The troughed sheet at C† is made in 0.7, 0.9 and 1.2 mm thicknesses and cover widths from 635 to 1 016 mm; the maximum length is 10.5 m. Using the 1.2 mm thickness the widest purlin spacing is 2.7 m.

Due to the corrugations or troughs these must be sealed at the ridge, eaves, gable, etc. Sealing is done in three ways: by shaping and flattening the sheet at top (see F) and bottom (see E); by making use of flashing strips (see D) or filler strips of expanded polyethylene about 75 mm thick (see H) which fit inside the trough or corrugation.

The typical ridge detail at G has filler strips placed beneath the aluminium alloy ridge cap. The eaves at H shows filler strips and aluminium alloy flashing. The verge at J makes use of an aluminium alloy angle trim.

The example in Fig. 63 shows aluminium roof covering in the form of sheeting. The details are of Fural‡ sheeting, part of the longitudinal section is drawn at D. It is obtainable in rolls 686 and 1 143 mm wide and 20.6 and 12.3 m long respectively as at E, and is 0.71 mm thick and weighs 2.8 kg/m^2; it is made in natural as well as other colours; the special shape allows for thermal movement. The minimum pitch is 6°, spar supports are at 610 mm centres, and fixing is by means of concealed retaining strips nailed to battens at the same centres. The same section is also made in copper.

The detail of the strip is given at H, this is fixed to the batten by clout nails through slotted holes to allow for expansion and contraction, the ribs of the sheeting engage in the lugs of the retaining strip. The detail at E also shows the eaves finish, and those at F, J and K are of verge, ridge and hip respectively. The heavy aluminium clamping band at J secures the ridge capping, the hip at K shows how the ribs of the sheeting are flattened and dressed up for covering with a capping. The treatment at the valley comprises a standard gutter pressing held by clips, over which the sheeting is dressed.

Wood-wool Decking (Fig. 64). Wood-wool has good sound absorbing and thermal insulation qualities which make it an excellent building material; it is used for many purposes such as partitioning, ceilings, insulation of cold storage rooms, shuttering and lagging of water tanks as well as roof decking. Wood-wool is made from wood fibre interwoven together and cement-bonded under pressure in a mould. The resulting slab, varying in thickness from 12 mm to 100 mm and 600 mm wide by up to 3.9 m long, is allowed to mature for a short while before use. B.S. 1105 describes the specification for the material and provides for Type A and Type B slabs; the latter is the roofing quality of minimum thickness 51 mm. The slabs can be cut with the usual wood-working tools, they should be handled "on edge", stored flat and kept dry. The surface has a rough texture,

* Manufactured by The British Aluminium Co. Ltd.
† Manufactured by Alcan Ltd.
‡ Manufactured by Roberts Adlard & Co. Ltd., Croydon, who also make the same section in copper.

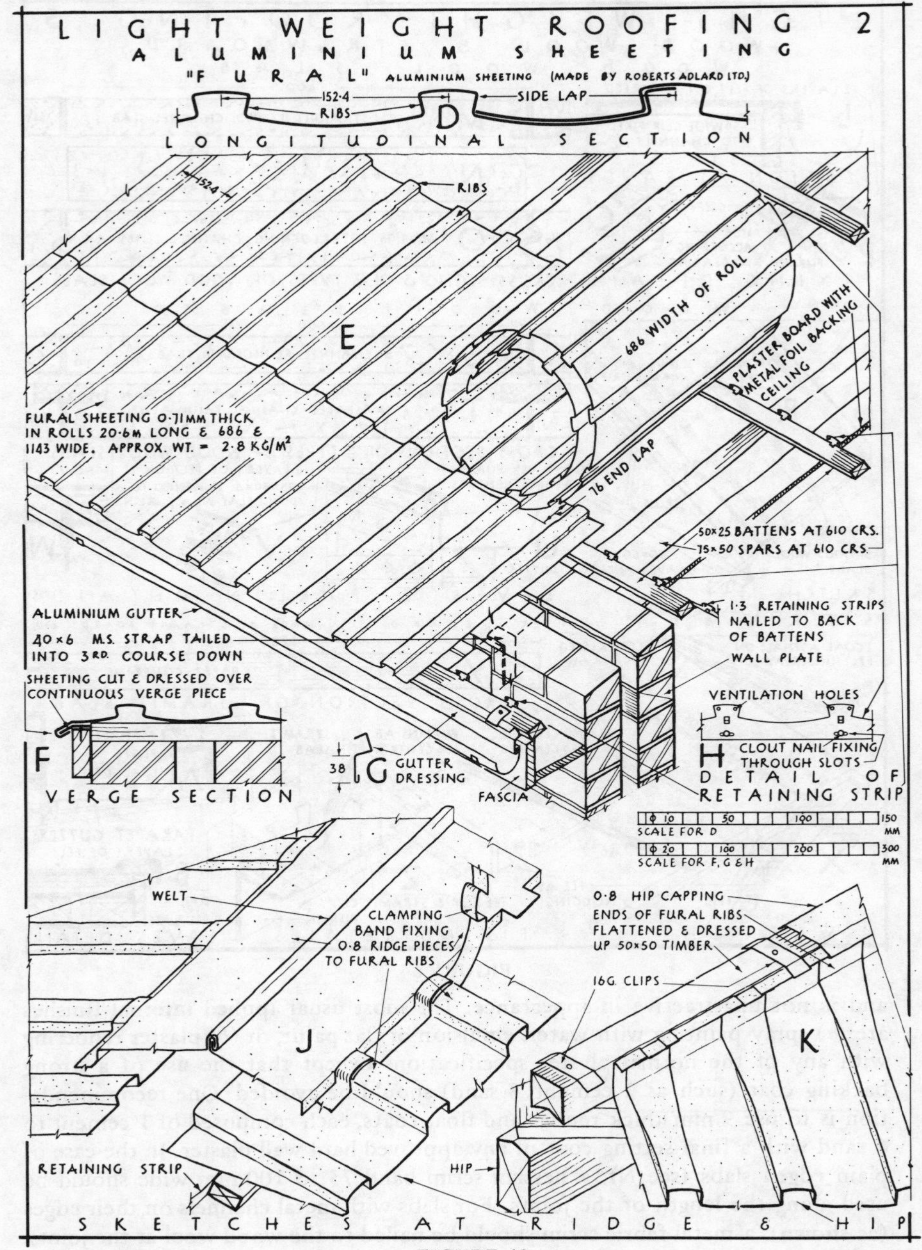

FIGURE 63

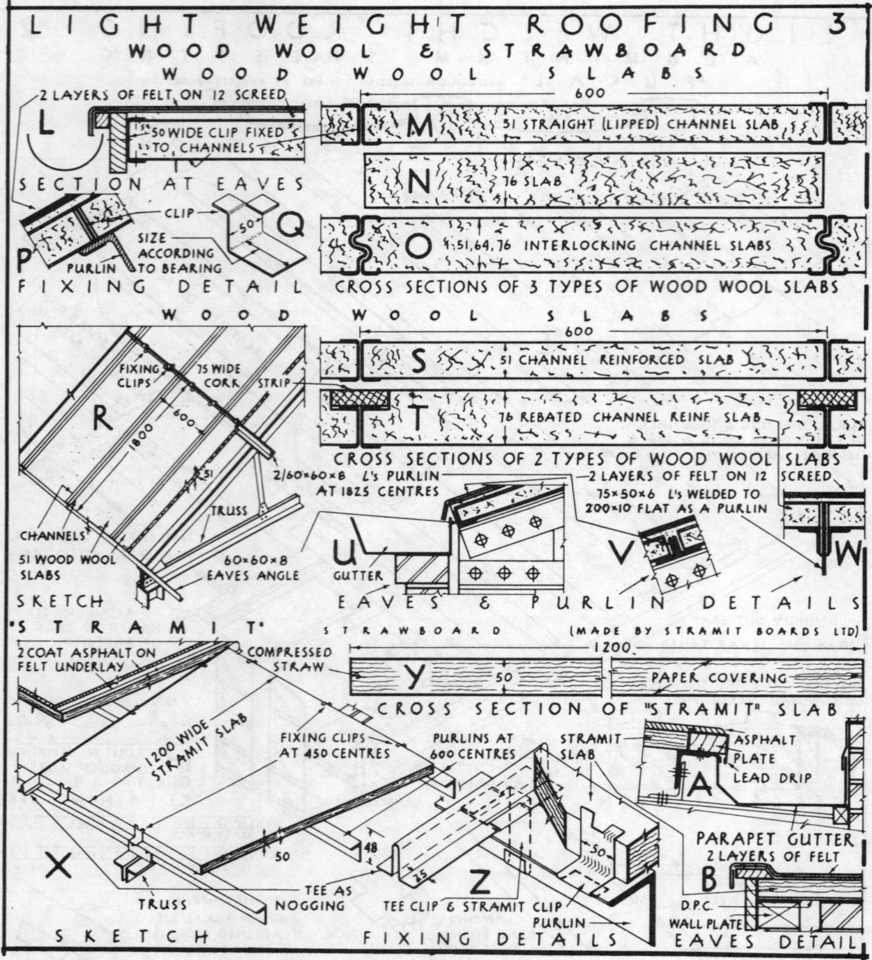

FIGURE 64

and is not unattractive in appearance. The most usual applied internal finishes are (*a*) spray painting with water, emulsion or flat paint, or (*b*) plaster rendering with any of the normal plaster specifications except that the use of a strong backing coat (such as 1 cement: 3 sand) should be avoided. One recommendation is to use 9 mm thick render and float coats, each composed of 1 cement to 6 sand with a final setting coat of any approved hard wall plaster. In the case of plain edged slabs (see N), a hessian scrim band 75 to 100 mm wide should be used along the length of the joints. For slabs with metal channels on their edges (as shown), a metal fabric scrim should be nailed to the wood-wool at the joints.

The top surface of a wood-wool roof must be sealed, *e.g.*, by a 12 mm thick cement and sand screed (or a cement slurry brushed on to close the interstices between the cemented fibres) covered with built-up felt roofing or asphalt.

The simplest type of wood-wool roof consists of 51 or 76 mm thick slabs as at N, nailed on timber joists at 600 and 900 mm centres respectively, the fixing to the joists is by 102 and 125 mm long clout nails, 125 mm apart. The maximum imposed load for these unreinforced slabs is 0.75 kN/m^2.

The strength of the panels can be increased by making them with light-gauge channels on the long edges as shown at M, O, S and T. The details L, M, O, S and T are wood-wool panels reinforced down their long edges with galvanised m.s. channels of different sections. This reinforcement increases the load carrying capacity of the 51 mm thick slab to 2 kN/m^2 over the maximum purlin centres of 2 m; for the 76 mm thick slab the corresponding values are 3.35 kN/m^2 over 3.9 m which values vary depending on the type of channel. The dead load of the material is 17 kg/m^2 per 25 mm thickness. Fixing of the reinforced slab is by means of clips shown at Q and by percolation of screed down the edges of the slabs. The eaves section of a flat roof (screed to falls being made by light-weight concrete) is shown at L where a 50 mm wide channel clip is secured to the abutting side channels of the slabs. Self-tapping screws fix the fascia to the clip. In the case of a pitched roof eaves, the lower edges of the units are secured by the more positive fixing of an angle as shown at R and U.

Various constructional details are given at R, U, V and W; the latter has a built-up purlin made with angles welded to both sides of a m.s. flat.

Wood-wool slabs can have various applied factory finishes on the upper face which obviate the need for the above mentioned on-site applied screed, which is required before the roof felting proceeds, viz.: The slabs can be pre-screeded with a cement: sand slurry or a bitumen: sand screed; or have a layer of felt bonded to the surface. The latter two when used with a self-adhesive waterproof tape over the joints ensure a showerproof roof prior to roof felting. Slab soffits also can have a cement: sand pre-applied slurry enabling direct decoration.

The thermal conductivity (k) of wood-wool is 0.081 W/m °C; the *U*-value of a 51 mm thick wood-wool slab with factory or site-applied cement or bitumen screed and three layers of felt is 1.21 W/m^2 °C (0.87 for the 76 mm thickness).

Strawboard Decking (Fig. 64). The details at X, Y, Z, A and B are of Stramit* board which is made of compressed straw with a thick paper covering conforming to B.S. 4046: Compressed Straw Building Slabs. The thickness is 50 mm, width 1.2 m and lengths of 1.8, 2.4, 2.7, 3 and 3.6 m. For roofing quality slabs, the paper is waterproofed sufficiently to withstand the effects of showers for a limited period until the covering is applied as described below. The board is also made with one layer of felt bonded to the upper surface; the lower surface is ready for immediate decoration. The board has other uses like wood-wool. When using this material for roofs it is important to have the roof space adequately ventilated.

* **Manufactured by Stramit Boards Ltd., see Chap. I, Vol. III.**

For roof decking the board must be supported at 600 mm centres and along all edges as shown at X. 1.2 m thick pressed steel nogging pieces as detailed at Z are used at the ends of the slab and fixing is by means of steel clips at 450 mm centres. When the slabs have been laid, the joints are taped with bitumen scrim and filled with mastic to render the roof showerproof before covering with felt or asphalt.

The parapet gutter detail at A shows a timber end plate secured to the purlin and a lead drip nailed to it on which the asphalt is dressed.

Strawboard has a density of 18.5 kg/m^2 for the 50 mm thickness, thermal conductivity (*Tc*) = 0.101 W/m °C. When used on a timber joist roof, felt weather-proofed and covered with chippings, the *U*-value is 1.027 W/m^2 °C (0.87 for the 76 mm thickness).

Aluminium Alloy and Steel Decking (Fig. 65). These two metals can be pressed to form troughed roof decking having a cross-section like that at B. The thickness of metal varies as shown in the table below; the depth of corrugations is 25, 35, 45, 65 and 85 mm to suit different loadings; sheet lengths are up to 10 m and widths vary from 450 to 900 mm. Some deckings have an additional soffit sheet as drawn at H which shows the general arrangement of the construction of a metal deck roof.

A felt vapour barrier is bonded with bitumen to the top of the deck on which an insulating media like fibreboard or expanded polystyrene is bonded to be covered with two or three layers of felt roofing; the top surface is finished with a layer of white stone chippings spread on bitumen to provide for solar reflectivity and reduce heat absorption in summer months. Using an insulating layer of 12.5 mm fibreboard or 38 mm polystyrene the *U*-value of such roofs would be 1.88 and 0.75 W/m^2 °C respectively.

The dead load of a 45 mm deep steel deck covered with two layers of felt on 12.5 mm fibreboard is 0.19 kN/m^2.

Examples of the maximum spans* for an imposed load of 0.75 kN/m^2 are in the following table.

Depth of Corrugation (mm)	Thickness of Metal (mm)	Maximum Span (m)			
		Aluminium		Steel	
		Single Span	Double Span	Single Span	Double Span
25	0.7			1.42	1.71
45	0.7			2.1	2.54
25	0.9	0.99	1.19	1.95	2.31
45	0.9	1.99	2.38	2.82	3.34
25	1.2	1.54	1.85		
45	1.2	2.25	2.67		
85	1.2	3.36	3.98		

* From Briggs Amasco Ltd., metal decks.

Where an aluminium deck is used in a building where humid conditions prevail then the deck should be insulated from the steel roof supports by a strip of felt or self-adhesive p.v.c. tape; also felt washers would be used for the fixings; these precautions are needed to prevent the danger of electrolytic action between the aluminium deck and the steel supports – see M.

The deck is fixed to the roof supports by hook bolts, or bolts and cleats (both shown at M) or by hammer drive screws, one being shown at C. The roof insulation is bonded with bitumen to the deck and also fastened down by self tapping screws (see A).

An eaves detail is drawn at E where an aluminium closure piece seals the open ends of the corrugations and has the final layer of felt dressed over it.

The construction at D shows how an expansion joint is formed in a deck roof; such a joint is needed at intervals of about 30 m.

Two ridge details are drawn at K and M showing the different methods of fixing the deck to the roof; in the latter the application of felt strips and washers illustrates the precautions mentioned above in regard to electrolytic action which can occur in humid conditions.

The purlin detail at G shows how the deck is lapped at the end joint between the sheets.

The simple verge detail at F has a welted apron flashing whilst the one at J has a pronounced projection formed with a galvanised steel trim.

The further application of metal roof decking is shown in Figs. 16, 17, 18 and 98.

Comparative Costs of Light-weight Roofing. Guidance on costs can be of a general nature only in a book of this type. The following information will be helpful and the costs quoted are in respect of the covering (as fixed) *only* and do not include the structure unless this is mentioned.

Considering the traditional roof of machine-made tiles on battens and felt (both included) to cost £*x* per m^2. Fibre sheeting plus 12 mm fibreboard lining costs the same. Metal decking with 12 mm fibreboard and three layers of felt costs 2.4*x*. Wood-wool slabs with three layers of felt on 12 mm screed costs approximately the same as the latter. A 150 mm concrete roof with screed, insulation board on bitumen and felt covering as before would be 3*x* including the concrete.

Ventilation. The section at L, Fig. 65, is of a typical roof *ventilator* made of 1.25 mm galvanized sheet steel covered with felt weatherproofing and bolted to a metal angle framework in the roof. The air flow depends on its height above the ground, the speed of the external air and the difference between the internal and external air temperatures. Assuming these three figures are 6 m, 5 km/hr and 7° C respectively, then the output of the ventilator is 28 m^3 of air per minute (the size of the opening in the roof being 300 mm by 600 mm). Alternatively, a 300 mm dia. fan installed in a 450 mm by 600 mm ventilator has an extraction capacity of 28 m^3/min, ignoring any assistance by natural conditions. The average factory requires about four air changes per hour.

LIGHT WEIGHT ROOFING 4

ALUMINIUM & STEEL DECKING

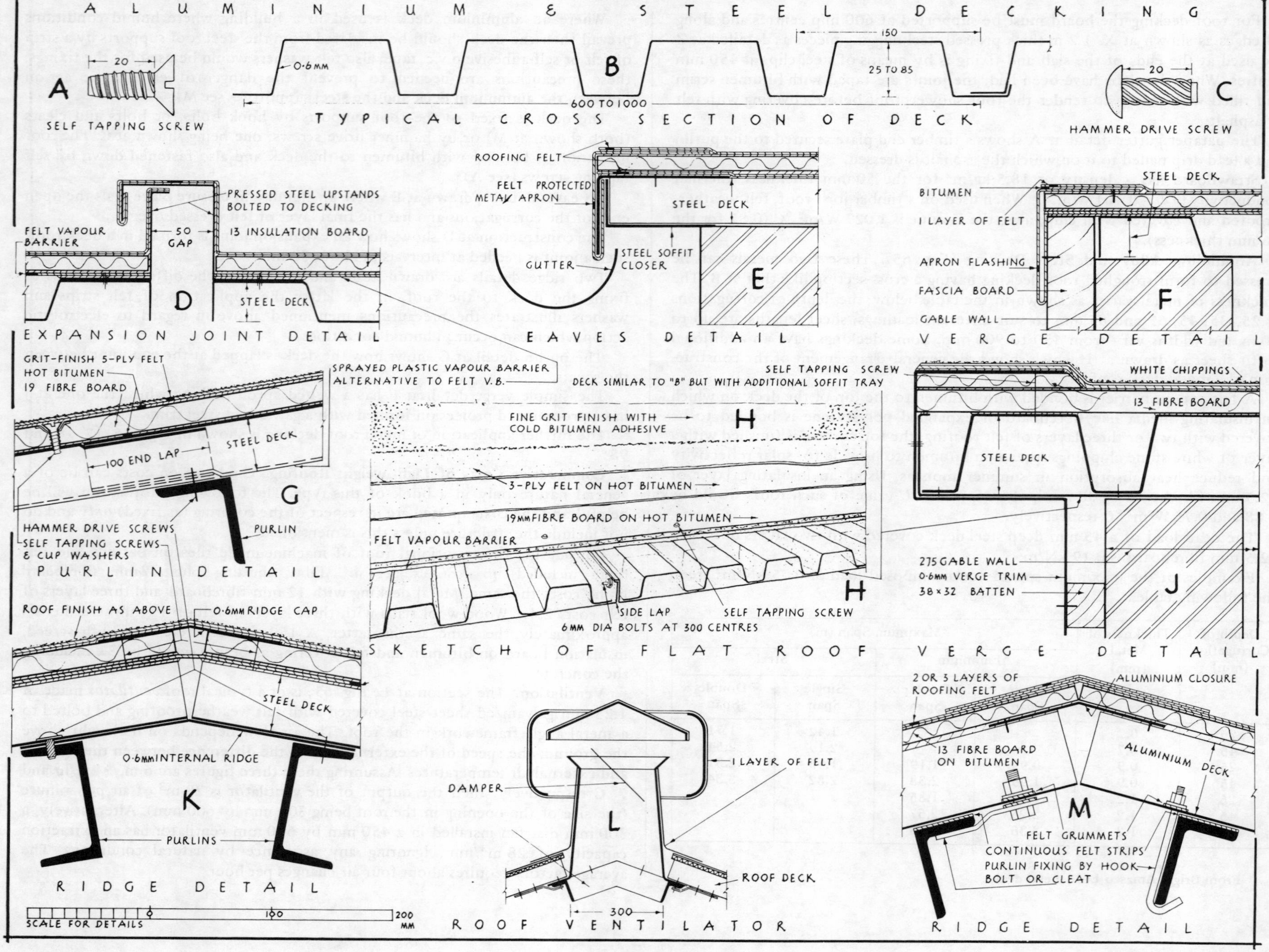

A
20
SELF TAPPING SCREW

B
0·6MM
150
25 TO 85
600 TO 1000
TYPICAL CROSS SECTION OF DECK

C
20
HAMMER DRIVE SCREW

PRESSED STEEL UPSTANDS BOLTED TO DECKING
FELT VAPOUR BARRIER
50 GAP
13 INSULATION BOARD
STEEL DECK
D
EXPANSION JOINT DETAIL

ROOFING FELT
FELT PROTECTED METAL APRON
STEEL DECK
STEEL SOFFIT CLOSER
GUTTER
E
EAVES DETAIL

STEEL DECK
BITUMEN
1 LAYER OF FELT
APRON FLASHING
FASCIA BOARD
GABLE WALL
F
VERGE DETAIL

GRIT-FINISH 5-PLY FELT
HOT BITUMEN
19 FIBRE BOARD
STEEL DECK
100 END LAP
G
HAMMER DRIVE SCREWS
SELF TAPPING SCREWS & CUP WASHERS
PURLIN
PURLIN DETAIL

SPRAYED PLASTIC VAPOUR BARRIER ALTERNATIVE TO FELT V.B.
DECK SIMILAR TO "B" BUT WITH ADDITIONAL SOFFIT TRAY
FINE GRIT FINISH WITH COLD BITUMEN ADHESIVE
H
3-PLY FELT ON HOT BITUMEN
19MM FIBRE BOARD ON HOT BITUMEN
FELT VAPOUR BARRIER
SIDE LAP
6MM DIA BOLTS AT 300 CENTRES
SELF TAPPING SCREW
H
SKETCH OF FLAT ROOF

SELF TAPPING SCREW
WHITE CHIPPINGS
13 FIBRE BOARD
STEEL DECK
275 GABLE WALL
0·6MM VERGE TRIM
38×32 BATTEN
J
VERGE DETAIL

ROOF FINISH AS ABOVE
0·6MM RIDGE CAP
STEEL DECK
0·6MM INTERNAL RIDGE
K
PURLINS
RIDGE DETAIL

1 LAYER OF FELT
DAMPER
L
ROOF DECK
300
ROOF VENTILATOR

2 OR 3 LAYERS OF ROOFING FELT
ALUMINIUM CLOSURE
13 FIBRE BOARD ON BITUMEN
ALUMINIUM DECK
M
FELT GRUMMETS
CONTINUOUS FELT STRIPS
PURLIN FIXING BY HOOK BOLT OR CLEAT
RIDGE DETAIL

0 100 200 MM
SCALE FOR DETAILS

FIGURE 65

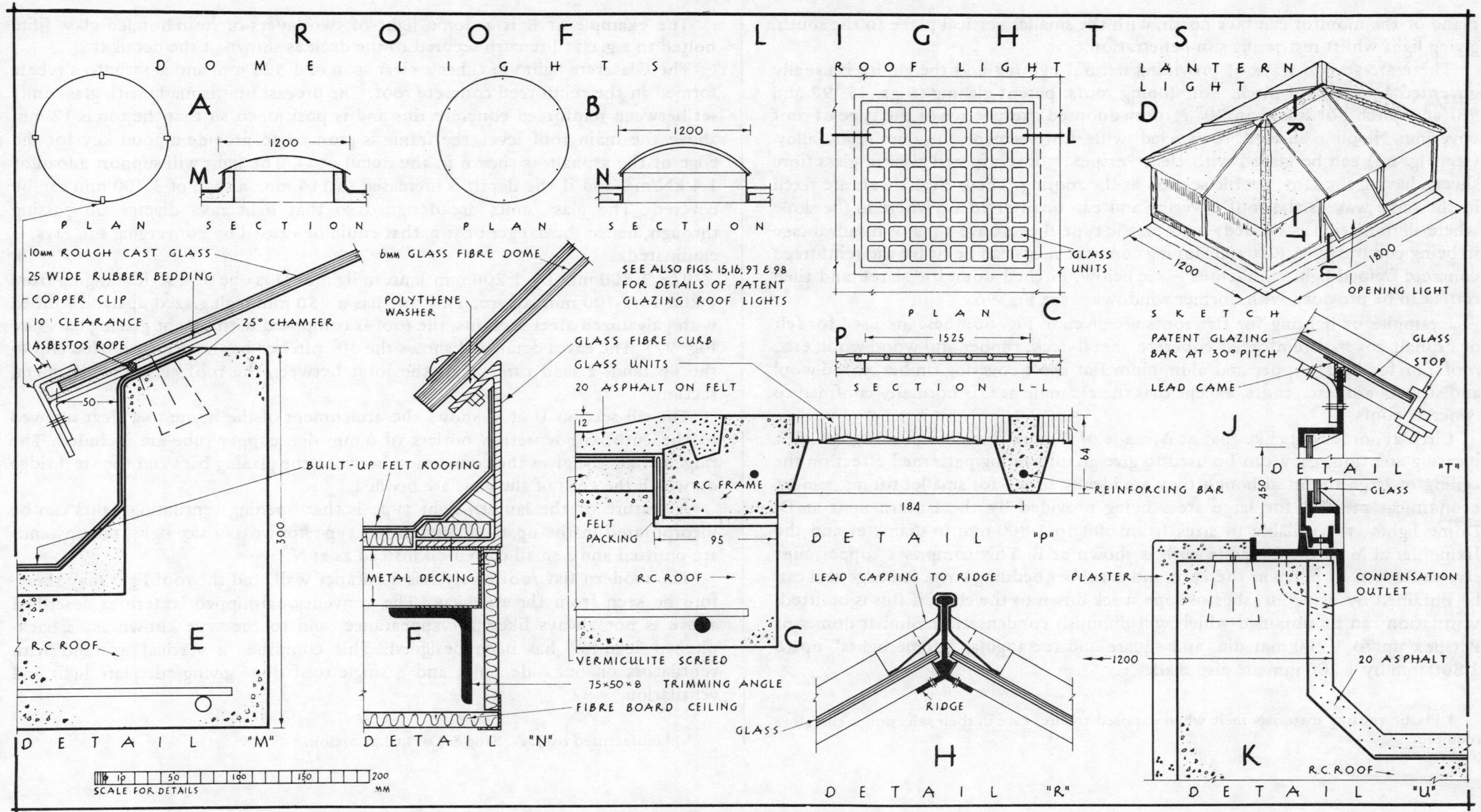

FIGURE 66

ROOF LIGHTS*

For spans over approximately 12 m (a dimension which is dependent on site conditions), the amount of natural lighting received from the sides of the building must normally be supplemented by roof lights. A 5 per cent daylight factor is the minimum for factories and it is generally better to distribute the light, rather than concentrate it, over the roof area. *Excessive* amounts of sunlight can be objectionable and so most of the glazing should face north; flat pitched lighting, rather than vertical, gives a better penetration of daylighting. Some roof structures give a more even distribution of natural light than others, for example the North light truss (see Fig. 15, with the light from one side only) tends to create shadows at the working plane and may not always be suitable. The monitor roof (see Fig. 16) is free from this objection and the longer sloping

* See also p. 221 for patent glazing.

plane of the monitor can face north, with the smaller vertical plane to the south, giving light whilst restricting sun penetration.

There are several ways of providing natural lighting and the choice is usually governed by the roof pitch. For sloping roofs, patent glazing (Figs. 15, 97 and 98) at a pitch not less than 20° is often adopted irrespective of the type of roof covering. Sloping sheeted roofs clad with fibre-cement or aluminium alloy (see Fig. 62) can be glazed with clear Perspex,† or reinforced glass or glass fibre sheets, having the same profile section as the roofing. These clear sheets are fixed in the same way as the roof covering and can be inserted anywhere in the slope where illumination is needed; such plastic-type sheets have a major disadvantage in being combustible. Flat and sloping concrete roofs can be lit by the reinforced concrete framed light with lenses – see below. Pitched domestic slated and tiled roofs can be provided with dormer windows – see Fig. 96.

Examples of lighting for flat roofs are given in Fig. 66; these are used for felt or asphalt covered reinforced concrete, metal deck, timber and wood-wool, etc., roofs; or for lead, copper and aluminium flat sheet covering timber, wood-wool and strawboard, etc., roofs, except that the example at C is normally confined to concrete roofs.

Circular dome lights like that at A, made of 10 mm thick rough-cast glass are a pleasing solution, they can be used to give an interesting patterned effect on the ceiling of large rooms although they are ideally suited for smaller rooms, a more economical method for large areas being provided by the lantern light at D. Dome lights are available in sizes from 600 to 1 800 mm in diameter and the fixing detail M at the concrete curb is shown at E. This comprises copper clips screwed down to plugs in the curb and a rubber bedding strip. An edge seal can be obtained by using an asbestos rope stuck down to the curb, if this is omitted, ventilation can be obtained which will diminish condensation. Similar domes of Perspex up to 1 200 mm dia. and square and rectangular "dome lights" up to 1 800 mm by 1 200 mm are also made.

† Plastic roofing materials melt when exposed to fire; care in their selection is therefore required.

The example at B is a dome light of two layers of resin-bonded glass fibre bolted to a glass fibre curb secured to the deck as shown at the detail at F.

The Glascrete light* at C has a clear span of 1 525 mm and is set into a rebate formed in the reinforced concrete roof. The precast unit is made with glass units set between reinforced concrete ribs and is positioned so that the top is 12 mm above the main roof level, the frame is grooved to provide a good key for the edge of the asphalt as shown in the detail at G. The light will support a load of 1.4 kN/m^2, and if the depth is increased to 114 mm, a span of 3 700 mm can be covered. The glass units are designed so that light rays diverge on passing through, hence the danger of fire, that could be caused by converging sun rays, is eliminated.

The 1 800 mm by 1 200 mm lantern light at D is one of a series ranging from 1 200 to 3 700 mm square. This one has a 450 mm high glazed upstand formed with galvanized steel sections, the roof is composed with patent glazing bars (see Fig. 97). The eaves detail at J shows the 30° pitched bar bolted through a clip to the upstand, a lead *came* seals the joint between the roof glass and the metal section.

The sill section U at K shows the attachment of the frame to a cleat screwed to the curb, condensation outlets of 6 mm dia. copper tube are included. The ridge detail at H gives the connection between the glazing bars and the steel ridge on which the ends of the glass are bedded.

A feature of the lantern light type is that opening ventilating lights can be incorporated in the upstand. In another type known as a sky light, the upstands are omitted and a small curb used instead as at N.

The modern flat roof rarely has a parapet wall, and the roof light may therefore be seen from the roadway. The conventional hipped lantern as described above is not always liked for appearance, and so the type known as "a back-pitched lean-to" has been designed. This comprises a vertical upstand with ventilators on one side only, and a single roof slope giving adequate light and ventilation.

* Manufactured by J. A. King & Co. Ltd., London.

CHAPTER SEVEN

BALCONIES AND CANOPIES

Syllabus. Timber, stone, precast and in-situ reinforced concrete balconies. Timber and steel canopies.

A balcony is an external balustraded platform with access from an upper floor.

The Building Regulations require a balcony handrail to be at a minimum height of 1.1 m.

TIMBER BALCONY

A simple domestic balcony of hardwood is shown in Fig. 67; it is framed into a wall opening 1 070 mm wide; elevation, plan and section are shown at H, N and J respectively with a sketch at K. The balcony floor is made from four joists bolted back (each with two bolts) to those of the room. The wall construction is a 100 mm thick inner leaf of light-weight concrete blocks with an outer leaf of common bricks rendered.

The balcony joists at 400 mm centres of planed 125 mm by 50 mm hardwood reduce to 95 mm by 50 mm where they project from the wall. Note that at P the joists are grooved where they pass through the cavity to prevent any rain which may travel along them from entering the inner leaf of the wall. They are covered with oak or keruing boards (12 mm apart) fixed with brass screws and cups. Two corner posts are fixed to the outer ends of the outer joists by means of brass screws and the dovetailed housed joint shown at W. Two wall posts are plugged to the wall above the outer joists, these posts are grooved at their sides as shown at M for the rendering to recess into them. Each side of the balcony then has a top and bottom rail tenoned into the wall post and corner post, t. g. and v. grooved boarding is screwed to the side rails. The top side rail fixing to the posts is shown at M and consists of a tenon joint with hardwood dowel. The bottom side rails are fixed in a similar way.

It will be appreciated that external joinery of this sort requires careful detailing of the joints so as to avoid the injurious effects of the weather. Timber expands and contracts due to the variation in moisture content and unsightly gaps can occur at joints which are then the first parts of the structure to decay. This effect is greatly minimized if the rails are inset for their full area into the post for a short distance before the tenon is made. Both tenon and mortice must be given one or two coats of paint before the joint is finally made, similarly the dowel should be painted before it is driven home.

The front of the balcony has top and bottom rails tenoned into the corner posts with hardwood balusters between. The front rails are cut from a piece of 75 mm by 55 mm as shown at V. Detail sections through the front rails are shown at S and U, where the construction of the hardwood balusters and the way they are housed into the rails is given.

After fixing the balcony joists the balustrade would be assembled as follows:

1. Cut joint shown at W between corner post and joist.
2. Cut tenons and mortices for the sides and temporarily frame the side panels together omitting dowel pins and screws.
3. Mark tenons and mortices for the front rails, cut these after the side panels have been taken down.
4. Temporarily fit all the bottom rails and again slide the front posts into their joints at the end of the joists, slide all top rails into position, square up framing and mark exact length of balusters. Mark off joint between balusters and rails.
5. Undo the whole once more and cut joints between balusters and rails, paint all joints one coat of paint, lay aside until dry and give second coat.
6. Finally, assemble all members, fix dowels and screws, wall posts back to plugs in wall, handrail, and screw side boarding to rails.

It is advisable to have cover flashings (copper would be most suitable) on top of the mitred joints in the handrail and also on the handrail and up behind the rendering next to the wall (see N).

The floor construction shown in this example is suitable for flats and other dwellings where the transmission of sound has to be minimized, it is detailed at R. Clean dry sand 50 mm thick is laid on the ceiling of expanded metal and plaster. A slag wool quilt (mineralized slag wool between sheets of strong paper and obtainable in rolls 1 m wide) is then laid on the joists but not nailed to them, it should be lapped 75 mm at all joints. The quilt must be carried up the edge of the boarding and underneath the skirting thus isolating the boarding from the rest of the structure. The boards themselves are framed up in panels (maximum size about 2.5 m by 2.5 m) to suit the shape of the room, 50 mm by

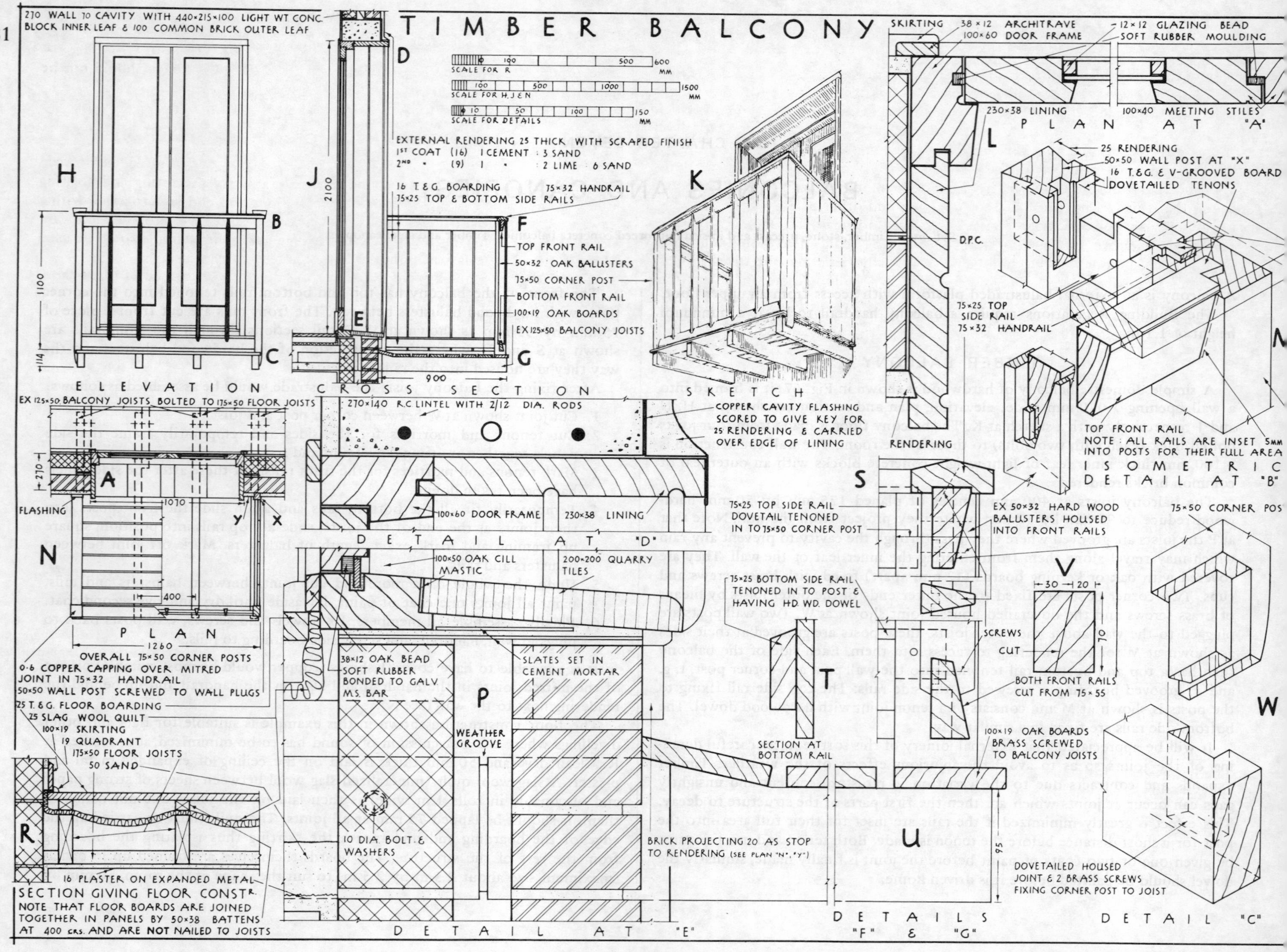
TIMBER BALCONY
270 WALL TO CAVITY WITH 440×215×100 LIGHT WT CONC BLOCK INNER LEAF & 100 COMMON BRICK OUTER LEAF
SCALE FOR R
SCALE FOR H, J & N
SCALE FOR DETAILS
EXTERNAL RENDERING 25 THICK WITH SCRAPED FINISH
1ST COAT (16) 1 CEMENT : 3 SAND
2ND " (9) 1 " : 2 LIME 6 SAND
16 T.&G. BOARDING
75×25 TOP & BOTTOM SIDE RAILS
75×32 HANDRAIL
TOP FRONT RAIL
50×32 OAK BALUSTERS
75×50 CORNER POST
BOTTOM FRONT RAIL
100×19 OAK BOARDS
EX 125×50 BALCONY JOISTS
ELEVATION
CROSS SECTION
SKETCH
EX 125×50 BALCONY JOISTS BOLTED TO 175×50 FLOOR JOISTS
270×140 R.C. LINTEL WITH 2/12 DIA. RODS
FLASHING
100×60 DOOR FRAME
230×38 LINING
DETAIL AT "D"
100×50 OAK CILL
MASTIC
200×200 QUARRY TILES
PLAN
OVERALL 75×50 CORNER POSTS
0·6 COPPER CAPPING OVER MITRED JOINT IN 75×32 HANDRAIL
50×50 WALL POST SCREWED TO WALL PLUGS
25 T.&G. FLOOR BOARDING
25 SLAG WOOL QUILT
100×19 SKIRTING
19 QUADRANT
175×50 FLOOR JOISTS
50 SAND
16 PLASTER ON EXPANDED METAL
SECTION GIVING FLOOR CONSTR.
NOTE THAT FLOOR BOARDS ARE JOINED TOGETHER IN PANELS BY 50×38 BATTENS AT 400 CRS. AND ARE NOT NAILED TO JOISTS
38×12 OAK BEAD
SOFT RUBBER BONDED TO GALV. M.S. BAR
WEATHER GROOVE
SLATES SET IN CEMENT MORTAR
10 DIA BOLT & WASHERS
BRICK PROJECTING 20 AS STOP TO RENDERING (SEE PLAN "N", "Y")
DETAIL AT "E"
SKIRTING
38×12 ARCHITRAVE
100×60 DOOR FRAME
12×12 GLAZING BEAD
SOFT RUBBER MOULDING
230×38 LINING
100×40 MEETING STILES
PLAN AT "A"
25 RENDERING
50×50 WALL POST AT "X"
16 T.&G. & V-GROOVED BOARD
DOVETAILED TENONS
D.P.C.
75×25 TOP SIDE RAIL
75×32 HANDRAIL
COPPER CAVITY FLASHING SCORED TO GIVE KEY FOR 25 RENDERING & CARRIED OVER EDGE OF LINING
RENDERING
TOP FRONT RAIL
NOTE ALL RAILS ARE INSET 5MM INTO POSTS FOR THEIR FULL AREA
ISOMETRIC DETAIL AT "B"
75×25 TOP SIDE RAIL DOVETAIL TENONED IN TO 75×50 CORNER POST
EX 50×32 HARD WOOD BALUSTERS HOUSED INTO FRONT RAILS
75×50 CORNER POST
75×25 BOTTOM SIDE RAIL TENONED IN TO POST & HAVING HD WD. DOWEL
SCREWS
CUT
BOTH FRONT RAILS CUT FROM 75×55
SECTION AT BOTTOM RAIL
100×19 OAK BOARDS BRASS SCREWED TO BALCONY JOISTS
DOVETAILED HOUSED JOINT & 2 BRASS SCREWS FIXING CORNER POST TO JOIST
DETAILS "F" & "G"
DETAIL "C"

FIGURE 67

38 mm battens underneath the boards secure them together. The boards are not nailed to the joists as this would impair the insulating properties of the system (the nails would provide a direct path for impact noises on the floor to travel through the joists and into the room below). It will be appreciated that although the quilt is compressed to a certain extent this compression will not be uniform (because of the position of furniture and other floor loads) throughout the floor area and therefore the floor will have a certain amount of spring in it. It may be found that this is a nuisance at door openings and other places where traffic is heavy, in such cases the boards may be screwed down to the floor but for the reason given above this sort of fixing should be reduced to a minimum. In bracing such a floor, herring bone strutting can be used for the deeper joists providing it is kept clear of the sand and quilt; for shallow floors, solid strutting will be necessary, laid flat.

At O the detail of the door head is given; a two-course reinforced concrete lintel is used, a d.p.c. passes across the cavity and down the lintel face and eventually over the edge of the 38 mm external timber door lining, the latter being grooved into the door frame and plugged to the lintel.

The threshold at P shows quarry tiles forming the step with an oak sill to the door. The galvanized steel weather bar set in the sill has a soft rubber strip bonded to it with rubber cement, thus forming a water-tight finish. The detail at L shows the plan of the door jamb and meeting stiles of the double doors which open inwards.

STONE BALCONY

The floor of this balcony shown in Fig. 68 is made of four pieces of selected hard York stone cantilevered out from the wall. The stone is weathered 12 mm from back to front and is 150 mm thick at the wall end, it is shaped on plan as shown and the pieces are joggle jointed as drawn at L, the outer edges being moulded as shown at K. The stones are held down by two steel beams 3.4 m long which extend on either side of the door opening and are built into the brick wall. The balcony is 2.68 m long by 1 m wide, the latter dimension allows 25 mm clearance between the edge of the opened door and the balustrade handrail. The door is fitted with brass extension hinges as shown at G which allow it to open back against the wall face where it can be held open by means of a cabin hook and eye. The galvanized mild steel balustrade consists of 20 mm by 20 mm standards, six of these are set in holes in the stone and caulked with lead as indicated at K. The central V-shaped members are 20 mm by 10 mm and the handrail is given at detail C.

In constructing the balcony, the brickwork would be built up to the underside level of the stone slabs and these would then be supported on scaffolding at the outer end and bedded on the wall at the other end. The steel beams are then placed in position and coupled together. A layer of cement grout is then run underneath the beams where it is essential to get a solid bedding as shown at M. The surrounding concrete is then placed along with the course of stone at the face of the outer beam. The scaffolding to the balcony stones should not be taken down until three weeks after the gable wall is completed.

PRECAST REINFORCED CONCRETE BALCONY

The example shown in Fig. 69 is constructed of normal grade reinforced concrete, it weighs just over a tonne and is suitable for precasting and hoisting into position. The balcony is composed of a floor and end wall together with a galvanized steel balustrade; the front elevation and two cross-sections are detailed at P, S and T respectively with the plan at Z. The example could be used in the construction flats as indicated in the sketch at U.

The reinforced concrete work can be considered to be formed of three parts, a beam at either end with a 125 mm thick slab spanning between them. The reinforcement details are given at A′, B′, C′ and D′. The left-hand beam is 580 mm wide and is formed within the slab thickness, it has five 12 mm dia. bars in the top of the slab. The right-hand beam is formed in the lower portion of the wall, it has two 12 mm dia. rods; a portion of it 150 mm deep extends 215 mm into a 103 mm cross wall which assists in providing counterweight to the balcony (see B′ and C′). In the wall above the beam there are 10 mm dia. rods running in both directions. The floor slab has five 10 mm rods spanning its length which are cranked round the beam bars at their ends. Note that as shown at D′ the floor unit next to the wall requires to be notched on the top side so as to avoid fouling the 165 mm deep portion of the curved reinforced concrete wall which is built into the 103 mm brick cross wall.

The balcony floor is covered with quarry tiles on mortar bedding and the balcony edge is flashed with 0.6 mm copper held by copper clips nailed to plugs in the concrete. One welt is required in the flashing at the corner as shown on plan at Z. The curved wall is cement painted on the outside with glazed tiles on the inner side, these tiles finish against the brickwall with a coved tile slip, and at the outer end against a 25 mm projection in the concrete.

The galvanized balustrade is constructed of a steel tube frame within which is welded at all points of contact a flat steel bar bent to the shape shown. The top of the tubular frame is 1.1 m above the balcony floor. The base of the frame has five 150 mm long legs welded to it which are welded to steel plates as shown at X and Y. The plates are holed for a rag-bolt fixing to grout holes cast in the concrete. The copper edge flashing is placed underneath the plates.

At V is one of the top fixings of the balustrade to the concrete wall, it is a short length of hooked tube which has been cast in the wall with a half lapped joint at the outer end for bolting to a short half lapped piece of tube welded to the frame. The other top fixing of the balustrade is shown at N and consists of a small lug welded to the frame which is bolted to a fish-tailed wall tie set in a joint of the brickwork.

The door threshold at Q indicates part of the bottom rail to the door with an inset weatherboard, the rail is rebated for striking against a galvanized m.s.

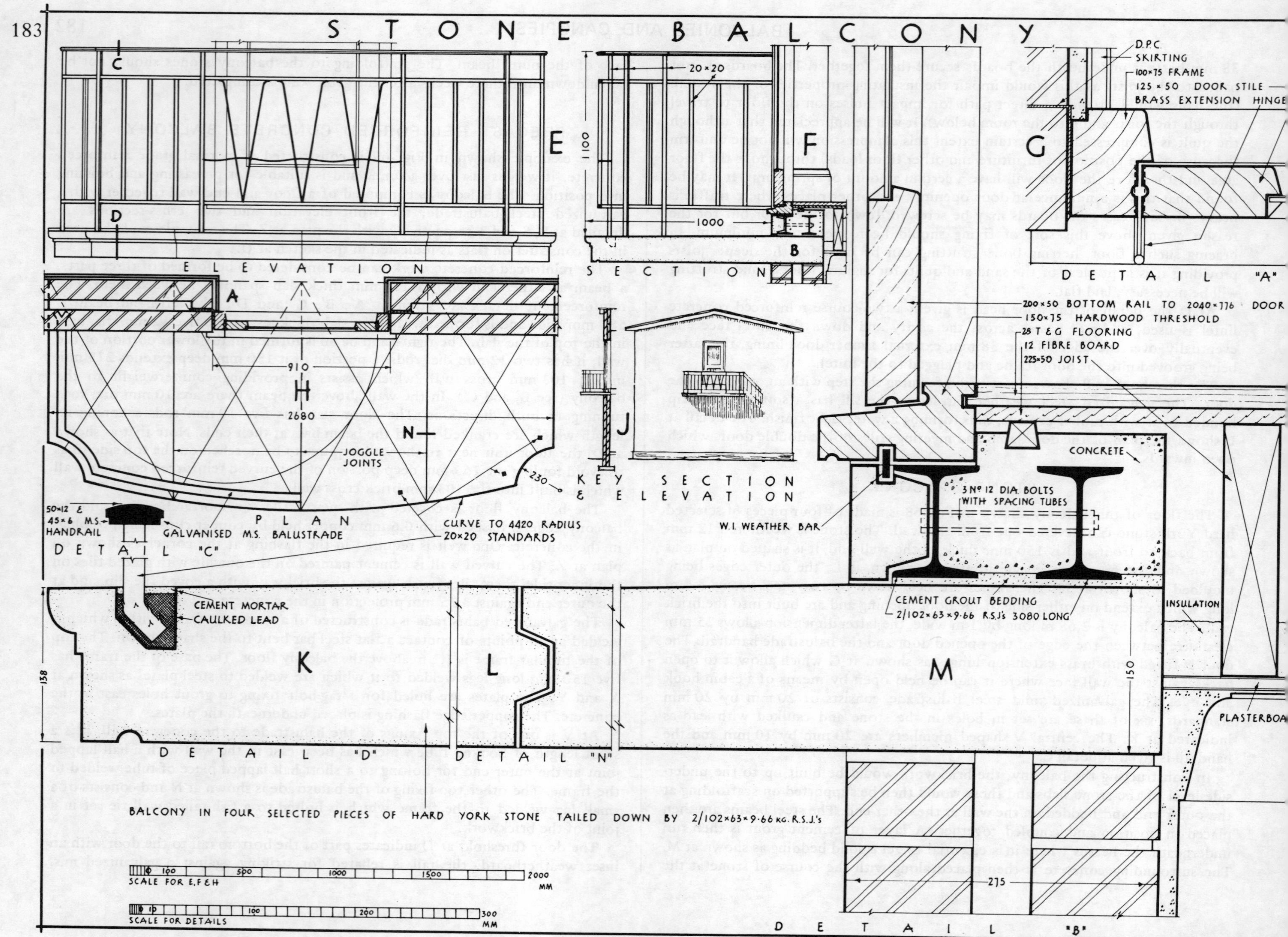

S T O N E B A L C O N Y
C
D
E
ELEVATION
1100
20×20
F
1000
B
SECTION
D.P.C.
SKIRTING
100×75 FRAME
125×50 DOOR STILE
BRASS EXTENSION HINGE
G
DETAIL "A"
A
910
H
2680
N
JOGGLE JOINTS
230
PLAN
CURVE TO 4420 RADIUS
20×20 STANDARDS
J
KEY SECTION & ELEVATION
200×50 BOTTOM RAIL TO 2040×776 DOOR
150×75 HARDWOOD THRESHOLD
28 T & G FLOORING
12 FIBRE BOARD
225×50 JOIST
CONCRETE
3 Nº 12 DIA. BOLTS WITH SPACING TUBES
W.I. WEATHER BAR
CEMENT GROUT BEDDING
2/102×63×9·66 R.S.J's 3080 LONG
INSULATION
PLASTERBOA
150
M
275
DETAIL "B"
50×12 & 45×6 M.S. HANDRAIL
GALVANISED M.S. BALUSTRADE
DETAIL "C"
CEMENT MORTAR
CAULKED LEAD
158
K
DETAIL "D"
L
DETAIL "N"
BALCONY IN FOUR SELECTED PIECES OF HARD YORK STONE TAILED DOWN BY 2/102×63×9·66 KG. R.S.J's
100
500
1000
1500
2000 MM
SCALE FOR E, F & H
10
100
200
300 MM
SCALE FOR DETAILS

FIGURE 68

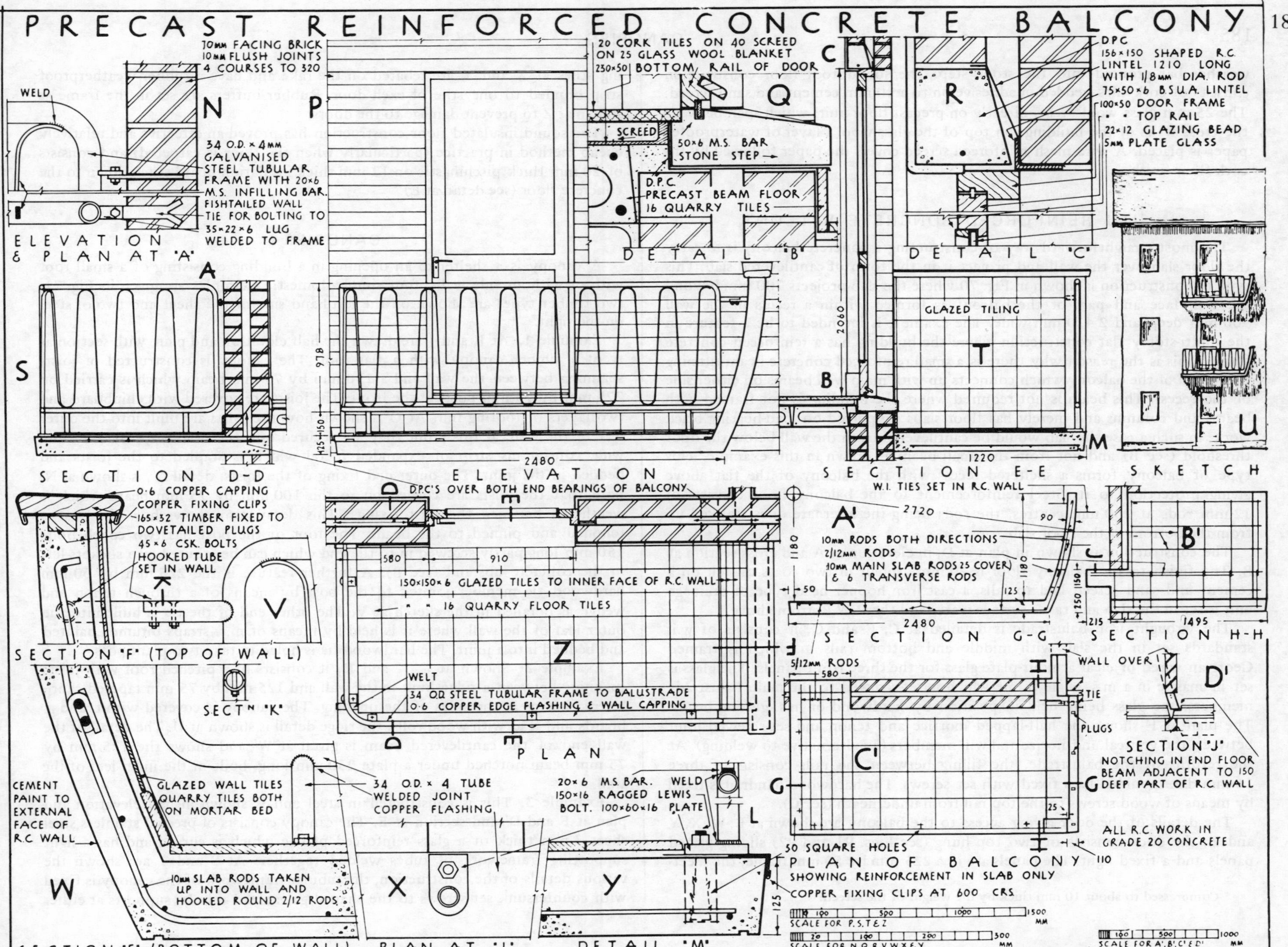
PRECAST REINFORCED CONCRETE BALCONY
10MM FACING BRICK
10MM FLUSH JOINTS
4 COURSES TO 320
WELD
N
P
34 O.D. × 4MM
GALVANISED
STEEL TUBULAR
FRAME WITH 20×6
M.S. INFILLING BAR.
FISHTAILED WALL
TIE FOR BOLTING TO
35×22×6 LUG
WELDED TO FRAME
ELEVATION
& PLAN AT 'A'
20 CORK TILES ON 40 SCREED
ON 25 GLASS WOOL BLANKET
250×50 BOTTOM RAIL OF DOOR
Q
SCREED
50×6 M.S. BAR
STONE STEP
D.P.C.
PRECAST BEAM FLOOR
16 QUARRY TILES
DETAIL 'B'
C
DPC
156×150 SHAPED R.C.
LINTEL 1210 LONG
WITH 1/8MM DIA. ROD
75×50×6 B.S.U.A. LINTEL
100×50 DOOR FRAME
TOP RAIL
22×12 GLAZING BEAD
5MM PLATE GLASS
R
DETAIL 'C'
A
S
918
150
125
2480
SECTION DD
ELEVATION
GLAZED TILING
2060
T
B
M
1220
SECTION EE
SKETCH
U
0·6 COPPER CAPPING
COPPER FIXING CLIPS
165×32 TIMBER FIXED TO
DOVETAILED PLUGS
45×6 CSK. BOLTS
HOOKED TUBE
SET IN WALL
K
V
SECTION 'F' (TOP OF WALL)
SECTN 'K'
D
E
DPC'S OVER BOTH END BEARINGS OF BALCONY
580
910
150×150×6 GLAZED TILES TO INNER FACE OF R.C. WALL
16 QUARRY FLOOR TILES
Z
WELT
34 OD STEEL TUBULAR FRAME TO BALUSTRADE
0·6 COPPER EDGE FLASHING & WALL CAPPING
PLAN
W.I. TIES SET IN R.C. WALL
A'
2720
90
180
10MM RODS BOTH DIRECTIONS
2/12MM RODS
10MM MAIN SLAB RODS (25 COVER)
& 6 TRANSVERSE RODS
50
125
250
1180
1150
B'
2480
215
1495
SECTION GG
SECTION H-H
5/12MM RODS
580
WALL OVER
TIE
PLUGS
D'
SECTION 'J'
NOTCHING IN END FLOOR
BEAM ADJACENT TO 150
DEEP PART OF R.C. WALL
C'
G
G
25
ALL R.C. WORK IN
GRADE 20 CONCRETE
110
CEMENT
PAINT TO
EXTERNAL
FACE OF
R.C. WALL
GLAZED WALL TILES
QUARRY TILES BOTH
ON MORTAR BED
34 O.D. × 4 TUBE
WELDED JOINT
COPPER FLASHING
20×6 M.S. BAR.
150×16 RAGGED LEWIS
BOLT. 100×60×16
WELD
PLATE
L
50 SQUARE HOLES
PLAN OF BALCONY
SHOWING REINFORCEMENT IN SLAB ONLY
COPPER FIXING CLIPS AT 600 CRS
10MM SLAB RODS TAKEN
UP INTO WALL AND
HOOKED ROUND 2/12 RODS
W
X
Y
125
SECTION 'F' (BOTTOM OF WALL)
PLAN AT 'L'
DETAIL 'M'
100
500
1000
1500
SCALE FOR P.S.T.E.Z
MM
20
100
200
500
SCALE FOR N.Q.R.V.W.X.E.Y
MM
100
500
1000
SCALE FOR A'.B'.C'.E.D'
MM

FIGURE 69

weather bar grouted into the stone step. The soundproof floor construction consists of cork tiles bedded in adhesive on to a 40 mm cement and sand screed. The 25 mm glass wool* rests directly on precast floor units which span between the cross walls of the building; on top of the glass wool a layer of waterproofed paper is placed. A wire mesh reinforced screed covers the paper followed by the cork floor finish.

IN-SITU REINFORCED CONCRETE BALCONY

The most straightforward way of constructing a concrete balcony is to carry the floor slab over the wall and project it in the form of cantilevered slab. This type of construction is shown in Fig. 70 where the slab projects 700 mm beyond the wall face and part of the balcony is formed within a recess in the wall 900 mm deep and 2 410 mm wide. The example is intended to be a feature in the multi-storey flat construction where the building has a reinforced concrete frame. This is the reason why there is a small reinforced concrete beam running the length of the balcony which connects up with main wall beams on either side of the recess. This beam is not required where the building is not framed with beams and columns and merely has floor slabs supported on load-bearing brick work; in such a case the slab would be cantilevered from the wall below the door threshold (see B) and not from the small beam as drawn in this example. This type of balcony forms a sheltered recess with the balcony of the flat above giving protection to it. Steel reinforcement to the balcony floor consists of 12 mm rods at 260 mm centres, the rods being the alternate ones cranked up from the bottom of the floor slab.

The construction is shown in plan at D, in elevation at A and cross section at B. The finish to the balcony floor is 20 mm asphalt in two coats on felt on a cement and sand screed laid to falls, a cast iron hopper head type of drainage unit is set in the slab and takes surface water and the R.W.P. from above.

The wrought iron balustrade is detailed at C, F and G, it consists of w.i. standards set in the slab with middle and bottom rails in which is framed Georgian wired or clear armour-plate glass for the three front panels. The glass is set in mastic in a m.s. angle frame which is set-screwed to the main balustrade members, the glass being held in position by hardwood or m.s. glazing beads. The plan at F shows the half-lapped mortice and tenon and set-screwed joint between the vertical and horizontal w.i. members (an alternative to welding). At the returns of the balustrade, the filling between the rails consists of three 16 mm dia. moulded bars fixed with set screws. The hardwood handrail is fixed by means of wood screws to the top rail from underneath (see C).

The details of the door giving access to the balcony are shown at E, W, X, Y and Z, the door consists of two top hung (see Figs. 91 and 92) sliding glazed panels and a fixed light. The panels are in a 225 mm by 50 mm frame, the meeting stiles at X and Y are rebated on the rake and have a rubber weatherproof strip bonded to one stile of each door. Rubber buffers are set in the frame as shown at Z to prevent damage to the doors.

The sound insulated floor construction has proved an effective and relatively cheap method in practice (particularly when the floor is carpeted) and consists of 20 mm thick pitchmastic on 12 mm thick insulation board stuck down to the concrete floor (see detail at E).

* Compressed to about 10 mm thick by the weight of the screed.

CANOPIES

A canopy is a shelter to an opening in a building consisting of a small roof with or without side walls; four simple domestic examples are given in Fig. 71, two timber types are shown on the left-hand side of the sheet and two of steel on the right.

Example 1. At B and J are drawn the half elevation and plan, with section at A of a timber canopy with a flat roof. The canopy is constructed of joists spanning between the wall and a 150 mm by 75 mm beam which is carried on 225 mm by 75 mm posts at the front. The joists are covered with chipboard and two layers of roofing felt. At O is shown how the joists are built into the outer leaf of the wall, at this point they are secured into the brickwork by a 75 mm wide continuous strip of expanded metal which is stapled to the joists and bedded in the joint. The outer end fixing of the joists, detail A′, is shown at N; note that the joists are cogged on to the 100 mm by 75 mm beam which is weathered between the joist fixings. This detail also shows how the post is tenoned and pinned to the beam. The foot of the post has two coach bolts 150 mm long partly screwed in to the end which can be grouted into sockets left in the concrete upstand (see B). A further feature is the 225 mm by 60 mm hardwood tie member jointed to the post by means of a through tenon and wedge as detailed in the sketch at V. The other end of the tie is built into the outer leaf of the wall where it is held by means of m.s. straps bitumen painted and bedded into a joint. The hardwood tie is holed to take two plant pots.

Example 2. Shown at C, K and D, it consists of a pitched roof with joists spanning between a ridge built in the wall and 125 mm by 75 mm tapered cantilevered beams at the sides of the opening. The canopy is covered with t. and g. boards and lead with wood rolls; the ridge detail is shown at U. The detail of the wall end of the cantilevered beam is given at W′ and shows the 125 mm by 75 mm beam notched under a plate 230 mm long, built in the inner leaf of the wall.

Example 3. This is constructed in steel and is shown in half elevation and plan at F and D′ and section at E. The canopy consists of pressed stainless steel sheet 3 mm thick or a glass reinforced plastic which is curved and has a light supporting framework of tubes welded together. At S and T are shown the various details of the construction, the tubular framework of the canopy is fixed with countersunk set screws to the shaped galvanized tubular supports at either

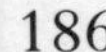

IN-SITU REINFORCED CONCRETE BALCONY

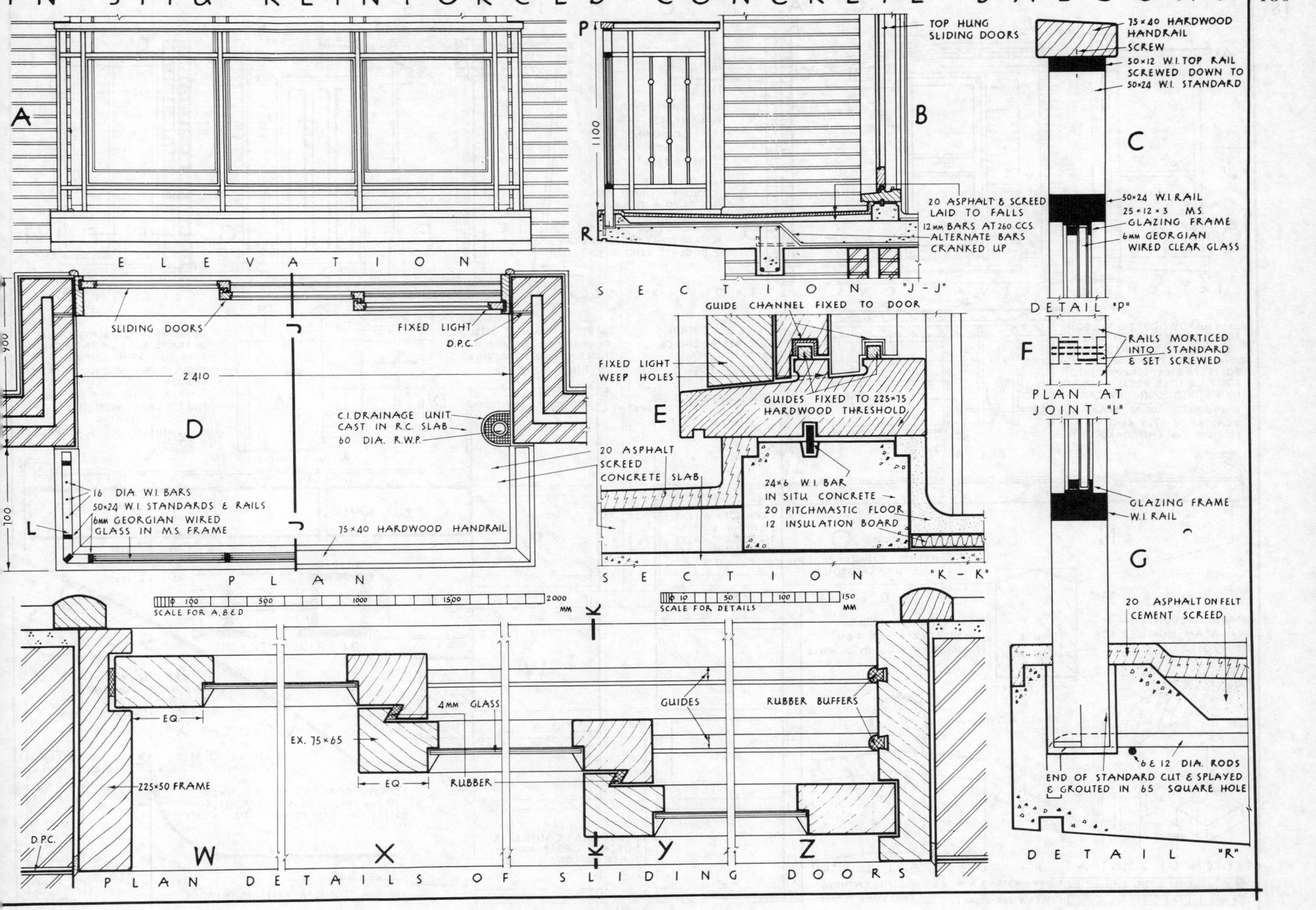

FIGURE 70

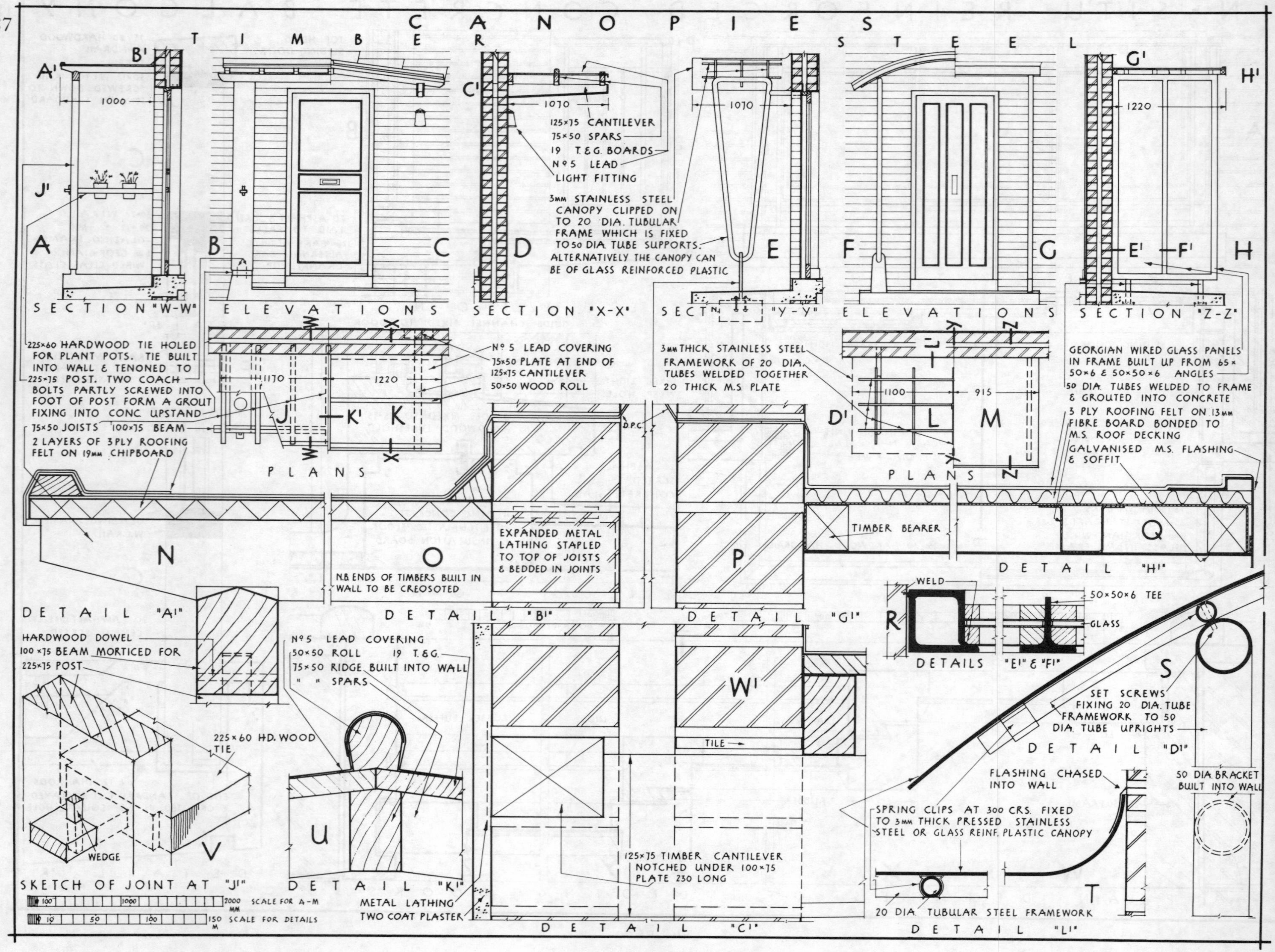

CANOPIES

TIMBER — STEEL

SECTION "W-W" — ELEVATIONS — SECTION "X-X" — SECTⁿ "Y-Y" — ELEVATIONS — SECTION "Z-Z"

1000

1070

125×75 CANTILEVER
75×50 SPARS
19 T.&G. BOARDS
Nº 5 LEAD
LIGHT FITTING

3MM STAINLESS STEEL CANOPY CLIPPED ON TO 20 DIA. TUBULAR FRAME WHICH IS FIXED TO 50 DIA. TUBE SUPPORTS. ALTERNATIVELY THE CANOPY CAN BE OF GLASS REINFORCED PLASTIC

1070

1220

225×60 HARDWOOD TIE HOLED FOR PLANT POTS. TIE BUILT INTO WALL & TENONED TO 225×75 POST. TWO COACH BOLTS PARTLY SCREWED INTO FOOT OF POST FORM A GROUT FIXING INTO CONC. UPSTAND

75×50 JOISTS 100×75 BEAM

2 LAYERS OF 3PLY ROOFING FELT ON 19MM CHIPBOARD

Nº 5 LEAD COVERING
75×50 PLATE AT END OF 125×75 CANTILEVER
50×50 WOOD ROLL

1170 — 1220

PLANS

3MM THICK STAINLESS STEEL FRAMEWORK OF 20 DIA. TUBES WELDED TOGETHER
20 THICK M.S. PLATE

1100 — 915

PLANS

GEORGIAN WIRED GLASS PANELS IN FRAME BUILT UP FROM 65×50×6 & 50×50×6 ANGLES
50 DIA. TUBES WELDED TO FRAME & GROUTED INTO CONCRETE
3 PLY ROOFING FELT ON 13MM FIBRE BOARD BONDED TO M.S. ROOF DECKING
GALVANISED M.S. FLASHING & SOFFIT

D.P.C.

TIMBER BEARER

DETAIL "H'"

EXPANDED METAL LATHING STAPLED TO TOP OF JOISTS & BEDDED IN JOINTS

N.B. ENDS OF TIMBERS BUILT IN WALL TO BE CREOSOTED

DETAIL "A'" — DETAIL "B'" — DETAIL "G'"

WELD
50×50×6 TEE
GLASS

DETAILS "E'" & "F'"

HARDWOOD DOWEL
100×75 BEAM MORTICED FOR 225×75 POST

225×60 HD. WOOD TIE

WEDGE

SKETCH OF JOINT AT "J'"

Nº 5 LEAD COVERING
50×50 ROLL 19 T.&G.
75×50 RIDGE BUILT INTO WALL
" " SPARS

DETAIL "K'"

METAL LATHING
TWO COAT PLASTER

TILE

125×75 TIMBER CANTILEVER NOTCHED UNDER 100×75 PLATE 230 LONG

DETAIL "C'"

SET SCREWS FIXING 20 DIA. TUBE FRAMEWORK TO 50 DIA. TUBE UPRIGHTS

DETAIL "D'"

FLASHING CHASED INTO WALL

50 DIA. BRACKET BUILT INTO WALL

SPRING CLIPS AT 300 CRS. FIXED TO 3MM THICK PRESSED STAINLESS STEEL OR GLASS REINF. PLASTIC CANOPY

20 DIA. TUBULAR STEEL FRAMEWORK

DETAIL "L'"

100 — 1000 — 2000 MM SCALE FOR A–M
19 — 50 — 100 — 150 MM SCALE FOR DETAILS

FIGURE 71

side of the canopy. The stainless steel covering has welded to it spring clips which engage firmly on to the canopy framework, as shown at S. The wall end of the stainless steel is curved up and flashed as shown at T. The 50 mm dia. vertical supports shown at E and F are fixed at the base by holding down bolts and at the top, a 50 mm dia. bracket is welded to the upright and built into the brickwork.

Example 4. This is shown at G, M and H, composed of 45 mm deep steel decking units (see p. 187) forming the canopy and resting on glazed side panels. The canopy is covered with insulation board and one layer of three-ply roofing felt with a galvanized mild steel soffit sheet fixed to the decking with sheradized self-tapping screws; this is detailed at P and Q (the frame of the side panel is not shown). The glazed side panels are made up of a frame consisting of angles welded together, the mullion is a steel tee (see R). The glazing frame has two tubular legs with base plates welded to them for concreting into the step, the top wall side of the frame has a small bracket welded to it and built into the brickwork.

CHAPTER EIGHT

INTERNAL FINISHES* TO WALLS AND CEILINGS

Syllabus. Wood panelling in traditional construction, contemporary panelling of plywood, laminboard and plastics. Marble and mosaic details. Patent suspended ceilings.

TIMBER PANELLING†

In the many old halls and castles of these islands, there are examples of traditional hardwood panelling that are without equal in most other countries. Although work of the same character is only occasionally adopted in new buildings, one cannot disregard the contribution these examples have made to this pleasing form of internal surface covering. It is difficult now to surpass the hand craftsmanship and elegance of the earlier panelling, but the same skills and treatment are still required in alteration, conversion and restoration work. Whenever one of these old buildings is demolished, the panelling is much in demand, it is highly valued for modification and re-erection in a new home. With the advent of modern woodworking machinery and the introduction of plywood, veneers, and other sheet materials, panelling has assumed a different form. There are many, who, for new buildings, prefer the traditional appearance of elaborate mouldings and carving, instead of the simpler effect which relies largely on the natural figuring of the timber. There is of course room for both expressions and an admixture of the two, and several examples of all kinds are given here. In all cases, the panelling has a backing of rough grounds, nailed to plugs in the wall, or fixed directly to the wall by patent fastenings.

There are several methods of securing the panel framing to the grounds. Wherever possible, secret fixings are adopted where the nail or screw is covered by another member, or placed in an unobtrusive position. In general the rails and muntins forming the framing, are secured by screws (shown in dotted outline or fine straight broken line) to the grounds; mouldings being fixed by fine metal pins (shown in thicker broken line). Where these cannot be concealed, screws may be recessed and covered with pellets (carefully selected small pieces of timber having the same appearance as the adjacent wood); alternatively, the screws can be recessed and covered with small turned buttons. Fixing pins or nails should be reasonably small, the finer ones can be broken off flush with the surface after being driven home, the larger ones can be punched home and the hole filled with matching stopping. 50 to 60 mm oval nails are often used for the heavier mouldings; the stopping should be done by the polisher, who can match the colour accurately. If the infilling panels (which was the usual practice before the introduction of plywood) are of solid timber, they should have a

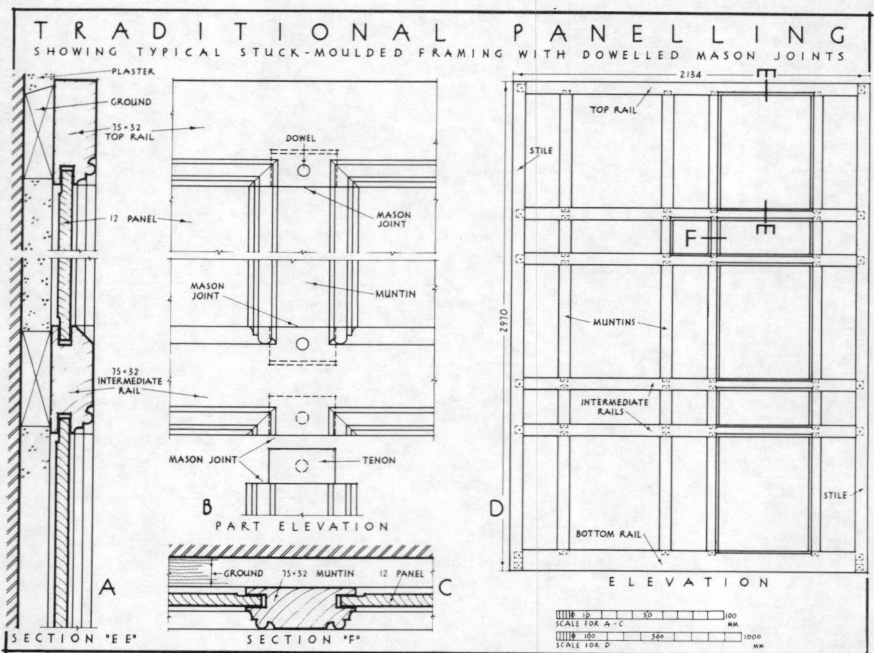

FIGURE 72

* Floor finishes have been described in Chap. I, Vol. III and plastering in Vol. I.

† Several illustrations of panelled doors have been given in the earlier volumes; at Fig. 46, Vol. I, the various types of mouldings (stuck, planted, and bolection), have been detailed. The application of plywood has been described in Vol. III.

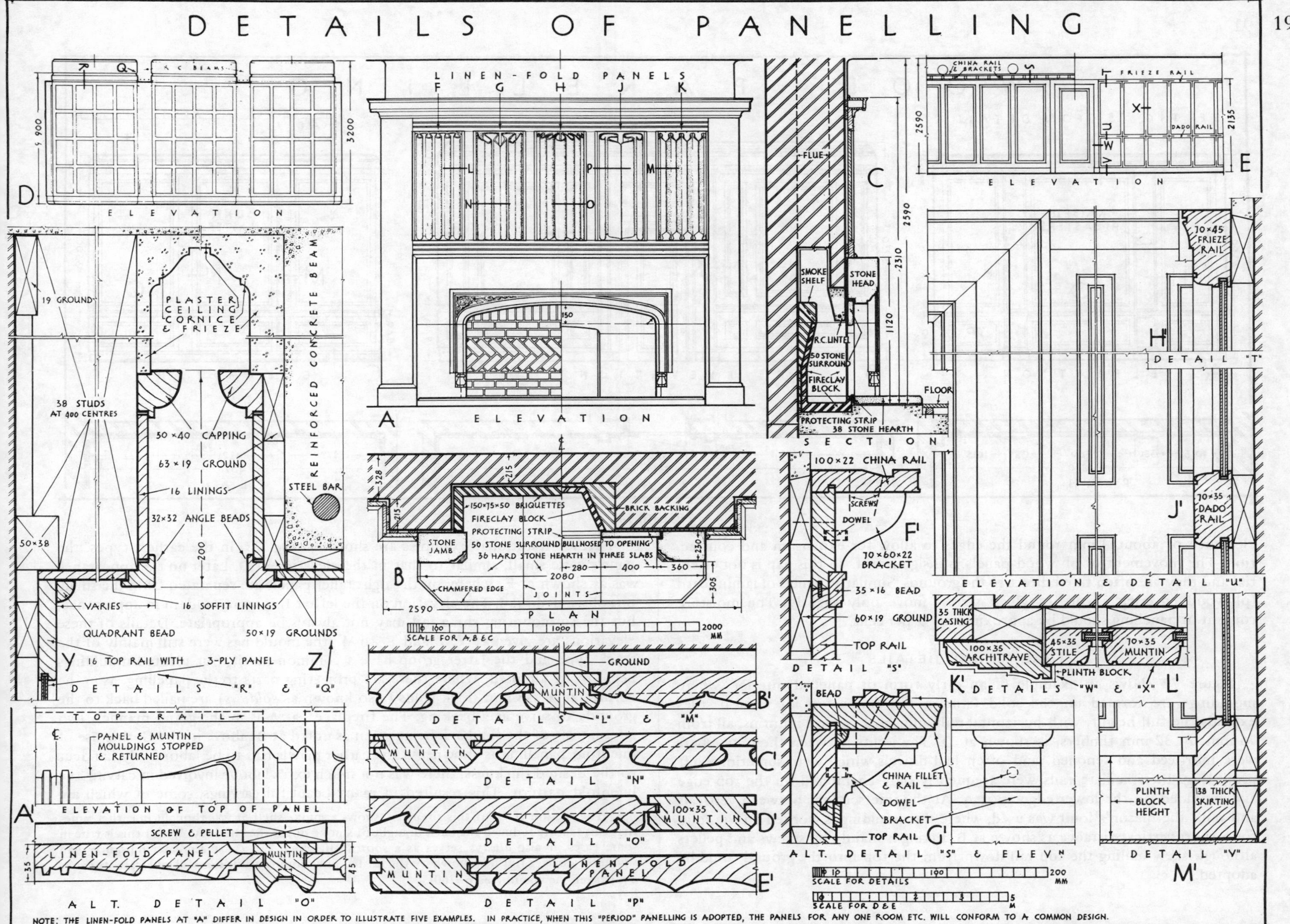
DETAILS OF PANELLING
LINEN-FOLD PANELS
NOTE: THE LINEN-FOLD PANELS AT "A" DIFFER IN DESIGN IN ORDER TO ILLUSTRATE FIVE EXAMPLES. IN PRACTICE, WHEN THIS "PERIOD" PANELLING IS ADOPTED, THE PANELS FOR ANY ONE ROOM ETC. WILL CONFORM TO A COMMON DESIGN.

FIGURE 73

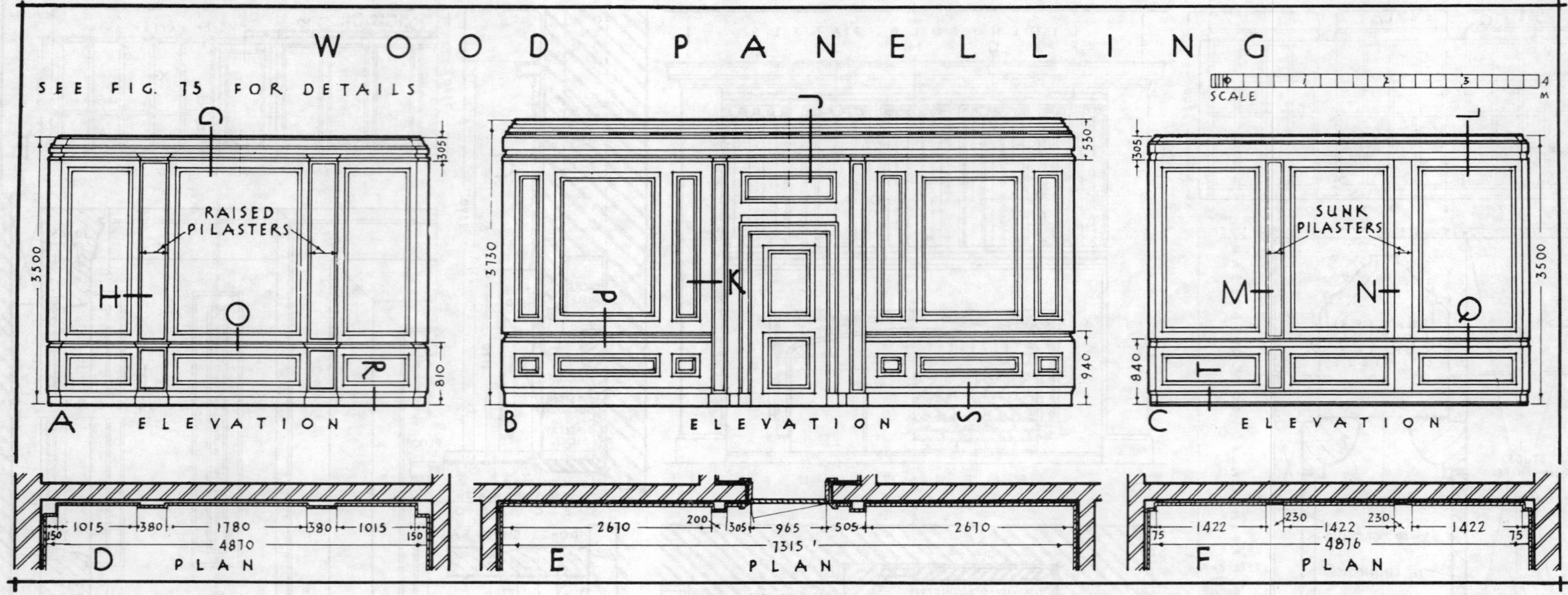

FIGURE 74

clearance of about 4 mm round the edges to allow for expansion and contraction. The movement of plywood panels is insignificant, so this gap is not essential and they are often fixed direct to the grounds. Similarly, panels of laminboard (plywood covering a core of glued strips) move only slightly. The moisture content of panelling should be approximately 9 per cent.

TRADITIONAL DETAILS

Figure 72 shows an example of an early form of panelled interior, where mouldings are formed on the solid (stuck). The framework of vertical stiles extends the full height, with horizontal rails and short vertical muntins, all from 75 mm by 32 mm timbers, is shown at D. The joints between these members were morticed and tenoned, and often had dowels which were sometimes left projecting. Intermediate rails were frequently only chamfered on the top edge and moulded on the lower edge as at A. At the intersections between verticals and rails, the mason's joint was used, where the moulding is worked on the solid for a short vertical distance as shown at B. Fixing is mainly by screws and pellets although skew nailing the top rail down from the top into the ground could be adopted.

Further traditional examples are shown in Fig. 73; in the earliest types, the panels were small, similar to that in the elevation at D. Later on the appearance was as shown at E, where, on the right taller panels are separated from the small ones by a dado rail. The elevation on the left at E is more modern in appearance, but the surmounting china rail may not always be appropriate. Details of these elevations are given at Y, Z and F′ to M′, the mouldings were still mainly of the stuck type and the latter group have a common motif, but planted mouldings begin to be adopted. Where there are projecting parts to the panelling, as in the cornice at Y, 38 mm thick studs (also known as *soldiers*) are nailed back to the grounds to serve as a backing. The fireplace* at A is in the grand manner, two alternatives of the fire back being given as noted at B; above it, the Gothic use of linenfold panelling is shown. As the earlier panels had to be laboriously handcut to the desired thickness, there was not much extra labour involved in carving the linenfold pattern. This resulted in many beautiful carvings, some of which are

* The section at C, of this fireplace, shows a smoke shelf, it was thought in earlier times that this feature reduced the back draught of smoke down the chimney. Whilst this is true in some cases, it also *always* serves as a *soot* shelf which can cause a greater nuisance than smoke – a better finish is shown by the dotted line. Some authorities still advocate its use – a mistaken viewpoint (see p. 260).

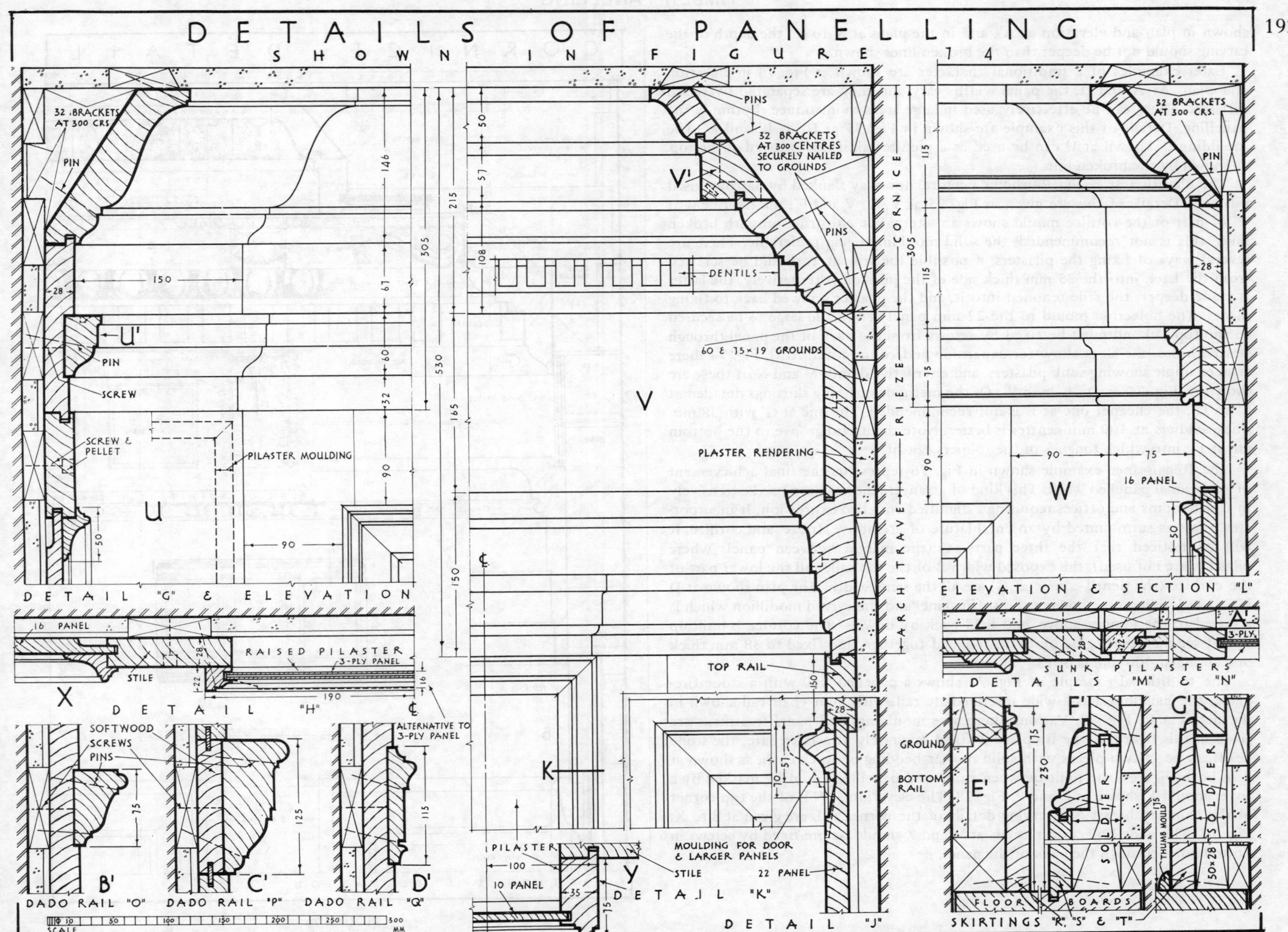
DETAILS OF PANELLING
SHOWN IN FIGURE 74
32 BRACKETS AT 300 CRS
PIN
U'
SCREW
SCREW & PELLET
PILASTER MOULDING
U
DETAIL "G" & ELEVATION
16 PANEL
RAISED PILASTER
3-PLY PANEL
STILE
X
DETAIL "H"
190
ALTERNATIVE TO 3-PLY PANEL
SOFTWOOD
SCREWS
PINS
B'
C'
D'
DADO RAIL "O"
DADO RAIL "P"
DADO RAIL "Q"
SCALE
MM
PINS
32 BRACKETS AT 300 CENTRES SECURELY NAILED TO GROUNDS
V'
DENTILS
60 & 75×19 GROUNDS
V
PLASTER RENDERING
CORNICE
FREIZE
ARCHITRAVE
TOP RAIL
GROUND
BOTTOM RAIL
K
PILASTER
10 PANEL
Y
STILE
DETAIL "K"
MOULDING FOR DOOR & LARGER PANELS
22 PANEL
DETAIL "J"
W
16 PANEL
ELEVATION & SECTION "L"
Z
A'
3-PLY
SUNK PLASTERS
DETAILS "M" & "N"
E'
F'
G'
SOLDIER
THUMB MOULD
50×28
FLOOR BOARDS
SKIRTINGS "R", "S" & "T"

FIGURE 75

shown in plan and elevation at A′, and in the plans at B′ to E′; the depth of the carving should not be deeper than the broken lines shown.

Later examples of a traditional character are shown at Fig. 74 in elevation and plan. At A and D, the panel widths vary and they are separated by raised pilasters. These can be effectively used in large areas to introduce rhythm in the panelling. Details of this example are shown in Fig. 75 at U, X, B′ and E′. The moulding U′ shown at U can be used as a picture rail if it is grooved at the top, as shown by the broken line.

The elevation at B, Fig. 74 shows a central doorway flanked by narrow raised pilasters. Details of this are given in Fig. 75 at Y, C′, V and F′; the treatment at V′ of part of the cornice mould shows an alternative construction with broken lines, this is not recommended, the solid moulding being preferable. There are several ways of fixing the pilasters, if possible the stile at Y should be screwed from the back into the 35 mm thick side of the pilaster. Alternatively, the latter is made deeper, the stile tenoned into it, and the pilaster screwed back to fixing pieces. The bolection mould to the 22 mm panel at V is too large to be secured to the top rail and must be fixed by screws from the back of the panel through slotted holes, the slots allow for expansion and contraction. At C, Fig. 74 there is an example showing sunk pilasters, and alternative details M and N of these are shown in Fig. 75 at D′, G′ and W. Of the methods of fixing skirtings detailed at E′ to G′, the cheaper one at E′ is not recommended. The one at G′ with 38 mm thick soldiers at 400 mm centres is better. Note the useful groove to the bottom rail at F′, into which tongues of the soldiers can fit.

The Renaissance example shown in Fig. 76 represents the final achievement of traditional panelled work. This kind of arrangement has been used extensively in court rooms and offices requiring a dignified enriched expression. It incorporates pilasters surmounted by an entablature of architrave, frieze, and cornice. It will be noticed that the three parts: C (the margin between panels where pilasters are not used), the exposed width B of the top rail, and the lower part of the cornice (the dentil course at G) are all the same width. The plan shown at D is a view looking up, showing the soffit panel and the carved modillion which is screwed to the joinery above, and held back by dowels. The cornice is built up out of separate parts glue blocked, tongued together, and fixed to 38 mm thick bracketing at 400 mm centres.

The traditional example at Fig. 77 shows a panelled wall with a stone fireplace, the panelling has a wide intermediate rail, with inset chair rail shown in the detail at R, Fig. 78. Various alternative mouldings and panel treatment are given in this figure. If the fireplace is fixed separately at a later date, the stone head can be in two pieces with solid mortar bedding between each, as shown at Z in both Figures; the joint between stone and panelling could be masked by a cover mould Y shown at Z and P, Fig. 78. The elevation at N is of the top corner of the chimney breast; six varying details of the corner at L are given at S to X, Fig. 78. The wide bolection moulds at M and Z should be pre-fixed by screws in slotted holes through the back of the panel.

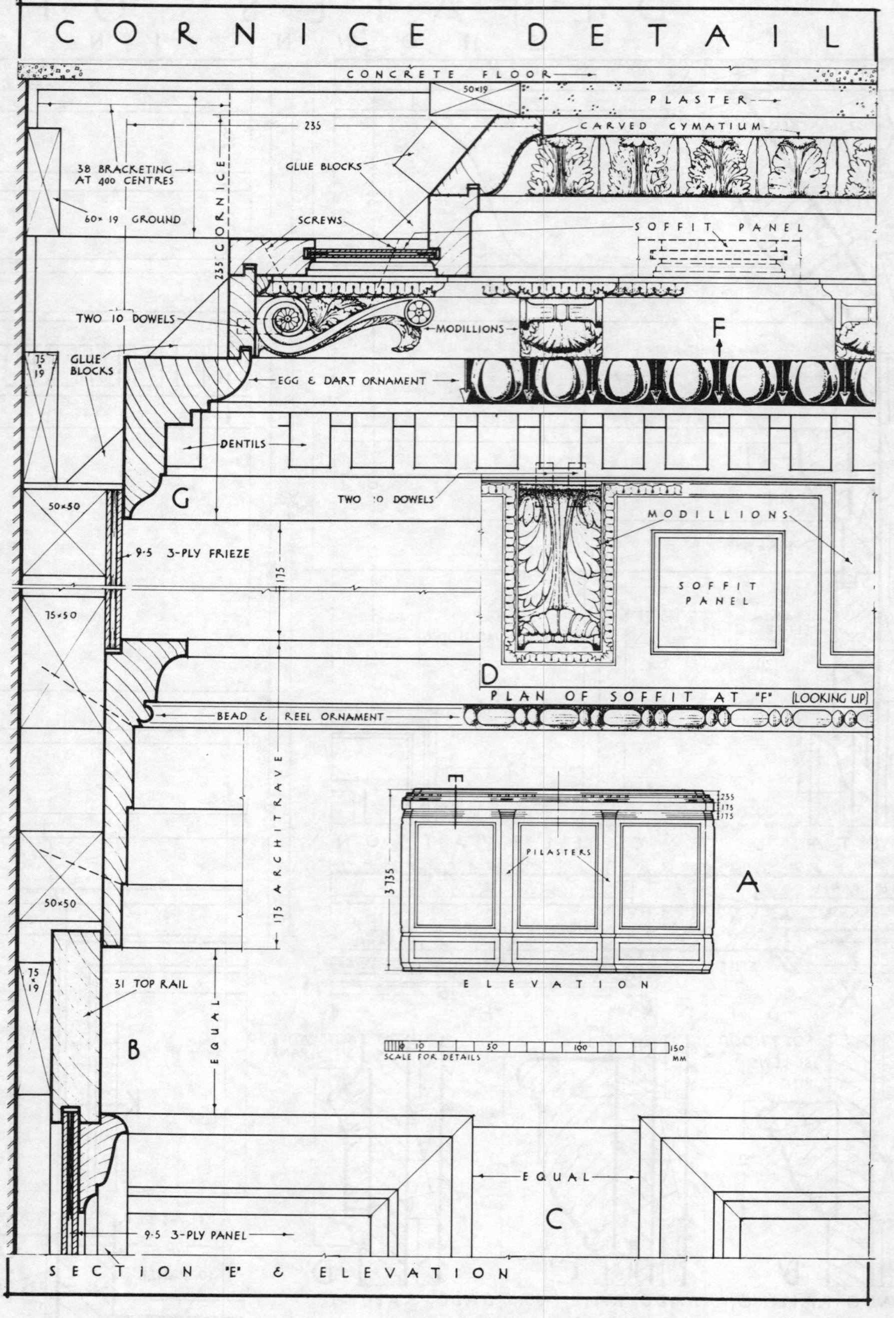

FIGURE 76

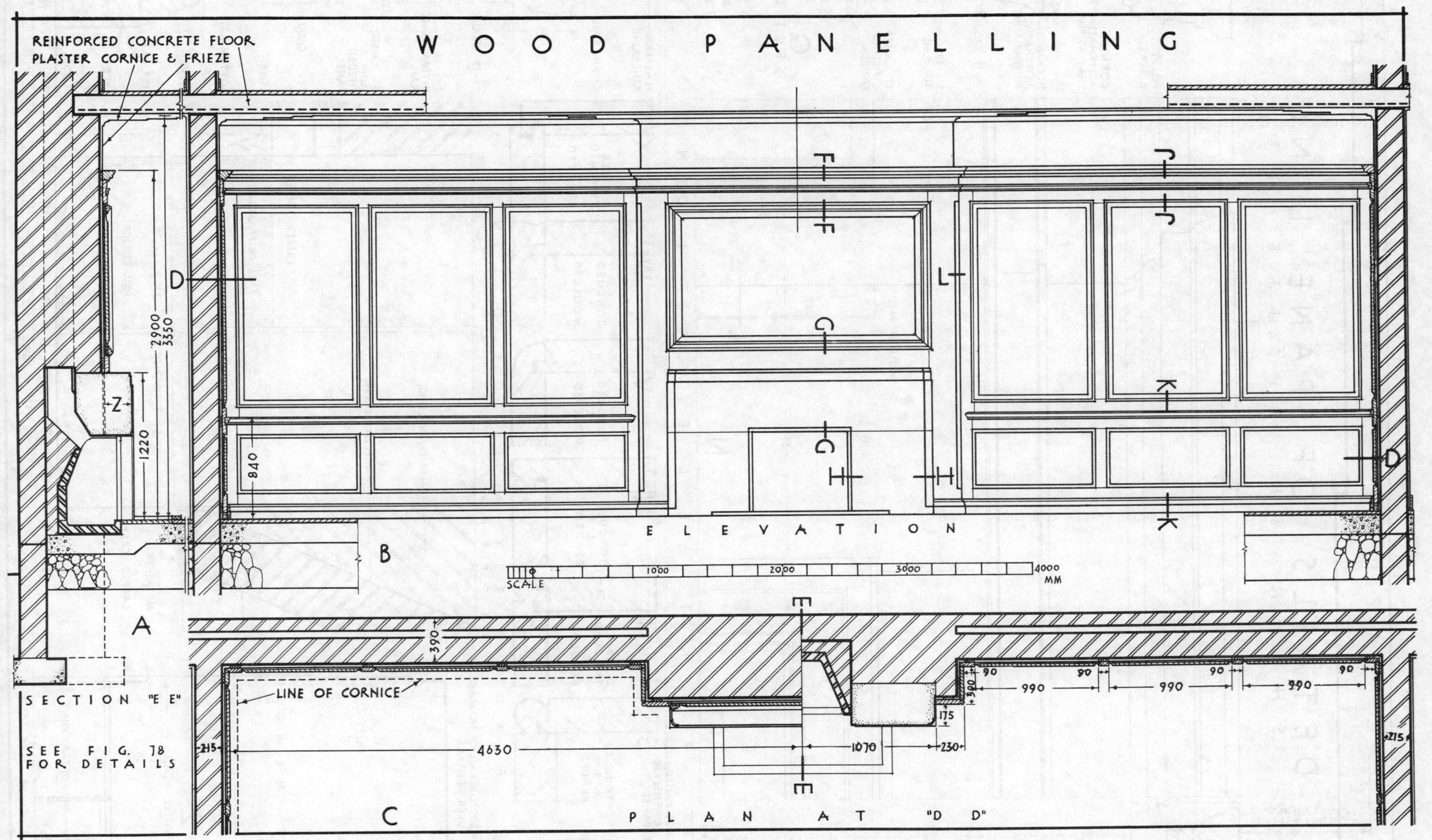
WOOD PANELLING
REINFORCED CONCRETE FLOOR
PLASTER CORNICE & FRIEZE
D
2900
3350
Z
1220
840
ELEVATION
SCALE
1000
2000
3000
4000 MM
A
B
SECTION "E E"
SEE FIG. 78 FOR DETAILS
390
LINE OF CORNICE
215
4630
1070
230
175
380
90
990
215
C
PLAN AT "D D"

FIGURE 77

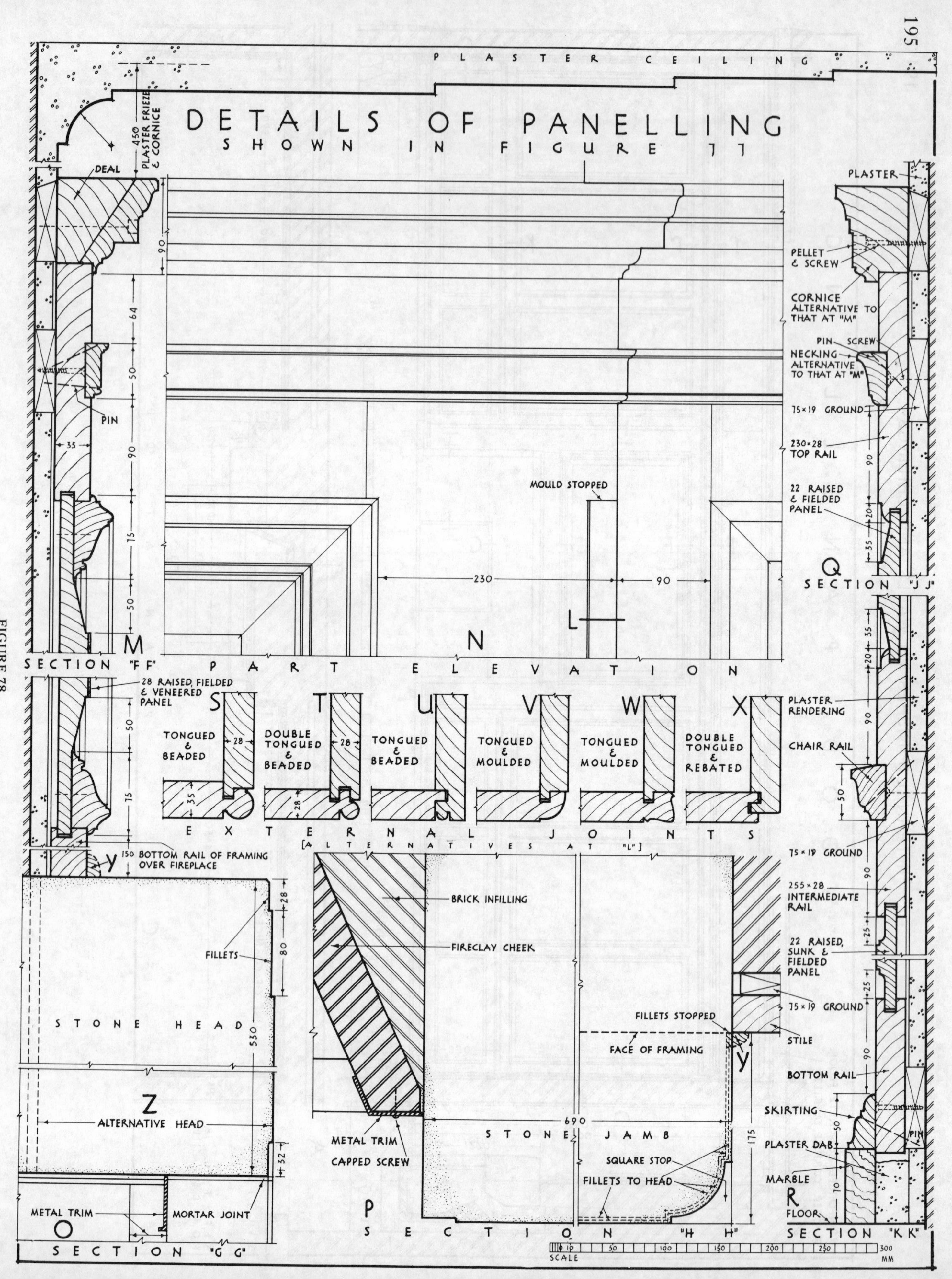
PLASTER CEILING
DETAILS OF PANELLING
SHOWN IN FIGURE 77
450 PLASTER FRIEZE & CORNICE
DEAL
PIN
M
SECTION "FF"
28 RAISED, FIELDED & VENEERED PANEL
150 BOTTOM RAIL OF FRAMING OVER FIREPLACE
MOULD STOPPED
L
N
PART ELEVATION
PLASTER
PELLET & SCREW
CORNICE ALTERNATIVE TO THAT AT "M"
PIN
SCREW
NECKING ALTERNATIVE TO THAT AT "M"
75×19 GROUND
230×28 TOP RAIL
22 RAISED & FIELDED PANEL
Q
SECTION "JJ"
S
TONGUED & BEADED
T
DOUBLE TONGUED & BEADED
U
TONGUED & BEADED
V
TONGUED & MOULDED
W
TONGUED & MOULDED
X
DOUBLE TONGUED & REBATED
EXTERNAL JOINTS
[ALTERNATIVES AT "L"]
PLASTER RENDERING
CHAIR RAIL
75×19 GROUND
255×28 INTERMEDIATE RAIL
22 RAISED, SUNK & FIELDED PANEL
75×19 GROUND
STILE
BOTTOM RAIL
SKIRTING
PIN
PLASTER DAB
MARBLE
R
FLOOR
SECTION "KK"
BRICK INFILLING
FIRECLAY CHEEK
FILLETS STOPPED
FACE OF FRAMING
STONE JAMB
SQUARE STOP
FILLETS TO HEAD
METAL TRIM
CAPPED SCREW
P
SECTION "HH"
FILLETS
STONE HEAD
Z
ALTERNATIVE HEAD
METAL TRIM
MORTAR JOINT
O
SECTION "GG"
SCALE
MM

FIGURE 78

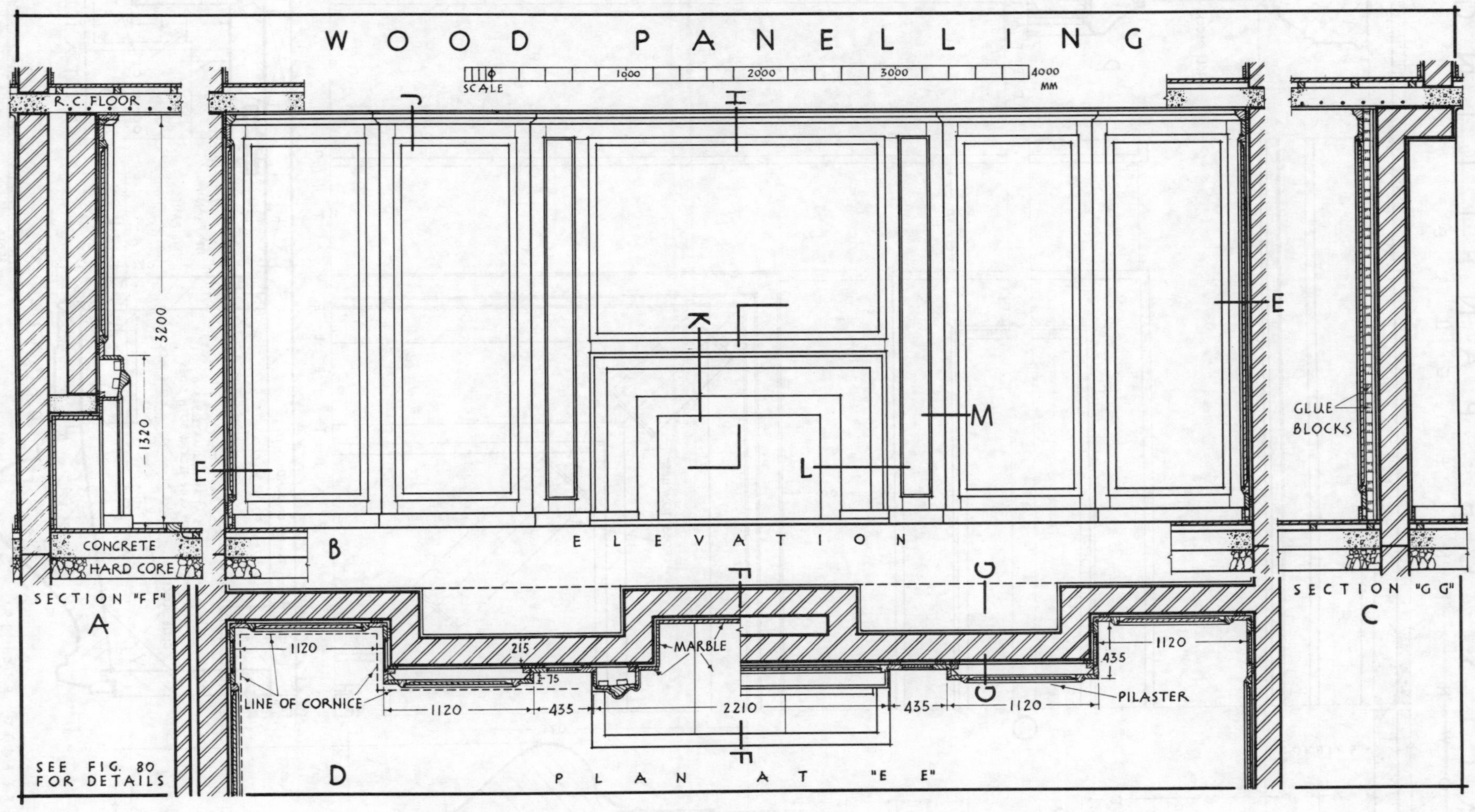

FIGURE 79

The example at Figs. 79 and 80 is more modern in feeling with large plain veneered panels set in different planes, with wide pilasters to the fireplace* breast. The veneer is applied to the laminboard backing, which is less liable to movement than solid wood. The fire opening is backed with marble and would be suitable for an electric radiator. The mantel and jambs to the fireplace are built up on brackets and incorporate a bold moulding, the parts being tongued and glue blocked together as shown in the various details.

Figure 80 shows the 320 mm wide moulded fireplace surround and panelling details, the framing at the sides is made up in the workshop, the joints X at Q and R between the 28 mm framing and the mantel moulding are screwed and tongued. The built-up section is then fixed by screws and pellets through the outer framing to the grounds round the outside; at the inside, the section is

* A further example of a marble fireplace with hardwood surround is shown in Fig. 107.

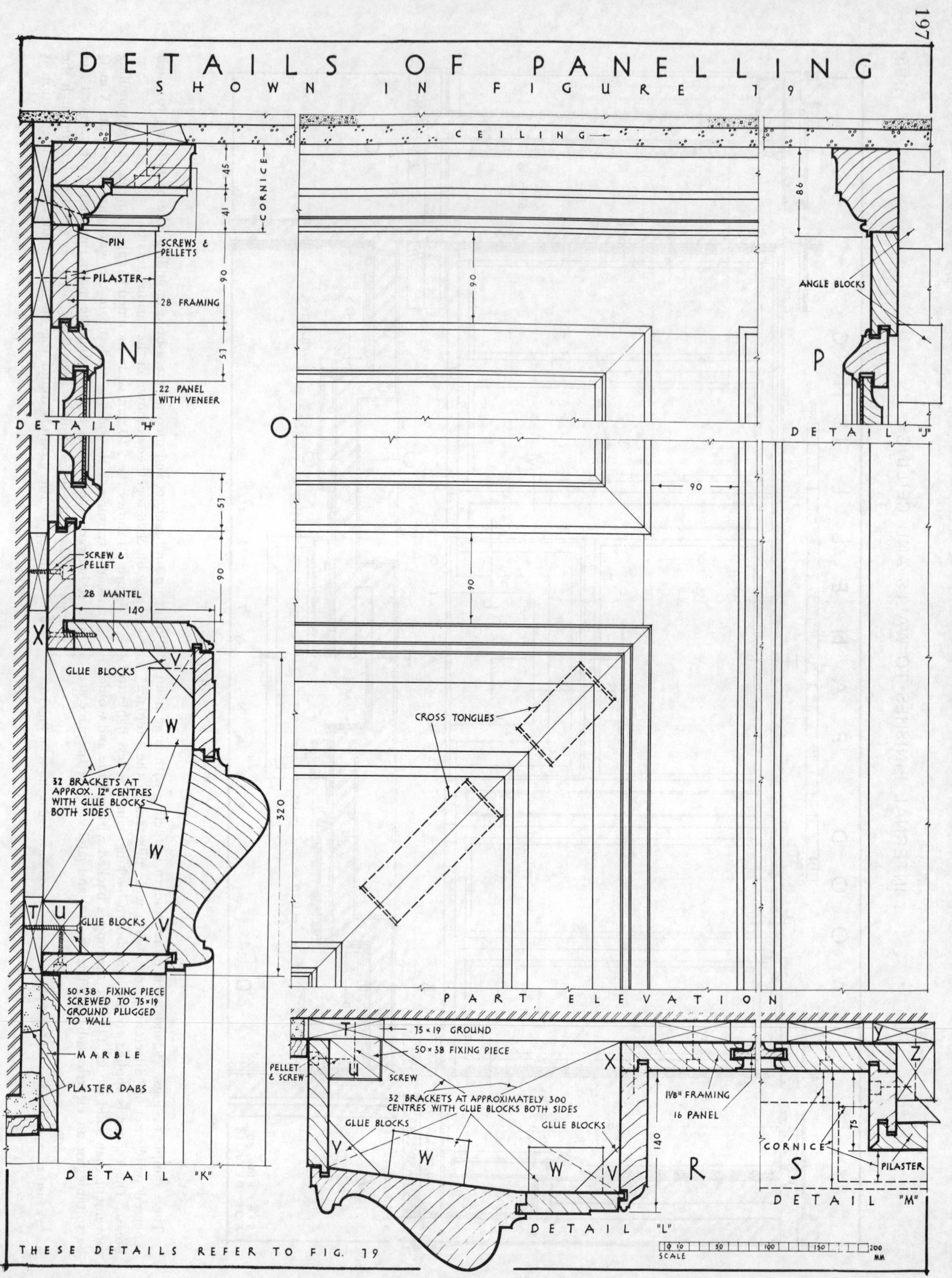
DETAILS OF PANELLING
SHOWN IN FIGURE 19
CEILING
CORNICE
45
41
90
51
PIN
SCREWS & PELLETS
PILASTER
28 FRAMING
N
22 PANEL WITH VENEER
DETAIL "H"
O
51
SCREW & PELLET
90
28 MANTEL
140
X
GLUE BLOCKS
V
W
32 BRACKETS AT APPROX. 12" CENTRES WITH GLUE BLOCKS BOTH SIDES
W
320
T
U
GLUE BLOCKS
V
50×38 FIXING PIECE SCREWED TO 75×19 GROUND PLUGGED TO WALL
MARBLE
PLASTER DABS
Q
DETAIL "K"
90
90
90
CROSS TONGUES
86
ANGLE BLOCKS
P
DETAIL "J"
PART ELEVATION
75×19 GROUND
50×38 FIXING PIECE
PELLET & SCREW
SCREW
32 BRACKETS AT APPROXIMATELY 300 CENTRES WITH GLUE BLOCKS BOTH SIDES
GLUE BLOCKS
GLUE BLOCKS
1 1/8" FRAMING
16 PANEL
140
R
DETAIL "L"
CORNICE
75
PILASTER
S
DETAIL "M"
THESE DETAILS REFER TO FIG. 19
0 10 50 100 150 200
SCALE
MM

FIGURE 80

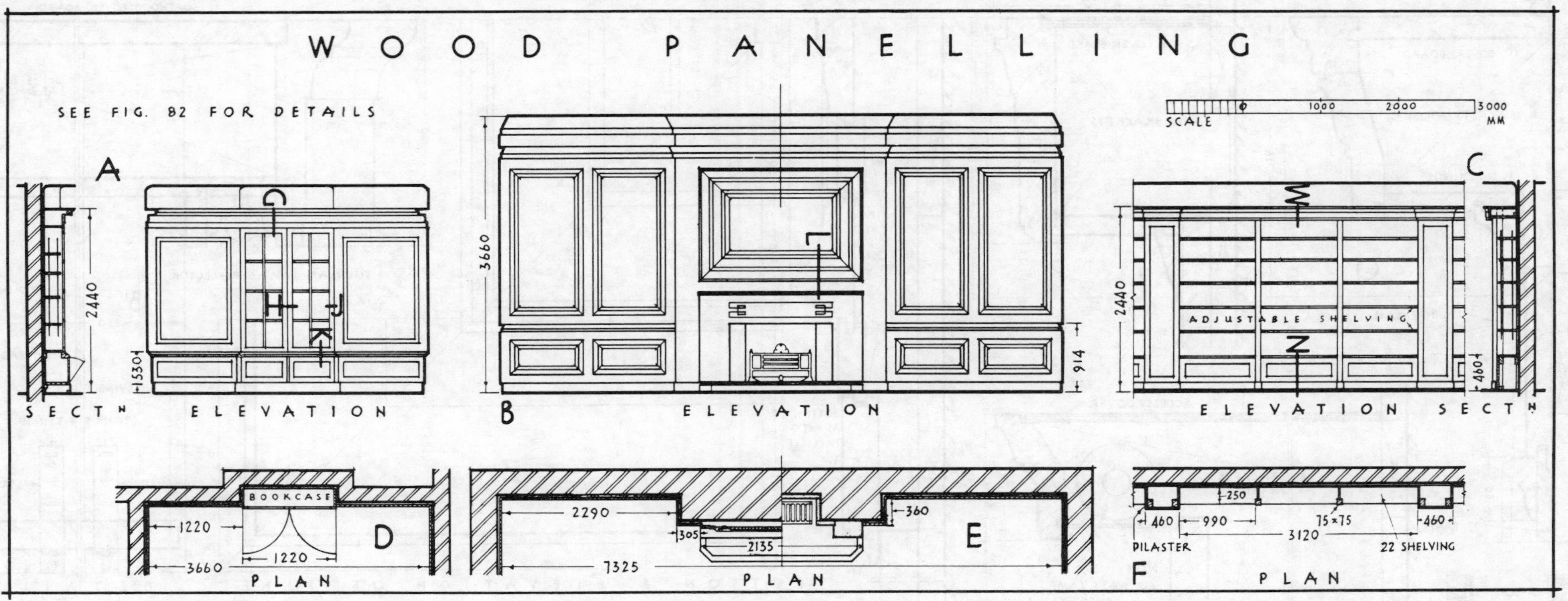

FIGURE 81

screwed to the fixing pieces U which are screwed to the grounds T. Cross tongues are used in the mitres as shown in the elevation. Methods of fixing marble are shown in greater detail in Fig. 88.

Further traditional examples are given in Fig. 81 with corresponding details in Fig. 82. The applications of shelving and necessary fittings, together with cornices, including the light fittings, are given. The shelving at R is carried by Tonk's fittings, these are two strips of slotted steel screwed to each supporting side. The height of the shelf can be adjusted by placing the loose cantilever brackets (which have a point that bites into the wood) into the appropriate slots.

The details in Fig. 83 represent a transitional stage between the older and newer types of panelling. Some of the elevations have large panels showing the greater use of plywood and simpler mouldings. That at A includes a doorway with the woodwork returned at an external corner G, and an internal angle at H, different details of these are given at L′ to P′. Alternative simple capping details are shown at Y, Z and A′, with plain skirtings at B′ to D′; two different treatments L and M at the door, are enlarged at E′ and G′. The panelling at elevation B is quite plain with rectangular panels and the details of the salient features are given. The elevations at C are more elaborate, in one case stuck moulds are used as at S′ with bolection moulding at T′. The elevation at E has been included to show another way of dividing the wall into panels, it contrasts with the later developments at B. The elevation at F shows the vertical t. and g. boarding known as matchboarding, where narrow strips of timber are used as indicated in the details at Q′ and R′; the boards are secret nailed back to the grounds at the joints. Another example of this form as applied to external work is shown in Figs. 17, 18 and 93 (detail at W).

MODERN PANELLING

At A, Fig. 84, the use of battened panelling (horizontal t. and g. boards) is shown and detailed at H to M, the battens tenon into the stile as at W, in the detail at J. The elevation at C, plan at D, and section at E show a central radiator with masking grille flanked by large panels, the relevant details are given at O and P. The radiator framing is formed with studs to which bearers are fixed that notch into a plate X fixed to the wall as shown at O and P. The grille is made with a 50 mm by 50 mm frame and 50 mm by 25 mm intermediate members, and is held in place by four Bales' catches (see X, Fig. 82). The plywood panel-

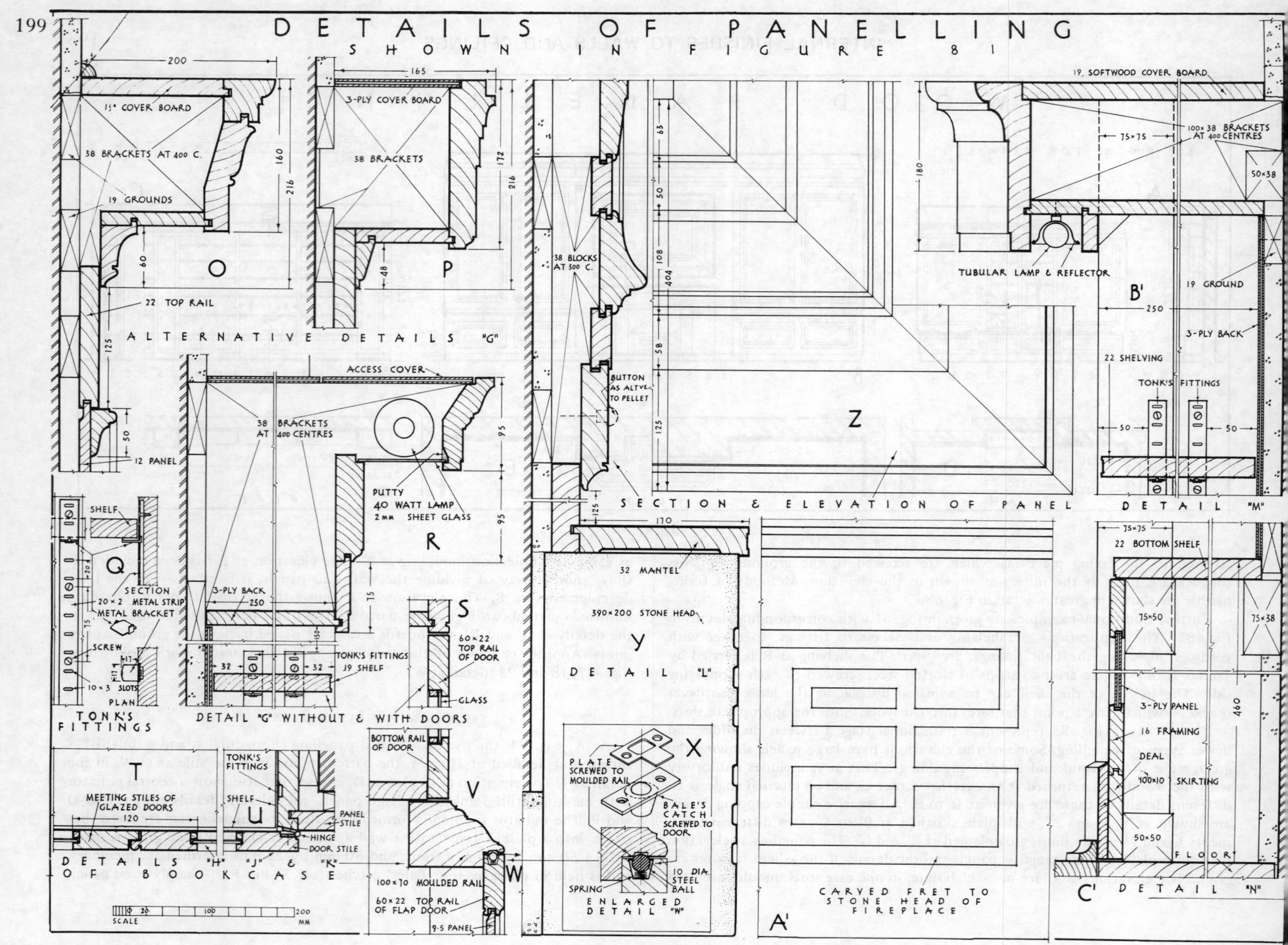

DETAILS OF PANELLING
SHOWN IN FIGURE 81
200
1½" COVER BOARD
38 BRACKETS AT 400 C.
19 GROUNDS
22 TOP RAIL
12 PANEL
O
165
3-PLY COVER BOARD
38 BRACKETS
P
ALTERNATIVE DETAILS "G"
ACCESS COVER
38 BRACKETS AT 400 CENTRES
PUTTY
40 WATT LAMP
2mm SHEET GLASS
R
3-PLY BACK
250
S
60×22 TOP RAIL OF DOOR
TONK'S FITTINGS
19 SHELF
GLASS
DETAIL "G" WITHOUT & WITH DOORS
SHELF
Q
SECTION
20×2 METAL STRIP
METAL BRACKET
SCREW
10×3 SLOTS
PLAN
TONK'S FITTINGS
BOTTOM RAIL OF DOOR
T
TONK'S FITTINGS
MEETING STILES OF GLAZED DOORS
SHELF
U
PANEL STILE
HINGE
DOOR STILE
120
V
W
100×70 MOULDED RAIL
60×22 TOP RAIL OF FLAP DOOR
9·5 PANEL
DETAILS "H" "J" & "K"
OF BOOKCASE
SCALE
MM
38 BLOCKS AT 300 C.
BUTTON AS ALTVE TO PELLET
170
32 MANTEL
390×200 STONE HEAD
Y
DETAIL "L"
PLATE SCREWED TO MOULDED RAIL
BALE'S CATCH SCREWED TO DOOR
X
SPRING
10 DIA. STEEL BALL
ENLARGED DETAIL "W"
Z
SECTION & ELEVATION OF PANEL
A'
CARVED FRET TO STONE HEAD OF FIREPLACE
19, SOFTWOOD COVER BOARD
100×38 BRACKETS AT 400 CENTRES
75×75
50×38
TUBULAR LAMP & REFLECTOR
B'
19 GROUND
250
3-PLY BACK
22 SHELVING
TONK'S FITTINGS
DETAIL "M"
75×75
22 BOTTOM SHELF
75×50
75×38
3-PLY PANEL
16 FRAMING
DEAL
400×10 SKIRTING
50×50
FLOOR
C'
DETAIL "N"

FIGURE 82

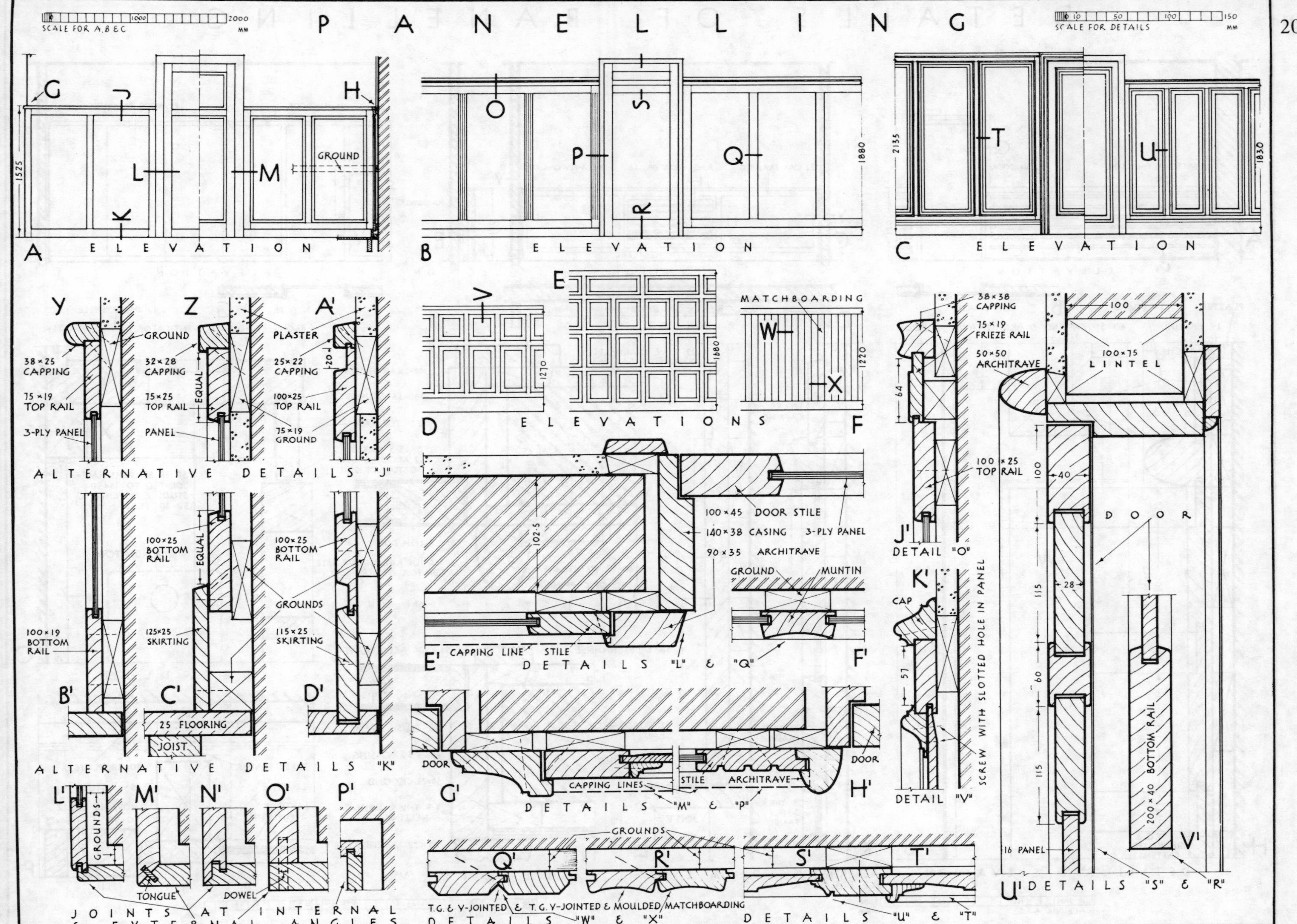

SCALE FOR A, B & C
PANELLING
SCALE FOR DETAILS
A ELEVATION
B ELEVATION
C ELEVATION
GROUND
D E F ELEVATIONS
MATCHBOARDING
38×38 CAPPING
75×19 FRIEZE RAIL
50×50 ARCHITRAVE
100×75 LINTEL
GROUND
PLASTER
38×25 CAPPING
32×28 CAPPING
25×22 CAPPING
75×19 TOP RAIL
75×25 TOP RAIL
100×25 TOP RAIL
3-PLY PANEL
PANEL
75×19 GROUND
ALTERNATIVE DETAILS "J"
100×45 DOOR STILE
140×38 CASING
3-PLY PANEL
90×35 ARCHITRAVE
MUNTIN
100×25 TOP RAIL
DETAIL "O"
DOOR
100×25 BOTTOM RAIL
GROUNDS
100×19 BOTTOM RAIL
125×25 SKIRTING
115×25 SKIRTING
CAP
CAPPING LINE
STILE
DETAILS "L" & "Q"
SCREW WITH SLOTTED HOLE IN PANEL
25 FLOORING
JOIST
ALTERNATIVE DETAILS "K"
CAPPING LINES
ARCHITRAVE
DETAILS "M" & "P"
DETAIL "V"
200×40 BOTTOM RAIL
16 PANEL
TONGUE
DOWEL
JOINTS AT INTERNAL & EXTERNAL ANGLES
T.G. & V-JOINTED & T.G. V-JOINTED & MOULDED MATCHBOARDING
DETAILS "W" & "X"
DETAILS "U" & "T"
DETAILS "S" & "R"

FIGURE 83

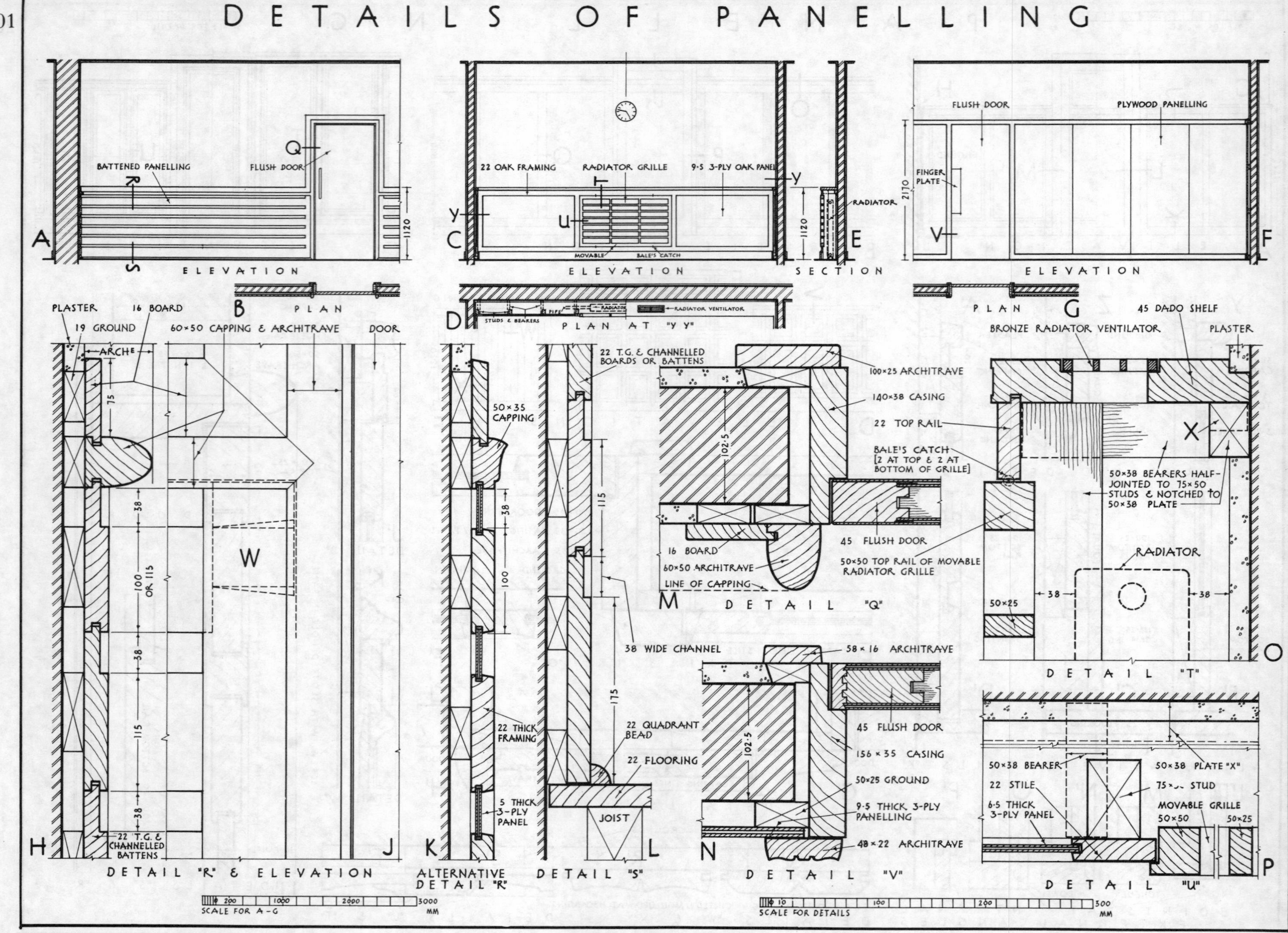
DETAILS OF PANELLING
BATTENED PANELLING
FLUSH DOOR
ELEVATION
PLAN
22 OAK FRAMING
RADIATOR GRILLE
9·5 3-PLY OAK PANEL
MOVABLE
BALE'S CATCH
ELEVATION
PLAN AT "Y Y"
RADIATOR
SECTION
FLUSH DOOR
PLYWOOD PANELLING
FINGER PLATE
ELEVATION
PLAN
PLASTER
16 BOARD
19 GROUND
60×50 CAPPING & ARCHITRAVE
DOOR
22 T.G. & CHANNELLED BATTENS
DETAIL "R" & ELEVATION
50×35 CAPPING
22 THICK FRAMING
5 THICK 3-PLY PANEL
ALTERNATIVE DETAIL "R"
22 T.G. & CHANNELLED BOARDS OR BATTENS
38 WIDE CHANNEL
22 QUADRANT BEAD
22 FLOORING
JOIST
DETAIL "S"
100×25 ARCHITRAVE
140×38 CASING
22 TOP RAIL
BALE'S CATCH [2 AT TOP & 2 AT BOTTOM OF GRILLE]
45 FLUSH DOOR
50×50 TOP RAIL OF MOVABLE RADIATOR GRILLE
16 BOARD
60×50 ARCHITRAVE
LINE OF CAPPING
DETAIL "Q"
58×16 ARCHITRAVE
45 FLUSH DOOR
156×35 CASING
50×25 GROUND
9·5 THICK 3-PLY PANELLING
48×22 ARCHITRAVE
DETAIL "V"
BRONZE RADIATOR VENTILATOR
45 DADO SHELF
PLASTER
50×38 BEARERS HALF-JOINTED TO 75×50 STUDS & NOTCHED TO 50×38 PLATE
RADIATOR
DETAIL "T"
50×38 BEARER
50×38 PLATE "X"
22 STILE
6·5 THICK 3-PLY PANEL
MOVABLE GRILLE
DETAIL "U"
SCALE FOR A-G
SCALE FOR DETAILS

FIGURE 84

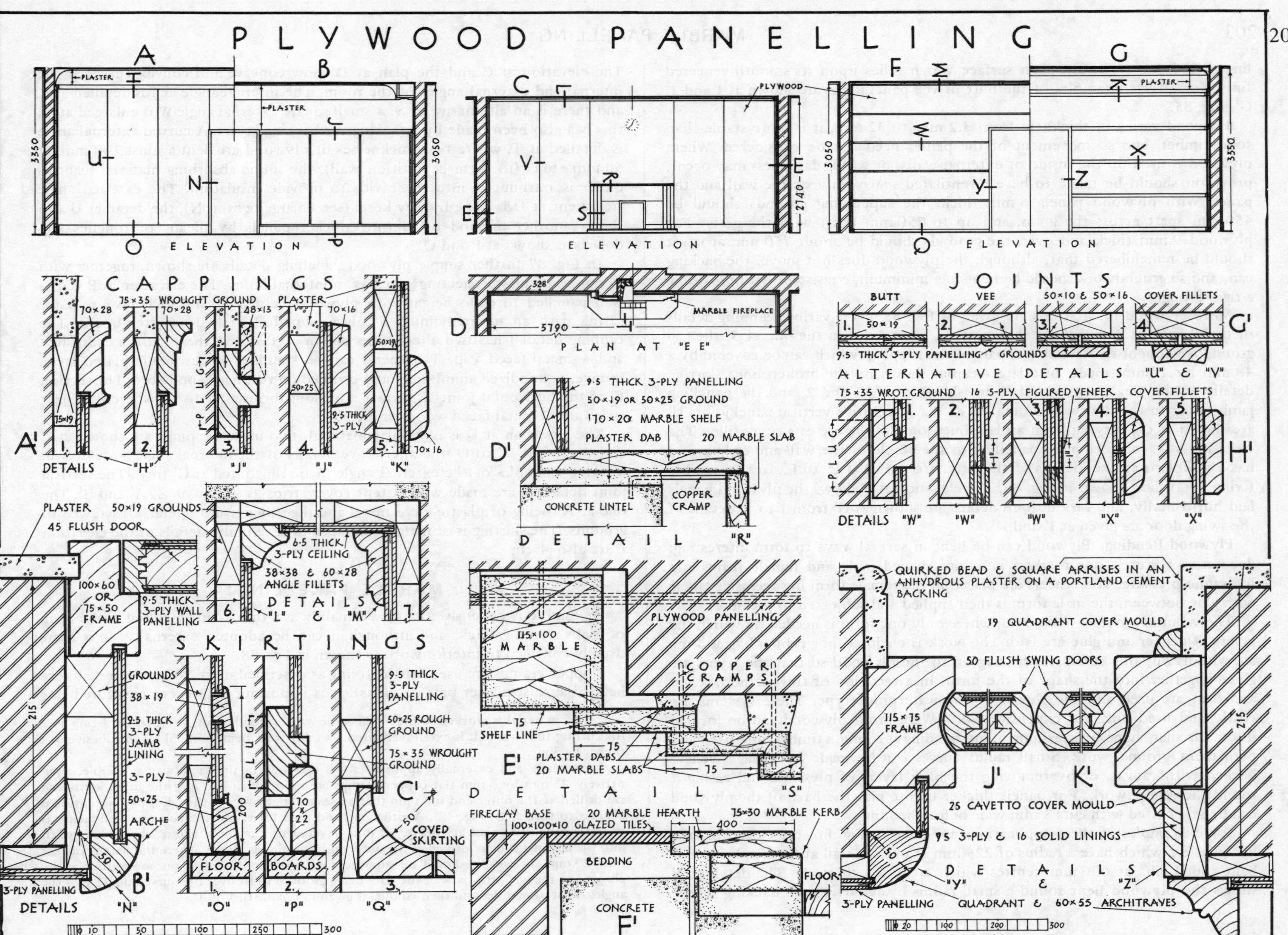
PLYWOOD PANELLING
ELEVATION
CAPPINGS
JOINTS
PLAN AT "E"
ALTERNATIVE DETAILS "U" & "V"
SKIRTINGS
DETAIL "R"
DETAIL "S"
DETAIL "T"
DETAILS "Y" & "Z"
SCALE FOR DETAILS
SCALE FOR A, B, C, D, F E G

FIGURE 85

ling at F has a relatively plain surface which relies upon its smooth veneered finish for effect. Examples of the butt or vee panel joints are shown at 1 and 2, G′, Fig. 85.

Plywood varies in thickness from 3.2 mm to 32 mm, it is more stable than solid timber, and so movement of the panels need not be considered. Where plywood is used on the inside of external walls, or where dampness may occur, provision should be made to have a ventilated space between the wall and the panel. With plywood panels 6 mm thick, the supporting grounds should be 450 mm apart across the grain, and up to 750 mm apart with the grain. For plywood 9 mm thick and over, the grounds should be about 750 mm apart; it should be remembered that, although the plywood does not move, the backing can, and so groundwork should be kept to a minimum, consistent with providing a rigid fixing.

More plywood illustrations are given in Fig. 85 where various capping details of the elevations A and B are shown at A′, from 1–4. In the one at 3, the top ground is wrought to serve also as part of the capping, which can be covered by a 48 mm by 13 mm piece, or a larger cap as shown by the broken line. Skirting details of the elevations A and B are shown at C′, 1 and 2, and the panelling jamb lining to the doorway is detailed at B′. Alternative vertical panel joints U, are shown at G′, varying from a plain butt joint to the use of a cover fillet. The elevation at C includes plain panelling to the whole of the wall and ceiling, and has a marble fireplace; details of the latter are shown at D′ to F′, further marble fixing details are shown in Fig. 88. The elevation at F shows the plywood panels laid horizontally, and various joint details are shown at H′ from 1 to 3, details of the swing door are given at J′ and K′.

Plywood Bending. Plywood can be bent in several ways to form interesting, decorative features, one method is to use shaped male and female forms and hydraulic pressure. The veneers are placed in the female form in successive layers with glue between, the male form is then applied and subjected to pressure.

The vacuum process is also used, where only one form is needed on which the layers of veneer and glue are laid. The work is enclosed in a rubber bag and the air withdrawn, this collapses the bag on to the plywood so that the layers are glued together into the shape of the form. In a variation of this method, steam and heat are used and the glue is of the waterproof type. These systems are costly and used only for expensive work. Waterproof plywood can be formed into a circular shape by steaming it and bending it round a timber core used as a permanent ground work. Small radius curves can be made by using a veneer backed with canvas, or by removing the back layers of plywood and easing it round the groundwork. For panels thicker than 6 mm the back of the plywood can be saw kerfed with cuts 3 mm wide before bending.

Some examples of these applications are given in Fig. 86, the elevation at A has pilasters which have a radius of 225 mm as in the detail at G, the plywood is bent round ribs at 600 mm centres which are fixed to studs. The detail at H shows the plywood bent round a small radius by removing the backing layers. The elevation at C and the plan at D show concave and convex curves at the internal and external angles of the room. The internal angle at J is detailed at R and there is an alternative at S; a small square external angle W is enlarged at O, this has also been made by removing the backing layers. A curved external angle is detailed at T, where two thicknesses of plywood are bent against 100 mm by 50 mm studs (to form a partition wall), the sound-absorbing material (cabot's quilt) is introduced into the cavity to provide insulation. The external angle treatment at U is done by saw kerfs (see enlargement at N), the detail at U also shows another method of jointing thicker panels by means of tongues and dowels as shown at P and Q.

In Fig. 87 further simple plywood panelling details are shown, together with examples of plastic sheeting* used as an internal lining. The elevation at B is of a wall panelled to dado height with plywood or plastic, and includes a radiator casing with an internal lining of aluminium foil backed asbestos board. The capping detail J has two alternatives drawn at T and U, these show a dado shelf and a metal-faced cap. The metal can be stainless or chromium-plated steel, bronze, or anodized aluminium, and is rolled on to a hardwood core. The section K of the horizontal joints is shown in various forms at C′ to F′, where the cover strips are of metal-faced wood, or metal.

The elevation at D is of similar material, two more cappings are shown at V and W, and at M′ to O′ the alternative details of the internal angle S are drawn. Varying examples of the external angle M are illustrated at G′ to J′. The vertical joint details N are made with patent cover strips as shown at Z, A′ and B′. The one at A′ being of plastic-faced metal and the other two of metal, all screwed to grounds. The skirting is of metal as detailed at K′. Similar details of the elevation F are also given.

MARBLE PANELLING†

As marble is expensive, it is used mainly as a thin facing material in the form of slabs 20 mm thick, and although it can be adopted externally, it is more usually confined to interior work as shown in Fig. 88.

Copper cramps are used for the fixing as described on p. 207 and the slabs are bedded against plaster pats (or dabs). It is important to prevent moisture being

* This material is worked in much the same way as wood, a fine toothed saw being used for cutting the sheets. It is extensively used for table tops, being secured by an adhesive to a timber backing.

† Internally and externally applied slate is attached in the same way as marble, alternatively 25 mm by 3 mm flat copper cramps are used which bed into the brick joints and are drilled at the outer end for a pin that passes through holes in the edges of adjacent slabs (similar to that at R, Fig. 48). Another method used for reinforced concrete wall facing, is to set channels like that at H, Fig. 52 (but dovetailed) into the concrete, shaped cramps fit into the channel and are drilled at the outer ends for pins as above. Where the slate is thicker than 20 mm, its weight should be supported at each storey height on non-ferrous angles plugged to the wall, the back of the slate being grooved to fit over the outstanding leg of the angle. A list of marbles and their colours is given in Chap. III, Vol. II.

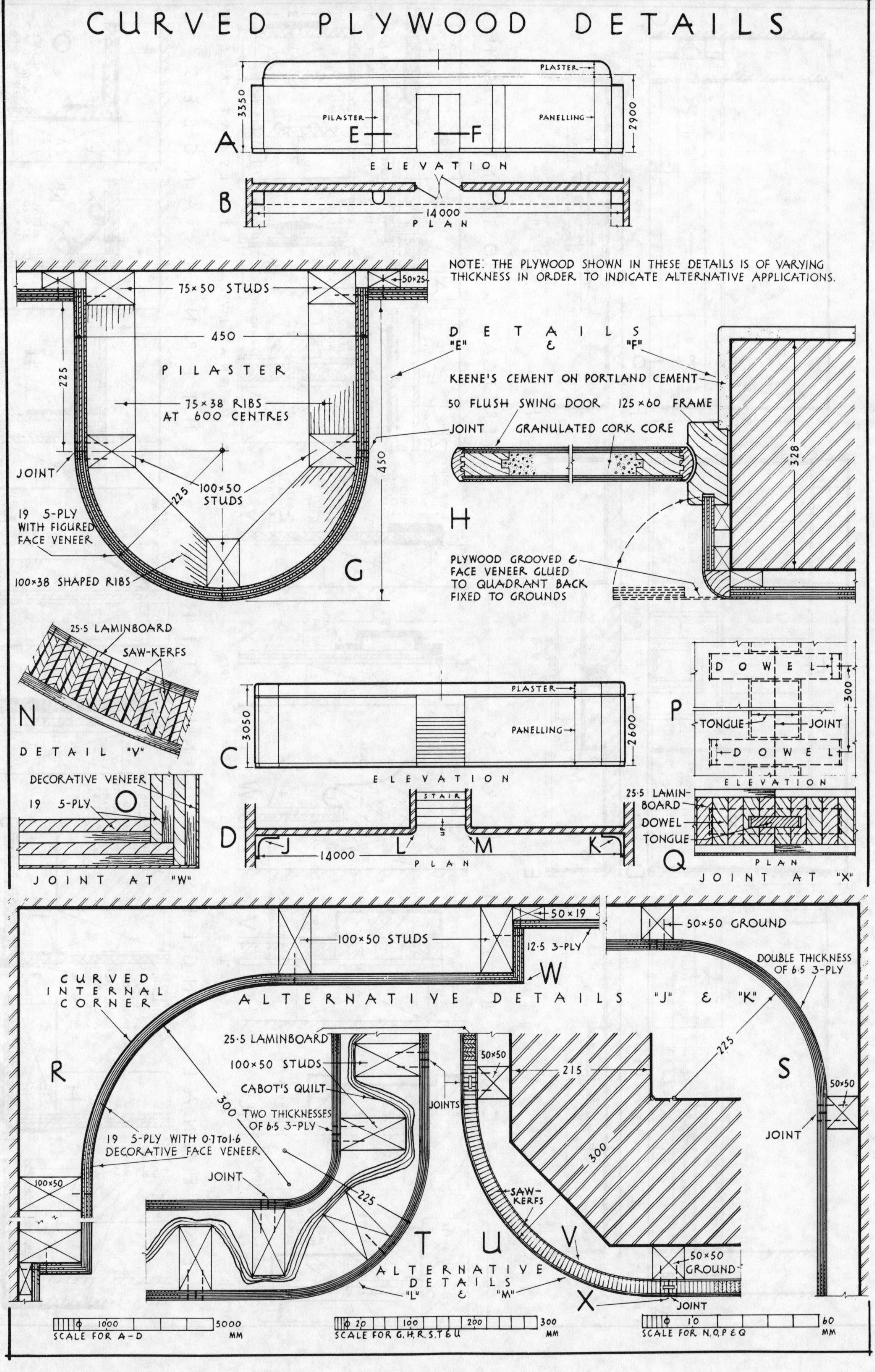
CURVED PLYWOOD DETAILS
PLASTER
PILASTER
PANELLING
3350
2900
A
E
F
ELEVATION
B
14000
PLAN
NOTE: THE PLYWOOD SHOWN IN THESE DETAILS IS OF VARYING THICKNESS IN ORDER TO INDICATE ALTERNATIVE APPLICATIONS.
75×50 STUDS
50×25
450
225
PILASTER
75×38 RIBS AT 600 CENTRES
JOINT
100×50 STUDS
19 5-PLY WITH FIGURED FACE VENEER
100×38 SHAPED RIBS
G
DETAILS "E" & "F"
KEENE'S CEMENT ON PORTLAND CEMENT
50 FLUSH SWING DOOR
125×60 FRAME
GRANULATED CORK CORE
328
H
PLYWOOD GROOVED & FACE VENEER GLUED TO QUADRANT BACK FIXED TO GROUNDS
25·5 LAMINBOARD
SAW-KERFS
N
DETAIL "V"
3050
2600
C
DOWEL
TONGUE
JOINT
300
P
DECORATIVE VENEER
19 5-PLY
O
JOINT AT "W"
STAIR
UP
D
J
L
M
K
25·5 LAMINBOARD
DOWEL
TONGUE
Q
JOINT AT "X"
100×50 STUDS
50×19
12·5 3-PLY
50×50 GROUND
DOUBLE THICKNESS OF 6·5 3-PLY
CURVED INTERNAL CORNER
W
ALTERNATIVE DETAILS "J" & "K"
R
25·5 LAMINBOARD
CABOT'S QUILT
TWO THICKNESSES OF 6·5 3-PLY
300
19 5-PLY WITH 0·7 TO 1·6 DECORATIVE FACE VENEER
JOINTS
50×50
215
S
100×50
SAW-KERFS
T
U
V
ALTERNATIVE DETAILS "L" & "M"
50×50 GROUND
X
SCALE FOR A-D
1000
5000 MM
SCALE FOR G, H, R, S, T & U
20
100
200
300 MM
SCALE FOR N, O, P & Q
10
60 MM

FIGURE 86

PLYWOOD & PLASTIC PANELLING

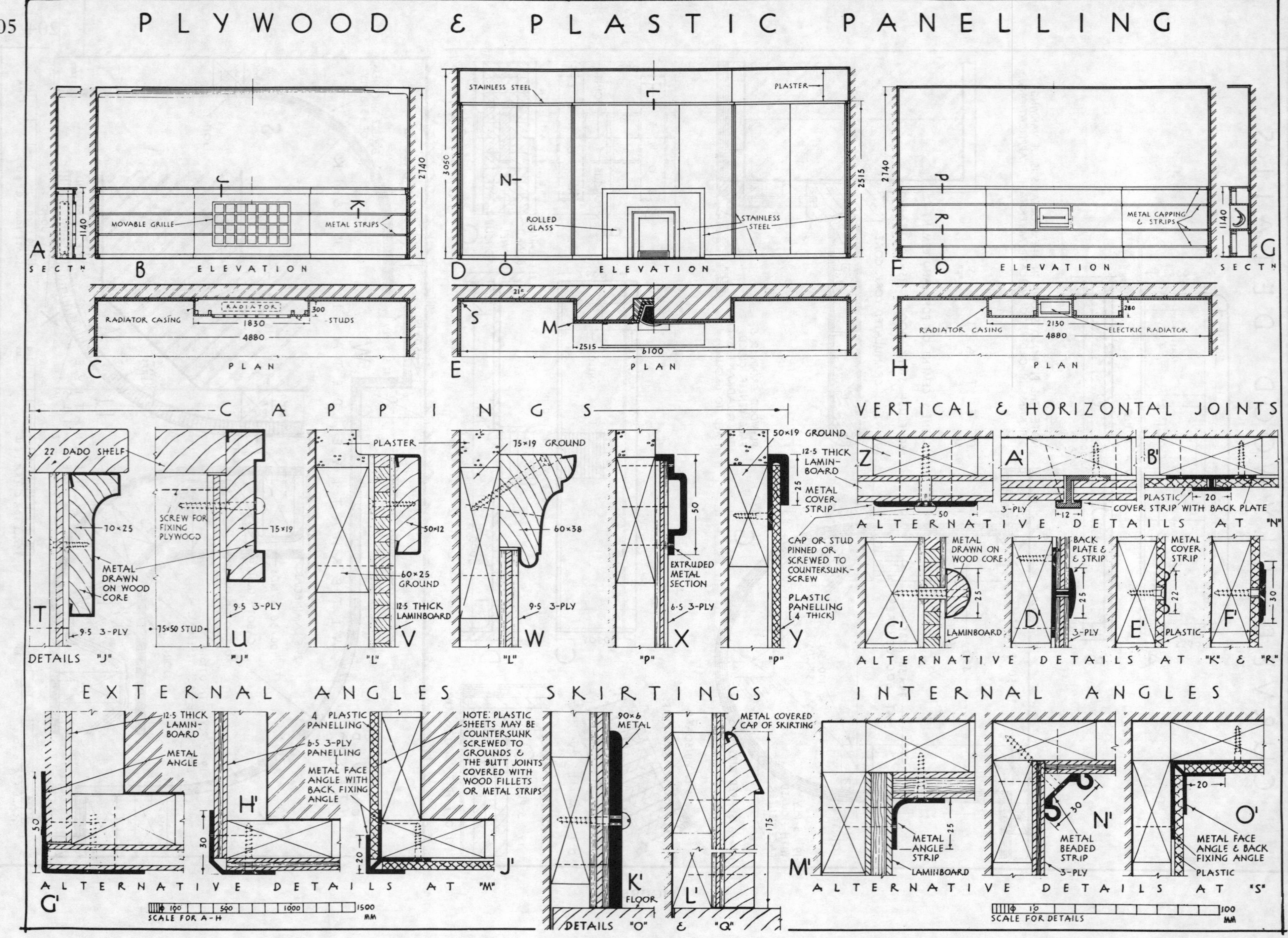

FIGURE 87

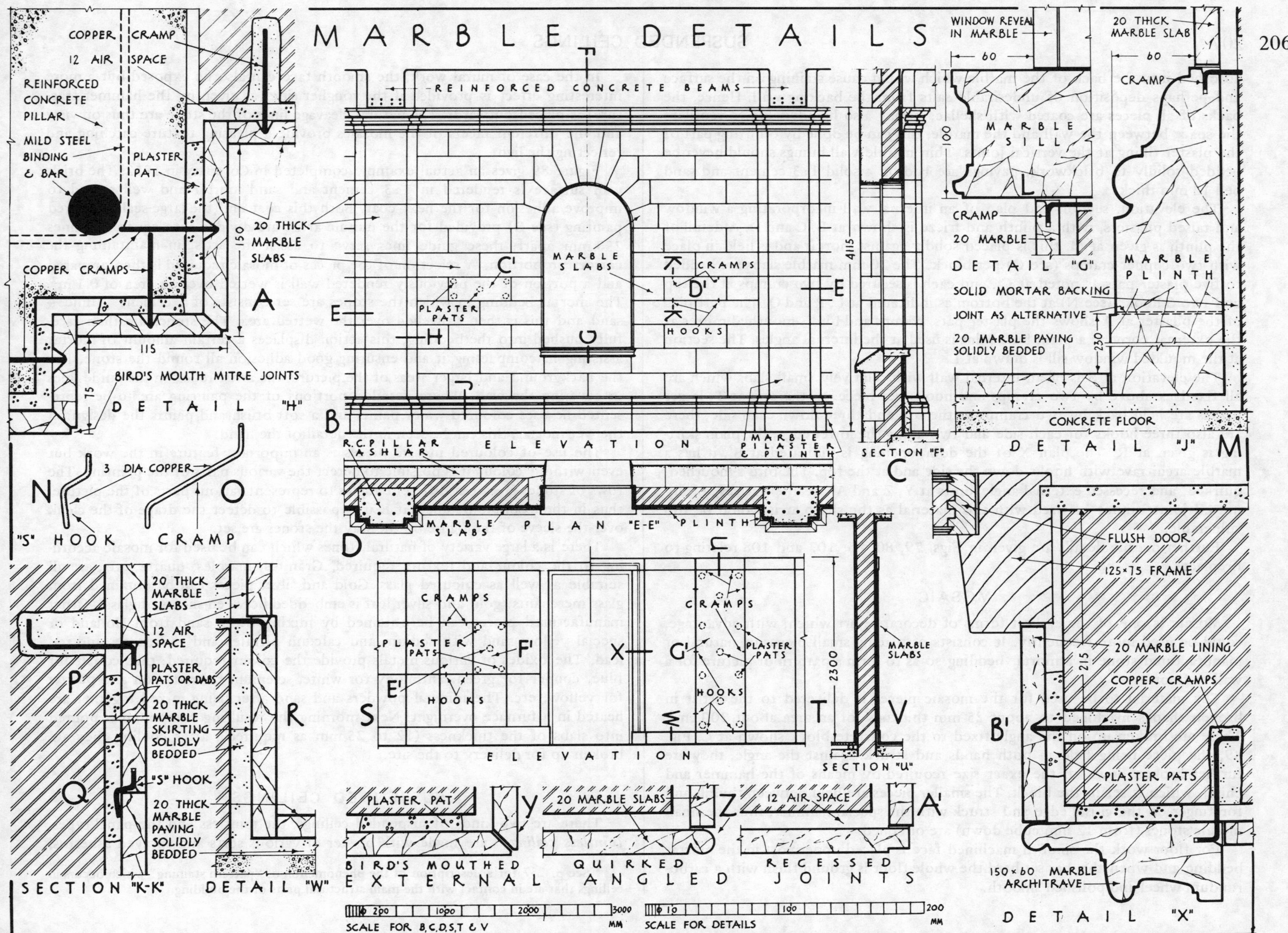
MARBLE DETAILS
COPPER CRAMP
12 AIR SPACE
REINFORCED CONCRETE PILLAR
MILD STEEL BINDING & BAR
PLASTER PAT
20 THICK MARBLE SLABS
COPPER CRAMPS
150
115
75
BIRD'S MOUTH MITRE JOINTS
DETAIL "H"
A
REINFORCED CONCRETE BEAMS
MARBLE SLABS
PLASTER PATS
CRAMPS
HOOKS
4115
E
H
G
J
K
C'
D'
B
R.C. PILLAR
ASHLAR
ELEVATION
MARBLE PILASTER PLINTH
SECTION "F"
C
PLAN "E-E"
MARBLE SLABS
PLINTH
D
WINDOW REVEAL IN MARBLE
60
100
CRAMP
MARBLE SILL
20 THICK MARBLE SLAB
CRAMP
20 MARBLE
DETAIL "G"
MARBLE PLINTH
SOLID MORTAR BACKING
JOINT AS ALTERNATIVE
20 MARBLE PAVING SOLIDLY BEDDED
230
CONCRETE FLOOR
DETAIL "J"
M
N
3 DIA. COPPER
O
"S" HOOK
CRAMP
20 THICK MARBLE SLABS
12 AIR SPACE
PLASTER PATS OR DABS
20 THICK MARBLE SKIRTING SOLIDLY BEDDED
"S" HOOK
20 THICK MARBLE PAVING SOLIDLY BEDDED
P
Q
R
SECTION "K-K"
DETAIL "W"
CRAMPS
PLASTER PATS
HOOKS
S
E'
F'
X
ELEVATION
CRAMPS
PLASTER PATS
HOOKS
MARBLE SLABS
2300
G'
U
T
V
SECTION "U"
FLUSH DOOR
125×75 FRAME
20 MARBLE LINING
215
COPPER CRAMPS
B'
PLASTER PATS
150×60 MARBLE ARCHITRAVE
DETAIL "X"
PLASTER PAT
20 MARBLE SLABS
12 AIR SPACE
Y
Z
A'
BIRD'S MOUTHED
QUIRKED
RECESSED
EXTERNAL ANGLED JOINTS
200
1000
2000
3000 MM
SCALE FOR B, C, D, S, T & V
10
100
200 MM
SCALE FOR DETAILS

FIGURE 88

absorbed into the back of the marble which would cause staining on the surface and perhaps deposition of undesirable salts from the backing wall. Hence, the backs of all pieces are coated with shellac; it may also be advisable to ventilate the space between the wall and the marble, this can be done by omitting part of the plaster filling at the vertical joints. Thin marble wall linings should never be bedded solidly to brickwork, pavings are laid on a solid 1 : 3 cement and sand bed 12 mm thick.

The elevation, section and plan of an internal wall incorporating a window and raised pilasters, with a plinth and frieze is shown at B, C and D. A detail of the plinth is given at M, this is placed solidly against mortar and is held in place with two copper cramps (see O) per block. The 20 mm marble slabs are bedded to five plaster pats as noted at C′, and each is secured by two cramps at the top and two S-hooks (see N) at the bottom as indicated at L, P and Q. The part plan of the pilaster at A shows the plaster pats, cramps and bird's-mouthed mitres at the external corners, a plain butt joint is used at the internal angles. The section at the moulded window sill is drawn at L.

The elevation at S is of an internal wall with relatively small slabs which are all fixed as above by two cramps and hooks per piece. In the one at T, larger panels are held back by two cramps at the top and three down each side, there are also three hooks for each side and two along the lower edge; the plain skirting is given at R. The plan X of the door opening is indicated at B′, it has a marble architrave with hooks down the side and at the top. The bird's-mouthed, quirked, and recessed external angle joints at Y, Z and A′ are alternatives, a fully mitred joint cannot be used with this material as the sharp arris would be too vulnerable.

Further marble details are given in Figs. 79, 80, 85, 107 and 108 relating to fireplaces.

MOSAIC

Mosaic is one of the earliest forms of decorative art which, with advantage, could be used more frequently. It consists of placing small pieces of natural or manufactured stone in a mortar bedding so as to form a pattern or picture for a wall or floor.

The material to be used for the mosaic pieces is delivered to the artist in broken shapes machined to about 25 mm thickness of an area about 200 cm^2. These are broken up on the angle fixed to the concrete block shown at C, Fig. 89, the piece being held in both hands and struck against the angle; they are further broken down to the exact size required by means of the hammer and chisel, which is set in the block. The smaller pieces are held between thumb and forefinger on the chisel edge and struck with the special hammer, thus the small mosaic stones (from 12 mm cube down) are obtained.

For floor work the smooth machined face is placed uppermost in the mortar bedding and when this has set hard the whole floor is ground flush with a carborundum wheel and polished smooth.

In the case of mural work, the smooth face can also be exposed but a more interesting effect is provided if the rougher side (as given by the hammer fracture) is placed outwards. The natural cleavage lines of the stone are thus on view and the different facets of the mosaics provide a pleasing texture catching and reflecting the light.

Figure 89 gives an actual example completed in Coventry in 1952. The brick wall surface is rendered in 1 : 3 cement and sand mortar and well scored to improve adhesion for the next coat. Both this coat and the large-scale coloured painting (see D) provided for the mosaic artist are divided into squares by lines 230 mm apart; these guide lines serve to assist the artist in maintaining the correct proportion. A selection of the pieces of mosaic required is then prepared and a portion of the previously rendered wall is wetted over an area of 0.1 m^2. The mortar bedding in which the stones are set consists of 1 cement : 4 lime : 4 sand and this is then trowelled over the wetted area. The stones are then carefully pushed into the bedding, this action displaces a certain amount of mortar assisting in compacting it and ensuring good adhesion all round the stone. For the background and larger areas of the picture, the artist relies on the guide lines in covering the wall. Where detailed portions of the painting are to be represented he uses coloured water paints and a soft brush and paints the design on the wet mortar; this can be seen in the detail of the hand.

The use of coloured mosaic pieces is an important feature in the work but even without colour it is possible to detect the various parts of the painting. The rows of stones are set at different angles to represent various parts of the picture; thus in the example detailed at E it is possible to detect the drape of the cloak over the sleeve of the figure by the way the stones are set.

There is a large variety of natural stones which can be used for mosaic according to the colour and texture required. Granites, marbles, quartz, etc., are all suitable as well as coloured glass. Gold and silver pieces can be obtained from glass merchants (gold and silver leaf is embedded between sheets of glass). Other manufactured pieces can be obtained by mixing white sand from Holland or special yellow sand with sodium and calcium nitrates and carbonates and red lead. The oxides of various metals provide the colour required; thus cobalt for blue, copper for green, antimony for white, selenium for red, iron and pewter for yellow, etc. The mineral powders and sand after being mixed together are heated in a furnace overnight. Next morning the resulting compound is poured into slabs of the thickness (12 to 25 mm as required), after cooling they are broken up for delivery to the site.

SUSPENDED CEILINGS

There are two kinds of suspended ceilings, the jointless and the panel types. *Jointless ceilings** are made with plaster of various sorts and sprayed asbestos,

*** See p. 257 for a description of the phenomenon of "pattern staining" which occurs in ceilings that are in contact with the main structural parts of the building.**

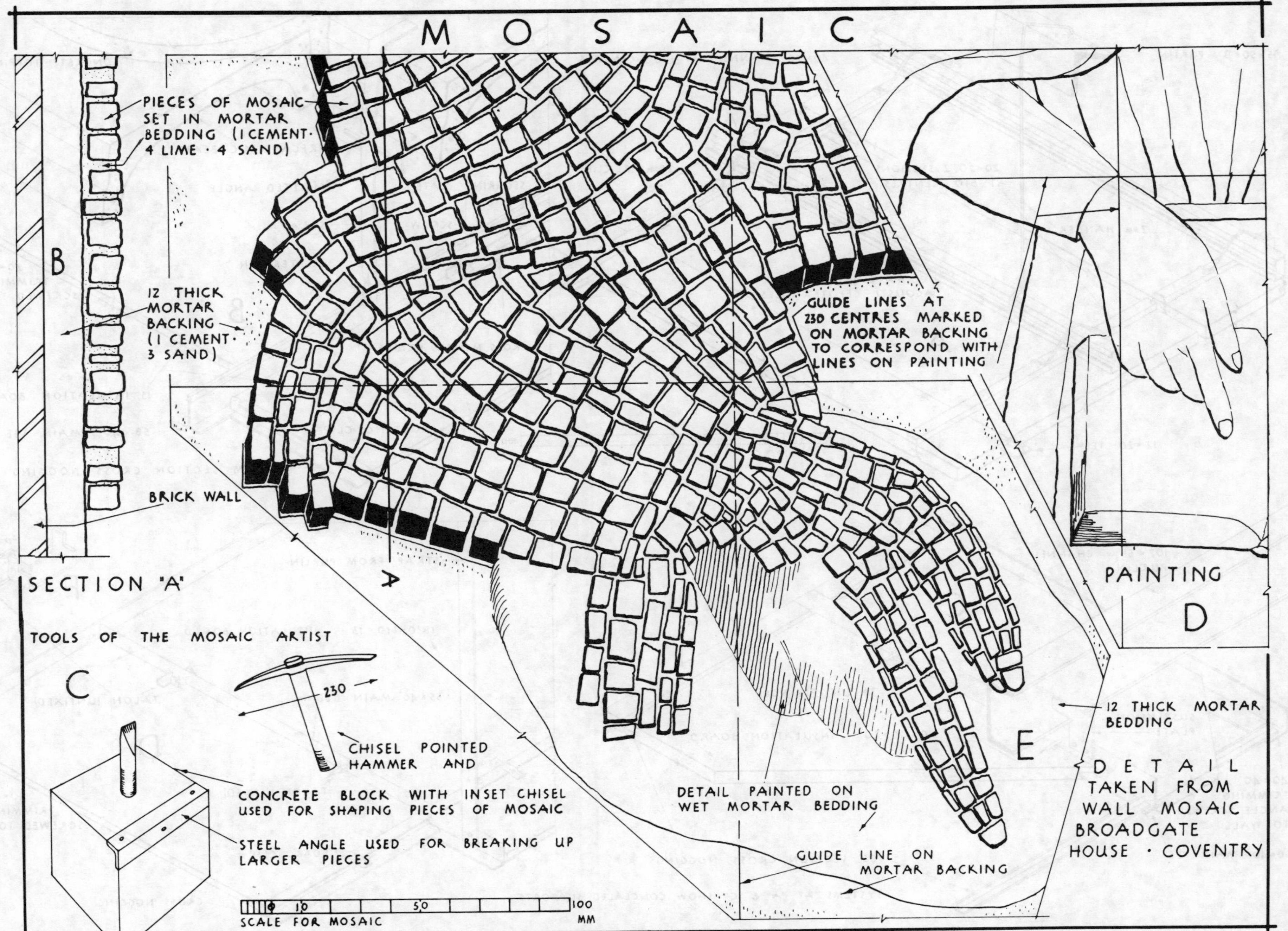
MOSAIC
PIECES OF MOSAIC SET IN MORTAR BEDDING (1 CEMENT · 4 LIME · 4 SAND)
B
12 THICK MORTAR BACKING (1 CEMENT · 3 SAND)
BRICK WALL
SECTION "A"
A
GUIDE LINES AT 230 CENTRES MARKED ON MORTAR BACKING TO CORRESPOND WITH LINES ON PAINTING
PAINTING
D
TOOLS OF THE MOSAIC ARTIST
C
230
CHISEL POINTED HAMMER AND
CONCRETE BLOCK WITH INSET CHISEL USED FOR SHAPING PIECES OF MOSAIC
STEEL ANGLE USED FOR BREAKING UP LARGER PIECES
0 10 50 100
SCALE FOR MOSAIC MM
DETAIL PAINTED ON WET MORTAR BEDDING
GUIDE LINE ON MORTAR BACKING
E
12 THICK MORTAR BEDDING
DETAIL TAKEN FROM WALL MOSAIC BROADGATE HOUSE · COVENTRY

FIGURE 89

PATENT CEILING SYSTEMS

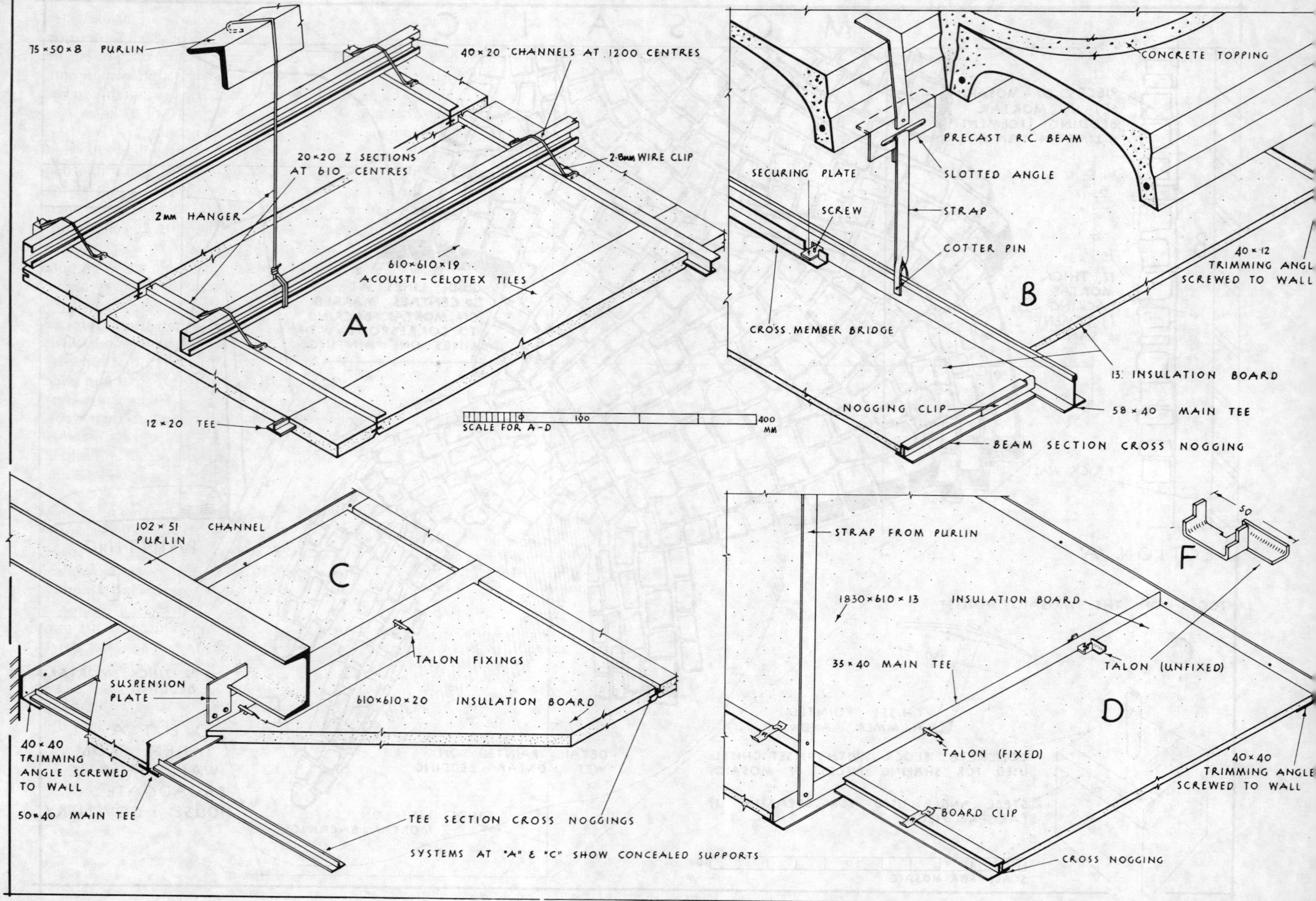

FIGURE 90

applied to a backing of expanded metal (see p. 48). The latter is of 6 mm size of the short way of the mesh, either galvanized steel or steel painted with asphaltum, examples of this material are shown at M, N, O, X, T and U, Fig. 19. The lathing is wired to a supporting framework of flat steel bars placed on edge, for example, 40 mm by 6 mm bars at 600 mm centres span 1.8 m, and these are suspended by straps or rods (a 6 mm dia. rod will carry 1.5 m^2 of ceiling). Plastering is done in three coats, there are several mixes and one of the best, which is relatively quick setting is metal lathing gypsum plaster. The first two coats consists of 1 volume of plaster to 1 volume of sand and have goat or cow hair mixed with them to the extent of 5 kg of hair to 1 m^3 of mixed plaster. The first coat is well pressed into the mesh to a thickness of 9 mm allowed to set and then scratched to form a key for the second coat. The final coat is about 5 mm thick and is of neat gypsum plaster. Vermiculite (an expanded form of mica – see p. 101) can be used instead of the sand, this results in better thermal insulation and a considerable saving of weight.*

Panel ceilings† can be made with dry materials, consequently they are more quickly completed than the jointless types. The panels are pre-formed, made of fibreboard, plaster, insulation materials, metal trays, cork, wood-wool and straw-board. Examples of the latter two are shown at L to Z, Fig. 64 as applied for roof decking. Most of the panel ceilings are made with fibreboard (see p. 101) which rests on metal framing members suspended from above. The board is obtainable in thicknesses from 12 mm to 50 mm and in sizes from 305 mm square to 1.2 m by 4.2 m, panels 610 mm square or 610 mm wide and 1.2 m long are commonly used. Some boards are perforated to within a short distance of the back with slots or small holes to improve sound absorption. Light-gauge rust-proofed steel or aluminium channel or tee sections are used to support the panel edges and these must be placed sufficiently close together to prevent sagging of the ceiling. The sections can be *exposed* or *concealed* and the panels should rest on flanges at least 16 mm wide to allow for possible movement. Tees are often used as supports, the main ones at 610 mm centres with cross tees (noggings) at the ends of the panel. Ideally, 610 mm square panels give the best results, but there are many cases (*i.e.*, in industrial buildings) where 1.8 m by 610 mm panels are suitable (fixed immediately above or below the purlins – the latter giving the best insulation is shown at G, Fig. 98, or at the level of the main tie of the truss). Fibreboard cannot be adopted where damp conditions exist, for this would cause distortion of the board; hence it should not be fixed until other materials employed in the construction of the building have dried out nor before the structure has been enclosed with doors and windows. Also, after completion, the surface of the board should be painted to prevent swelling attributable to the absorption of condensation. The finished ceiling weighs from 10 to 12 kg/m^2.

Four examples of suspended panel ceilings are given in Fig. 90.

The concealed type at A employs 610 mm square or 610 mm by 305 mm Acousti-Celotex tiles with chamfered edges, this is fibreboard with 5 mm dia. holes at 50 mm centres on the surface which penetrate to within 3 mm of the back. The panels are 19 mm or 32 mm thick weighing 10 to 11 kg/m^2 respectively and have their edges grooved. 2 mm thick wire hangers at centres not exceeding 1.81 or 2 m (according to the tile thickness) carry 2 mm galvanized channels on edge at 1 200 mm centres. 2.8 mm wire clips from these support 0.6 mm galvanized steel Z-section bearers which engage in the grooves of the ceiling tiles at 610 mm centres.

The detail at B shows the suspension of an exposed system from a precast beam floor. A short strap is cast into the joint between the beams and this is subsequently bolted to a slotted angle which carries another strap that supports the 58 mm by 40 mm main tee. These tees are at centres to suit 610 mm wide sheets of 12 mm thick fibreboard. Cross noggings at 1.2 m or 1.8 m centres rest on the main tee flange through special nogging clips which slide on to their webs. The ceiling lining is clamped between the base of the tee and a *cross member bridge*. The latter comprises a pair of angles on either side of the tee and is held down by *securing plates* (at 305 mm centres) which are fixed by screws passing up through the tee flange from below.

The arrangement at C is a concealed one where 610 mm squares of 20 mm thick fibreboard having grooved edges slot into the supporting tees. The suspension from the channel purlin to the main tee is through a plate, the space between the ceiling and the purlin being smaller than in the previous examples. Two sizes of aluminium alloy main tee are made, the one shown being 50 mm by 40 mm, for a maximum span of 3 m. When this is reduced to 2.1 m, the tee is 35 mm by 40 mm. Special board fixings known as *talons* are used at 305 mm centres, one of these is enlarged at F in the unfixed position. The talon slides through a slot in the tee and is rotated for fixing so that the prongs bite into the board.

The system at D shows an exposed aluminium alloy framework with 1.83 m by 610 mm panels of 13 mm fibreboard secured by talons in the main tees and by board clips on the noggings.

* Ordinary plaster weighs about 1 540 kg/m^3 and vermiculite plaster from 480 to 640 kg/m^3.

† The Metal Fixing Association issue a Code of Practice for light-weight fixing systems used for ceiling construction.

CHAPTER NINE

SPECIAL DOORS AND WINDOWS

Syllabus. Sliding, and sliding-folding doors and partitions; revolving door. Double glazed windows; dormer window. Patent glazing.

SPECIAL DOORS*

SLIDING DOORS AND SLIDING-FOLDING DOORS

For small glass or timber sliding doors, used for cupboards and other minor fittings, no special provisions are required and it is merely necessary to provide grooves of hardwood, felt-lined metal or plastic track in which the door can slide. Provision for insertion of the panel is made by having the top track sufficiently deep so the panel can be lifted up into it and then lowered into the bottom track. When glass sliding panels are used, the edges must be rounded and polished smooth, projecting handles should be avoided and recessed finger holds used instead.

Sliding doors can be arranged in very many different ways, there are however two basic types: (1) plain sliding doors, and (2) sliding-folding doors; both can be suspended from above by hangers using top rollers and usually bottom guides, this arrangement is known as a *top-running set*; alternatively, the doors can operate by means of top guides with the weight taken on bottom rollers, this is known as a *bottom-running set*. Different manufacturers of the special equipment needed to move the door have their own preferences as to whether a top-running or bottom-running set gives the best results for a particular situation. Where the choice is open and there are no limiting site factors it is generally thought that the bottom-running method gives a better trouble-free service, this is particularly so for large heavy doors. Where the floor does not give a solid foundation, bottom rollers would not run smoothly and a top-running set is preferable. If the weight cannot be carried from above or the supporting lintel is insufficiently strong to prevent the deflection that may be caused by the extra weight of the door, then bottom rollers must be used. In either case the door must be properly framed together using stiles not less than 100 mm wide for domestic-sized doors and larger for bigger doors. The rails of the door have to be sufficiently wide to accommodate the rollers, and for a top-hung door it is important to remember that the normal minimum width of 100 mm will not suffice; the tenons of the top rail in such a door carry most of the weight and the rail should therefore be from 150 to 225 mm wide.

Although sliding doors are more expensive than side-hung ones, there are several instances where the additional cost is justifiable. For example when space is restricted and there is insufficient room for the swing of the door; they are also useful when combined together to make a movable partition to subdivide a large room into two smaller ones.

(1) Sliding Doors* (Fig. 91). According to the width of the opening there will be one or several leaves, the leaf width must not exceed the height or be much less than half the height, the leaf can slide to the right or left; when double tracks are used a 12 mm gap must be provided between each set. A single-leaved internal domestic sliding door is shown at A; a double-leaved arrangement is shown at B, where both leaves slide to the right and a double track is used; the construction would be similar if the pair of doors opened outwards on the same track, one door to the left and the other to the right; this is often done and it is

* Swing doors also belong to this category, but their construction is not materially different to ordinary hinged doors; at J′ and K′, Fig. 85 the details at the stiles of a swing door are shown, as they are generally made to open both ways the frame cannot be rebated. The movement of the door is controlled by special pivots, the bottom one is set in the floor and has a double check action spring, this allows the door to be opened in both directions and checks the swinging movement as the door closes.

Internal swing doors for factories are sometimes made in tough rubber sheet so that they can be pushed open directly by the small trucks used to transport materials.

Another type of special door, which can be made to swing is formed with 12 mm thick toughened plate glass, housed in top and bottom metal rails containing the pivots, the exposed vertical edges of the glass are rounded off and polished.

Doors requiring to be of sound insulating construction depend for their efficiency on weight and adequacy of the edge seal (cf. windows, p. 218). A 50 mm solid core door with rubber beading bonded to the rebates of the frame and with a draught excluder set in the bottom edge (which rises as the door is opened) is reasonably satisfactory, giving a reduction of about 30 dB. A 35-dB door is provided if, in addition to being of 50 mm solid construction, it has also a sheet of lead incorporated in the thickness.

Ordinary side-hung folding doors are described in Chap. IV, Vol. I, and Chap. II, Vol. III. See Chap. III, this volume, for fire-resisting doors and roller shutters.

* A fireproof steel sliding door is described on p. 109 and shown in Fig. 35.

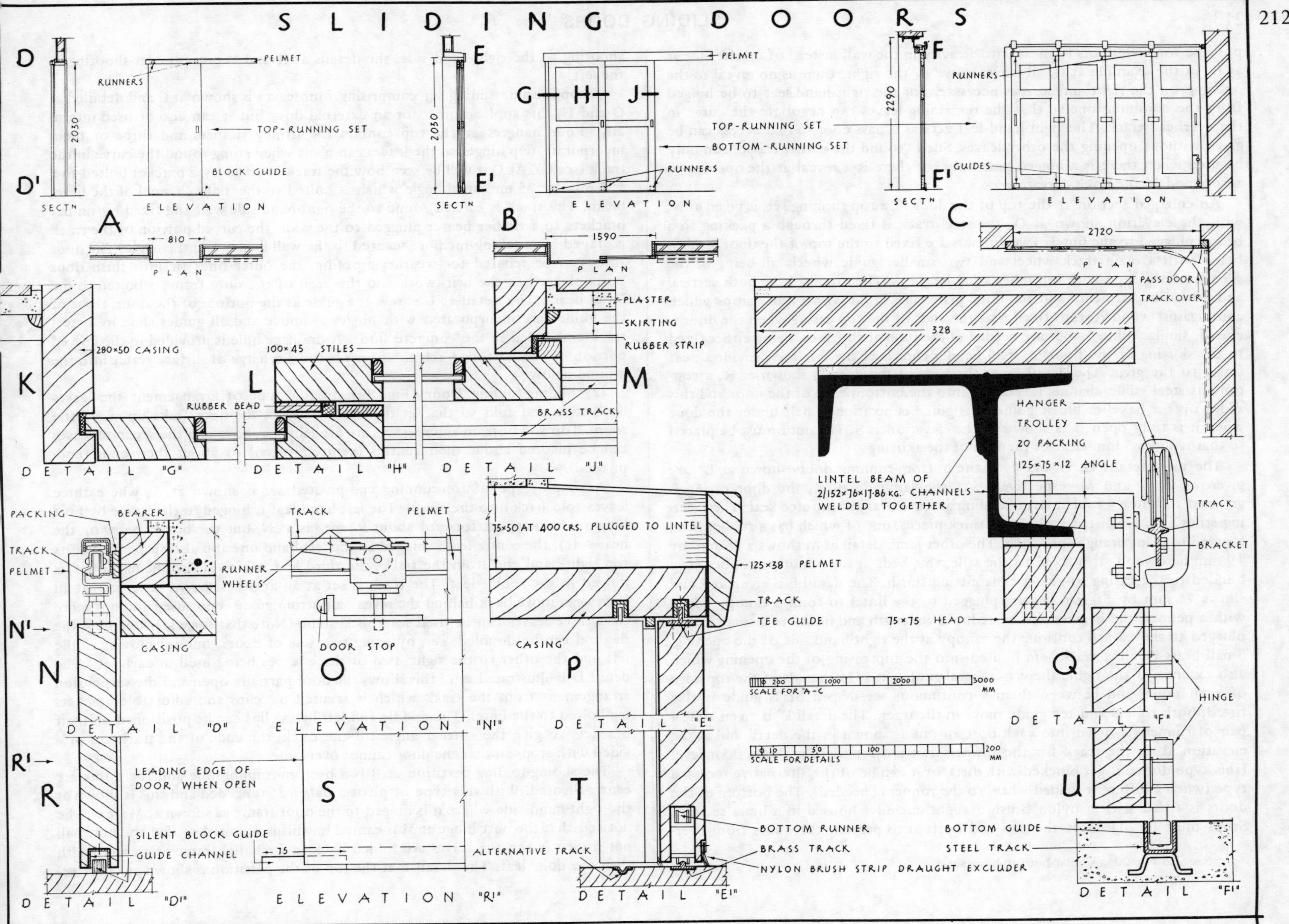
SLIDING DOORS
D
D'
SECTN
PELMET
RUNNERS
2030
TOP-RUNNING SET
BLOCK GUIDE
ELEVATION
E
E'
SECTN
H
J
2050
TOP-RUNNING SET
BOTTOM-RUNNING SET
RUNNERS
F
F'
SECTN
2290
PELMET
RUNNERS
GUIDES
ELEVATION
A
810
PLAN
B
1590
PLAN
C
2120
PLAN
PLASTER
SKIRTING
RUBBER STRIP
PASS DOOR
TRACK OVER
328
280×50 CASING
100×45 STILES
K
L
M
RUBBER BEAD
BRASS TRACK
HANGER
TROLLEY
20 PACKING
125×75×12 ANGLE
DETAIL "G"
DETAIL "H"
DETAIL "J"
LINTEL BEAM OF
2/152×76×17.88 KG. CHANNELS
WELDED TOGETHER
TRACK
PACKING
BEARER
TRACK
PELMET
75×50 AT 400 CRS. PLUGGED TO LINTEL
TRACK
PELMET
RUNNER
WHEELS
BRACKET
125×38 PELMET
TRACK
TEE GUIDE
75×75 HEAD
N'
CASING
DOOR STOP
CASING
N
O
P
Q
SCALE FOR A-C
200
1000
2000
3000 MM
SCALE FOR DETAILS
0
10
50
100
200 MM
HINGE
DETAIL "D"
ELEVATION "N"
DETAIL "E"
DETAIL "F"
R'
LEADING EDGE OF
DOOR WHEN OPEN
R
S
T
U
SILENT BLOCK GUIDE
GUIDE CHANNEL
15
ALTERNATIVE TRACK
BOTTOM RUNNER
BRASS TRACK
NYLON BRUSH STRIP DRAUGHT EXCLUDER
BOTTOM GUIDE
STEEL TRACK
DETAIL "D'"
ELEVATION "R"
DETAIL "E'"
DETAIL "F'"

FIGURE 91

possible for such doors to move into a cavity in the wall instead of on the face as at B. In the example at C, all leaves move to the right, there is no reveal to the opening on the right and so it is necessary for the right-hand leaf to be hinged from the adjoining one so that the remaining leaves can negotiate the curve in the overhead track. The right-hand leaf acts as a pass door so that access can be given without opening the other leaves. Such "round the corner track" can only be used when there is a hinged pass door, or there is a reveal at the opening to accommodate the track curvature.

An enlarged section at the top of the door A, a top-running set, is given at N, with the elevation shown at O; the steel track is fixed through a packing to a bearer plugged to the lintel. Two runners are fixed to the top of the door, each is fitted with a main track wheel and two smaller guide wheels all being of the silent running type with self-lubricating bearings. The runners have both vertical and lateral adjustments and the door plates are fitted with rubber stops which abut against wooden stops fixed near the ends of the top casing when the door is closed; similar rubber stops are needed at the base of the door, being either fixed to the skirting or the floor. A steel pelmet clips over the track to provide a neat finish to the gear. The detail D′ at the base of the door is shown at R, a continuous steel guide channel is recessed into the bottom edge of the door and this slides over a bakelite block guide; this guide is positioned half under the door when it is fully opened as shown in the elevation at S. The door must be placed so that it slides 3 mm clear of the face of the skirting.

The plan details G, H and J of the bottom-running doors shown at B* are given at K, L and M respectively. At the jamb detail K, the door casing is grooved to house a rubber strip bedding giving a draught-proofed seal. The meeting stiles at L are fitted with 9 mm thick pieces, one of which has a rubber bead bonded to it for draught-proofing. The other jamb detail at M shows a 25 mm by 19 mm hardwood strip fixed to the stile, this beds against another rubber strip bonded to the casing to give a close fitting finish. The detail E is given at P and shows 75 mm by 50 mm bearers plugged to the lintel to form a canopy edged with a pelmet; the bearers will be reduced in length and nailed to a small bearer plugged to the wall to continue the canopy at the right-hand side of the opening. Small brass or alloy tracks are housed into the top casing of the opening which also extends to the right; there is a metal guide pin at both ends of the top edge of each door, and between them a continuous tee-shaped brass guide is also fitted, both rollers and tee guide move in the track. The detail E′ is given at T, a pair of runners is fitted into each bottom rail as shown in the detail and at the elevation at B; the track for the runners can project slightly above floor level (this type does not get blocked with dirt), or it can be of the alternative recessed type (when a different shaped wheel to the runner is needed). The bottom of the doors is fitted with a nylon brush draught excluder housed in a brass section. Stops must be placed at the top and bottom to prevent the doors from over-shooting to the right-hand side, the details at K and M prevent over-shooting to the left.

A top-running sliding set comprising four leaves is shown at C and detailed at Q and U; this application is for an external door but it can also be used internally. Four hangers at the top contain the trolley runners and three of them incorporate flap hinges so the leaves can pivot when going round the curve in the track (see C). At Q it will be seen how the track is offset by a bracket bolted to a 125 mm by 75 mm steel angle which is bolted to the inner channel of the lintel beam. The track is carried round to the right-hand side wall and fixed by similar brackets to a timber bearer plugged to the wall, the curved portion of the track is stayed by a raking member secured to the wall bearer and the angle. The door stiles can be rebated for weather-proofing, the outer ones fit into flush door posts plugged to the brickwork and the head of the door frame is bolted to the lintel beam. The detail at U shows the guide at the bottom of the door, three of the guides are incorporated with hinges as above and all guides slide in a steel track embedded in the concrete floor. A drainage hole is provided in the curved portion of the bottom track to allow for the discharge of surface water into the ground below.

(2) Sliding-folding Door (Fig. 92). In this type of arrangement the leaves both slide and fold so that in the open position the doors take up very little room. Top and bottom-running sets are available as above and the separate leaves can be pivoted about their centres (centre-pivoted) or about their ends (end-pivoted).

A simple type of top-running end-pivoted set is shown at A, where three leaves fold back into the reveal. The left-hand leaf is hinged to the frame by butt hinges which are set forward about 9 mm (as at N, but the hinges being on the near side), the centre leaf is hinged to the left-hand one and also suspended at its top right-hand end from the track; the third leaf, which is also the pass door, is hinged to the centre leaf. The track is set at an angle as shown at A, so that all leaves can move back behind the reveal, a bottom guide is not used and not more than three leaves can be used for this system. (Note that for wider openings the method can be doubled, *i.e.*, by using two sets of doors, one set moving to the left and the other to the right; two or three leaves being used in each set.) The detail D is illustrated at L, this shows the door partially open and the suspension arrangement from the track which is secured by clips and adjustable brackets rag-bolted to the lintel. The middle and left-hand clips can be positioned on their brackets to give the correct angle for the track; the ends of the track are provided with stops so that the door cannot over-run.

The sliding-folding partition at B is a bottom-running one and the doors are centre-pivoted. With this type of pivot a *half leaf* is needed and this is shown at the right-hand side where it is hinged to the door frame as shown at M. It will be noticed that the butt hinge at M is canted in, this is required so that the butt will not project when the leaves are folded back in a rebated frame of greater width than the door leaf. The detail E at the top of the partition is shown at Q, a steel

* See also Fig. 70, a similar but top-hung set.

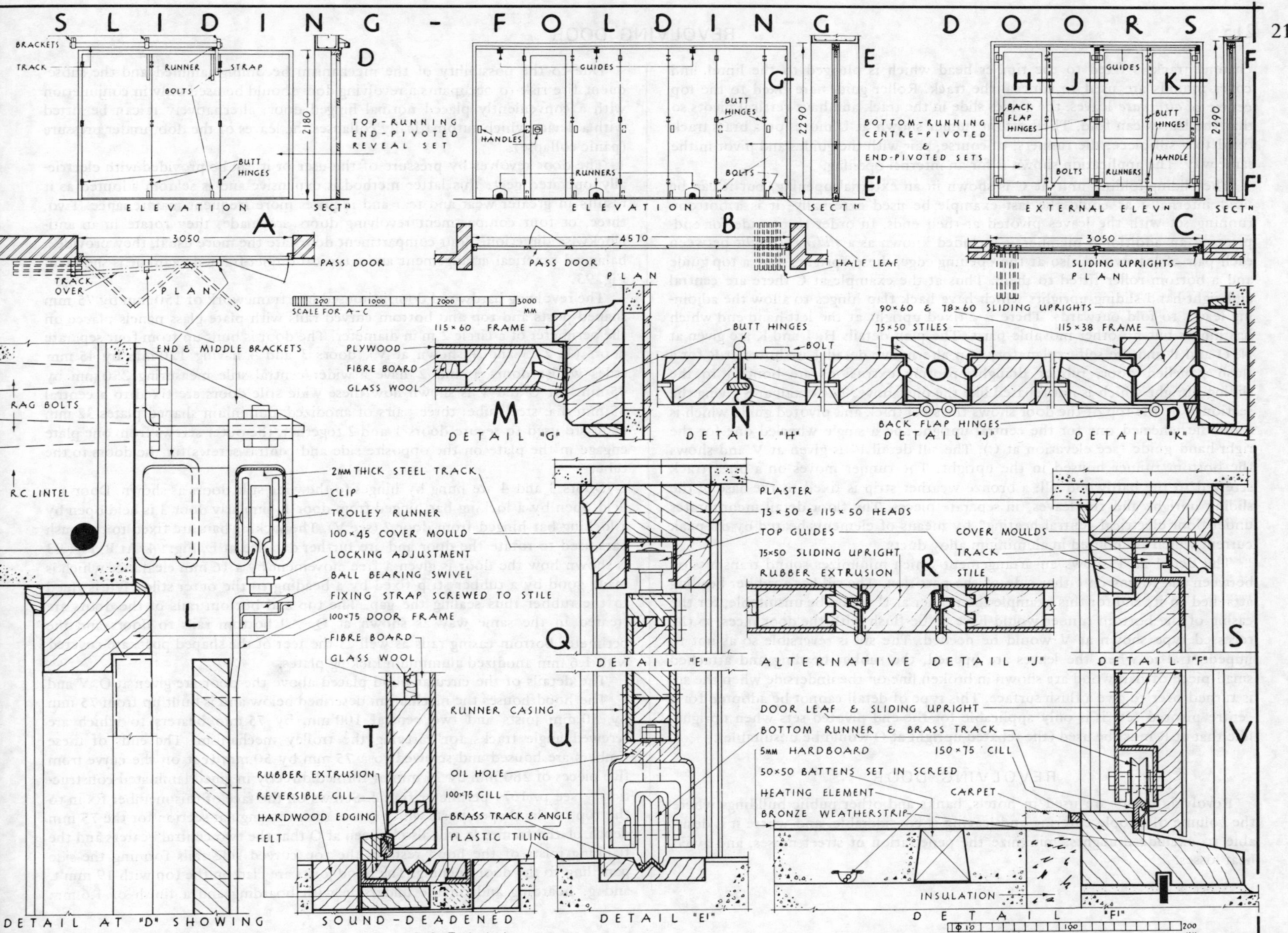

SLIDING-FOLDING DOORS
BRACKETS
TRACK
RUNNER
STRAP
BOLTS
BUTT HINGES
TOP-RUNNING END-PIVOTED REVEAL SET
2180
ELEVATION
SECTN
A
D
GUIDES
HANDLES
RUNNERS
B
BUTT HINGES
2290
BOLTS
G
BOTTOM-RUNNING CENTRE-PIVOTED & END-PIVOTED SETS
E
E'
H
J
K
BACK FLAP HINGES
HANDLE
EXTERNAL ELEVN
C
F
F'
3050
4570
PASS DOOR
TRACK OVER
PLAN
HALF LEAF
SLIDING UPRIGHTS
SCALE FOR A-C
200
1000
2000
3000 MM
115×60 FRAME
PLYWOOD
FIBRE BOARD
GLASS WOOL
M
DETAIL "G"
END & MIDDLE BRACKETS
RAG BOLTS
R.C. LINTEL
90×60 & 78×60 SLIDING UPRIGHTS
75×50 STILES
115×38 FRAME
BUTT HINGES
BOLT
N
O
P
BACK FLAP HINGES
DETAIL "H"
DETAIL "J"
DETAIL "K"
2MM THICK STEEL TRACK
CLIP
TROLLEY RUNNER
100×45 COVER MOULD
LOCKING ADJUSTMENT
BALL BEARING SWIVEL
FIXING STRAP SCREWED TO STILE
100×75 DOOR FRAME
FIBRE BOARD
GLASS WOOL
L
PLASTER
75×50 & 115×50 HEADS
TOP GUIDES
75×50 SLIDING UPRIGHT
RUBBER EXTRUSION
COVER MOULDS
TRACK
STILE
Q
R
DETAIL "E"
ALTERNATIVE DETAIL "J"
DETAIL "F"
S
RUNNER CASING
T
U
RUBBER EXTRUSION
REVERSIBLE CILL
HARDWOOD EDGING
FELT
OIL HOLE
100×75 CILL
BRASS TRACK & ANGLE
PLASTIC TILING
DOOR LEAF & SLIDING UPRIGHT
BOTTOM RUNNER & BRASS TRACK
5MM HARDBOARD
150×75 CILL
50×50 BATTENS SET IN SCREED
HEATING ELEMENT
CARPET
BRONZE WEATHERSTRIP
V
INSULATION
DETAIL AT "D" SHOWING DOOR PARTIALLY OPEN
SOUND-DEADENED CILL DETAIL
DETAIL "E'"
DETAIL "F'"
SCALE FOR DETAILS
0
10
100
200 MM

FIGURE 92

channel track is fixed to the timber head which is plugged to the lintel, and cover moulds are used to conceal the track. Roller guides are fixed to the top centre of *alternate* leaves, the guides slide in the track and have vertical pivots so that the leaves can fold. The bottom runner shown at U moves on a brass track fixed to a sill piece; the runners, of course, pair with the guides and pivot in the same way. The application shown is for an internal opening.

The sliding-folding unit at C is shown in an external opening, but it can be used internally as could the last example be used externally; it is a bottom-running set with the leaves pivoted at their ends. In order to provide for end-pivoting an additional member is included known as a *sliding upright* between each pair of leaves and also at the opening edge, these uprights have a top guide and a bottom roller fitted to them. Thus at the example at C there are central and right-hand sliding uprights which have back flap hinges to allow the adjoining leaves to fold outwards. There is a fixed upright at the left-hand end which has hinges but no other movable parts. The plan details H, J and K are given at N, O and P and are self-explanatory. An alternative detail J is shown at R for a flush panelled door, rubber draught-proofing extrusions are bonded to the sliding upright which is not rebated like the one above. The detail at S giving the section F at the top of the door shows the steel track and pivoted guide which is a double wheeled one for the central upright and a single wheeled one for the right-hand guide (see elevation at C). The sill detail F′ is given at V and shows the bottom runner housed in the upright. The runner moves on a brass track screwed to the hardwood sill; a bronze weather strip is fixed to the base of the sliding upright and the leaves, in separate pieces. The floor detail incorporates under-floor electrical central heating* by means of elements heated by off-peak current which are housed in aluminium alloy ducts.

The detail at T shows an arrangement which minimizes sound transmission between the rooms on either side of the partition. The sill has a rubber beading attached to it, and for this example the runner at U would be unsuitable, for the casing of the bottom runner would have to be flush with the door faces, so the recessed type shown at V would be needed. The sill is reversible so as not to impede traffic when the leaves are opened, the rubber beading and attached small piece of hardwood are shown in broken line on the underside when the sill is turned over to give a flush surface. This type of detail cannot be adopted for a centre pivoted set, it is only applicable for the end pivoted sets when uprights like that at R must be used (the rebated upright at O would be unsuitable).

REVOLVING DOOR

Revolving doors are used in hotels, banks and other public buildings where the volume of people entering and leaving is considerable, and where it is desirable to exclude draughts, minimize the penetration of street noises, and avoid heat losses.

* See p. 267.

Due to the possibility of the mechanism becoming jammed and the subsequent fire risk to occupants a revolving door should be used only in conjunction with a conveniently placed normal hinged door; alternatively it can be fitted with a device which automatically collapses the leaves of the door under pressure (panic collapse).

The door revolves by pressure of the user or it can be provided with electrically operated gear; this latter method is expensive and is seldom adopted as it results in greater wear and tear and requires more frequent maintenance. Two, three, or four compartment revolving doors are made, they rotate in an anti-clockwise direction. Four compartment doors are the more usual, they provide a balanced practical arrangement and a typical timber-framed example is shown in Fig. 93.

The revolving hardwood door is housed in a framework of 150 mm by 75 mm shaped posts and top and bottom curved rails with plate glass panels placed on the perimeter of a circle 2 m in diameter. The door is built up from four separate doors (1, 2, 3 and 4 shown at V), doors 3 and 4 having 120 mm by 45 mm stiles whilst doors 1 and 2 have a wider central stile measuring 250 mm by 45 mm. At U and V is shown how these wide stile doors are fixed to a central 35 mm dia. steel tube; three pairs of anodized aluminium shaped plates 32 mm wide are used to secure doors 1 and 2 together, the outer screws from one plate engage in the plate on the opposite side and central screws fix the doors to the tube.

Doors 3 and 4 are hung by hinges to the wide stile doors as shown. Door 4 is held open by a locking bar hinged from door 1, similarly door 3 is held open by a locking bar hinged from door 2 (see V). The locking bars are fixed to the push bars used to rotate the door and are further detailed at E, Fig. 94. At P, Fig. 93 is shown how the door is given a free movement by a 16 mm clearance which is made good by a rubber strip fixed by a beading to the outer stiles, felt is glued to the rubber thus sealing the gap. The top and bottom rails of the doors are treated in the same way as shown at Q. All bottom rails to doors and the perimeter bottom casing rails as well as the feet of the shaped posts are covered with 1.6 mm anodized aluminium kicking plates.

The details of the circular hood placed above the door are given at O, Y and T. The hood houses the mechanism described below and is built up from 75 mm by 50 mm joists and two central 100 mm by 75 mm bearers to which are screwed angle tracks for carrying the trolley mechanism. The ends of these timbers are housed and screwed to a 75 mm by 50 mm (cut on the curve from five pieces of 280 mm by 75 mm or formed directly in glued laminated construction – see p. 167) perimeter frame. Screws on the face of this member fix in to the top of the shaped posts which retain their rectangular section for the 75 mm depth of the frame. It will also be seen at O that the two central bearers and the flanking joists of the hood rest on the top curved side rails forming the side panelling to the door opening. The hood joists are clad on the top with 19 mm t. and g. boarding and on the underside with boarding and a finish of 1.6 mm

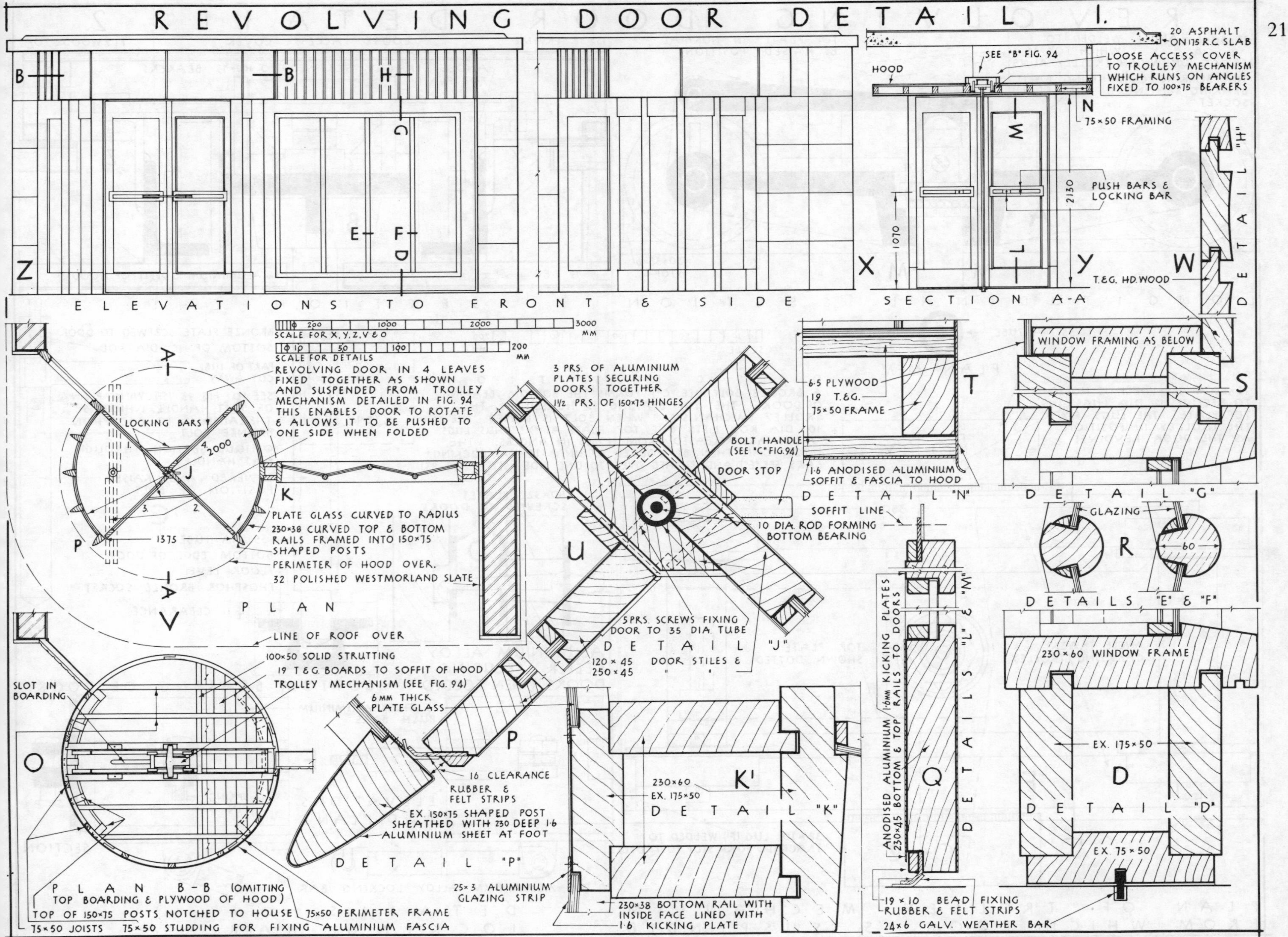
REVOLVING DOOR DETAIL.
ELEVATIONS TO FRONT & SIDE
SECTION A-A
20 ASPHALT ON 115 R.C. SLAB
SEE "B" FIG. 94
HOOD
LOOSE ACCESS COVER TO TROLLEY MECHANISM WHICH RUNS ON ANGLES FIXED TO 100×75 BEARERS
75×50 FRAMING
PUSH BARS & LOCKING BAR
DETAIL "H"
T.& G. HD. WOOD
SCALE FOR X, Y, Z, V & O
SCALE FOR DETAILS
REVOLVING DOOR IN 4 LEAVES FIXED TOGETHER AS SHOWN AND SUSPENDED FROM TROLLEY MECHANISM DETAILED IN FIG. 94 THIS ENABLES DOOR TO ROTATE & ALLOWS IT TO BE PUSHED TO ONE SIDE WHEN FOLDED
LOCKING BARS
PLATE GLASS CURVED TO RADIUS
230×38 CURVED TOP & BOTTOM RAILS FRAMED INTO 150×75 SHAPED POSTS
PERIMETER OF HOOD OVER.
32 POLISHED WESTMORLAND SLATE
PLAN
LINE OF ROOF OVER
100×50 SOLID STRUTTING
19 T&G BOARDS TO SOFFIT OF HOOD
TROLLEY MECHANISM (SEE FIG. 94)
SLOT IN BOARDING
PLAN B-B (OMITTING TOP BOARDING & PLYWOOD OF HOOD)
TOP OF 150×75 POSTS NOTCHED TO HOUSE 75×50 JOISTS
75×50 STUDDING FOR FIXING ALUMINIUM FASCIA
75×50 PERIMETER FRAME
3 PRS. OF ALUMINIUM PLATES SECURING DOORS TOGETHER
1½ PRS. OF 150×75 HINGES
5 PRS. SCREWS FIXING DOOR TO 35 DIA. TUBE
DETAIL "J"
DOOR STILES & 120×45 250×45
10 DIA. ROD FORMING BOTTOM BEARING
BOLT HANDLE (SEE "C" FIG. 94)
DOOR STOP
6·5 PLYWOOD
19 T.&G.
75×50 FRAME
1·6 ANODISED ALUMINIUM SOFFIT & FASCIA TO HOOD
DETAIL "N"
WINDOW FRAMING AS BELOW
DETAIL "G"
GLAZING
DETAILS "E" & "F"
SOFFIT LINE
6MM THICK PLATE GLASS
16 CLEARANCE
RUBBER & FELT STRIPS
EX. 150×75 SHAPED POST SHEATHED WITH 230 DEEP 1·6 ALUMINIUM SHEET AT FOOT
DETAIL "P"
25×3 ALUMINIUM GLAZING STRIP
230×60
EX. 175×50
DETAIL "K"
230×38 BOTTOM RAIL WITH INSIDE FACE LINED WITH 1·6 KICKING PLATE
ANODISED ALUMINIUM 1·6MM KICKING PLATES 230×45 BOTTOM & TOP RAILS TO DOORS
DETAILS "L" & "M"
19×10 BEAD FIXING RUBBER & FELT STRIPS
24×6 GALV. WEATHER BAR
230×60 WINDOW FRAME
EX. 175×50
EX. 75×50
DETAIL "D"

FIGURE 93

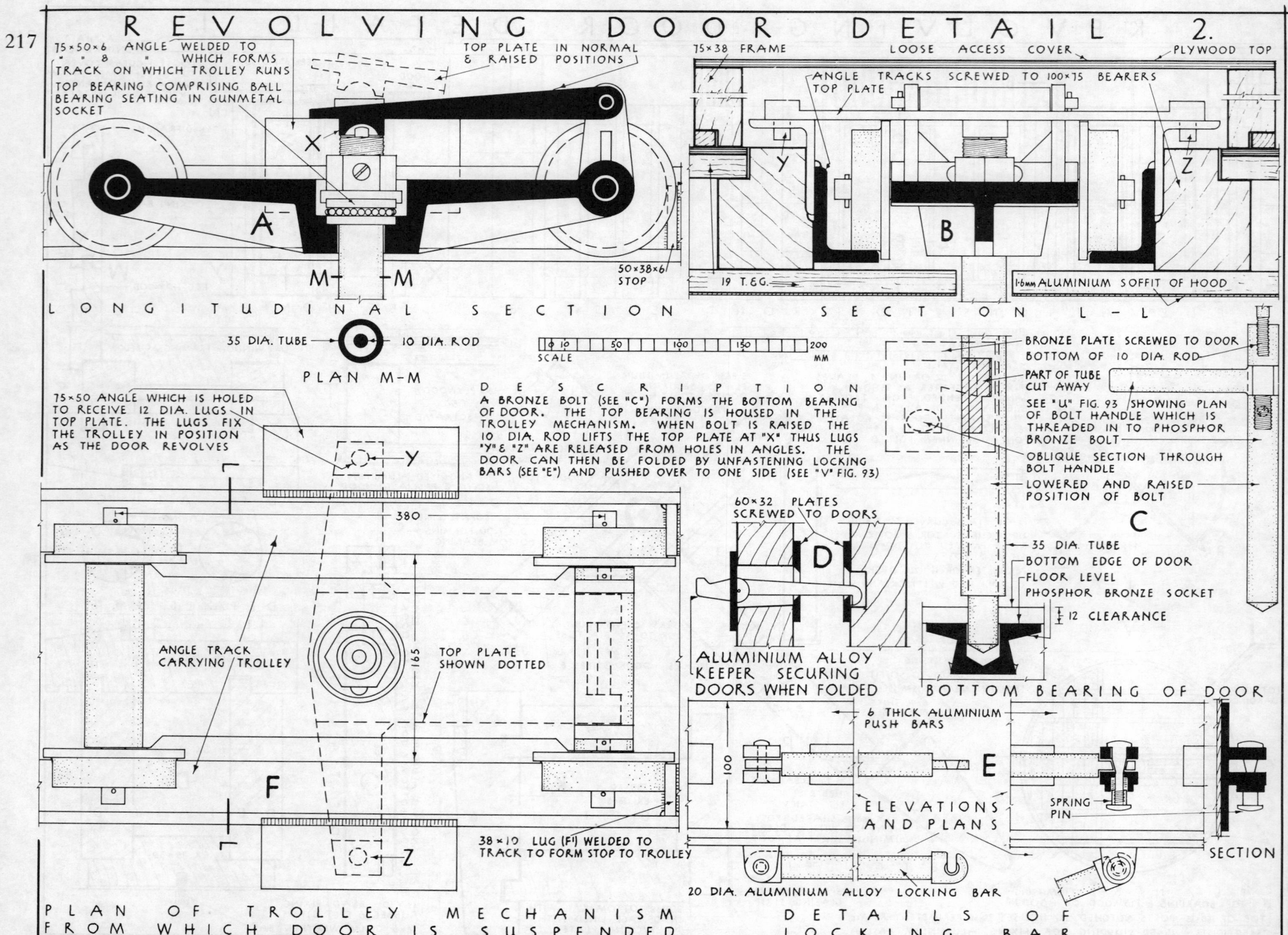
REVOLVING DOOR DETAIL 2.
75×50×6 ANGLE WELDED TO
" " 8 " WHICH FORMS
TRACK ON WHICH TROLLEY RUNS
TOP BEARING COMPRISING BALL BEARING SEATING IN GUNMETAL SOCKET
TOP PLATE IN NORMAL & RAISED POSITIONS
X
A
M-M
50×38×6 STOP
LONGITUDINAL SECTION
75×38 FRAME
LOOSE ACCESS COVER
PLYWOOD TOP
ANGLE TRACKS SCREWED TO 100×75 BEARERS
TOP PLATE
Y
Z
B
19 T.&G.
1·6mm ALUMINIUM SOFFIT OF HOOD
SECTION L-L
35 DIA. TUBE
10 DIA. ROD
PLAN M-M
SCALE
0 10 50 100 150 200 MM
DESCRIPTION
A BRONZE BOLT (SEE "C") FORMS THE BOTTOM BEARING OF DOOR. THE TOP BEARING IS HOUSED IN THE TROLLEY MECHANISM. WHEN BOLT IS RAISED THE 10 DIA. ROD LIFTS THE TOP PLATE AT "X" THUS LUGS "Y" & "Z" ARE RELEASED FROM HOLES IN ANGLES. THE DOOR CAN THEN BE FOLDED BY UNFASTENING LOCKING BARS (SEE "E") AND PUSHED OVER TO ONE SIDE (SEE "V" FIG. 93)
75×50 ANGLE WHICH IS HOLED TO RECEIVE 12 DIA. LUGS IN TOP PLATE. THE LUGS FIX THE TROLLEY IN POSITION AS THE DOOR REVOLVES
Y
380
165
ANGLE TRACK CARRYING TROLLEY
TOP PLATE SHOWN DOTTED
F
38×10 LUG (F¹) WELDED TO TRACK TO FORM STOP TO TROLLEY
Z
PLAN OF TROLLEY MECHANISM FROM WHICH DOOR IS SUSPENDED
BRONZE PLATE SCREWED TO DOOR
BOTTOM OF 10 DIA. ROD
PART OF TUBE CUT AWAY
SEE "U" FIG. 93 SHOWING PLAN OF BOLT HANDLE WHICH IS THREADED IN TO PHOSPHOR BRONZE BOLT
OBLIQUE SECTION THROUGH BOLT HANDLE
LOWERED AND RAISED POSITION OF BOLT
C
35 DIA. TUBE
BOTTOM EDGE OF DOOR
FLOOR LEVEL
PHOSPHOR BRONZE SOCKET
12 CLEARANCE
BOTTOM BEARING OF DOOR
60×32 PLATES SCREWED TO DOORS
D
ALUMINIUM ALLOY KEEPER SECURING DOORS WHEN FOLDED
6 THICK ALUMINIUM PUSH BARS
100
E
ELEVATIONS AND PLANS
SPRING PIN
SECTION
20 DIA. ALUMINIUM ALLOY LOCKING BAR
DETAILS OF LOCKING BAR

FIGURE 94

anodized aluminium forming a smooth soffit. 75 mm by 50 mm studs are housed at the bottom in the perimeter frame of the hood and at the top to a similarly curved timber fixed to the concrete roof. The outer face of the studs and frame is covered with an aluminium fascia shown at T.

To the right of the door is a window detailed at K′, D, R and S, all in hardwood and with circular glazing mullions. The vertical strip panelling above the window is enlarged at W.

Mechanism. Figure 94 shows in greater detail the various fittings and parts required to operate the revolving door. The bottom bearing of the door is shown at C and consists of a phosphor bronze bolt threaded and screwed to the 10 mm dia. rod running the height of the door inside the 35 mm dia. tube to which the door is secured. The bolt turns in a phosphor bronze socket let in to the floor finish, this is a bearing guide, the door being suspended from above. The bolt handle can be seen protruding from door 2 at U, Fig. 93.

The top bearing of the door is placed in the trolley mechanism (A, B and F, Fig. 94) from which the door is suspended. The trolley consists of four steel wheels on a cast iron chassis which is holed in the centre to allow the 35 mm dia. tube to pass through. A nut is threaded on to the top of the tube and secured by two bolts, beneath the nut is a ball-bearing seating in a gunmetal socket resting in a recess in the chassis of the trolley. The door is thus free to rotate in the two bearings provided.

The trolley is supported on angle tracks screwed to the 100 mm by 75 mm bearers in the hood, lugs (F′ at F) welded to the tracks prevent the trolley from over-running. In its normal rotating position, the door is held in place by means of a cast iron top plate hinged above the right-hand axle of the trolley. At F is shown the dotted outline of this plate at the free extremities of which are pins Y and Z which engage in holes in the short 75 mm by 50 mm angles welded to the track.

When the door is required to be folded back the bolt at the bottom (see handle at U, Fig. 93) is lifted to its raised position in the plate at C, Fig. 94. This action raises the rod in the tube and lifts the top plate of the trolley at X, Fig. 94. Thus the two retaining pins are released from their holes and the door (after being folded, see below) can be moved over to the left by sliding it along the track. It is held in this open position by a further set of holes for the retaining pins and also by another socket bearing set in the floor.

It is important to allow top access to the mechanism for occasional greasing and maintenance, the space between the top of the hood and the concrete roof in this example should be regarded as a minimum.

The combined locking bar and push bars are detailed at E, Fig. 94. These are fixed between doors 1 and 4, and 3 and 2; they consist of a 20 mm dia. locking bar hinged on to the 100 mm by 6 mm twin push bars; one end of the locking bar can be released from the push bar by means of a spring pin, thus the doors can be folded back and pushed to one side as shown by the broken lines at V, Fig. 93.

Ordinary push bars (without a locking bar) are placed on the side of each door opposite to the combined fitting. The doors are retained in the folded position by means of aluminium alloy keepers detailed at D, Fig. 94.

SPECIAL WINDOWS*

DOUBLE GLAZED WINDOWS

Double-glazed windows are used to improve thermal and sound insulation and to reduce condensation. As well as the double-glazing system consisting of two sheets of glass bonded together with a sealed cavity between as described on p. 154, there are other methods as follows.

The most obvious arrangement is to have two separate windows, one on the outside opening out, and one on the inside opening in. This might entail the additional cost of the second frame which is not justified for thermal reasons although it does give better sound insulation. The provision of tight-fitting windows without air gaps round their edges is most important when sound transmission has to be reduced. One means of sealing is shown in the metal window at C and G, Fig. 52; others are given at A and B, Fig. 95. Ordinary timber sashes cannot be made tight fitting because they swell and contract as the moisture content changes; in this respect, the lipped (storm-proofed) section at C, Fig. 95 is better, for it can be made to fit relatively closely behind the lip. When two windows, glazed with 4 mm glass, having sealed edges are placed 100 to 200 mm apart and sound absorbents are placed on the reveals, lintel and sill between them, then they have a sound insulation value of about 33 dB: this is about twice the value given by an ordinary window without special edge seals; the thermal improvement is approximately of the same order. If the space is reduced to 19 mm the same thermal gain is obtained but the sound insulation is improved by only approximately 20 per cent over an ordinary window.

Examples of double-glazed windows for use where sound reduction is not the major factor are illustrated in Fig. 95. The one at C† has a timber frame with the familiar storm-lipped outer sash and weather stripping, the inner sash is hinged to the closing stile of the outer sash. Both sashes are held together by couplers enabling them to be opened as one unit or separately.

The aluminium alloy section at A‡ has a main frame (with fine concrete filling) to which the window is hinged with centre-hung friction pivots, allowing it to be opened fully and reversed. It has an inner glazed portion with an outer glazed part coupled to it by bottom-hung continuous integral pivots. When the window is reversed, the outer sash is brought to the inside so that it is now top hung and can be opened separately and held by stays. This enables both sides of

* See pp. 153–154 for types of glass.
† Made by members of the British Woodwork Federation.
‡ Made by Crittall-Hope Ltd., Braintree.

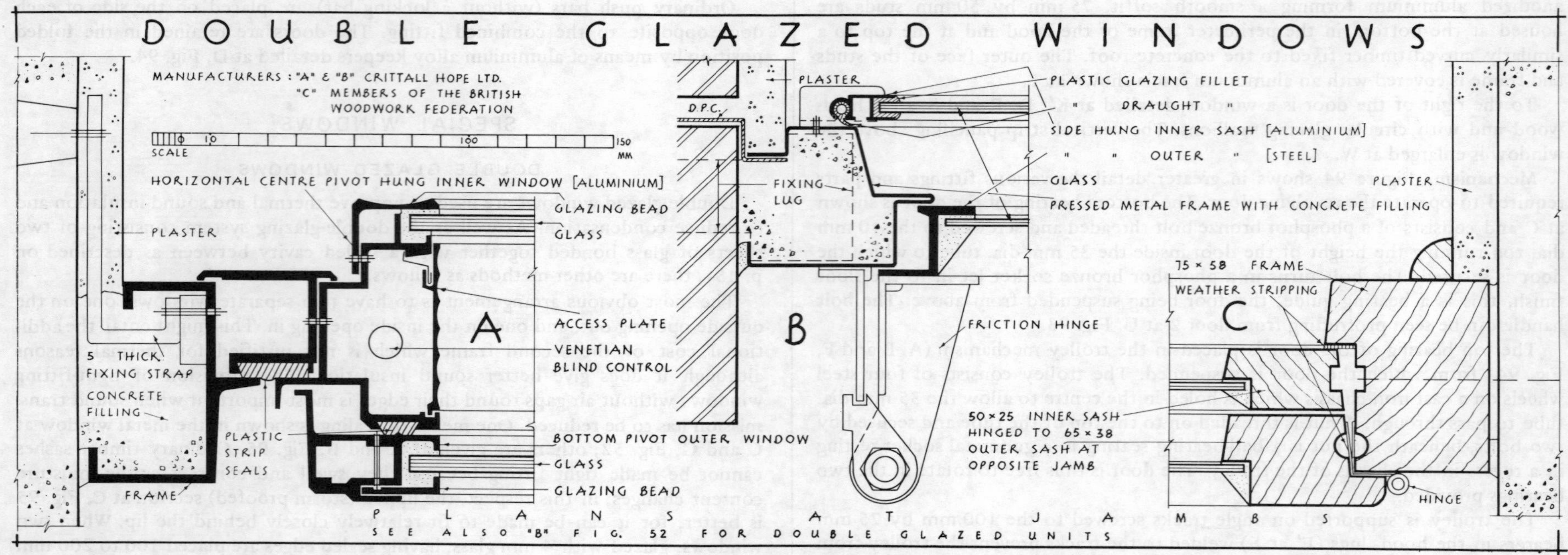

FIGURE 95

the outer glass and the outside of the inner glass to be cleaned from inside the room. Efficient plastic strip weather seals are employed between the frame and the opening main part and also between the latter and the outer sash. If desired, a venetian blind can be incorporated to pass between the sheets of glass and this can be controlled when the window is open or shut.

The simpler example at B* has an ordinary metal sash section for the outer window which is side hung with friction hinges to a pressed metal frame. A light alloy section with the glass set in plastic fillets is side pivoted to the inside of the frame and there is a plastic draught seal between the two. This inner sash can be lifted off its pivots for storage during the summer months if desired.

DORMER WINDOW

A dormer window, Fig. 96, is one which projects from the roof† as shown in the key section at E or as an extension of the main windows as in the elevation at F. It is used to provide daylighting within the roof space when this is used as a room, and provides an architectural feature of interest which could, with advantage, be used more frequently. Dormers are useful in bungalow construction for providing additional habitable rooms within the normal roof structure. It should be remembered that where rooms are placed in the roof, the Building Regulations state that the ceiling height of such a room must be at least 2.3 m over not less than half the area of the room measured at a height of 1.5 m above the floor level. The roof covering to a dormer will normally be of the same material as the main roof and both pitched and flat dormers covered with tiles, slates and lead are used. Pitched dormers are particularly attractive when tiled as in the example, especially when they are constructed so that they fit well down on to the roof and there is the minimum amount of "upstand" between the window sill and the main roof (see C).

At A, half of the elevation and section are given, a further section is shown at B and a part plan at D. To form the opening in the roof, 100 mm by 100 mm trimming spars are used on either side, and an upper 100 mm by 100 mm and a lower 150 mm by 100 mm trimmer are jointed to the trimming spars. The joints may be of the bevelled housed type or tusk-tenoned for half the thickness of the trimmer, as shown. A window frame forming the front of the dormer and having 100 mm by 100 mm posts and head with a 200 mm by 100 mm sill rests on the

* The Campaigner storm sash window by Crittall-Hope Ltd.
† See also A, Fig. 55.

DORMER WINDOW

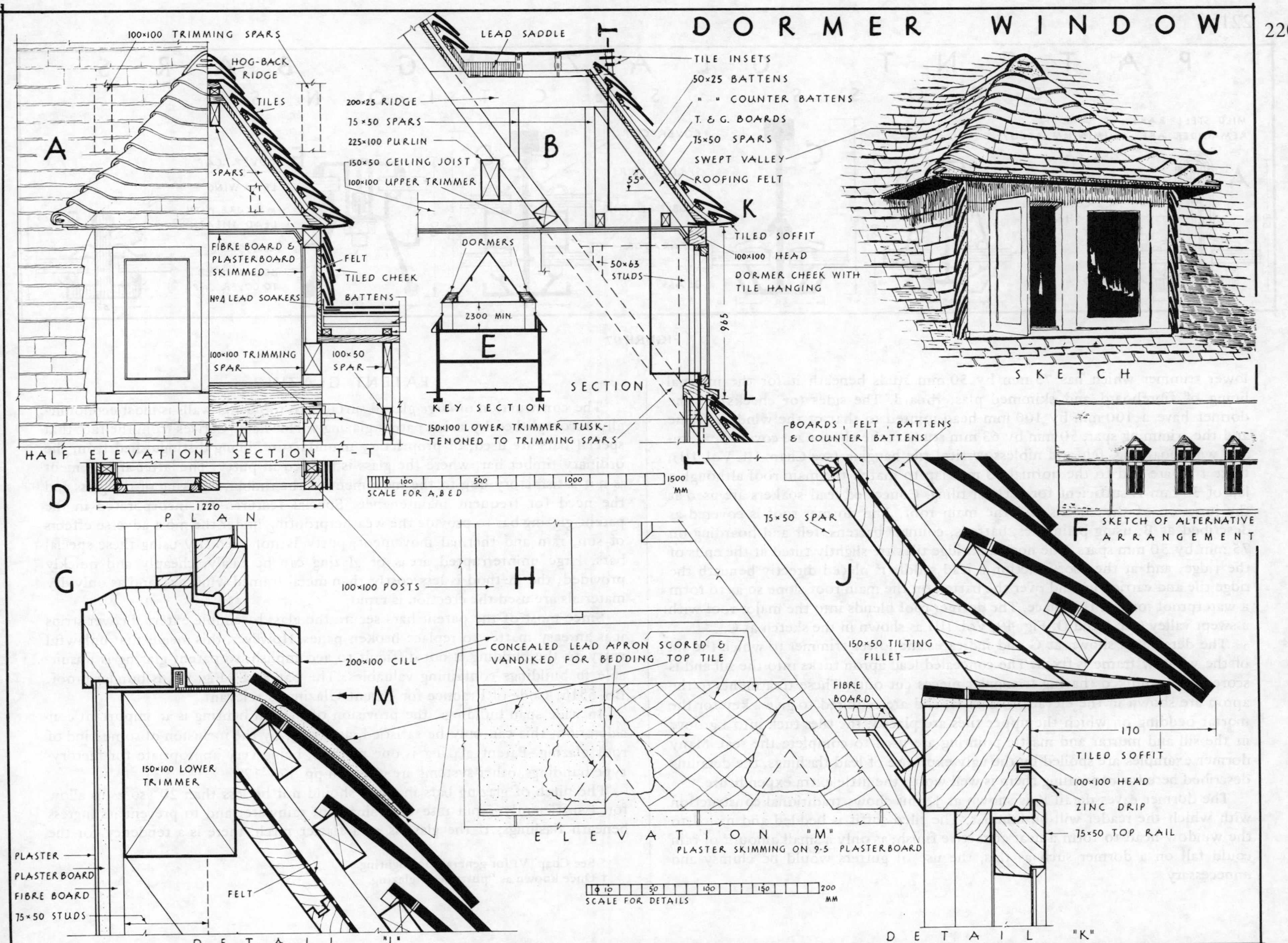

FIGURE 96

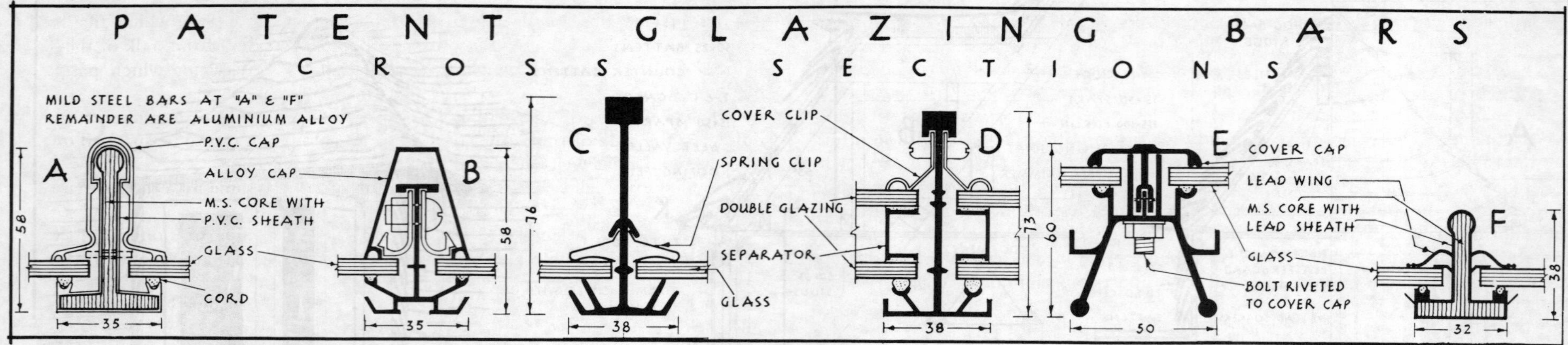

FIGURE 97

lower trimmer which has 75 mm by 50 mm studs beneath it for the internal lining of fibreboard and skimmed plasterboard. The sides (or cheeks) of the dormer have a 100 mm by 100 mm head jointed to that of the window frame and the trimming spar, 50 mm by 63 mm studs at the cheeks are covered externally with boarding, felt and nibless vertical tile hanging (see Chap. III, Vol. III); these tiles are laid to the normal 63 mm lap to match the main roof although a lap of 38 mm is sufficient for vertical tiling. Concealed lead soakers are used at the junction of the cheeks and the main roof. The dormer roof is covered as described at B, using plain tiles, battens, counter battens, felt and boarding on 75 mm by 50 mm spars. The hog-back ridge tiles are slightly tilted at the ends of the ridge; and at the roof junction a lead saddle is placed directly beneath the ridge tile and carried up and over the batten on the main roof slope so as to form a waterproof joint at this place. The dormer roof blends into the major roof with a swept valley (see J and O, Fig. 49, Vol. III) as shown in the sketch at C.

The detail L is shown at G and indicates the lower trimmer to which the sill of the window frame is fixed. The concealed lead apron tucks into the sill and is scored and vandiked (having triangular pieces cut out). These treatments to the apron are shown in the elevation M at H, and are required to give a key for the mortar bedding on which the upper tiles are placed; the tiles tuck into a groove in the sill and mortar and mastic pointing are used to complete the seal. Many dormer examples are spoiled by the ugly exposure of lead flashings, the detailing described here for concealing them is well worth the little extra expenditure.

The dormer eaves detail K is shown at J, this shows traditional construction with which the reader will be familiar. The tiled soffit is bedded and nailed to the window head to form a neat attractive finish; as only a small amount of rain could fall on a dormer such as this, the use of gutters would be clumsy and unnecessary.

PATENT GLAZING*

The construction of *large* glazed surfaces to roofs and walls is most economically accomplished by using patent glazing.† This name derives from the fact that special bars are used, of proprietary manufacture, being distinguished from the ordinary timber bar, where the glass is bedded in putty. The latter arrangement is not satisfactory due to the movement of the timber, cracking of the glass and the need for frequent maintenance. Special features are incorporated in the patent glazing bar to provide the weatherproofing under the most adverse effects of sun, rain and thermal movement; putty is not used. By using these special bars, large uninterrupted areas of glazing can be easily, cheaply and quickly provided; the method is less costly than metal framed windows, and as only dry materials are used the erection is rapid.

Since most of the patent bars secure the glass by simple external cover strips it is an easy matter to replace broken panes. However, this means that unlawful entry to the building is not difficult to accomplish; so patent glazing is unsuitable in buildings containing valuables. The bar at E, Fig. 97, is burglar-proof. BS 5516: Code of Practice for Patent Glazing is relevant.

In wide span buildings, the provision of natural lighting is an important consideration, this can only be satisfied, as a rule, by the inclusion of some kind of roof glazing. Patent glazing is one method, being very appropriate for factory-type buildings, other systems are given on pp. 178–179.

The pitch of glazing bars in roofs should not be less than 20° so as to allow for a sufficiently rapid rate of drainage of rainwater and to prevent its ingress beneath flashings. If the glass is at a flatter pitch, there is a tendency for the

* See Chap. VI for general roof lighting.
† Once known as "putty-less" glazing.

condensation, which forms on the underside, to fall in drops directly from it, instead of being led down the drainage channels to the outside.

The bars are made of the following materials:* aluminium alloy (usually type HE9P); galvanized steel; or steel covered in lead (the core being first galvanized or treated with a rust-proofing paint), the lead is No. 2 thickness and is extruded on to the bar to enclose it *completely*; or rust-proofed steel clad with jointless unplasticised p.v.c. The decision on the choice of one of these for a particular building will depend on several factors. The nature of the manufacturing processes in the building may be of importance, *e.g.*, fumes from alkalis and chlorides have a destructive effect on aluminium, and lead is affected by acetic acid vapours. Lead-clothed bars are to be preferred in smoke-laden atmospheres. The weight of the glazing may be a consideration, aluminium glazing weighs about 96 N/m^2 less than the lead type. The latter weighs approximately 287 N/m^2, both figures include the weight of 6 mm thick glass.

There are many types of bar on the market and most of them have the following basic features: (1) The glass usually rests on a continuous seating of oiled asbestos cord, plastic strip, or beads formed in the lead extrusion. (2) The glass is secured on the outside by continuous lead wings formed in the lead sheathing, or by cappings of aluminium, p.v.c. or lead; these extend about 16 mm on to the glass. Finishes of this kind allow for the easy replacement of broken panes; with the burglar-proof type bars, the capping is secured from below. (3) At least one set of channels (often two are provided) is incorporated to allow for the dispersal of any water which may seep under the wings or cappings. (4) Rustproof bolts are used to secure the top and bottom of the bar to the structure; the bolts being in slotted holes so that the bar is free to expand and contract. Provision is made to prevent the glass from slipping down the bar, and a draught fillet is supplied to seal the space below the glass and the bottom structural member (see M, Fig. 98).

Bars are normally placed at centres just exceeding 610 mm to suit glass of this width; it is not advisable to increase this dimension due to the difficulty of handling large panes of glass on top of the roof and the additional cost of replacement. For roof lighting, 6 mm thick wired glass is used (the wire improves the glass strength and helps to hold the pane in position, even if it is broken by fire or other damage). The same glass can be used for side lighting; alternatively, 4 or 6 mm clear glass is suitable. Panels of glazing can be arranged to open by hand, electrical or hydraulic operation.

The depth of the glazing bar increases as the span increases. In Fig. 97 six examples of different kinds of bar are given.

The one at A† is a rolled steel T-bar which is dipped in calcium plumbate paint and totally enclosed in a jointless unplasticised p.v.c. sheath. The glass is laid on greased fibre cords and held in place by a p.v.c. cap which fits by snap-action over the bulb at the top of the bar. Both sides of the stalk of the T have a drainage channel which can conduct away any water which passes beneath the cap.

* Reinforced concrete glazing bars are also used, but these are heavy and generally more appropriate for side glazing.

† Manufactured by Crittall-Hope Ltd.

The bar at B* is of aluminium alloy; the glass is secured by aluminium strips bolted to the stalk of the T; the strips allow an aluminium cap to be snapped on. This example looks well when used for vertical patent glazing.

The aluminium alloy bar at C† has a spring clip of the same material to secure the glass.

The one at D‡ is similar to the last but the cover clips are bolted on; the application shows double glazing where two sheets of glass are separated by a spacer section.

The bar at E is made of aluminium alloy; it is a burglar-proof type in that the cover cap on the top is secured by a bolt from within — see p. 221.

The T-section bar at F is of mild steel sheathed in lead; it has two lead wings either side of the stalk for dressing over the glass. The lead sheathed bar is the forerunner of all others and has proved to be eminently durable.

Figure 98 shows the application of patent glazing (see also Figs. 15, 16 and 66), the key sketch at H is of a factory building with a light steel framework of trusses and stanchions, covered with light-weight cladding, both roof and side lighting are shown. Detail A at G is the typical one at the top of the roof lighting, showing a steel purlin fixed by a cleat to the truss, a metal deck roof with built-up felt roofing is indicated (see Fig. 65). The glazing bars rest on a 50 mm by 50 mm shelf angle fixed with countersunk bolts to the purlin. The attachment of the bar to the angle is by means of a fixing plate similar to that given at N, the plate has a 20 mm by 22 mm slotted hole for a 10 mm dia. rust-proofed bolt. The bar manufacturers specify the position of the shelf angle below the top of the purlin to suit the bar used, the stalk of deeper bars is often swaged or cut off at a bevel to give clearance beneath the roof overhang. A lead flashing is clipped round the purlin and dressed over the glass and the top of the bar. This detail also shows that the roof is underdrawn with insulation board below the top member of the truss; this board rests between tees slung from the purlins in a similar way to that at D, Fig. 90.

Detail B at M shows the usual treatment at the bottom edge of the roof glazing, the purlin fixing is as before, but its top leg points down the roof. As the bottom end of the bars is above the roof level, the pitch of glazing bars is always flatter than the roof covering, and the bottom seating has to be raised above the purlins. In this detail, the raising is done by means of a 150 mm by 6 mm plate bolted to the purlin back, the shelf angle being fixed to the plate. The bar shown is like the double glazing one at D, Fig. 97 the top pane of glass is prevented from slipping down by the aluminium alloy glass stop drawn at L, which is

* Manufactured by Crittall-Hope Ltd.

† Manufactured by Heywood Williams Ltd., Huddersfield.

‡ Manufactured by Pillar Patent Glazing Ltd., London.

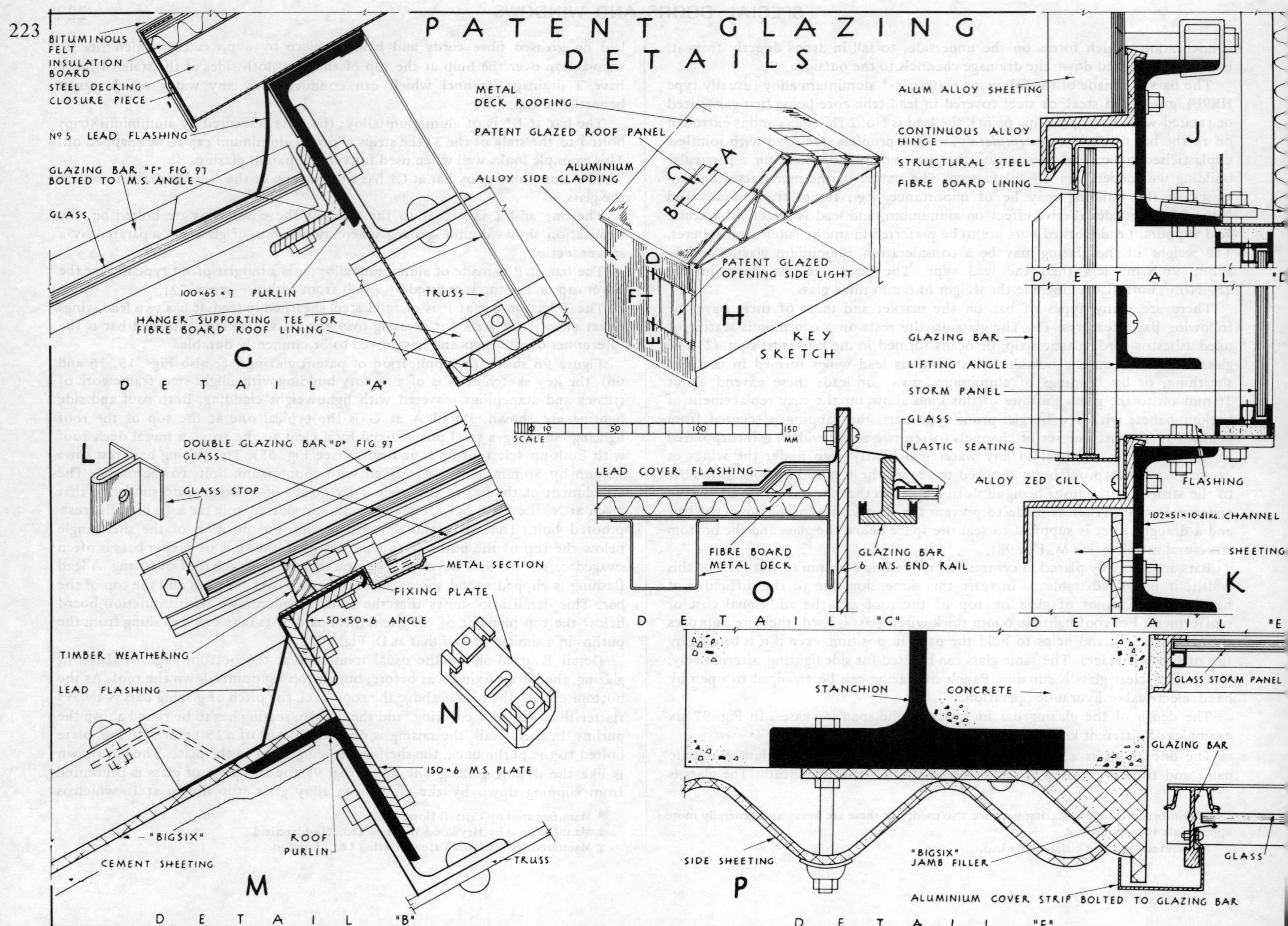

PATENT GLAZING DETAILS
BITUMINOUS FELT
INSULATION BOARD
STEEL DECKING
CLOSURE PIECE
METAL DECK ROOFING
Nº 5 LEAD FLASHING
PATENT GLAZED ROOF PANEL
GLAZING BAR "F" FIG. 97 BOLTED TO M.S. ANGLE
ALUMINIUM ALLOY SIDE CLADDING
GLASS
100×65×7 PURLIN
TRUSS
HANGER SUPPORTING TEE FOR FIBRE BOARD ROOF LINING
G
DETAIL "A"
B
C
A
D
E
F
PATENT GLAZED OPENING SIDE LIGHT
H
KEY SKETCH
ALUM. ALLOY SHEETING
CONTINUOUS ALLOY HINGE
STRUCTURAL STEEL
FIBRE BOARD LINING
J
DETAIL "D"
GLAZING BAR
LIFTING ANGLE
STORM PANEL
GLASS
PLASTIC SEATING
FLASHING
ALLOY ZED CILL
102×51×10·4 kg. CHANNEL
SHEETING
K
DETAIL "E"
SCALE 0 10 50 100 150 MM
DOUBLE GLAZING BAR "D" FIG. 97
GLASS
L
GLASS STOP
LEAD COVER FLASHING
FIBRE BOARD
METAL DECK
GLAZING BAR
6 M.S. END RAIL
O
DETAIL "C"
METAL SECTION
FIXING PLATE
50×50×6 ANGLE
TIMBER WEATHERING
LEAD FLASHING
N
150×6 M.S. PLATE
"BIGSIX"
CEMENT SHEETING
ROOF PURLIN
TRUSS
M
DETAIL "B"
STANCHION
CONCRETE
GLASS STORM PANEL
GLAZING BAR
SIDE SHEETING
"BIGSIX" JAMB FILLER
GLASS
P
ALUMINIUM COVER STRIP BOLTED TO GLAZING BAR
DETAIL "F"

FIGURE 98

bolted to the bar. The inner pane of glass is bedded along the lower edge in glazing compound contained in a metal section which is secured to the shelf angle by the same bolts that secure the fixing plate, the latter is detailed at N and described above. Note that the inner glass does not come into contact with the outer air, for this would impair the insulation value of the construction. The 25 mm air space between the glasses is sealed at the bottom by a timber weathering which is clipped to the fixing plate. Asbestos-cement roof sheeting is used as an alternative to that at G, being held by bent clips to the top leg of the purlin (hook bolts cannot be accommodated in this position), weatherproofing is completed by the lead cover flashing which is dressed over the corrugations and extends round the shelf angle.

The detail at O is of the junction between the roof and the end of a panel of glazing. Due to the different slopes of the glass and the roof, the weathering is accomplished by inserting a steel end plate between the upper and lower purlins. The width of the end plate is such that its top is not less than 50 mm above the roof slope; a lead flashing is dressed over and stitch bolted to it.

The remaining details in the figure show the application of patent glazing bars in a vertical position to provide openable side lighting. Up to twenty or so 610 mm wide panes can be fixed together into one opening panel operated by window gear. The bars are secured by top and bottom members, the former rests in a continuous aluminium alloy hinge of Z-section as shown at J, and is bolted to the channel framing of the structure; the internal fibreboard lining is trimmed at the bottom by a special angle.

The detail E at K shows the lower edge of the glazing where there is another alloy Z-section forming a protective sill to the sheeting. The storm panel of glass in 900 mm wide frame is used at the ends of the glazing run only, this prevents rain from being blown into the building at each end when the window is opened.

The plan detail at P shows the junction between the vertical side sheeting and the patent glazing. The gap between the two is covered by a cover strip which is stitch bolted to the bar and overlaps the asbestos-cement jamb filler piece.

CHAPTER TEN

INTERNAL PLUMBING*

Syllabus. Water collection. Temporary and permanent hardness. Purification, settlement, sterilization, softening. Acidity and alkalinity. Distribution. Copper, polythene, galvanized steel and lead pipes, manufacture, fixing, capillary and compression joints. Domestic water installations, direct and indirect systems. Pipe sizing. Taps and valves. Sanitary appliances, types and manufacture, wash-down and syphonic W.C.s.

Soil and waste installations, single-stack, two-pipe, one-pipe and single-stack plus vent-stack systems. Self and induced siphonage, back pressure. Soil and waste pipe-work.

WATER COLLECTION, TREATMENT AND SUPPLY

Water is a compound of two atoms of hydrogen and one of oxygen and derives from rain falling to the catchment areas. From these places the water percolates and eventually collects at the sources of supply such as reservoirs, lakes, rivers and deep wells. In its original form the rain is pure and is known as soft water. Although it is pure, it is a good dissolving agent and should not be delivered in lead pipes as this would cause lead poisoning. For a similar reason, zinc containers should not be used; rain water has also a fairly rapid corrosive effect on iron pipes. As the rain falls through the atmosphere it absorbs some of the gases, principally carbon dioxide.

According to the locality of the catchment area and the nature of the strata through which the water percolates to the supply source, various impurities are absorbed. For example, water from peaty areas becomes acidic and has to be treated as described below to prevent corrosion of supply pipes and to render it more palatable. In limestone areas, water which has passed through rocky strata containing the carbonates and sulphates of calcium and magnesium dissolves some of these minerals and takes them into solution. This dissolving action changes the water from *soft* to *hard* and is made possible, in the case of temporary hard water (see below), by the presence of carbon dioxide absorbed by the rain which changes the carbonate into bicarbonate. The higher the concentration of this gas, the greater is the absorption of the carbonates† with corresponding increase in hardness. Hardness is classified in terms of calcium carbonate, and water having under 50 milligrams per litre of hardness is graded soft. That which has 50 to 100 milligrams is moderately soft; 100 to 150 milligrams – slightly hard; 150 to 250 milligrams – moderately hard; 250 to 350 milligrams – hard; over 350 milligrams – very hard. The amount of hardness is noted by the readiness with which the water combines with soap to form a lather. Soft water lathers easily and hard water does so with difficulty thus wasting soap* in the formation of an insoluble surface scum.

There are two kinds of hardness, *temporary* and *permanent*.§ Temporary hardness can be removed by boiling the water which drives off the carbon dioxide and releases the calcium and magnesium carbonates as precipitates. It is this deposit in the form of hard scale or *fur* which collects in boilers, water-heaters, pipes and kettles (particularly round the elements); it is especially troublesome and has to be eliminated. Obviously, the boiling of temporary hard water as a method of reducing its hardness is not practicable on a large scale and other methods given below are used.

Permanent hardness is the amount of hardness remaining after a sample of water has been boiled, it is commonly due to the presence of sulphates of calcium and magnesium which are soluble in water without the presence of carbon dioxide. Consequently, if permanent hard water is boiled there is not deposition‡ of scale and this is of value in plumbing arrangements.

* External plumbing, including lead work and lead pipe jointing, and some cast iron rainwater goods have been described in Vol. I. Aluminium, pressed galvanized steel, zinc, vitreous enamelled cast iron and plastic rainwater goods are also available in a variety of sections, their jointing and fixing being similar to that for cast iron. Copper roofing which may be the work of the plumber or coppersmith is mentioned in Vol. I, and described fully in Vol. III. Domestic water services are introduced in Vol. I.

† The dissolving of sulphates is not dependent on the CO_2 content – see later.

* For this reason the use of soapless detergents for washing clothes is advocated in hard water districts.

§ This is a popular misnomer, as permanent hardness can be removed as described below.

‡ The substances are deposited by evaporation and so the use of this water in steam boilers has to be avoided.

WATER PURIFICATION, SOFTENING AND SUPPLY

For domestic purposes,§ the aim is to provide pure, palatable water which will lather without difficulty. Water of zero hardness, such as rain, has an insipid taste, as has boiled water; it also produces poisonous solutions in pipes other than copper and plastic ones. Slightly hard water is desirable; when it is harder than this, the supply authorities are asked by the Ministry of Health to soften it. The treatment required to provide the desired standard depends on the state of the supply water and either hardening or softening may be required. In the case of most reservoir waters, the typical treatments are: *settlement* and *filtration* to eliminate suspended matter, *sterilization* to remove dissolved matter and *adjustment of hardness*, all usually by gravity delivery.

Settlement occurs by storage in the reservoir where the larger impurities fall to the bottom and many of the harmful bacteria die. Sometimes, the water is fed to local service reservoirs where further removal of bacteria occurs by storage. Chemical coagulants, such as alum, may be added to hasten the process.

Filtration. In the *filters*, the water discharges from a head of 1.2 to 1.5 m on to beds of sand up to 1 m thick which overlie a layer of coarse gravel 0.5 m deep; here the water is slowly strained and the smaller particles removed. The filters also provide a further substantial reduction of bacteria accomplished by the collection of the suspended matter as a film on the sand surface. Microbe organisms develop in this film which break down organic matter and prevent the passage of other microbes. The organisms steadily multiply on the surface layer and it should not be disturbed; periodically it has to be removed when the percolation rate becomes uneconomically slow. When this happens the surface layer of sand is skimmed off and the water allowed to run to waste over it until a new film has developed. More rapid filters are also used with greater heads of water, these give less bacteriological purification and the water from them needs a greater degree of sterilization.

Sterilization. This destroys the remaining harmful bacteria and is usually effected by the addition of a calculated amount of chlorine. Other sterilization agents are bleaching powder, and ammonium plus chlorine, which react to give chloramine.

Adjustment of Hardness. Temporary hardness is removed by the addition of lime in proportion to the degree of hardness, the lime combines with the bicarbonate present in the water and is deposited as a precipitate of insoluble calcium carbonate.

Permanent hardness is reduced by the addition of sodium carbonate (washing soda), this reacts with the calcium sulphate (causing the hardness) and calcium carbonate is precipitated.

For waters having both types of hardness, the above two reactions can be combined in the soda-lime softening process.

An alternative softening method is the base exchange ("zeolite") process where the reagent is a sodium compound which exchanges the sodium ion for the calcium and magnesium ions in solution, thus softening the water.

When an increase of hardness is needed as with water from peat areas, this is done by adding lime which also has the effect of reducing the dangerous acidity.

The acidity of water is usually given in terms of pH* units. When the pH is between 8 and 6, the water is neutral; when it is less than 6 – acidic; if pH exceeds 8, the water is alkaline. Certain dyes are used as indicators to determine the pH value, for example, neutrality is shown when bromo-thymol blue is added to the water and it becomes bluish green; if it turns green or yellow then acidity is indicated, if it gives a blue colour then it is alkaline. Different indicators, such as methyl orange and cresyl blue change colour within reasonably narrow limits of pH value. Alternatively, when accurate analysis is required a special electrical meter can be used.

Supply. After treatment the water is fed in cast iron* pipes to the supply areas where a ring main network of pipes 0.76 to 1 m deep is located. These pipes have stop valves at approximately every 900 m and at branch junctions. At low points there are wash-out valves for cleansing the system, and at high points, air valves are placed for removal of trapped air. In built-up areas, fire hydrant connections are placed also at regular intervals.

The diameter of the *supply pipe* from the *main* to the premises depends on the size of the building and the number of occupants, a 12 mm dia. bore pipe is normally sufficient for a house. In connecting these two pipes, a watertight box is clamped to the main, this contains a drill for cutting the hole and a tapping tool for forming the thread. Incorporated in the box is a ferrule (which may include a stop valve) which can be rotated into position over the hole and screwed down. The swarf from the tapping can be washed out, and if the ferrule has a stop valve the operation can be completed without turning the main supply off. The short connecting pipe to the ferrule is usually of plastic and this extends to just outside the boundary of the building. At this point, a stop valve is fitted and enclosed at the bottom of a small accessible chamber built with bricks, or, more often a 150 mm dia. earthenware pipe is used and provided with a cast iron hinged lid.

§ Certain industries require special types of water, for example laundries and dye works often install additional equipment to reduce hardness.

* This is a value of the concentration of the hydrogen ions in the water and refers to a chemical method of expressing the reaction of the water.

TUBES

Tubes for water supply† installations are made of *copper, polythene, galvanized steel* and *stainless steel*. For the reasons mentioned on p. 225, lead pipes are no longer used.

Copper Pipes. Much plumbing work is done in this material; it has several merits, *e.g.*, it has considerable strength, reasonable ductility, is obtainable in long lengths, has a good resistance to corrosion and need not be painted. There are two types of copper water service pipes, *heavy-gauge* and *light-gauge*. The former can be threaded and is used for high pressure work in industrial layouts. For general purpose work where the pressure does not exceed 1 379 kN/m^2,§ the most commonly used pipe for internal domestic work is the light-gauge tube conforming to B.S. 2871; it is available in straight lengths (4.5 to 6 m) the usual sizes for domestic work being 12, 15, 18, 22 and 28 mm nominal external diameter.

For underground work,‡ as for the pipe from the main to the building, special copper tube is used having a heavier gauge. This conforms to B.S. 1386 and is in two grades: *half hard*, which is most generally used, or, *fully annealed*. In the half-hard temper, the tubes are in straight pieces 4.5 to 6 m long; the fully

* Fibre-cement pressure pipes are being increasingly used for water supply; they are particularly suitable in soft water districts.

† See p. 243 for sanitation pipes.

§ Corresponding to a head of 140 m.

‡ Certain soils such as ashes, red clay and furnace clinker are corrosive to pipe exteriors and although some relief can be obtained by improving the drainage and surrounding the pipe in limestone chippings, it is desirable to paint the tube with bitumen.

annealed quality is also obtainable in similar straight lengths or in coils 9 to 18 m long.

Bending† *of Copper Tubes*. This can be done by hand or machine; for manual bending, the tube should be filled (known as loading) so as to preserve the bore. One method of supporting the bore is to use a flexible spiral steel spring, bends with a radius (to the inner curve) of three times the tube diameter can be made by this means; tubes up to 22 mm dia. can be bent in the same way, but for the larger diameters the tube has also to be heated.

Bending machines vary from small hand-operated models to those assisted by a ratchet or gears or a hydraulic press. They all work on a similar principle, consisting of a quadrant or steel former with a semi-circular grooved edge to fit the inner radius of the bend in the tube; for the outer radius, a hollowed piece of steel forms the back guide on which is pressed an adjustable roller used in bending the tube round the quadrant. When a bending machine is used, loading or heating of the tube is not needed up to diameters of 22 mm, and comparatively sharp bends of inner radius equal to three times the tube diameter can be made; tubes of greater size have to be softened by heating (annealed) prior to bending. For smaller radius bends the pipe has to be loaded, or alternatively, a *draw* bar bending machine can be used. This equipment may be power assisted and it has a former and guide as before, plus a draw bar (a mandrel) which fits inside the tube to support it up to the point where the bend is made.

Fixing of Copper Tubes. These are fixed to a timber plate by pipe clips which incorporate a separate spacing piece (see I at J′, Fig. 99), or they may be enclosed in the type of clip that is built into the wall (2 at J′). Clips should be placed from 1.2 to 1.8 m apart on horizontal runs and up to 1.8 m apart on vertical runs.

Manufacture of Copper pipes. Small amounts of phosphorus and sometimes arsenic are added to the melted copper which is cast into billets 1.2 m long and up to 150 mm dia. The heated billet is pierced to form it into a shell, either by passing it through special rollers and over a mandrel, or by extrusion using a ram to force the metal through the annular space between an outer circular die and a centrally placed mandrel. The shell is reduced in diameter by cold drawing processes using a series of decreasing dies and mandrels. This deformation causes hardening of the metal and so periodic annealing (see p. 29) is required; hard, half-hard, or soft quality tubing is obtained by suitable annealing and drawing in the later stages of manufacture. The appropriate British Standards specify tests which the batches of tube must satisfy before being passed for use.

Copper Tube Joints. There are three types of joint for connecting copper tube: *capillary*, *compression* and *welded*, and the fittings used are of alloys of copper or brass.*

† Bends should be used wherever possible in preference to elbows and other fittings, they can be made to a slower radius than fittings and thereby minimize resistance to flow and plumbing noises.

* In corrosive waters, brass fittings are unsuitable for copper tubes because of the zinc content; they are liable to dezincification or galvanic corrosion by electrolytic action. In such circumstances special alloys are used by the pipe-fitting manufacturers.

The Capillary Joint (see C†, Fig. 99). This comprises a copper alloy socket with an internal recessed groove or ring containing solder. The space between the outside of the tube and the inside of the socket (a tee piece in this example) is about 1 mm. In making the joint, the tube end is cut square, the burr removed and its outside cleaned with fine sandpaper or steel wool for a depth just exceeding that of the socket. The inside of the socket is wiped free from the protective coating and cleaned, if necessary, as before. The contacting surfaces of the tube and fitting are coated with a resin-based flux, they are then brought together so that the tube fits against the shoulder of the fitting. By heating the joint with a blow lamp, the solder is melted and flows by capillary action to fill the annular space between tube and socket.

This type of joint has the neatest appearance of all and is available in all the usual fittings such as tees (as at C), elbows, bends, etc.

Compression Joints. These are of two types: *non-manipulative* and *manipulative*.

Non-manipulative Compression Joint (see D*, K, and N, Fig. 99). This consists of an externally threaded brass alloy coupling, or socket, with an internal shoulder (or shoulders) acting as a distance stop. The end of the tube is cut square as above, and a nut and annealed brass compression ring are slid over the end. The ring seats against the mouth of the coupling, and by tightening the nut, the ring is made to grip the tube and provide a watertight joint.

Manipulative Compression Joint. An example of this type is shown at E*, it is made of gunmetal alloy and is suitable for underground work. The coupling and coupling nut containing a friction ring are placed over the tubes, these are then flared out by driving in a tapered steel drift. A shaped cone‡ ring is placed inside the ends of the tubes and the coupling nut is tightened. This action compresses the shaped end of the tubes between the compensating ring and the cone to make a reliable joint.

Welded Joint. Although there are several types of welding technique, the bronze-welded joint is the most convenient one for general plumbing work. In this, the end of one tube is flared out by a drift and the end of the other one has its outside arris filed off. Phosphor bronze or brass alloy filler rods are used and melted by an oxy-acetylene flame into the space between the two tube ends. The finished appearance of the joint is very similar to the taft joint shown at B′, Fig. 77, Vol. I, and an example is shown in this volume at E, Fig. 100. This shows a 90 mm dia. soil pipe that has been reduced in diameter by cutting

† This is a fitting made by the Yorkshire Imperial Metals Ltd and incorporates the correct amount of solder. In other makes, the solder is applied externally through a touch hole in the socket. Various types of solder are available, for domestic work the most usual is composed of equal parts of lead and tin, another type has 39 per cent tin, 60 per cent lead and 1 per cent antimony.

* Made by the Yorkshire Imperial Metals Ltd.

‡ The cone is loose in the straight coupling only and forms part of the body in the other fittings.

shaped pieces out of it, flaring out the end and welding together. Welded joints are seldom necessary.

Polythene Pipes. These are being increasingly used internally and externally for *cold* water service pipes only; they have better thermal insulation properties than metal pipes, thus reducing the possibility of freezing up, nor do they burst on thawing as metal pipes are inclined to do; they are easy to bend and do not corrode.‡ Polythene tube is available in two grades: normal gauge and heavy gauge and is specified in B.S. 3505, it is made in coils up to 150 m long and the same internal diameters as copper pipes. The normal grade is suitable for domestic work and can be jointed with compression fittings like that at D, Fig. 99; as it has a greater wall thickness than copper, the fittings have to be one size larger than would be the case for a copper tube. The heavy gauge tube can be threaded and joined by a sleeve as described below for galvanized steel pipe.

Bending of Polythene Pipes. This is easily accomplished by immersing the tube in boiling water for five minutes, inserting a bending spring in the tube, bending it to the desired shape and holding it until cold. The minimum radius for such a bend is three times the outside diameter.

Fixing of Polythene Pipes. As the material has a relatively high rate of expansion, expansion loops are needed for long runs. Standard clips as for metal pipes are used but at closer centres and to allow for slight movement. For horizontal runs, clips are spaced at intervals of about twelve times the outside tube diameter for 22 mm sizes and less, and eight times for the larger sizes; for vertical runs a spacing of twenty-four tube diameters is usual.

Manufacture of Polythene Pipes. They are made from thermoplastic materials, such as polythene, polyvinyl chloride, polystyrene and cellulose acetate. The heated raw materials are forced through a die having a central pin, the tubular shape is thus obtained by passage through the annular space. The machine is known as an extruder and consists of a barrel in which a revolving screw carries the material forward to the die. The barrel is heated to the correct temperature, and as the soft tube emerges it is passed through baths of water. The rate of extrusion is controlled by a pulling machine which grips and hauls the tube through the baths. After coiling, the dimensions are checked and a small piece is sent to the laboratory for testing.

Polythene Tube Joints. The heavy gauge tube can be threaded and joined by similar fittings are used for galvanized steel tubes described below. The two most widely used joints for the normal gauge tube are the flanged joint and the compression joint. An example of the former is shown at F, Fig. 99; this is a bend produced by the Yorkshire Imperial Metals Ltd. and is made of a high grade polythene known as "Plastronga"; tees and the usual range of couplings are made of the same material. For this joint, the tube is provided with a flanged* end and the bend is threaded externally and has an internal socket to receive the tube flange.

‡ They are unaffected by sulphuric acid but attacked by nitric acid, petrol, benzine and heat.

* Tubes can be supplied with this end already formed, or, alternatively, by using a special flanging tool on the site and applying gentle heat from a blow lamp, the tube is softened, moulded and flanged.

An example of the compression joint, made by the same firm is shown at G, Fig. 99, this comprises an alloy fitting with external thread and internal socket. In order to resist the compressive force, a copper liner or insert is placed within the tube; this is done by immersing the tube in boiling water for half a minute to soften it and facilitate the insertion of the liner. This particular fitting is of a lighter grade than the similar one at D and both can be used for copper and polythene pipe jointing, although the heavier one makes a better joint for plastic tubes.

Welding can also be used for polythene joints, the tube ends are chamfered off at about 50° and a polythene welding rod and nitrogen gas torch used. Tubes can be butt jointed in this way for the smaller sizes, the larger ones can have polythene flanges welded on for a bolted connection. Yet another type of joint is similar to F, but made of polythene with built-in electrodes; the fitting and tube are fused together when an electric current is passed through the joint.

Galvanized Steel Pipes.* These are used mainly in the larger schemes, where the water is suitable; they are cheaper than copper. Steel tubes corrode more readily in soft and acid waters and are not so easily manipulated as copper, although they are stronger and can be used in hard water districts† when they withstand the hammering needed to remove scale. Galvanized steel tubes are available in light, medium and heavy grades up to 150 mm bore conforming to B.S. 1387; most authorities only permit the use of the heavy grade which have to withstand a hydraulic test pressure of 4.8 MN/m^2. Tubes are made in random lengths up to 7 m with both ends threaded and one end provided with screwed socket for jointing.

Steel tubes are bent by machine benders as previously described to a minimum radius of eight diameters. Pipe clips are spaced at 2.4 m centres vertically and at 1.8 m centres horizontally.

Galvanized Steel Tube Joints. Taper threads are provided to the tubes with parallel threads to the sockets; the usual range of tees, bends, etc., are available as well as short lengths 100 to 250 mm long. In making the joint, the threads are painted with a mixture of red and white lead to give a watertight fitting.

Manufacture of Galvanized Steel Tube. Two methods are in use: *butt welding* and the *seamless process.*

In the butt welding method, the heated steel strip is pulled through a bell-shaped die which gives the tubular section and compresses the edge to form a continuous weld. The tube then passes through a series of rollers to compress and elongate it to a uniform diameter, the tube is stretched in one series of rollers so that the desired thickness and

* Ungalvanized steel tubes are also used but are mainly confined to heating circuits for hot water and steam radiators.

† In such areas where furring occurs it is advisable to use the heavy grade pipes one size larger than normally required. Thus, the supply from the main should be 18 mm dia. instead of 12 or 15 mm, circulating pipes should be at least 35 mm dia. and access plates are needed to remove deposits.

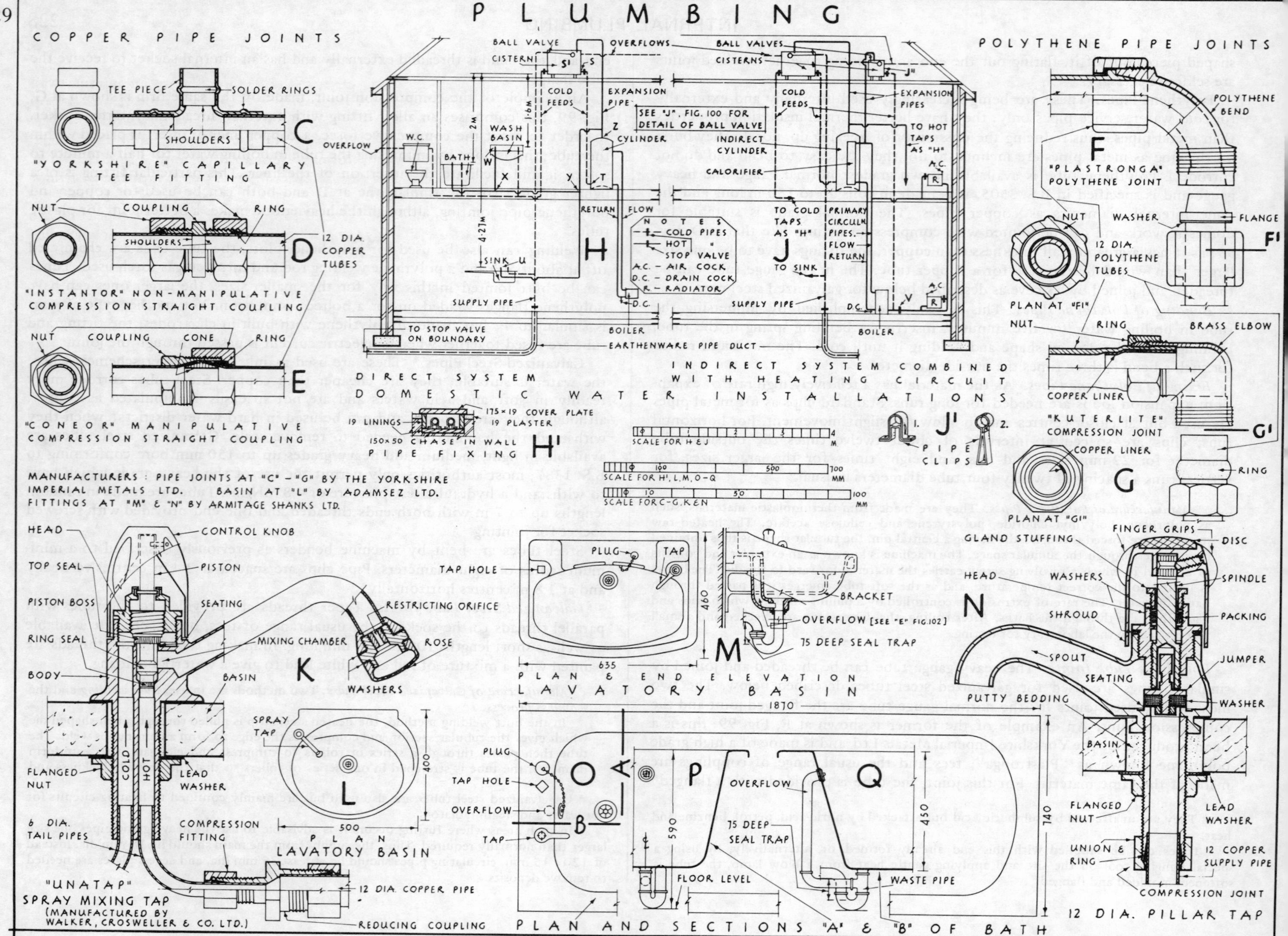
PLUMBING
COPPER PIPE JOINTS
TEE PIECE
SOLDER RINGS
SHOULDERS
C
"YORKSHIRE" CAPILLARY TEE FITTING
NUT
COUPLING
RING
SHOULDERS
D
12 DIA. COPPER TUBES
"INSTANTOR" NON-MANIPULATIVE COMPRESSION STRAIGHT COUPLING
NUT
COUPLING
CONE
RING
E
"CONEOR" MANIPULATIVE COMPRESSION STRAIGHT COUPLING
MANUFACTURERS: PIPE JOINTS AT "C" – "G" BY THE YORKSHIRE IMPERIAL METALS LTD. BASIN AT "L" BY ADAMSEZ LTD. FITTINGS AT "M" & "N" BY ARMITAGE SHANKS LTD.
BALL VALVE
CISTERN
S'
S
OVERFLOWS
COLD FEEDS
EXPANSION PIPE
WASH BASIN
W.C.
OVERFLOW
BATH
W
X
Y
Z
T
CYLINDER
RETURN
FLOW
SINK
U
SUPPLY PIPE
TO STOP VALVE ON BOUNDARY
2m
1.6m
4.27m
H
DIRECT SYSTEM
BALL VALVES
CISTERNS
J"
COLD FEEDS
EXPANSION PIPES
SEE "J", FIG. 100 FOR DETAIL OF BALL VALVE
TO HOT TAPS AS "H"
INDIRECT CYLINDER
CALORIFIER
A.C.
R
NOTES
— COLD PIPES
— HOT "
STOP VALVE
A.C. – AIR COCK
D.C. – DRAIN COCK
R – RADIATOR
TO COLD TAPS AS "H"
PRIMARY CIRCULN. PIPES. FLOW RETURN
J
TO SINK
SUPPLY PIPE
D.C.
V
BOILER
EARTHENWARE PIPE DUCT
INDIRECT SYSTEM COMBINED WITH HEATING CIRCUIT
DOMESTIC WATER INSTALLATIONS
19 LININGS
175×19 COVER PLATE
19 PLASTER
150×50 CHASE IN WALL
H'
PIPE FIXING
J'
PIPE CLIPS
SCALE FOR H & J
4 M
SCALE FOR H', L, M, O–Q
100
500
700 MM
SCALE FOR C–G, K, & N
10
50
100 MM
POLYTHENE PIPE JOINTS
POLYTHENE BEND
F
"PLASTRONGA" POLYTHENE JOINT
NUT
WASHER
FLANGE
F'
12 DIA. POLYTHENE TUBES
PLAN AT "F'"
NUT
RING
BRASS ELBOW
COPPER LINER
"KUTERLITE" COMPRESSION JOINT
G'
COPPER LINER
RING
G
PLAN AT "G'"
HEAD
CONTROL KNOB
TOP SEAL
PISTON
PISTON BOSS
SEATING
RING SEAL
MIXING CHAMBER
BODY
BASIN
FLANGED NUT
COLD
HOT
LEAD WASHER
6 DIA. TAIL PIPES
COMPRESSION FITTING
"UNATAP" SPRAY MIXING TAP
(MANUFACTURED BY WALKER, CROSWELLER & CO. LTD.)
TAP HOLE
RESTRICTING ORIFICE
ROSE
WASHERS
K
12 DIA. COPPER PIPE
REDUCING COUPLING
SPRAY TAP
PLUG
TAP HOLE
OVERFLOW
TAP
400
500
L
PLAN LAVATORY BASIN
PLUG
TAP
480
BRACKET
OVERFLOW [SEE "E" FIG.102]
75 DEEP SEAL TRAP
635
M
PLAN & END ELEVATION LAVATORY BASIN
1870
A
B
O
P
Q
OVERFLOW
590
75 DEEP SEAL TRAP
450
740
FLOOR LEVEL
WASTE PIPE
PLAN AND SECTIONS "A" & "B" OF BATH
FINGER GRIPS
GLAND STUFFING
DISC
HEAD
WASHERS
SPINDLE
SHROUD
PACKING
N
SPOUT
JUMPER
SEATING
PUTTY BEDDING
WASHER
BASIN
FLANGED NUT
LEAD WASHER
UNION & RING
12 COPPER SUPPLY PIPE
COMPRESSION JOINT
12 DIA. PILLAR TAP

FIGURE 99

diameter are obtained, this also removes the welding scale that has been formed. After resting on cooling racks, being finally quenched in water to remove loose scale, the tube is passed through another set of rollers for straightening, it is then galvanized by the hot-dip process (see p. 29).

In the seamless process, the heated steel billet (a solid round bar) is passed through rollers which have a piercing mandrel between them. The resulting pierced shell travels through several sets of rollers with central mandrels which increase its length and reduce its diameter and wall thickness; these processes give a true bore to the pipe, remove scale and burnish the surfaces. Tubes down to 35 mm dia. are made in this way, but for the smaller sizes, further cold drawing is required. After the tube has cooled, it is washed in weak sulphuric acid to finally remove scale, and after further washing and immersion in a lubricant it is ready for cold drawing. This may be *either* a tensile action, consisting of a reducing die with mandrel, the tube being pulled through the die to reduce its diameter and wall thickness; *or* a compressive action using semicircular rotating dies with tapered semi-circular grooves in their faces and a tapered mandrel. Cold drawing hardens the tube, so it is annealed, washed and lubricated between each reduction. Finally the tube is straightened in rollers, cut to length, tested for soundness and galvanized.

Installation of Pipe-Work. In domestic work, it is usual to conceal the pipe runs in small ducts such as a chase in the wall or behind skirtings, they should not be buried directly in the plaster finish or be notched into floor joists; their position should be determined before work starts and be accessible in case of repair. A typical arrangement is shown at H′, Fig. 99, the wall is chased and lined with a back board for the fixing of the pipes and at the sides for the screwed-on cover plate. Typical copper pipe clips are shown at J′, that at 1 is in two parts and allows sufficient space from the back board for the coupling nut of a compression fitting; the one at 2 is the holderbat type which can be built into the wall, the ring is in two parts and is secured by a nut and bolt.

DOMESTIC WATER INSTALLATIONS

These are shown in Fig. 99. From the boundary stop valve, the supply pipe is extended to the building in any suitable pipe material that is resistant to soil corrosion; underground quality copper tube or polythene are used for this purpose. 12 mm dia. soft copper 1.8 to 1.25 mm thick is often used for the branch pipe* from the main. Polythene tube is increasingly used for all cold supply pipes, especially externally, due to its good resistance to frost damage. If this material is used for the main underground delivery pipe, then it should be remembered that it is not suitable as an earth† for the electrical service.

To prevent damage by frost and traffic, the supply pipe must be placed 0.76 m below ground level and this depth must be maintained until it is inside* the building; similarly, the rising pipe should be brought up an internal wall rather than the colder external wall where it may be affected by frost. A stop valve is placed immediately above ground floor level, sometimes a drain cock is placed just above the stop valve to allow for the complete emptying of the system — although a sink tap will normally serve this purpose. From the valve, the supply pipe rises directly to a storage cistern (see H and J) near the first floor ceiling.†

The pipes so far described are termed supply pipes or service pipes and are subject to mains pressure, those taking water from the cistern are known as distribution or feed pipes and are subject to the much lower pressure from the cistern.

In the planning of the building, care should have been taken to centralize the plumbing so as to give an efficient and economical layout of the appliances requiring water. Hence, the bathroom would be as near as possible over the kitchen, and the distance between boiler and cylinder would be kept short; this latter provision has a marked effect on the efficiency of the heating arrangements.

The branch pipes to the first floor appliances should be given a slight fall away from the taps, the branch to the sink should fall towards the tap; the observance of these rules ensures that the system can be drained. It will be seen at H, that the cold feed pipe to the first floor appliances cannot be drained in this way, it can only be partially emptied by closing its valve at the cistern and turning on the bath tap. The pipe could be emptied by siphoning off water at the bath tap, or the feed could be extended to ground floor level and fitted with a drain cock (see p. 234).

In determining the metals to be used for the distribution pipes, the advice of the water authority should be sought. The use of certain metals may be prohibited because of the corrosion caused by waters of acid reaction, *e.g.*, galvanized tubes in peat districts. For soft or acid waters it is unwise to use pipes and fittings (cisterns and cylinder) of differing metals in the same system, this can produce bi-metallic corrosion due to the water acting as an electrolyte. Copper in solution from copper pipes attacks the zinc in the galvanized surfaces of the cistern; this action is accelerated where hot water is present. It is therefore good practice to specify that all pipes and fittings should be of the same metal; this will usually be copper.

There are two main systems for the distribution of water in the house, (1) the direct system, and (2) the indirect system.

* Where the supply pipe is long (as to isolated farms), the copper or polythene pipe can be economically laid by *mole plough* which dispenses with the excavation of a trench. This consists of a cutting blade which is pulled by a tractor along the pipeline to cut a slit 0.76 m deep in the ground. The mole is a torpedo shaped piece of steel fixed to the bottom of the blade and it forms a hole for the pipe which is coupled behind it and drawn in as the cut is made.

† Metal pipes are frequently used for earthing purposes, see p. 250.

* The pipe should pass beneath the building inside a sleeve of agricultural pipes, and if it rises through a suspended floor it should be lagged.

† The cistern can be in the roof space as shown or just above the hot water cylinder (see below for minimum height); in the former event, the cistern and attached pipes must be properly lagged. Cistern lagging can be of several materials; strawboard, insulation board or polystyrene are suitable; pipe lagging can be of felt, hessian or foamed plastic, etc.

(1) THE DIRECT SYSTEM

This is widely adopted for small houses, being the most economical; it is not recommended where hardness deposits develop. The diagrammatic layout of the arrangement is shown at H, Fig. 99; its main elements are the cold water storage cistern, the hot water storage cylinder and the boiler for heating the water. The supply pipe (normally 12 mm dia.) rises from the internal stop valve to the cold storage cistern. Branch pipes are taken off the supply riser for drinking water; in a house, there will be usually just one branch to the kitchen sink. It is considered good practice to supply all remaining cold feeds from the cistern and not from the main supply pipe; this is enforced by some authorities so as to reduce demand on the mains at peak periods of the day. The arrangement also provides a small emergency supply in the case of failure, and the pipes from the cistern can be less heavy than those under mains pressure. The water enters the cistern through a ball valve (see J, Fig. 100, and p. 235) which is controlled by a ball floating on the surface. The cistern has a 22 mm bore overflow (also known as a water waste preventer or warning pipe) which prevents flooding in the case of a fault in the valve. The overflow must discharge outside the building; in the event of overflowing occurring whilst the house is unoccupied, the authority can prevent wastage by turning off the supply at the outside stop valve. The overflow pipe should be fitted with a hinged flap at the outer end to prevent the access of cold air to the cistern and reduce the possibility of freezing.

Feed pipes 64 mm above the bottom of the cistern are taken to appliances that have not been supplied with cold water from the supply riser, these pipes must be provided with stop valves as shown, the right-hand feed delivers water to the base of the hot water cylinder.

Cisterns. These are made from galvanized steel, copper, asbestos and plastic, the latter being the most common. They are made in various sizes to suit the demand, and for a house a capacity of between 136 and 200 litres is usual; in order to give an adequate flow the cistern should be placed not less than 1.5 m above the highest appliance.

Hot Water Storage Cylinders. These are usually of copper, although galvanized steel is used also in hard water areas. Copper cylinders* have a dished bottom and curved top to resist water pressure. The cylinder capacity should be between 27 and 50 litres per head. Thus, for a household of five, the size would be from 135 to 250 litres.

A cylinder has four pipe connections; on opposite sides near the bottom are those for the cold feed inlet and the return pipe to the boiler. A quarter of the way down the cylinder and above the return pipe there is the flow connection from the boiler, and on the larger sizes there is another connection on the opposite side. The flow and return pipes comprise the primary circulation (see below). The last connection is from the top of the cylinder and is for the expansion pipe. This pipe allows for the escape of any steam or rising boiling water and is carried up to discharge over the cistern. A branch is taken off the expansion pipe to serve the hot taps and forms the secondary circulation. Cylinders can also be obtained with an access plate for connection of an electric immersion heater; this is a valuable supplementary method of giving hot water and should be fitted with a thermostatic control and temperature adjustment to provide automatic and economical usage. Heaters are obtainable in several sizes, they would have a loading of 2 to 3 kW for a house. The cylinder should be lagged and is normally placed in an airing cupboard adjacent to or in the bathroom.

Boilers. These are made of iron, steel, stainless steel or copper, and may be in an independent stove or behind a fire as a back boiler similar to that in Fig. 110. A typical copper back boiler measures 250 mm by 150 mm by 200 mm and is made of 6.4 mm thick metal; it has two connections, the upper one for the flow pipe to the cylinder and the lower one for the return pipe from the cylinder (see Fig. 110). At a small extra cost, iron boilers can be specially treated by *bower barffing* to render them rustproof and less liable to corrosion. For soft water districts, a copper boiler is advocated with an all-copper installation. The boiler can be fitted with a safety valve (see p. 235) to prevent boiler explosions, this is particularly desirable in hard water districts where "furring" can cause pipe blockages. Also, in such areas, the boiler should have an access plate so that it can be regularly descaled. Another type of boiler is the high-output boiler, see p. 263.

Circulation. The circulation of water is a convection movement started by its expansion when heated, the water becomes less dense and so rises in the flow* pipe. The warmed water in the boiler is replaced by cooler and heavier water from the cylinder, this is warmed in turn to continue the circulation. In order to have an adequate flow in the pipes, the storage cistern should be at least 1.5 m above the highest tap, this provides enough pressure to force warmed water from the cylinder to the taps. For the greatest efficiency, the flow pipe should rise throughout its length, and be free from horizontal runs, dips and bends; both it and the return pipe should be kept as short as possible; the manufacturers of heating appliances normally specify the maximum length of these runs that will satisfactorily heat the cylinder. A drain cock should be placed at the lowest

* B.S. 699 specifies copper cylinders of three grades for maximum working heads of 25, 15 and 10 m, the first being grade 1 in the following sizes: (capacities vary from 74 to 450 litres, the three given being popular sizes):

BS Type Reference	Actual Capacity (litres)	Diameter (mm)	Height (mm)	Thickness of copper (mm)
7	120	450	900	1.6
9	166	450	1 200	1.8
10	200	500	1 200	1.8

The thickness figures are for the body and top, the cylinder bottom is 0.4 mm thicker for types 7 and 9 and 0.7 mm thicker for type 10.

* It will be observed at H that the flow pipe rises from the *top* of the boiler to the *top* of the cylinder, whereas the return pipe travels from the *bottom* of the cylinder to the *bottom* of the boiler.

point in the return pipe so that the cylinder can be emptied. Bends in the cold water supply pipe should be gradual, if they are sharp they can produce "water hammer"; this is a thumping noise created by water at mains pressure and can cause vibration of the pipes. Where possible, the secondary circulation pipes should fall away from the expansion pipe so that this acts as a vent in preventing the formation of air locks. Where a branch from the expansion pipe has to rise to a high level fitting (such as a shower), then another expansion pipe must be provided to rise from the highest point in the circuit.

Towel Rails. A heated towel rail can be incorporated in the layout providing the manufacturer states this to be within the capacity of the heating appliance. Such a towel rail should have top and bottom connections for fixing to the return pipe to the boiler, a control valve and an air cock (see p. 235) for the release of trapped air at weekly intervals.

Instantaneous Water Heaters. These are operated by gas or electricity to provide immediate hot water at the appliance. The heater has its own tap and cold feed connection from the cistern; when the supply authority is agreeable, the heater may be fed direct from the mains supply pipe to a small cistern having a ball valve incorporated in it.

Lagging. The importance of this has already been mentioned, it is worth while lagging all the hot pipes, cylinder and cistern. The cost is relatively small, frost damage and unnecessary heat losses are prevented and fuel saving is achieved.

(2) THE INDIRECT SYSTEM

The remarks given above on cisterns, boilers, circulation, water heaters, and lagging apply also to this system, it differs from the direct system by having additional piping for the hot water supply – see J, Fig. 99. The name of the method derives from the type of cylinder which has an outer container enclosing another vessel or *calorifier* of annular cross section or a pipe coil; it is known as an indirect cylinder* and may be of copper or galvanized steel. The calorifier is connected to the primary circulation pipes (flow and return) to the boiler, it is fed by its own small storage cistern (J″) having a capacity of not less than 50 litres and there is a connection from the primary flow to the radiator circuit. Each radiator must have a control valve to regulate its temperature and disconnect it and must have an air cock as for a towel rail.

The main body of water in the cylinder (which is supplied from the main storage cistern) is therefore heated indirectly by the calorifier and supplies hot tap water through the secondary circulation like the direct system at H. The indirect system therefore has the double purpose of supplying washing water via the secondary circuit and radiators on the primary circuit which can be disconnected by the valve at V. For small domestic† installations, the boiler manufacturer will state the area of radiator heating surface, cylinder capacity and length of pipe-work that the boiler will heat; a towel rail could be coupled to the heating circuit.

An indirect* system is necessary where radiators are required, and it has the advantage that hardness deposits do not accumulate because the primary water is not constantly being changed, it is therefore suitable for hard water areas.

Determination of Pipe Sizes. The following pipe diameters (mm) are useful as a general guide: Supply pipe to cistern, 12 or 15; Flow and return, 18 to 35; Hot water to bath, 18; Hot and cold taps to lavatory basin and sink, 12 (branches off 18 mm or 28 mm main feed); Expansion pipe, 28; Cold feed pipe to cylinder, 28.

The factors governing the sizes of pipes are: the rate of flow required at the tap, the head of water available, the length of the pipe and number and type of

TABLE 36 RATES OF FLOW FOR LOSSES IN HEAD

Loss of Head (m per m run of pipe)	Flow in Litres per second for Copper and Plastic Pipes for the following pipe diameters (mm)					
	12	15	18	22	28	35
0.01	–	–	0.065	0.12	0.2	0.42
0.02	–	0.064	0.103	0.19	0.325	0.67
0.03	–	0.082	0.126	0.25	0.41	0.86
0.04	0.05	0.097	0.156	0.28	0.49	1
0.05	0.06	0.11	0.177	0.33	0.56	1.16
0.06	0.067	0.125	0.2	0.37	0.62	1.3
0.07	0.073	0.136	0.22	0.395	0.68	1.41
0.08	0.078	0.147	0.24	0.43	0.73	1.52
0.09	0.084	0.16	0.256	0.46	0.79	1.65
0.1	0.09	0.17	0.267	0.49	0.84	1.75
0.2	0.137	0.26	0.4	0.73	1.27	2.7
0.3	0.176	0.32	0.52	0.93	1.6	3.4
0.4	0.21	0.38	0.62	1.1	1.9	4
0.5	0.25	0.43	0.7	1.26	2.2	4.6
0.6	0.275	0.48	0.78	1.4	2.5	5
0.7	0.3	0.53	0.87	1.54	2.7	5.7
0.8	0.32	0.58	0.93	1.66	2.9	6
0.9	0.34	0.62	1	1.76	3.1	6.5
1	0.37	0.67	1.07	1.9	3.4	7

* Copper indirect cylinders are specified in B.S. 1566 in two grades (Grades 2 and 3) for maximum heads of 15 and 10 m respectively. Particulars of three types are:

BS Type Reference	Approx. Capacity (litres)	Diameter (mm)	Height (mm)
8	140	450	1 050
9	162	450	1 200
11	245	500	1 500

† The design of larger heating schemes is described in Vol. V.

* There is a special cylinder known as the "Primatic", manufactured by Range Boilers Ltd, Stalybridge, which contains a special calorifier which eliminates the need for the duplicate cistern required for the ordinary indirect cylinder.

fittings in it, and the frictional resistance to flow of the water in the pipe. The recommended rates of flow in litres/second for the various appliances are: W.C. cisterns, 0.1; both taps to the wash basin, 0.15; both bath taps, 0.3; 15 mm sink taps, 0.2. The head of water at the tap is the vertical distance from the base of the cistern to the tap, this allows a small margin of safety of about 0.6 m corresponding to depth of the cistern water. The loss of head of water due to friction in a pipe depends on its length, number of bends and trees, etc., its diameter and smoothness, and the speed of the water. The frictional resistance of copper pipes is less than that of steel ones. Table 36 gives the flow rate in litres/minute, in copper and plastic pipes of different diameters, for losses in head of metres per metre run of pipe. In Table 37 the resistance offered by various pipe fittings is expressed in equivalent lengths of straight pipe.

TABLE 37 RESISTANCE OF FITTINGS IN EQUIVALENT LENGTHS

Fitting	Resistance to Flow by Different Fittings expressed as Equivalent Lengths in metres of Straight Pipes for Various Pipe Diameters (mm)					
	12	15	18	22	28	35
Bend	0.21	0.27	0.32	0.42	0.6	0.75
Elbow	0.47	0.6	0.74	0.95	1.2	1.5
Tee	0.57	0.74	0.93	1.23	1.7	2.25
Reduction	0.11	0.13	0.2	0.23	0.33	0.44
Enlargement	0.18	0.27	0.34	0.51	0.94	0.95
Valve or Tap	2.7	4	5	7	9	12

Example at H, Fig. 99 *showing Method of ascertaining Pipe Sizes*. Measuring the actual pipe lengths from the drawing and using the pipe sizes from the guide above, we have the following information:

Pipe	Diameter (mm)	Actual Length (m)
ST and ZY	28	2.75 and 2.06
XW	15	1
YU	12	3.81
YX	22	1.83

Assume that the maximum demand will be when the bath and sink hot taps are in use together. Pipes have to be sized to give the maximum flow at the point where the head of water is least and this is usually at the bathroom wash basin (tap at W).

Find Bore of Pipes ST *and* ZW. Head of water at W = 1.6 m.
Length SW = ST + ZY + YX + XW = 7.64 m.
Equivalent length of fittings from Table 29:

	m
2 bends (28 mm) in ST	1.2
cistern outlet and cylinder inlet	1.27
cylinder outlet	0.94
28 mm branch tee above Z	1.7
28 mm bend	0.6
28 to 22 mm branch tee at Y	1.7
reduction at Y	0.23
22 to 15 mm branch tee at X	0.74
reduction at X	0.13
15 mm tap at W	4
Total	12.51

Therefore total length = 7.64 + 12.51 = 20.15 m

$$\text{Rate of loss of head} = \frac{1.6}{20.15} = 0.08 \text{ m/m.}$$

For this loss of head, from Table 28, the rates of flow in the various pipes are:

0.147 litres per second in a 15 mm pipe
0.43 litres per second in 22 mm pipe
0.73 litres per second in a 28 mm pipe.

So the pipe sizes are correct for: the 28 mm dia. lengths ST and ZY needing 0.5 as against 0.73 litres/second provided for bath and sink; the 22 mm dia. length YX needing 0.3 as against 0.43 litres/second provided for the bath; the 15 mm dia. length XW requires 0.15 litres/second and is provided with 0.147 litres/second, so this pipe is a little undersized – however, the arrangement is satisfactory because the bath would normally not be used at the same time as the wash basin where both appliances are in the same room. If they are in separate rooms a larger pipe would be needed to serve the basin.

Find Bore of Pipe YU. From the above, the loss of head in length ZY = 0.08 m/m.

Length of ZY = 2.06 m.

Equivalent length of fittings from Table 36

28 mm tee = 1.7
28 mm bend = 0.6
Total 2.3 m

Total length = 2.06 + 2.3 = 4.36 m.

Head used up in ZY = 4.36 x 0.08 = 0.35 m.

By measurement from the drawing, the head at U = 4.27 m, so head to be used up in friction in YU = 4.27 − 0.35 = 3.92 m.

Length of YU = 3.81 m.

Equivalent length of fittings from Table 37:

reducer at Y	= 0.33
two 12 mm bends	= 0.42
12 mm tap	= 2.7
	3.45 m

Therefore total length of YU = 3.81 + 3.45 = 7.26 m.

$$\text{Rate of loss of head} = \frac{3.92}{7.26} = 0.54 \text{ m/m.}$$

From Table 28, for this loss of head a 12 mm pipe delivers 0.26 litres/second and as this is 0.06 litres above the requirement for the tap at U then a 12 mm pipe is satisfactory.

A similar calculation will show that the bath tap must be served by a 22 mm tap.

Taps. These are of two types, *(a) bib taps*, which deliver water to the open, and *(b) stop taps* or *stop valves*, which are used to control the flow of water within a pipe.

(a) Bib Taps are of two kinds, pillar taps and side entry taps; the former are fixed to the appliance, the water rising from a connection below. Side entry taps are screwed to the wall above the appliance and the water delivers at right angles to the back of the tap. Apart from these distinctions, their construction and operation are similar.

A 12 or 15 mm dia. chromium-plated brass pillar tap is shown at N, Fig. 99. It is provided with a threaded tail piece for the pipe connection by means of a compression joint. The tap is bedded in putty and fixed with a lead washer and flanged nut to the basin. The spout is part of the body of the tap, the body being threaded to receive the head. A spindle screws inside the head, the bottom of the spindle being recessed to contain the top of the jumper, the latter has a washer bolted to it which bears on to the seating. The top of the spindle is grooved to provide a key for the grub screw which fixes the shroud, the latter incorporates projecting finger grips and a plastic disc with the letter H or C is fitted in the top. The inner portion of the shroud fits over the spindle and the contacting surfaces are serrated so that by turning the shroud, the spindle is rotated. The detail shows the tap in the off position, an anti-clockwise motion of the shroud turns the lower threaded portion of the spindle in the head; this releases the jumper, admitting water to the body. The escape of water into the shroud is prevented by the gland stuffing which screws into the top of the head and bears on to a packing.

Another type of pillar tap* is shown at K, Fig. 99. This is a spray† mixing tap, where the water is discharged as a spray and not as a jet like the one at N. Spray taps are recommended for public buildings, offices, schools, etc., in these places they have the advantage over the previous type in giving a 50 per cent saving in fuel and water. With a spray tap, the hands are washed directly under the spray and not in a pool in the basin, hence the basin plug and overflow can be omitted. In any case, only one tap per basin is needed, and the time spent in filling the basin is saved. In the example shown, both hot and cold tails of 6 mm dia. are provided and these are soldered into the body of the tap, they connect to the 12 mm dia. feed pipes via a reducing coupling of the compression type. The body has two water ways, a mixing chamber and the delivery tube; a piston fits into the hot water way and can be raised and lowered by the control knob or shroud which has depressions for finger grips. The detail shows the tap closed with the piston at its lowest point; the ring seal on the bottom of the piston prevents egress of hot water, and the top seal on the piston is tight on the seating so that cold water cannot pass down round the piston to the mixing chamber. An anti-clockwise motion of the knob raises the top seal so as to admit cold water to the mixing chamber; simultaneously, the bottom ring seal rises an equal amount, but this moves in a cylinder and so hot water is not yet released. Further turning of the knob lifts the ring seal into the enlarged part of the cylinder allowing hot water to be discharged in increasing amount, and there is a corresponding reduction in cold water flow as the piston boss approaches the underside of the cold water seating. This arrangement provides a variable water temperature with the quantity remaining constant.

(b) Stop Tap or Valve‡ (see H and J, Fig. 99). A stop valve is fitted into the pipe run and is used to turn off the supply; its construction is similar to the pillar tap described above except that the water is not discharged into the open.

Drain Cock and Air Cock (see H and J, Fig. 99). These have been mentioned on pp. 228 and 230. The *drain cock* (or draw-off tap) is used to empty a pipe, it comprises a tee junction fitted into the pipe run. The branch of the tee is closed by a small plug which can be unscrewed to allow the escape of water; the outside

* Manufactured by Walker, Crosweller and Co. Ltd., by whom it was designed in conjunction with the B.R.E. The tap must connect to supplies of equal pressure.

† Another type of this is the ordinary spray tap with one supply at the correct temperature (say 40° C). The supply may be from a storage tank at the required temperature or from having passed through a mixing valve used to serve a range of spray taps.

‡ Another type of control fitting capable of turning off the supply is the *stop cock* which has a plug with a handle. The plug passes through the water way and so cuts off the supply; it has a hole in it so that water will pass on turning the handle at right angles. The stop cock is a crude device because it can turn off the water too quickly, this causes a sudden increase of pressure which may break the pipe joints, many authorities prohibit their use. The stop *valve* has a superior mechanism as described and is a preferable fitting.

of the branch is serrated so that a hose pipe can be connected. The *air cock* is of similar construction and permits the escape of air from local high points in the installation such as radiators. Trapped air in radiators cannot reach the expansion pipe; if it were allowed to accumulate, the flow of water in the radiator would eventually cease.

Valves. These are of three types:* stop valve or stop tap described above, safety valve and ball valve.

A *safety valve* is a guard to prevent boiler explosions which may occur if the circulation pipes become frozen or blocked by hardness deposits; such blockages cause the accumulation of steam which can lead to serious explosions. The spring-loaded safety valve is a reliable fitting which can be adjusted so that it is released when the pressure rises to just above normal. It should be fitted to the top of the boiler or in the flow pipe to the boiler. Some authorities prefer another type – the "dead-weight" pattern.

The *ball valve* is used to give automatic control of the admission of water to a cold water storage cistern or the flushing cistern of a W.C., it is fitted at a high-level in the appliance. One type of ball valve is the Kingley B.R.E. valve† detailed at J, Fig. 100, and used in the storage cisterns shown at H and J, Fig. 99. It has a threaded shank for fixing with back nuts and lead washers to the wall of the tank, and for the attachment of the supply pipe via a compression fitting. The water passes through a nylon nozzle which is screwed into the brass body of the valve; the nozzle is specially shaped so as to minimize the noise from the disturbed water. The outlet from the nozzle is closed and opened by the rubber diaphragm which is actuated by a plunger, the latter acts like a piston in the end plate which is secured to the body by the threaded cap plate. The plunger can be pushed inwards by the lever arm which is hinged to the end plate. At the outer end of the brass lever arm a plastic ball float is fitted, the adjustment screw enables the float to be placed at the correct level. The operation of the valve is self-explanatory, the admission of water being controlled by its own level. The water enters the tank via a submerged vertical pipe to reduce noise, small holes near the top of this pipe prevent water being siphoned back through the nozzle. This make of valve operates more silently than any other kind, and the only moving part in contact with water is the diaphragm.

Another type of ball valve is the "Portsmouth" pattern which has a lever arm and float as above. The other end of the arm is cranked up to fit inside a slot with a horizontal sliding piston, the arm pivots on a pin below the piston. As the water level rises, the cranked arm pushes the piston sideways until contact is made between the valve seating (through which water passes) and the rubber washer set in the end of the piston; on contact being made, the supply ceases. This type of valve is incorporated in the W.C. cistern at D, Fig. 100.

* Mixing valves and other types are described in Vol. V.

† Manufactured by the King's Langley Engineering Co. Ltd., and designed by them in collaboration with the B.R.E.

SANITARY APPLIANCES*

The four main sanitary appliances† are bath, wash basin, sink, and water closet.

Baths (see O, P and Q, Fig. 99). These are made in many sizes, typical rectangular plan baths vary from 1 500 mm by 600 mm by 400 mm high to 2 000 mm by 820 mm by 500 mm high, the one illustrated being of intermediate size; circular and triangular (or corner-fitting) shapes are also made. They are provided with tap holes, plug and chain; also overflow and waste connections which are usually coupled together as shown (see p. 241) for waste collection. The taps may be positioned as shown or at one corner or along one side.

Baths are made in the following materials: cast iron to B.S. 1189; acrylic plastic to B.S. 4305; glass reinforced plastic (g.r.p.) and vitreous enamelled sheet steel to B.S. 1390. The coordinating sizes are 1 700 mm by 700 mm, heights rising in 50 mm multiples – 350 mm being common (finished sizes are about 4 mm less). Rectangular baths are described as left-hand or right-hand. A left-hand bath is one which when looking at it from the "approach" side has the taps and waste outlet on the left.

Manufacture of Cast Iron Baths. Firstly, a timber pattern block replica of the bath is made, this is covered with sheet lead and from it cast iron production patterns are made; these patterns are in two halves representing the inside and outside of the bath. Each is filled in turn with semi-synthetic sand by a *speed slinger*, this throws the sand at high velocity (in effect, ramming) into the halves. Thus, two sand moulds are formed for the inner and outer surfaces, these are then brought together for the molten metal to be poured into the space (6 to 9 mm) between them. Twin ladles are used to pour the iron down into each side of the mould simultaneously. After a 20 min. cooling period, the top part of the moulding and the bottom part containing the casting are placed on the "knock-out". This is a vibrating table which loosens the sand from the moulding box and the casting, the sand falls on to a conveyor belt and travels to the reconditioning plant.

The bath casting is then sand blasted, dressed and cleaned and is now ready for the enamelling process. To bond the enamel to the casting, it is first sprayed with a ground coat and then placed in the bath furnace where it is brought to red heat. Porcelain enamel powder is now applied to the red-hot casting from a duster (a sieve which is pneumatically vibrated), and the bath is returned to the furnace for the powder to fuse. In all, two or three powder coatings are given, the bath being held in a cradle operated by foot pedals, this allows it to be swung in any desired position for the skilled operation of dusting. After cooling, the bath is inspected, and a protective layer of paint is given to the outside. It is sent out from the works with the adjustable feet, chromium-plated outlet and overflow grating separate for these to be fixed on site.

Manufacture of Plastic Baths. These are made of glass reinforced plastic; they are of laminated construction comprising about 60 per cent glass fibre reinforcement and about 40 per cent resin in which a hardener is incorporated. The resin is sprayed onto a mould, covered with a mat of glass fibre, sprayed again and rolled or pressed. Alternatively, roving (a reel of strands of glass fibre) is wound into a spray gun to which the resin and

* An introduction to these has been given in Chap. II on Drainage in Vol. II.

† Others are, the drinking fountain, see p. 242 and H, Fig. 102; the urinal, see p. 241 and A and B, Fig. 102; and the bidet which is similar to the W.C. pedestal but being connected to both hot and cold water supplies to provide an ascending spray of water.

hardener is also fed. The spray gun incorporates a chopper which cuts the fibre into short strands with the result that the three materials are blown onto the mould.

Wash basins (M and L, Fig. 99). These are made of g.r.p. or more generally from one of the ceramic materials, *i.e.*: glazed earthenware, glazed fireclay and vitreous china. The two latter are the more costly, having superior wearing qualities. Sizes and shapes vary considerably, they are often rectangular from 460 mm by 280 mm to 700 mm by 500 mm, the one at M‡, made of vitreous china, is a reasonable size for a bathroom. It is 12 mm thick at the bowl, has two tap holes and overflow which connects to the waste outlet (see also E, Fig. 102). In a well designed wash-basin, the taps are placed near to the back corners so that they are clear of the user's head as he bends over the bowl; an adequate rim is provided to prevent spillage over the sides and front. The basin at L* is of glazed fireclay and specially designed for use with the spray tap (see p. 234); hence, the plug, chain and overflow are superfluous and only one tap is needed. Basins are supported on chromium-plated or porcelain-enamelled brackets as at M, or on a ceramic pedestal, or on a corbel block which is integral with the basin and is built into the wall.

B.S. 1188 deals with fireclay and vitreous china wash basins of sizes 635 mm by 457 mm and 559 mm by 406 mm.

Manufacture of Vitreous China Basins. The basin is cast from a mould prepared from a model, mould and model being of plaster of Paris. The raw materials for the basin are of small particle size and are mixed with water in a *blunger* (a tank having rotating blades to agitate the contents) and the liquid is pumped up to and passed through a filter press. This is a horizontal press of rectangular trays containing nylon sieves which produce slabs of filter pressed clay. This clay is again blunged after water, silicate of soda and soda ash have been added. The liquid called slip is pumped up a rising main and along pipes to overhead feed points situated at intervals over the benches in the casting shed. The mould† consists of an inner block or drum and an outer case, together with plaster plugs at the outlet. The liquid slip is poured through funnels into the cavity between the parts of the mould. After allowing sufficient time for the slip to build up to the required thickness, the excess slip is drained off and the mould opened. This is known as a *drain cast* process, and the action in the mould is one of drying out, caused by the plaster drawing moisture from the slip until a sufficient residue thickness is obtained. The casting is then placed in a plaster seat and after finishing (removal of blemishes and touching up), is allowed to dry.

The casting is then glazed by spraying on the liquid glaze which is a mixture of Cornish stone, whiting, flint, tin, etc. Finally, the basin is placed in a gas-fired kiln where it is gradually subjected to a maximum temperature of 1 200° C.

Sinks. These are made of the same materials as basins (except vitreous china) and also of stainless steel, g.r.p. and vitreous enamelled steel. They are of two types: the Belfast pattern with outlet and overflow at one end, the taps being the side entry type fixed to the wall; and the shelf pattern which has a 75 to 100 mm wide shelf along the side next to the wall for connection of the pillar taps, the outlet and overflow are centrally placed along the shelf side. Sizes vary from 460 mm by 380 mm by 200 mm to 1 200 mm by 610 mm by 300 mm in thicknesses from 38 to 50 mm for the ceramic type; these lengths may be increased by the incorporation of a draining board. The ceramic sinks are manufactured by a similar method to that described for china basins, those of fireclay and earthenware are *engobed* (brushed or sprayed with a liquid, to give a white finish†, which consists of china clay, felspar and certain fluxes) before being glazed. With some clays, an additional firing (known as biscuit firing) in the kiln precedes the glazing. Coloured ceramic appliances are made by incorporating the oxides of certain ores in the glaze.

Stainless steel sinks are made from the sheet metal which is machine pressed into shape, the vitreous enamelled types are similarly made from plain strip steel which is sprayed with the enamel liquid and then fired at a high temperature.

Water Closets. These are made from the ceramic materials given above in many patterns, their manufacture is similar to that described for wash-basins, they are subdivided into two types: (*a*) the wash-down pedestal, and (*b*) the siphonic pedestal, each in a suite comprising a flushing cistern* and pedestal pan. The cistern contains 9, 12 or 13.6 litres of flushing water delivered by a ball valve (see p. 235). The most popular arrangement is the "low down suite"¶ like that at D, E and F, Fig. 100, where cistern and pan are adjacent; in another, more compact type (the close-coupled suite), the flush pipe is omitted and the cistern sits directly on the pan; in some examples, instead of resting on the floor, the pan is provided with a corbel piece at the back for building into the wall.

The cistern shown at D‡ has a 13.6 litre capacity and is made of vitreous china, it rests on chromium-plated brackets and is fixed back to the wall near the top by brass screws and washers. There is a ball valve and a china siphon screwed to the cistern at the flushing pipe joint. On depressing the chromium-plated handle, the connecting link raises a rod which lifts the attached blade and diaphragm washer inside the siphon. This lifts water over the weir into the left-hand side of the siphon and produces the siphonic action§ for emptying the main body of water down the 38 mm dia. flush pipe. The 12 mm dia. inlet and 18 mm dia. overflow can be placed in alternative positions as shown. This cistern conforms to B.S. 1125, and having a valveless siphon, is of the type demanded

‡ Manufactured by Armitage Shanks & Co. Ltd.

* Manufactured by Adamsez Ltd.

† The mould (case and drum) is made from a model of reverse shape; the model is well coated with shellac to prevent the plaster of Paris (which is poured into it to form either the case or the drum) from sticking to the model.

† Vitreous china is white throughout and so does not need to be engobed.

* In certain areas, where a 9 litre cistern is the maximum size allowed, a siphonic pedestal is most desirable. A few authorities permit the use of a flushing valve which takes the place of the cistern. In this arrangement, the valve is hand operated for the flush, it is inserted in a feed pipe from a separate cistern adjacent to the main storage cistern and some authorities require it to be fed through a meter.

¶ A high level suite is indicated at E, Fig. 36, Vol. II.

‡ Manufactured by Armitage Shanks & Co., Ltd.

§ This siphonic action relates to the emptying of the *cistern* and should not be confused with the secondary flushing action of the siphonic type of *pedestal* (see (*b*), p. 238).

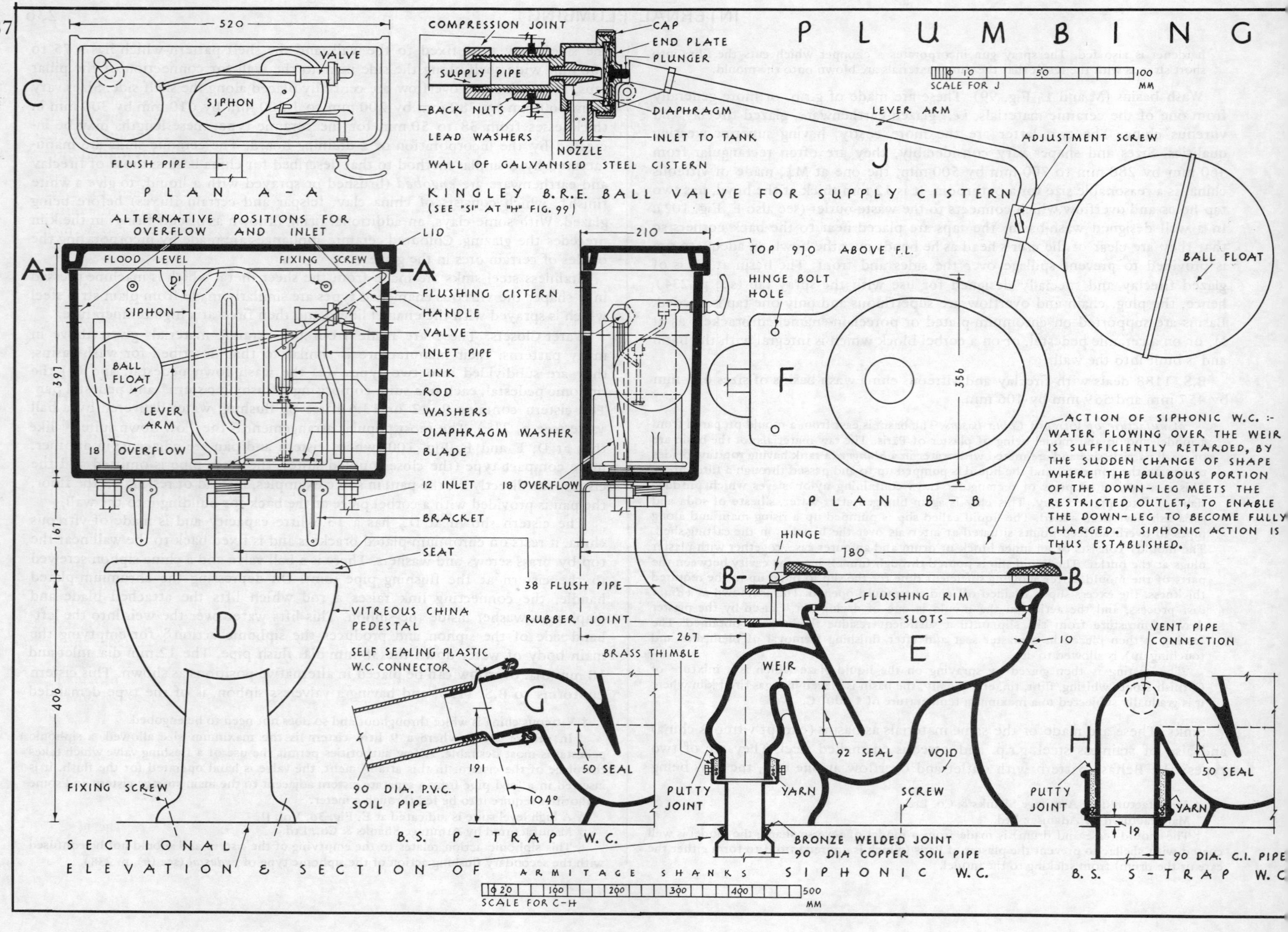

P L U M B I N G

C

520

COMPRESSION JOINT

CAP

END PLATE

PLUNGER

VALVE

SUPPLY PIPE

SIPHON

BACK NUTS

DIAPHRAGM

LEAD WASHERS

INLET TO TANK

NOZZLE

FLUSH PIPE

WALL OF GALVANIZED STEEL CISTERN

SCALE FOR J 0 10 50 100 MM

LEVER ARM

ADJUSTMENT SCREW

J

P L A N A - A

KINGLEY B.R.E. BALL VALVE FOR SUPPLY CISTERN

(SEE "S" AT "H" FIG. 99)

ALTERNATIVE POSITIONS FOR OVERFLOW AND INLET

LID

210

TOP 970 ABOVE F.L.

BALL FLOAT

A-

FLOOD LEVEL

FIXING SCREW

-A

D

HINGE BOLT HOLE

FLUSHING CISTERN

SIPHON

HANDLE

VALVE

INLET PIPE

LINK

ROD

WASHERS

DIAPHRAGM WASHER

BLADE

391

BALL FLOAT

LEVER ARM

18 OVERFLOW

12 INLET

18 OVERFLOW

F

356

ACTION OF SIPHONIC W.C. :- WATER FLOWING OVER THE WEIR IS SUFFICIENTLY RETARDED, BY THE SUDDEN CHANGE OF SHAPE WHERE THE BULBOUS PORTION OF THE DOWN-LEG MEETS THE RESTRICTED OUTLET, TO ENABLE THE DOWN-LEG TO BECOME FULLY CHARGED. SIPHONIC ACTION IS THUS ESTABLISHED.

161

BRACKET

P L A N B B

HINGE

180

SEAT

B-

-B

38 FLUSH PIPE

FLUSHING RIM

VITREOUS CHINA PEDESTAL

RUBBER JOINT

SLOTS

D

267

10

VENT PIPE CONNECTION

BRASS THIMBLE

E

SELF SEALING PLASTIC W.C. CONNECTOR

WEIR

406

G

92 SEAL

VOID

H

50 SEAL

50 SEAL

FIXING SCREW

191

90 DIA. P.V.C. SOIL PIPE

104°

PUTTY JOINT

YARN

SCREW

PUTTY JOINT

YARN

19

B.S. P-TRAP W.C.

BRONZE WELDED JOINT

90 DIA COPPER SOIL PIPE

90 DIA. C.I. PIPE

SECTIONAL ELEVATION & SECTION OF ARMITAGE SHANKS

SIPHONIC W.C.

B.S. S-TRAP W.C

0 20 100 200 300 400 500 MM

SCALE FOR C-H

FIGURE 100

by virtually every water undertaking in England and Wales. The requirements lay down that the internal weir at the top of the siphon shall be higher¶ than the flood or spill-over level of the cistern. This flood level must be 64 mm above the water level, and the overflow point must be 25 mm above the water level. Due to the B.S. requirements, the crown or extreme top of the siphon is bound to project considerably above the flood level of the cistern – which must therefore be made with a very deep cover or, as shown, to make the shell of the cistern slightly deeper than is necessary and by forming a cut-out (see D′ at D) in the back it is possible to have a shallow and much neater cover.

Pans are fixed to the floor by two or four brass screws and lead washers; in order to deaden the noise from the pan, the void shown at E can be packed with a cement and sawdust mortar before fixing. Pans are fitted with a plastic seat (with or without lid) fixed by chromium-plated bolts incorporating the hinge.

B.S. 1213 establishes certain main dimensions of the pan, *e.g.*, top of rim to floor level is 406 mm, outlet positions as described below, front of flushing rim to back of S-trap outlet varies from 520 mm to 635 mm. These measurements, and those giving the height of the top of the cistern above floor level, and the projection of the rim from the wall, are all important in determining the size of the W.C. compartment, window sill level, and position of the soil pipe connection. The lowest cistern height is 760 mm* for the close-coupled suite, giving a projection of 813 mm.* In the example at E and D, Fig. 100, these two dimensions are 970 mm and 780 mm respectively. If the flush pipe were lengthened vertically by 280 mm,* the cistern top would be raised by the same amount and this would reduce the projection by 50 mm* (for the seat would now fold back to the pipe).

As well as being made from a non-porous, smooth, well glazed material, a W.C. should, (i) be free from corners which would harbour dirt, (ii) have a minimum depth of seal of 50 mm, (iii) be well shaped and curved towards the outlet, (iv) hold sufficient water to submerge the deposit, and (v) have a flushing rim that efficiently washes the inside of the pan. The latter is accomplished by having small holes at about 25 mm intervals round the underside of the rim, also by slots about 50 mm long beneath the rim at front and rear (see E, Fig. 100).

(*a*) *Wash-down Pedestal*. This, the simpler of the two types, is shown at E, in Fig. 36, Vol. II; it is also partly shown at the outlets at G and H, Fig. 100 in this volume. Water from the flush pipe travels round the flushing rim and out through small holes into the pan; a 50 mm water seal is provided. Outlets from the pan are either P-trap, or S-trap, the former is drawn at G and shows the centre of the 90 mm dia. outlet being 191 mm above floor level at the angle shown.‡ This example shows the connection made to a.p.v.c. soil branch via a self-sealing W.C. connector which has a sealing ring where it fits over the W.C. outlet and two more sealing rings (not shown) which rest between the projecting fins on the outside of the connector at the lower end. The detail at H is of an S-trap outlet pan where the outlet finishes 19 mm above floor level and is jointed direct to a cast iron soil pipe with a yarn and putty† joint.

Both types of outlet can be provided with a short projecting arm for a vent pipe connection (see p. 240) as at H. In the details G and H shown, the outlets are straight on the main axis of the pan; these pan outlets can also be made having the discharge at right angles to the axis, these are known as side outlets (P or S), either left or right-hand to suite the soil pipe position.

(*b*) *Siphonic Pedestals*. These are of a more elaborate construction at the outlet than the simple wash-down type, they give a more efficient emptying of the pan due to the combined siphonic and washing-down actions which produce an improved discharge. There are two types of siphonic pan, one has a special shaped outlet and the other has a double trap. An example of the former is drawn at D, E and F*, Fig. 100; this has a bulbous portion at the outgo which is connected to a brass thimble of restricted diameter. When water passes over the weir, the flow is retarded at the bulbous part and the whole of the down leg becomes charged with water, this starts the siphonic action which empties the pan. The restricted diameter thimble is an essential feature in the design; it has three brass screws to locate it centrally and the joint is of putty and yarn as before. The copper soil branch has a flared end formed in it; this is done by cutting four diamond-shaped pieces out of the sides of the end of the pipe (to reduce its diameter). Bronze welding seals these cuts and makes the joint to the thimble. Alternatively, a reducing socket can be used.

In the second type of siphonic pan a second trap is provided and situated beyond the first one, this increases the bulk of the appliance but provides for thorough flushing by siphonage and washing-down effect.

Siphonic pans must *always* be connected to a soil pipe which is open to the atmosphere at the top. Alternatively a vent pipe must be taken from the soil branch pipe (see p. 240).

Provision of Sanitary Appliances. The numbers of these to be provided in certain buildings is laid down in the Washing Facilities Regulations 1964 for wash basins and in the Sanitary Conveniences Regulations 1964 for W.C.s and urinals. The Regulations form Statutory Instruments No. 965 and 966 respectively; they relate to offices, shops and railway premises and form a useful guide for other buildings as shown in the Table which follows:

¶ The reason why water by-laws demand that the internal weir at the top of the siphon be higher than the spill-over level of the cistern is to ensure that in the event of a choked overflow and defective ball valve, the siphon itself would not work as an overflow in allowing water to run to waste into the *pan*; the provision of the cut-out, in such circumstances, ensures that the water runs to waste on to the *floor*, necessitating the remedying of the defects and conservation of water.

* Approximate dimensions, the manufacturer's catalogue normally provides this information.

‡ Instead of being angled the outlet can be horizontal at the same level.

† The 1 : 3 cement and sand joint (as used for stoneware drains – Chap. II, Vol. II) is sometimes used, but the putty joint is more flexible, allowing for some settlement of the building, and so prevents breakage at the pan outlet. The use of putty also means that replacement is more easily made.

* The "Acra" siphonic suite by Armitage Shanks & Co. Ltd.

For Males and Females		For Females and for Males where Urinals are not Provided	For Males where Urinals are Provided		
No. of Persons	No. of Washbasins	No. of W.C.s	No. of Persons	No. of W.C.s	No. of Urinals
1–15	1	1	1–15	1	1
16–30	2	2	16–20	1	1
31–50	3	3	21–30	2	1
51–75	4	4	31–45	2	2
76–100	5	5	46–60	3	2
			61–75	3	3
			76–90	4	3
			91–100	4	4

SOIL AND WASTE INSTALLATIONS

The old way of providing pipe-work for the carrying of soil and waste water from a house is shown in diagrammatic form at A, Fig. 101, where all the pipes are on the outside. The disadvantages of this are that the pipes detract from the appearance of the house and may freeze up during winter. This has now been recognized by the Building Regulations which state that no soil or waste pipe shall be placed *outside* a building if it has more than 3 storeys (except that a waste pipe from an appliance at or near ground level may be placed outside buildings of any height). Apart from ground level waste pipes it is good practice to put all other pipes inside regardless of the number of storeys.

The most economical way of conducting soil and waste water from a house is by means of the single-stack system shown at B, Fig. 101, where all the pipe-work other than that for rainwater is inside the building. It will be observed at B that there is only one main pipe and that the hopper head and the gully are omitted; as a result of these two omissions† no objections remain to the placing of the installation inside. As well as serving as collection points for pipes, both a hopper and a gully are sure safeguards against the admission of drain air into the building; they must be replaced by equal safeguards if the danger of self-siphonage and other effects mentioned below are to be avoided. The precautions that have to be taken are given below; they include the introduction of waste traps having a 75 mm deep water seal, or alternatively the use of such traps* with a network of anti-siphonage pipes (or vent pipes, see below) to maintain the atmospheric pressure in the branch pipes and minimize the reduction of the seals. Loss of seal can happen in several ways, and the pipe-work has to be designed so that at least 25 mm of seal (corresponding to a negative pressure in the pipe of 375 N/m^2) is retained at each appliance and the admission of drain air is prevented.

The effects ¶ that have to be considered in achieving an adequate standard are as follows: (*a*) self-siphonage, (*b*) induced-siphonage, and (*c*) back pressure.

(a) **Self-siphonage.** This can happen when the discharge from an appliance sucks part of its own seal away. It occurs when the branch pipe is running full bore at the outfall end, being only partly filled between this point and the trap, some of the seal water is thus siphoned away; as the solid core of water slows down, the remaining suction draws the core back towards the trap. Providing a P-trap and not an S-trap is used and the solid core returns sufficiently near to it, the trap will be partially refilled when the branch gradient is not too steep. This action is confined mainly to small bore pipes, especially wash basins and small sinks; it is controlled by giving the correct fall to the particular length of pipe as described in the single stack system given below. It does not happen in bath wastes unless, perhaps, they are over 1.8 m long (in any case the final slow trickle of water from these appliances will refill the trap); as the W.C. should always be placed near to the soil stack, self-siphonage of this appliance is a rarity.

(b) **Induced-siphonage.** This is the effect of the discharge from one appliance siphoning off part of the seal in another. When the stack is temporarily and partially filled by a short column of water from a discharge from above and this passes a branch junction, the branch trap is subject to induced-siphonage. The effect of this filling of the stack or pipe is to reduce the pressure below atmospheric level in varying degree down its length causing loss of seal in other appliances. W.C.s are mainly responsible for this phenomenon, particularly when the junction is not curved as at K′, K, Fig. 102. The adoption of 75 mm seal traps for flats up to five storeys, and these traps plus anti-siphonage pipes (or a 150 mm stack up to ten storeys) for taller buildings limit the effects of induced-siphonage. Ground floor appliances in blocks above five storeys high may be vulnerable to the effect, and for this reason are preferably connected to the drain at an inspection chamber.

(c) **Back Pressure.** This happens when the pressure in the pipes exceeds the atmospheric level, it may be sufficiently strong to cause the admission of drain air to the room. It develops near the bottom of a partially filled stack, particularly when the common drain to which several stacks connect is running fairly full and is unable to accommodate the air that is drawn down with the discharge. In the event of the flow from a branch being unable to enter the stack and overcome the resistance of the liquid already there, the ensuing pressure can force the flow back along the branch so that it enters the appliance along with drain air. Further, the returning flow can make the U-shaped column of trap water move up and down, this results in a loss of seal after cessation of the movement. Back pressure can also develop due to the excessive use of detergents, the froth that these produce impedes the flow at the bottom of the stack; this is more evident in two-pipe systems where small diameter main waste pipes are used, the use of a pipe not less than 75 mm dia. for the bottom length of the waste pipe will reduce this effect. In single-stack systems, the discharge of W.C.s helps to remove the froth. The use

† Hopper heads cannot be used internally because of the offensive smell produced. Back inlet gullies, where the waste pipe is connected to the gully by a sealed joint have been used internally, but this construction is sub-standard.

*B.S. 5572 specifies some design criteria for soil and waste pipes above ground. It permits the use of 38 mm seal traps when vent pipes are used. However, many local authorities require the deeper traps even though the pipes are vented. The extra cost is small and the practice is a sound one.

¶ In addition to the three effects given, there is another smaller one. This is the loss of trap seal due to evaporation, which amounts to about 12 mm per month. This can only be prevented by the addition of water and could not be objectionable unless premises were left unoccupied for several months.

of an external gully for the ground floor sink is often advocated to overcome this nuisance, the branch drain from the gully acts as a relief pipe for the foam. Such a gully also serves as a useful warning device in the event of flooding occurring due to a blockage in the drain; the gulley allows flooding to occur *outside* the building – the absence of it would cause flooding inside the building at the lowest connected appliances. Back pressure is limited by the adoption of the measures given in (*b*) above, it is of greater importance in installations serving the larger flows from buildings above twelve storeys high.

For flats and other multi-storey buildings erected between the two world wars, the four systems of sanitation plumbing were: (1) the fully-vented two-pipe system, which is now obsolete, (2) the modified two-pipe system with the soil branches only vented, (3) the fully vented one-pipe system, and (4) the modified one-pipe system, with the soil branches only vented.

For a rectangular block of flats up to five-storeys in height, having a compact layout of appliances, methods (2), (3) and (4) have been replaced by (5) the more economical 100 mm dia. single-stack system. For taller flats the dia. size of the single-stack is increased thus: In the case of twelve- and twenty-five-storey blocks to 125 and 150 mm dia. respectively. Thus for these three-storey heights vent pipes are omitted entirely if the appropriate soil-stack dia. is chosen. Instead of using a larger dia. soil-stack, the single-stack plus vent-stack system (method (6)) which is like method (5) plus a vent-stack that is connected to the soil-stack at each floor, can be used.

In the planning of such buildings, it is the usual practice to have the same number of appliances in the same position on each floor so that the soil and waste collections can be concentrated in a main sanitation pipe set in a vertical duct. Each flat would have a W.C., wash basin, bath and sink connected to a single stack in the duct* (see C and D, Fig. 102). For example, the typical arrangement for a five-storey flat block having six flats per floor would be to have six ducts each serving a tier of five flats. Alternatively the number of ducts could be halved if two flats on *each* floor deliver to the same duct; *i.e.*, each stack serves two sets of appliances at each floor – see Table 40.

Consideration is now given to the various systems of carrying soil and waste water in multi-storey buildings. The systems are shown in diagrammatic form in Fig. 101. Note that ground floor appliances may deliver to an inspection chamber (see (*b*) and (*c*) above) instead of to the main sanitation pipes; and that all pipes terminate above the roof as vent pipes. Note that all pipes emerging from the roof should not be placed near to the corners or parapets of buildings for the suction effects, which can impair water seals, are greater there than at the centre of the roof.

(1) The Fully Vented Two-pipe System (see C). This was once widely used for tall buildings but has now been replaced by one or other of the systems below.

Briefly, the system has two main vertical pipes, *a main waste pipe* (M.W.P.) discharging over a gully and *a main soil pipe* (M.S.P.) connected direct to the drain, both being open to the air above eaves level. From the wash-basin, bath and sink, *branch waste pipes* (B.W.P.s) with 38 mm seals (see footnote *, p. 239) connect direct to the M.W.P. and a *branch soil pipe* (B.S.P.) is taken from the W.C. to the M.S.P. In order to limit the effects, given above, that may cause loss of seal, and to maintain atmospheric pressure in the branches, these are all fitted with an *anti-siphonage pipe* (also known as a *vent pipe*) placed within 75 mm and 300 mm from the seals. The usual size for the wash-basin waste is 32 mm dia. and 40 mm dia. for the sink and bath wastes; a *branch waste vent pipe* (B.W.V.P.) normally of the same size as the waste pipe to which it is connected joins a common *main waste vent pipe* (M.W.V.P.) which may be 40 mm or 50 mm dia. A 50 mm dia. *branch soil vent pipe* (B.S.V.P.) is taken from each W.C. branch and joined to a *main soil vent pipe* (M.S.V.P.) of 50 mm dia. Both the main vent pipes are open to the atmosphere at the top, and the M.S.V.P. joins the M.S.P. between 230 and 600 mm below the lowest branch connection. To save piping, the main vent pipes can join the M.S.P. and the M.W.P. at a point not less than 900 mm above the highest appliance. There are thus four main pipes with branches and anti-siphonage pipes resulting in an elaborate and costly arrangement.

(2) The Modified Two-pipe System (see D) with soil pipe only vented. A M.S.P. and a M.W.P. are used as (1), but only the W.C. branches have anti-siphonage pipes. Instead of having vent pipes to the bath, basin and sink, these appliances are fitted with 75 mm deep seal traps, the M.W.P. thus becomes a main waste stack (M.W.S.). In comparison with the system (1), there is thus the saving of the M.W.V.P. and its vent branches and the introduction of the M.W.S. which is vented at the top and leads directly to the drain below without the use of a gully. The waste pipes must be designed as described in (5) below.

This arrangement could be appropriate when a long branch soil pipe is needed to serve a W.C. some distance away from the other appliances; in other, more normal circumstances, it has been replaced by one or other of the following.

(3) The Fully Vented One-pipe System (see E). This consists of a common main sanitation pipe for both soil and waste (M.S.W.P.) and a common main vent pipe (M.V.P.) for the vent branches from all appliances; waste traps are the 75 mm seal variety. Both main pipes are open to the atmosphere at the top, there are no hoppers or gullies and so an internal arrangement of pipe-work is

* As well as housing the stack pipe, the duct may also be used for the incoming water and gas supply pipes, the electricity and telephone cables and for the meters. In some areas, the local supply Boards require the gas and electricity services to be in separate compartments in the duct. The barrel of all pipes should be 50 mm clear of the walls to facilitate joint making. The minimum size for a duct containing all the services is about 750 mm by 610 mm to allow space for the fitters. It should be accessible at each floor level for inspection and insertion of the stack which may be in two-storey lengths. It should not be near the pantry unless the stack is lagged to prevent transmission of heat from discharged hot water.

As ducts provide a ready channel for the passage of sound from one flat to another, they should not be placed next to living quarters; duct doors should be tight fitting with sealed edges.

As a rule, the duct floor, or a large part of it cannot be laid until the pipe-work has been completed. The simplest type of floor construction is to use a 100 mm thick lightly reinforced slab resting on a 50 mm wide corbelled ledge formed in the duct wall; a metal tray with holes for the pipes being used as shuttering. A sleeve is formed for each pipe out of a 100 mm wide strip of metal, this is sufficiently long so that when it is bent round the pipe it forms a 15 mm wide annular space. The strip acts as vertical shuttering and the space between pipe and concrete can be eventually packed with asbestos rope or other fireproof insulation. Duct side walls should be of $\frac{1}{2}$ brick thick or concrete block; if the duct is on a party wall, the latter should be of 1 brick thickness or equivalent.

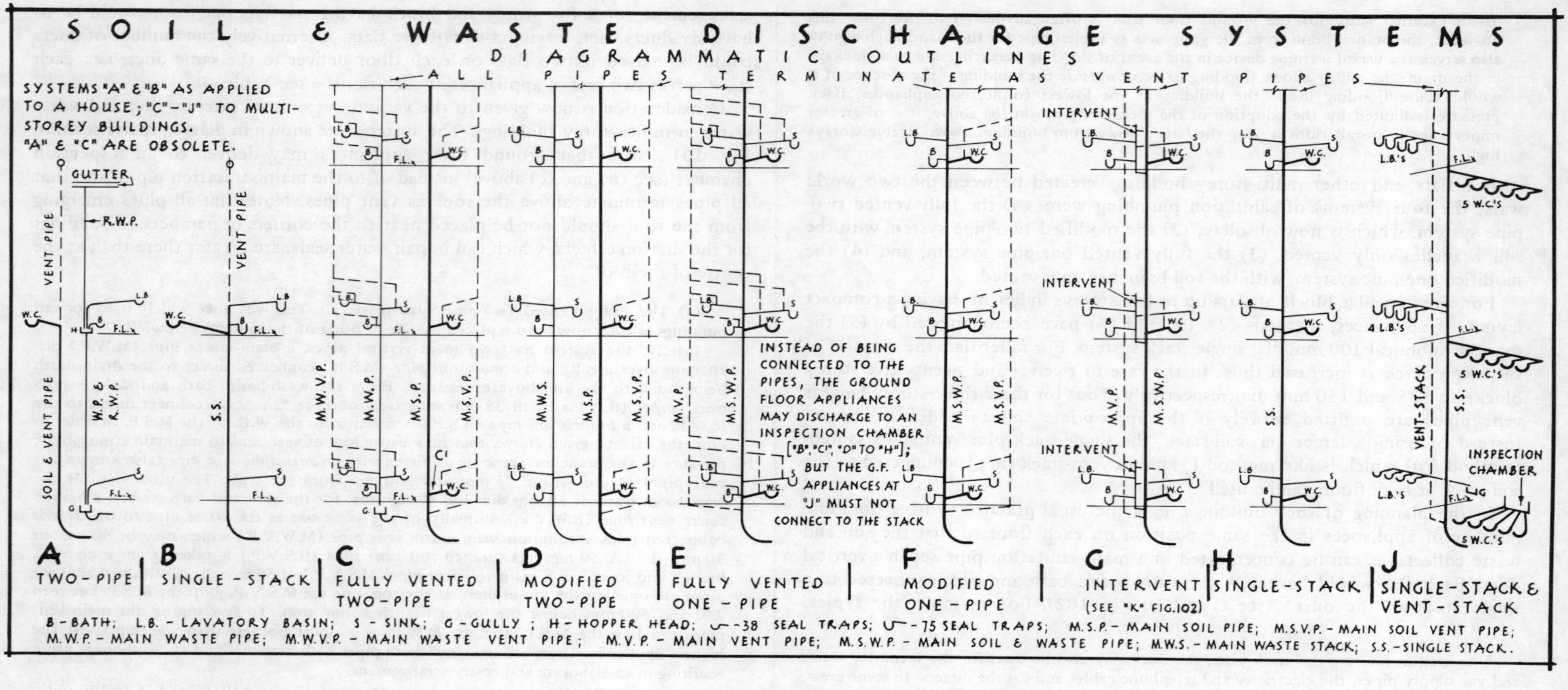

SOIL & WASTE DISCHARGE SYSTEMS

DIAGRAMMATIC OUTLINES

ALL PIPES TERMINATE AS VENT PIPES

SYSTEMS "A" & "B" AS APPLIED TO A HOUSE, "C"–"J" TO MULTI-STOREY BUILDINGS. "A" & "C" ARE OBSOLETE.

GUTTER; R.W.P.; VENT PIPE; SOIL & VENT PIPE; INTERVENT; VENT-STACK; INSPECTION CHAMBER; L.B.'S; 4 L.B.'S; S.W.C.'S

INSTEAD OF BEING CONNECTED TO THE PIPES, THE GROUND FLOOR APPLIANCES MAY DISCHARGE TO AN INSPECTION CHAMBER ["B" "C", "D" TO "H"], BUT THE G.F. APPLIANCES AT "J" MUST NOT CONNECT TO THE STACK

A TWO PIPE | B SINGLE STACK | C FULLY VENTED TWO-PIPE | D MODIFIED TWO-PIPE | E FULLY VENTED ONE-PIPE | F MODIFIED ONE-PIPE | G INTERVENT (SEE "K" FIG. 102) | H SINGLE-STACK | J SINGLE-STACK & VENT-STACK

B–BATH; L.B. LAVATORY BASIN; S SINK; G GULLY; H–HOPPER HEAD; ∪–38 SEAL TRAPS; ∪–75 SEAL TRAPS; M.S.P.–MAIN SOIL PIPE; M.S.V.P.–MAIN SOIL VENT PIPE; M.W.P.–MAIN WASTE PIPE; M.W.V.P.–MAIN WASTE VENT PIPE; M.V.P.–MAIN VENT PIPE; M.S.W.P.–MAIN SOIL & WASTE PIPE; M.W.S.–MAIN WASTE STACK; S.S.–SINGLE STACK.

FIGURE 101

practicable. The method has been widely used for tall buildings, being particularly suitable for those exceeding twenty-five storeys in height. It is also extensively used in tall buildings having several W.C.s, wash-basins, urinals, etc., grouped together at each floor as at A, Fig. 102, one trap only being used for each range of basins and urinals with a branch vent pipe to each trap. In flats, a common waste pipe is sometimes used for both the wash-basin and bath, each with their own trap but a common vent pipe (see A, Fig. 102, second floor). If this is done, care has to be taken to prevent the waste from the wash-basin running into the bath; this is avoided by having sufficient fall on the bath waste.

In comparison with the previous methods, the fully vented one-pipe arrangement is a notable advance in reducing the amount of pipe-work; the fittings J, K and L, Fig. 102 and described on p. 243 are useful for this method.

An example of the fully vented one-pipe system is shown at A, Fig. 102. The main soil and waste pipe is 100 mm dia. with a 50 mm dia. main vent pipe; on the third floor a range of four W.C.s is connected to the M.S.W.P., each W.C. has a 50 mm dia. branch vent pipe connected to the main branch vent pipe of the same size. At the same level there is a range of four slab urinals which have a glazed channel as shown at the detail W, at B. The channel is laid to fall towards a 50 mm dia. cast iron P-trap with a 40 or 50 mm dia. vent connection. An alternative type of individual urinal is shown in a range of three at the second floor, these are connected to a common 40 mm dia. branch soil pipe. The 75 mm deep seal trap for this range is shown inverted so that the soil branch is always full of liquid, this prevents the odour that would occur if the pipe were allowed to dry out. Also on the floor there is a bath and lavatory basin connected to a 38 mm dia. common waste pipe with a deep seal trap. On the first floor, four basins and a drinking fountain are coupled as shown in the detail X at H, this illustrates the point that a drinking fountain should always be separately trapped. The ground floor appliances are generally more conveniently joined direct to the drain at an inspection chamber unless there is a gulley connected to an inspection chamber which would reveal flooding in the event of drain blockage.

(4) The Modified One-pipe System (see F). This comprises a M.S.W.P. as at E, a main vent pipe for the vent branches from the W.C.s, and unvented waste connections with 75 mm seal traps for the baths, basins, and sinks; hoppers and gullies are not required; the waste pipes must be designed in accordance with the rules given in (5) below. If a 50 mm dia. main vent pipe is used the system can be used for flat blocks between twelve and fifteen storeys high when the stack can serve the appliances from *two* flats at each floor. For sixteen to twenty storey flats using a 100 mm dia. soil stack with a 50 mm dia. main vent pipe the system will serve the appliances from one flat at each floor; by increasing the main vent pipe to 75 mm dia. it will serve two flats at each floor in such a building. For a six to eleven storey flat block a variation of the system where vent branches to the W.C.s are placed on alternate floors only is satisfactory; in this case the vent pipe is 50 mm dia. and the soil stack 100 mm – this will serve up to two flats on each floor.

A further modification of the one-pipe system is shown at G, Fig. 101, and K, Fig. 102, and this is suitable for blocks over ten storeys in height. It incorporates an "intervent"* unit placed at each floor level for the waste connections; this has a 64 mm dia. intervent pipe if all the waste appliances connect to it, and 50 mm dia. if it is just used for the bath and wash-basin wastes. Near the top of the vent, a connection is made to the main vent pipe and there is a branch vent for the W.C. A removable plug is provided at the top of the intervent for rodding purposes.

(5) The Single-stack System (see B and H). This has been introduced on p. 240 where the stack sizes and conditions for which it is suitable are given. The system serves a triple purpose, *i.e.*, as a M.S.P., M.W.P. and M.V.P.; 75 mm seal P-traps are used, there are no anti-siphonage pipes, hoppers or gullies. Although the anti-siphonage pipes are omitted, there is no danger from the pressure and siphonage effects, described on p. 239, provided the following rules are observed:

(*a*) The appliances must be arranged in a compact layout near to the duct.

(*b*) The soil branches must be kept short and have swept junctions to the stack as at K′, K, Fig. 102.

* Manufactured by Econa Modern Products Ltd.

(*c*) 75 mm deep seal P-traps to be used for the waste appliances, and wastes must enter the stack above the W.C. branch or not nearer than 200 mm below it.

(*d*) In order to prevent the siphonage of basin and sink wastes, these appliances should be as near to the stack as possible and the following maximum gradient figures in Table 38 for lengths of waste should not be exceeded.† The minimum desirable slope is $1\frac{1}{4}°$.

TABLE 38 MAXIMUM LENGTH AND SLOPE OF WASTE PIPES

Length of Waste Pipe from Trap Weir to Stack (mm)	Maximum Slope	
	Degrees	Gradient
1 700	1¼	1:46 = 20.8 mm/m
1 300	2	1:28.6 = 35 mm/m
990	3	1:19 = 52.6 mm/m
825	4	1:14.3 = 70 mm/m

(*e*) The stack should be joined to the drain by large radius pipes, preferably not less than one-eighth circle bends being used (see Chap. II, Vol. II).

Table 31 shows the sizes of soil stacks required for different storey numbers; it also shows when a vent-stack is needed as described in system (6).

An example of a compact layout for a single-stack system is shown at C and D, Fig. 102. The stack is located in a duct behind the wash-basin and is accessible from a door below the sink or basin. To clear any blockages that develop, the stack can have an access boss for rodding from the duct; alternatively, rodding can be done by unscrewing one of the waste pipes. A further method for giving rodding access is to use the type of W.C. that has provision for a vent pipe connection (see H, Fig. 100), this is a common device for single-stack systems. For the reasons given on p. 239, for multi-storey buildings it is good practice to connect the groundfloor appliances direct to the drain in the normal way.

(6) The Single-Stack Plus Vent-Stack System (see J). This consists of a soil-stack and a vent-stack; at each floor level, above the highest range of appliances, a short branch vent pipe connects the soil-stack to the vent stack. None of the appliances are separately vented. The arrangement is particularly suitable for tall office blocks where there is a range of W.C.s, lavatory basins and urinals at each floor level. The number of appliances depends on the occupancy; in a large building there may be more than one group of appliances at each floor, or alternate floors, usually near the staircases. The maximum group size is usually five

† Where the correct distances and gradients cannot be observed, and the waste length does not exceed 3 m, then resealing traps can be used (see p. 246).

TABLE 39 SIZES OF DRAINAGE STACK AND VENT STACK (dia. in mm) FOR BLOCKS OF FLATS

Type	Stack diameter (mm)	Requirements	Requirements
House (Single-family dwellings up to 3 storeys)	90		
Flats		*Stack serving one group‡ on each floor*	*Stack serving two groups‡ on each floor*
Up to 5 storeys	100	Single-stack	Single-stack
6 to 10	100	Single-stack	50 mm vent stack with one connection on alternate floors
11 to 15	100	40 mm vent stack with one connection on alternate floors	50 mm vent stack with one connection on each floor
16 to 20	100	60 mm vent stack with one connection on alternate floors	60 mm vent stack with one connection on each floor
Up to 12 storeys	125	Single-stack	Single-stack
12 to 15	125	Single-stack	50 mm vent stack with one connection on alternate floors
Up to 25 storeys	150	Single-stack	Single-stack

‡ Each group consists of a W.C., bath, basin and sink. Where dwellings contain more appliances, it may be necessary to provide more vents.

Note: The above recommendations apply to systems with swept-inlet W.C. branches like K′, K, Fig. 102. With straight-inlet branches, a 100 mm stack with no vents has been found satisfactory for up to four storeys; a 150 mm stack with no vents has been found satisfactory for up to fifteen storeys.

W.C.s, five urinals and five wash-basins all of which are given the collective name here of a *five-group*. In a four-storey building with a five-group at each floor just a single-stack and no vent stack is needed. For other groups and taller buildings see Table 40 which gives the vent stack diameters for 100 and 150 mm soil stacks. Note that in the table the word "group" includes one *each* of the above three appliances.

TABLE 40 SIZES OF DRAINAGE STACK AND VENT STACK (dia. in mm) FOR OFFICE BUILDINGS

	100 mm dia. stack			150 mm dia. stack				
No. of Floors	5	8	12	8	12	16	20	24
Group 1 and 2	○	○	30	○	○	○	○	○
Group 3	○	30	40	○	○	○	○	○
Group 4 and 5	○	40	50	○	40	40	50	60

Note: The word *group* means one W.C., one wash-basin, one urinal; and a three-group installation includes three of *each* type of appliance. The symbol ○ denotes that a vent stack is not required.

Soil and Waste Pipe-work. Cast iron*, galvanized† steel, pitch fibre, asbestos-cement, plastics and copper are used in this class of work for the main sanitation pipes; the smaller branch pipes are usually in copper or plastic. Preformed galvanized steel can be used for the main sanitation pipes; it is more adaptable than cast iron, less bulky and can be obtained in longer lengths, often extending through two storeys in height. Short lengths of pipe incorporating the waste and soil connections are available in steel and cast iron. Two galvanized steel examples are shown at J‡ and K‡, Fig. 102. The one at J is for an S-trap W.C. and has bosses for the waste pipes, these can be formed at any angle on plan and at the heights required; a similar fitting for a P-trap W.C. branch is also made. The waste bosses should be above the soil branch intersection or at a distance over 200 mm below this intersection. The fitting at K is the "intervent" unit described above. The fitting at L shows the cast iron "Spruce-thrower"§ unit which simplifies the jointing of pipe-work in this metal.

The use of plastic soil and waste pipes is increasing rapidly; made of black or grey unplasticized polyvinyl chloride (p.v.c.) they provide a very smooth bore and are cheaper than other materials. P.v.c. pipes are made in diameters rising by 25 mm increments from 50 to 150 mm dia. and in 4 m lengths; they have a socket at one end and a spigot at the other; the thickness of the pipe wall varies according to the manufacturer and the pipe dia. being about 3 mm. The joints between lengths of soil pipe are made by slipping a circular neoprene ring over the spigot end and pushing this into the socket of the connecting pipe. This simple effective joint allows for some expansion movement so necessary for this material. The connection between a waste pipe and a soil pipe is made by cutting a hole in the soil pipe and inserting a boss fitting which is attached to the soil pipe by a solvent weld cement. The boss has a tapered socket for receiving the

* See Fig. 36, Vol. II.

† Joints between galvanized steel and copper should have an insulating connector, as at E, Fig. 102, to prevent electrolytic action.

‡ Manufactured by Econa Modern Products Ltd.

§ Manufactured by B. Finch & Co. Ltd.

SOIL & WASTE PIPEWORK

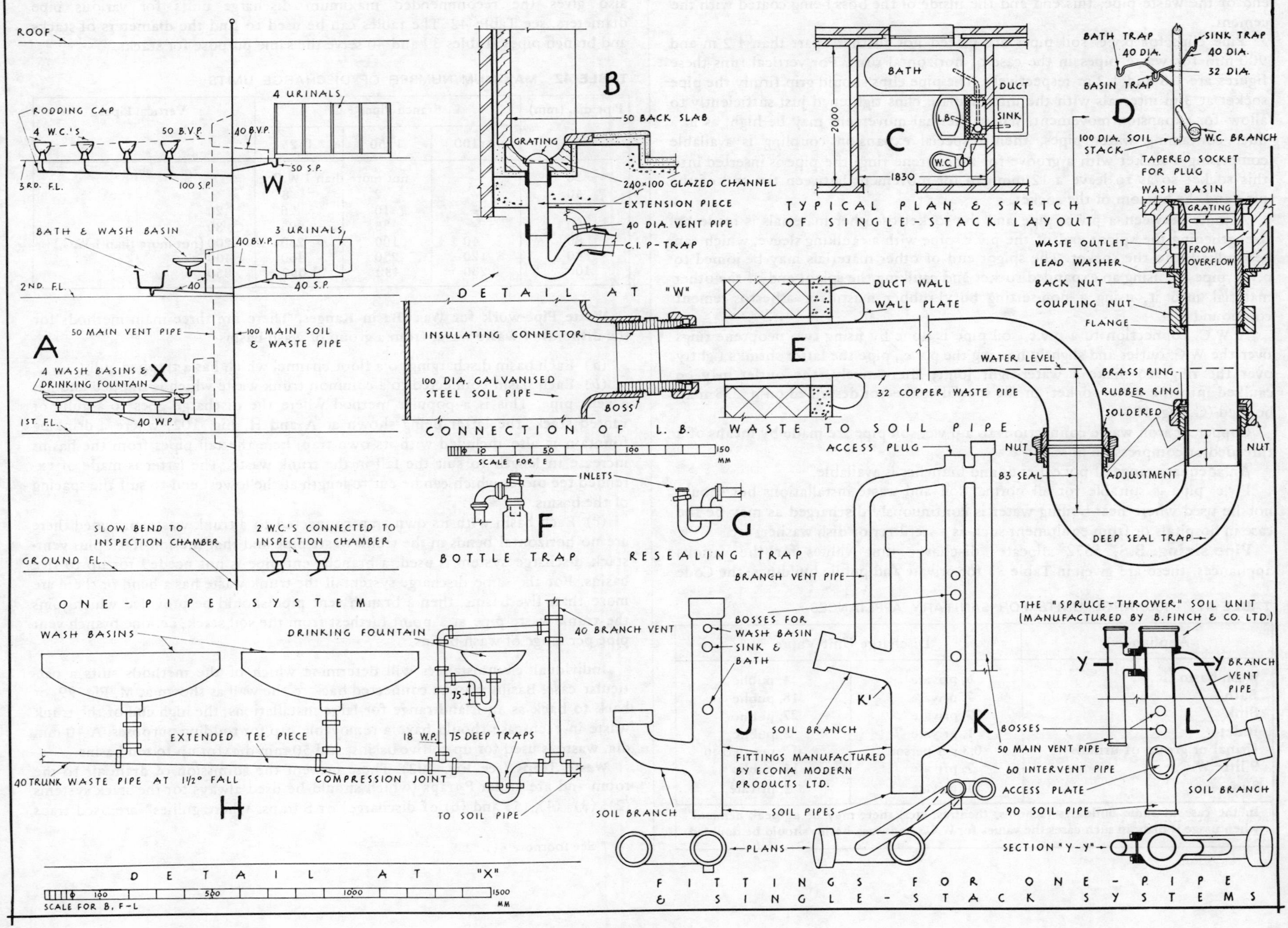

ROOF
RODDING CAP
4 W.C.'S
50 B.V.P.
40 B.V.P.
50 S.P.
100 S.P.
3RD. FL.
4 URINALS
W
BATH & WASH BASIN
40 B.V.P.
3 URINALS
40
40 S.P.
2ND. FL.
50 MAIN VENT PIPE
100 MAIN SOIL & WASTE PIPE
A
4 WASH BASINS & DRINKING FOUNTAIN
X
1ST. FL.
40 W.P.
SLOW BEND TO INSPECTION CHAMBER
2 W.C.'S CONNECTED TO INSPECTION CHAMBER
GROUND FL.
ONE-PIPE SYSTEM

B
50 BACK SLAB
GRATING
240×100 GLAZED CHANNEL
EXTENSION PIECE
40 DIA. VENT PIPE
C.I.P.-TRAP
DETAIL AT "W"

BATH
DUCT
L.B.
SINK
W.C.
2000
1830
C
TYPICAL PLAN & SKETCH OF SINGLE STACK LAYOUT

BATH TRAP
40 DIA.
SINK TRAP
40 DIA.
32 DIA.
BASIN TRAP
D
100 DIA. SOIL STACK
W.C. BRANCH
TAPERED SOCKET FOR PLUG
WASH BASIN
GRATING
WASTE OUTLET
FROM OVERFLOW
LEAD WASHER
BACK NUT
COUPLING NUT
FLANGE

INSULATING CONNECTOR
100 DIA. GALVANISED STEEL SOIL PIPE
BOSS
DUCT WALL
WALL PLATE
E
32 COPPER WASTE PIPE
CONNECTION OF L.B. WASTE TO SOIL PIPE
10 50 100 150 MM
SCALE FOR E

WATER LEVEL
BRASS RING
RUBBER RING
SOLDERED
NUT
NUT
ADJUSTMENT
83 SEAL
ACCESS PLUG
DEEP SEAL TRAP

INLETS
F
BOTTLE TRAP
G
RESEALING TRAP

WASH BASINS
DRINKING FOUNTAIN
40 BRANCH VENT
75
EXTENDED TEE PIECE
18 W.P.
75 DEEP TRAPS
40 TRUNK WASTE PIPE AT 1½° FALL
COMPRESSION JOINT
H
TO SOIL PIPE
DETAIL AT "X"
0 100 500 1000 1500 MM
SCALE FOR B, F-L

BRANCH VENT PIPE
BOSSES FOR WASH BASIN
SINK & BATH
K'
J
SOIL BRANCH
FITTINGS MANUFACTURED BY ECONA MODERN PRODUCTS LTD.
K
SOIL BRANCH
SOIL PIPES
PLANS

THE "SPRUCE-THROWER" SOIL UNIT (MANUFACTURED BY B. FINCH & CO. LTD.)
Y
Y
BRANCH VENT PIPE
BOSSES
50 MAIN VENT PIPE
60 INTERVENT PIPE
ACCESS PLATE
90 SOIL PIPE
L
SOIL BRANCH
SECTION "Y-Y"

FITTINGS FOR ONE-PIPE & SINGLE-STACK SYSTEMS

FIGURE 102

end of the waste pipe, this end and the inside of the boss being coated with the cement.

Pipe clips for p.v.c. soil pipes are placed not further apart than 1.2 m and 900 mm for waste pipes in the case of horizontal runs. For vertical runs these figures are 1.8 and 1.2 m respectively. The pipe clips should grip firmly the pipe socket at 3 m intervals with the intermediate clips tightened just sufficiently to allow for expansion movement. Where thermal movement may be high, as in a duct containing water pipes, then a special expansion coupling is available comprising a socket with a groove for a neoprene ring; the pipe is inserted into this socket so as to leave a 12 mm gap for movement between the end of the pipe and the bottom of the socket.

A joint between a p.v.c. pipe and the socket of other materials is made by strengthening the spigot end of the p.v.c. pipe with a caulking sleeve, which can be caulked into the socket. The spigot end of other materials may be joined to p.v.c. pipe by using an expanded socket and caulking the spigot end of the other material into it, using a non-setting butyl-rubber mastic or asbestos-cement compound.

A W.C. connection to a p.v.c. soil pipe is done by using two neoprene rings over the W.C. outlet and slightly heating the p.v.c., pipe the latter shrinks tightly over the rings to make a water-tight joint; alternatively, the outlet may be caulked into the p.v.c. socket; or the special connector described on p. 238 may be used (G, Fig. 100).

Copper or iron waste connections to a p.v.c. soil pipe are made by means of a threaded or compression boss.

An adequate range of p.v.c. bends and branches is available.

P.v.c. pipe is suitable for all normal soil and waste installations but should not be used where near-boiling water is continuously discharged as may be the case in hospitals or from equipment such as a sterilizer or dish washer, etc.

Pipe sizing. B.S. 5572 allocates discharge unit values for the various appliances, these are given in Table 33 for private and public buildings; the Code also gives the recommended maximum discharge units for various pipe diameters, see Table 42. The tables can be used to find the diameters of stacks and branch pipes. Tables 39 and 40 serve the same purpose for stacks.

TABLE 41 DISCHARGE UNITS FOR SANITARY APPLIANCES

Appliance	Discharge Unit Value	
Wash-basin	6, private	4, public
Bath	7, private	18, public
Sink	27, private	27, public
Bidet	1, private	2, public
Urinal or group of urinals	0.3 per person	0.3 per person
9 litre W.C.	7, private	14, public
Shower	1, private	2, private

In the case of some buildings (schools, theatres, etc.) there may be a "peak demand" when usage is high: in such cases the values for W.C.s and wash-basins should be doubled.

TABLE 42 MAXIMUM NUMBER OF DISCHARGE UNITS

Pipe dia. (mm)	Branch Pipes Fall			Vertical Pipes
	1:100	1:50	1:25	
30	–	not more than 1 W.C.		–
40	–	2	8	–
50	–	10	26	20
60	–	35	95	80
80	40	100	230	200 (not more than 1 W.C.)
90	120	230	460	400
100	230	430	1 050	850

Waste Pipe-work for Wash-Basin Ranges. There are three main methods for the disposal of waste water from a group of wash-basins:

(*a*) Each basin discharging to a floor channel which has a trapped gully.

(*b*) Each basin connected to a common trunk waste which is trapped and has a vent pipe. This is a popular method where the discharge goes to a gully or vented stack; the latter being shown at A and H, Fig. 102, where a drinking fountain is also included with its own trap; here the tail pipes from the basins increase in length to suit the fall in the trunk waste. The latter is made of extended tee pieces which can be cut to length at the lowest end to suit the spacing of the basins.

(*c*) Each basin with its own trap connected to a trunk waste; provided there are no horizontal bends in the trunk waste pipe and that the soil-stack plus vent-stack discharge system is used, a branch vent pipe is not needed for up to five basins. For the same discharge system, if the trunk waste has a bend or there are more than five basins, then a branch vent pipe should be provided which joins the trunk waste pipe at a point furthest from the soil stack; *i.e.* one branch vent pipe per range of wash-basins.

Individual circumstances will determine which of the methods suits a particular case. Basins may be connected back to the wall as shown at M, Fig. 99, or back to back as an island range for large installations; the high end of the trunk waste in each case should have a removable cap for rodding purposes. A 40 mm dia. waste is used for up to five basins, and 50 mm dia. for up to ten basins.

Waste Traps (see Fig. 102). These prevent the admission of drain air to the room and are either P-traps (which should be used always for the stack systems (2), (3), (4), (5) and (6) of discharge) or S-traps. Where gullies* are used traps

* See footnote ¶, p. 239.

should have a seal depth of 38 mm; this is increased to 75 mm where gullies are omitted in systems B and D to J, Fig. 101.

The detail of one kind† of 75 mm deep seal trap is shown at E, this particular make‡ allows for an adjustment of 22 mm to be made. The trap has two couplings of the compressive type which allow the fitting to be swivelled in any direction. The top coupling nut bears against a flange brazed to the pipe and makes the joint to the threaded outlet from the basin. The joint below has a threaded piece soldered to the pipe for a compression nut, the nut fits against a brass ring and a rubber ring, the third joint near the outgo is also of the compressive type. A similar type, made by the same firm, for a bath and incorporating the overflow is shown at P and Q, Fig. 99.

Another type of trap§ is the bottle trap shown at F; it has a 75 mm seal and employs a glass bottle (metal bottles are also used). With the glass type, the accumulation of dirt can be seen, the bottle can be unscrewed for cleansing, it is therefore a suitable trap for sinks.

The resealing trap shown at G is a useful type which incorporates a chamber holding a reserve supply of water; the reserve of water reseals the trap should some of the water be siphoned off. Such traps can be used with discretion on single-stack systems where the requirements for fall (see p. 240) cannot be met.

Testing and Installation. In addition to ensuring that the appliances function and discharge correctly, that the minimum trap seal is maintained (p. 237), and there are no blockages, the pipe-work and its joints must also be tested for soundness. There are the three tests: by water, air and smoke.

† Traps of this type can be obtained with removable caps (for cleaning) at the bottom. These are not recommended as they tend to cause blockages; in any case, the trap can easily be uncoupled and cleaned out if necessary.

‡ A P-trap, manufactured by Armitage Shanks & Co. Ltd.

§ Manufactured by Econa Modern Products Ltd.

The water test is used for drainage systems (see Chap. II, Vol. II), but is too exacting for assembled pipe-work. It can, however, be applied to unfixed lengths of the main soil and vent pipes and stacks, which can be filled with water (the branches being plugged) to check the absence of blow holes in the metal.

Air Test. At an inspection chamber, the branch drain is plugged by means of a rubber diaphragm which can be expanded to seal the drain, its fit is checked by passing some water into the branch. The top of the vent pipe is similarly plugged and all traps filled with water. At a convenient W.C. the open end of a rubber tube is passed through the water seal into the soil pipe. The other end of the tube is fitted to a tee-piece having a valve at one branch through which air can be blown, the other branch is connected to a U-tube or manometer having a measuring gauge. Air is blown in via the tee-piece, through the rubber tube and into the installation so that a pressure equivalent to a head of not less than 38 mm* of water is maintained for three minutes. Loss of pressure indicates a fault somewhere in the system and if this cannot be located by inspection it has to be found by using the smoke test.

Smoke test. As the test is somewhat awkward to accomplish it may be convenient for the operatives to wear respirators. A smoke generating machine is used to supply smoke which is admitted to the pipe-work at the inspection chamber through a rubber tube. In order to fill all the branch pipes with smoke it is preferable to have the seals of the appliances emptied of water. The top of the vent pipe is then plugged and smoke is introduced; as soon as this becomes visible in a room the 75 mm seals are filled with water, those of less depth require plugging. The plug at the top of the vent pipe should be removed for a while to allow air to escape and smoke emerge, it is then replaced and smoke production continued until a pressure of 38 mm* water-gauge obtains. The test is efficient, giving immediate location of faults.

* A Building Regulation requirement.

CHAPTER ELEVEN

ELECTRICAL AND GAS SERVICES

Syllabus. Electrical services. Definitions, units. Production, distribution, tariffs. Domestic, commercial and industrial installations. Wiring, control equipment, earthing. Gas services, units, production and distribution; installation and pipe-work; burners.

ELECTRICAL INSTALLATIONS*

Definitions. The ampere is the unit of current, or rate of flow of an electric current, the volt is the unit of pressure, the ohm is the unit of resistance to flow, and the watt is the unit of power, measuring the rate at which electricity is used by an appliance (see p. 253). Hence:

$$\text{watts} = \text{amps} \times \text{volts} \qquad (1)\dagger$$

From Ohm's law it is deduced that

$$\text{amps} = \frac{\text{volts}}{\text{ohms}} \qquad (2)$$

Electricity flows in a conductor and if this is of length l m and cross-sectional area a m^2 then its

$$\text{resistance (ohms)} = \rho l/a \qquad (3)$$

where ρ is a constant depending on the material of the conductor. These three basic formulae are important criteria in the design of the supply network and electrical installation in a building.

The term "unit of electricity" is often used where 1 unit = 1 kW (*e.g.* a 150 W lamp switched on for 10 hours consumes 1.5 kW or 1.5 units of electricity).

Production of Electricity. Electricity is produced by an alternator which comprises an electromagnet rotating in triple stationary windings, current being generated in each winding. The magnet can be turned by water power, or steam turbine, the steam being made by coal or oil firing, or from the heat of nuclear reaction. The alternator generates electricity (alternating* current, so-called because it rises and falls as the magnet rotates). The rate of variation is called the frequency, normally having a value of 50 cycles per second. The current is described as three-phase alternating current, requiring three conductors for its transmission.

Transmission and Distribution. The main distribution network is by overhead cables carried on pylons. Voltages are high for economic reasons, being 275 kV or 400 kV on the super grid and 132 kV on the primary grid. At points along the lines, the voltage is stepped down at transformer stations to 66 kV; up to this stage the generation and supply is the responsibility of the Central Electricity Generating Board. Local Electricity Boards take their supply from these main sub-stations, and serve their areas with 66, 33 and 11 kV lines. They control smaller sub-stations at all voltage changes, and at 11 kV stations the power is reduced to 415/240 volts. The 11 kV sub-stations serve the domestic and industrial premises, although some manufacturers who require higher voltages have their own sub-station.

A 240-volt single-phase supply is used for house and similar properties, and the cable includes a phase wire and a neutral wire. The 415-volt three-phase supply is needed for larger premises. The supply authorities have to ensure that the voltage provided at the consumer's terminal does not vary more than ±6 per cent nor the frequency vary more than ±1 per cent.

Tariffs. Premises are divided into seven main groups having different tariffs:— domestic, farms, various combinations of commercial/domestic, churches and industry. Tariff prices vary widely and increase as the cost of generating fuel rises. For certain heating installations (e.g. electric floor warming – see p. 268) "restricted hour tariffs" are available which give a reduction in the cost per unit of about 50%. These "off-peak" tariffs operate mostly at night when generating plant is not working to a maximum output.

* See p. 266 for electric heating systems.

† This is true for direct current circuits. It also applies in single-phase alternating current circuits when the *power factor* is unity. The power factor equals the true power (kW) divided by the apparent power (kVA) and is less than unity in circuits containing motors, for in such circuits the current lags behind the voltage. The apparent power is the sum of the two parts of the current used by a motor, viz. (*a*) the part creating rotation of the motor shaft, and (*b*) the working part giving the output of power. Hence, a low power factor in a.c. circuits increases the current for a given load.

* Another type of power is *direct* current produced in earlier times and is still required for certain machines such as welding gear or in motors of variable speed.

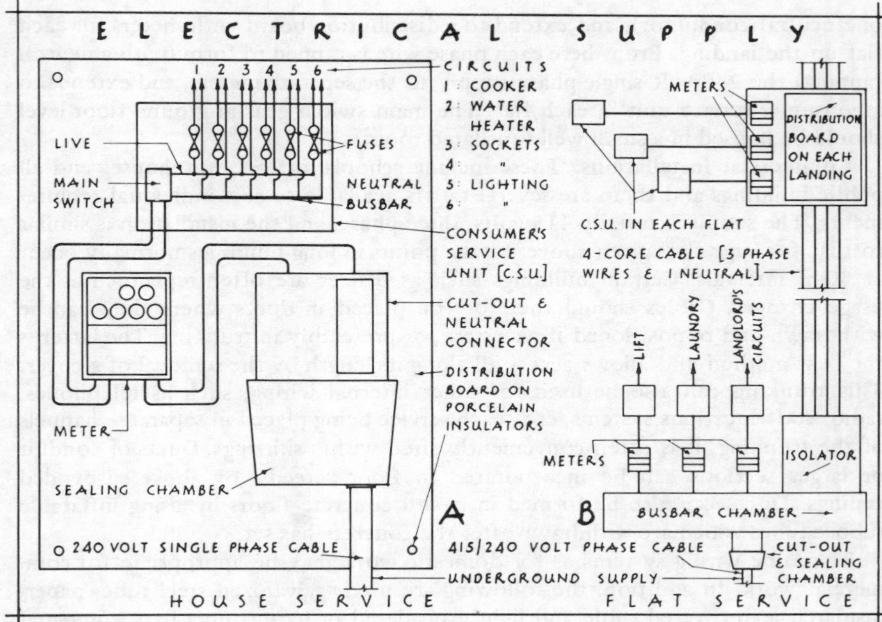

FIGURE 103

Domestic Installations. The regulations of the Institute of Electrical Engineers provide guidance on the methods used in the work to ensure good construction and elimination of the danger of fire and shock, etc. The incoming wires to a house comprise a live insulated phase conductor and an insulated neutral conductor which is earthed at the sub-station. The cable enters the building near the service position (a board fixed to the wall with porcelain insulators to accommodate the gear), where the Board's equipment of cut-out and meter is placed (see A, Fig. 103). The supply may be from overhead or underground, and in the latter case, the cable enters the sealing box before the cut-out. Leads from the meter join the consumer's service unit of main switch and fuse board. The service is divided at the fuse board into sub-circuits each emanating from a branch off the live conductor (via a fuse) and a branch off the neutral conductor. Standard equipment for this gear, in a house, consists of small metal-clad boxes occupying a minimum of space, or may be combined together in the form of a consumer's control unit. The fuse board has six or more fuses, one each for the cooker (up to 30 amp) and water heater, two for the socket outlets (power plug points) and two for the lighting circuits. A final sub-circuit rated at 30 amp may supply an electric cooker connected by means of a cooker control unit having a main switch and rated at 30 amp and which may also include one socket outlet for a kettle. The water heater circuit would be of 13 or 15 amp, and the two lighting circuits (for each 90 m^2 of floor area) would each be of 5 amp for the ground floor and first-floor lights.

In a lighting circuit, the phase and neutral leads are looped into one terminal in the switch and light respectively, a switch wire connects the other terminals of the switch and light, and is made live when the switch is placed in the "on" position (see Fig. 105). The current rating in a lighting circuit supplying more than one lamp is not to exceed 15 amp.

The most economical method of supplying the sockets is the *ring main* system (see Fig. 104), one ring being used for each 90 m^2 of floor area. The plug tops in the ring have their own fuse of 2, 5, 10 or 13 amp rating to suit the loading of the appliance to which they are connected. By reference to formula (1), with the standard 240 voltage, a 2-amp fuse is suitable for lights and appliances up to 480 watts rating, 5 amp for 480 to 1 200 watts, 10 amp for 1 200 to 2 400 watts, etc. In domestic work the number of 13-amp socket outlets in the ring main is unlimited if the floor area is under 90 m^2; and spurs off the ring are allowed, providing there are not more than two sockets or one fixed appliance per spur, and not more than half the number of points are served by spurs. The ring main is supplied through a 30-amp fuse at the fuse board. In any installation, the number of outlets per ring should be approximately equal, to balance the load. The principles of the ring main are shown in the diagram at A, Fig. 104; there are five socket outlets in the ring with three spurs off it. The bottom spur has one more outlet, the one on the right is for a water heater or fixed radiator having a separate switch and spur fuse box, and the top spur is for two more socket outlets. The house plan at B shows the application for a circuit of fourteen socket outlets where the ring main is in the living room. Three spurs for six outlets lead to the kitchen, study and garage; some of the outlets are of the two-gang type – see p. 250.

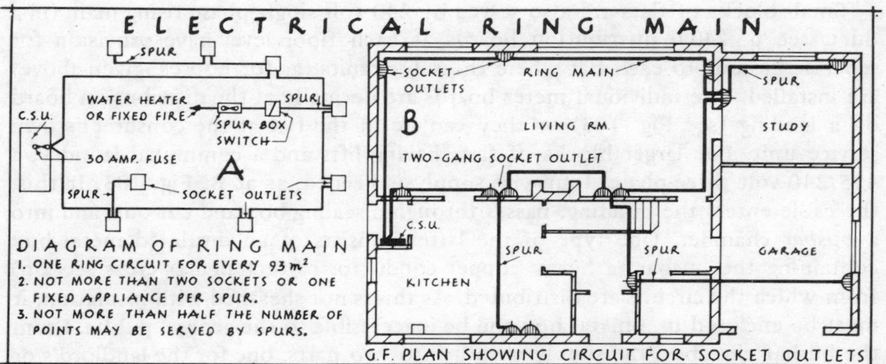

FIGURE 104

There are three main wiring systems in domestic work, the cheapest and most commonly used being polyvinyl-chloride sheathed cable (p.v.c.s.); secondly, p.v.c. insulated cable inside black enamelled circular conduit, this is 75 per cent dearer than the first; thirdly, mineral insulated copper sheathed cable (m.i.c.s.) which is twice as costly as the first. Cables that are buried in plaster or other materials should be inside conduit, cable between floor joists or in the roof space need only be p.v.c. Cables are also described according to the number and diameter of strands. For example a 3/0.74 cable has three strands each 0.74 mm dia. In addition to having an adequate load-carrying capacity, a conductor must have sufficient strength to resist damage during installation, service and repair. Its cross-sectional area has to be large enough to ensure that the circuit resistance is less than that which would cause an excessive *voltage drop*. As current passes through a conductor, its pressure (voltage) is reduced in overcoming the resistance of the cable. This is known as voltage drop and is least in short thick cables. From the consumer's terminals on a 240 volt supply, the voltage drop to any point in the installation must not exceed 5.8 volts when the full current load is being carried. Table 43 shows the current rating and length of cable in metres for a drop of 1-volt for two single-core p.v.c. insulated cables enclosed in one conduit or one twin p.v.c. sheathed cable; the table can be used to determine cable sizes for an installation.

TABLE 43 PERMISSIBLE VOLTAGE DROP

Cable size (mm)	3/0.74	3/0.91	7/0.74	7/0.91	7/1.12	7/1.32	7/1.63
Current rating (amps)	10	15	20	28	36	43	53
Length of run per 1 volt drop (m)	3	3.35	3.66	3.96	4.88	5.49	7

Small blocks of flats are also served by 240-volt single-phase rising main (in a duct, see p. 240); distribution boards at each floor level have provision for separate circuits to each flat where the sub-circuits (as for houses, given above) are installed. The individual meter boards are normally at the distribution board on a landing (see Fig. 103) or they can be in the flat at the consumer's own service unit. For larger blocks of flats having lifts and a communal laundry, a 415/240-volt three-phase, four-wire supply is needed, as at B, Fig. 103. In this, the cable enters the building, passes through a sealing box and cut-out, and into a *busbar* chamber. One type of the latter consists of an insulated metal box containing the busbar (a heavy copper conductor of rectangular cross section) from which the circuits are distributed. As this is not sheathed with insulation, it must be enclosed in a metal box and be inaccessible to the general public. From the busbar chamber, the supply is split into two parts, one for the landlord's or porter's domestic circuit, lift and laundry (each separately metered), and one for the flats via an isolator. The cables from the latter are four-core (three-phase and one neutral conductor), and extend to a distribution board with meters for each flat on the landing. From here each phase wire is tapped to form (with a neutral tapping) the 240-volt single-phase supply to the separate meters, and extends to a consumer service unit in each flat. The main switch gear at ground floor level should be housed in a small well ventilated room.

Commercial Installations. These include schools, offices, warehouses and all public buildings and there are several tariffs available to suit individual requirements. The supply is usually 415 volts, three-phase, and the installation is similar to that for large flats given above. Intake points in long buildings normally occur at 30 m intervals. Certain buildings such as offices are often replanned as the usage changes. Cables should therefore be placed in ducts where they can be withdrawn and re-positioned if necessary, or preferably in trunking. The latter is the best method and allows access all along its length by the removal of a cover. This trunking can also be used for other internal wiring, such as telephones, radio, staff locations systems, etc., each service being placed in separate channels of the trunking; it is often conveniently sited within skirtings. Ducts of conduit or larger sections can be incorporated in floor screeds, or above suspended ceilings. Ducts can also be formed in in-situ concrete floors by using inflatable rubber tubes which are withdrawn after the concrete has set.

The same wiring systems as for domestic work may be appropriate for commercial work. In addition, the following are used: galvanized steel tube, paper-insulated lead-covered cable and lightly insulated or bare copper bars supported on insulators in metal ducts.

Large commercial consumers often have their own sub-station in the building and this would have an 11 kV supply. It would be placed near to the switching equipment already described, and have two compartments, one for the high voltage intake and switch gear, and the other for the transformer. Wide doors and good access are needed to the sub-station to allow for the possible replacement of transformers.

Industrial Installations. Depending on the size of the manufacturing process, the supply may be three-phase 415/240 volts, or 3.3 kV or 11 kV requiring a separate sub-station. The installation will be similar to commercial undertakings, but allowing for greater flexibility of the wiring. Most of this will be on the surface and a convenient form for machines is the busbar trunking given above. The trunking is supported from overhead to keep the floor space clear. Galvanized conduit would be used for the lighting circuit. The maximum number of outlets from a ring main in an industrial layout is ten.

Control Equipment. This comprises switches and fuse gear, distribution boards, control gear for motors, light switches, ceiling roses, socket outlets and plug tops.

The primary control beyond the cable entry is the main switch which may be single pole or triple pole according to the number of phases. This switch is placed in a small metal-clad box which cannot be opened until the switch is in the "off" position. Each pole has its own fuse to control the outgoing sub-mains and is associated with a meter. Certain heavy duty switches have a circuit breaker instead of a fuse; this is an electromagnetically or thermally operated trip which cuts off the supply should the circuit become overloaded.

From the switch-gear, the circuits are controlled via a main distribution board used where a circuit sub-divides, several boards being needed to suit the requirements. Further distribution boards may be provided to sub-divide the supply into final circuits and sub-circuits. Fuses are placed in the boards at each subdivision and these operate to open the circuit in the event of overload.

Fuses are of two types, the rewirable and the cartridge, and they melt in the event of the current increasing; the former type can be renewed with a fresh length of bare wire. In the cartridge fuse, the wire is enclosed in a case containing a powder which prevents the formation of an arc when fusing occurs; it is this type which is fitted into the standard 13 amp plug top, and the whole cartridge has to be replaced when the fuse melts. In places where the interruption of supply, as a result of fusing, is serious and time cannot be spared to replace a broken fuse, then a small circuit breaker (an automatic switch which operates to open in the event of overloading, see below) can be used as an alternative.

An electric motor has its own individual circuit controlled by a fuse board as above, it will also have a starter switch. As the current varies from a maximum, when the motor is newly started, to a less amount when it is running normally, then the starting switch must allow for gradual operation. Means of isolation, and a device to prevent the motor restarting in the event of supply failure, must be incorporated in the starter.

Most electric light switches are of the 5-amp type with a slow silent make-and-break device; there are three types – Fig. 105. Firstly, the one-way switch for a lamp or lamps from one point as in the example at A, where two lamps are each controlled by their own switch. Then the two-way switch (commonly used on staircase landings), where the same lamp (as at B) or lamps can be controlled from two points. Thirdly, intermediate switches used at several points in conjunction with a pair of two-way switches; this is shown at C, where an intermediate switch is placed between two two-way switches; both lights can be controlled from any of the three positions. All types are available as either flush

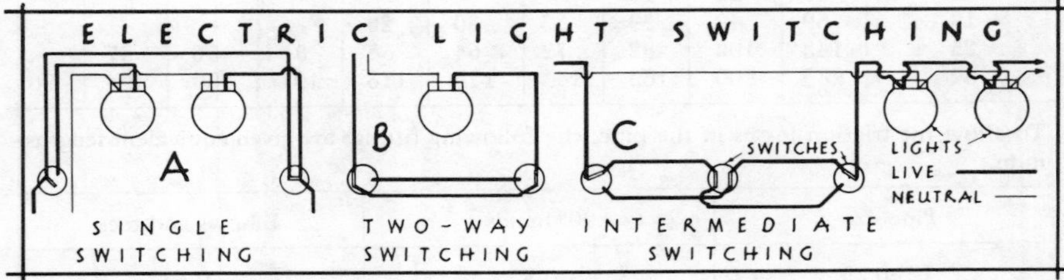

FIGURE 105

pattern or surface fittings. The flush pattern is inset into the 16 mm plaster thickness, the mechanism being placed in a wooden box screwed to the wall and covered with a metal or plastic plate. The surface switch is similar but having a metal base and is not recessed. Ceiling switches operated by a cord are also used and these are necessary inside a bathroom to prevent the danger of shock. Other types, such as door switches (fixed to the door frame) are operated by the opening and closing of the door, some burglar alarm switches are of this type. The time-lag switch is another, this automatically turns off the light after an interval. Other special switches are the thermostats which operate at a given temperature, the waterproof, and the flameproof type, and time switches used in lighting and heating circuits which function by a clock mechanism.

There are innumerable kinds of ceiling rose of insulated construction, they have two or three terminals, the third terminal being used for looping in.

The socket outlet and plug used for new work is the 13-amp type, this has three flat pins for the two main wires and the earth connections respectively. In some types, the neutral and live sockets are protected by shutters so that they are sealed off when not in use. They can have a switch and may be flush or surface mounted. The plug top is fitted with a 2, 5, 10 or 13 amp fuse to suit the appliance. Socket outlets can be combined as at B, Fig. 104 to form two-gang outlets in the same fitting.

Electrical Protection and Earthing. In the event of mechanical damage, faults in the cable or appliance, or a short circuit, automatic provision must be made to render the installation safe. An earth wire is always included in the circuit and one end of it connects to the third terminal of the plug, and the other to the metal casing of the appliance. Also a fuse or circuit breaker is always included, and these precautions prevent the risk of shock or fire. A short circuit occurs when direct contact is made between a live conductor and an earth wire, or between a live conductor and neutral, and its effect is to blow the fuse, or "trip" the circuit breaker. Overloading happens when an appliance is connected to a socket outlet of lower current-carrying capacity.

The earthing connection can be made from the conduit (where this is used), or the cable can have an earth wire, or the sheath of the incoming cable can serve. The water pipe (never the gas pipe) is sometimes used as an earthing terminal although the practice is decreasing, and the Electricity Board often provides an earth terminal at the supply position. A non-metallic water pipe (*i.e.*, plastic) is unsuitable for earthing and an earth leakage circuit breaker* has to be incorporated which cuts off the supply in the event of a fault.

Practical Aspects of Wiring. It is important to determine the position of all cable runs prior to the construction starting and to make provision for their easy

* This device, being demanded by some Boards, gives satisfactory earthing protection, it is particularly useful when old property is being rewired; a separate insulated earth wire is taken from it to a copper earth electrode. This is a plate, rod or tube (*e.g.*, 20 mm dia., 600 mm long for a house) placed in ground which is preferably damp.

insertion. Vertical ducts are used for multiple runs; for individual cables, the use of the oval conduit will obviate the need for much chasing as it can be within the plaster thickness, the ends of such conduit should be covered with a rubber grommet to prevent damage to the cable. P.v.c. cable is suitable where there is no risk of mechanical damage, *e.g.*, in timber suspended floors this cable is clipped to the sides of the joists. The notching of timber joists should be avoided, and where runs at right angles to the joists are needed they should pass through holes bored in the centre of the depth of the beam.

The method of housing cables in concrete floors will depend on the construction. Conduit, metal or plastic trunking or ducts from inflatable tubes may be adopted, and these are preferably placed on top of the floor within a screed. 20 mm dia. conduit is commonly employed and as this cannot be bent to a sharper inner radius than 65 mm provision for bends must be made, the minimum screed thickness for such conduit is 35 mm; for trunking, a depth of 45 mm or more may be needed. With in-situ solid slabs, the conduit can be placed on the formwork; alternatively ducts may be formed in the top of the slab for later fixing of conduit. Drops through such a floor to lighting points, and vertical ducts must be formed by shuttering. For hollow block floors (see Fig. 28), the trunking has to be in the top of the floor, holes can be formed by cutting the tiles, or leaving them out. Ducts and trunking should always be sufficiently large to allow modifications to be made to suit changing circumstances. Conduit should always be laid to a slight fall so that condensation and water that accumulates during construction can be drained off before the cable is inserted.

GAS INSTALLATIONS†

Gas is mainly composed of hydrogen, carbon monoxide and hydrocarbons, and the principal source is natural gas. The calorific value of gas is 19 MJ/m^3, it is distributed by the Area Gas Boards and charged to the consumer on a cubic metre basis. Some areas are now supplied from a grid where the pressure may be up to 0.55 MN/m^2 or more; this is reduced normally to about 150 mm water gauge at governor stations for distribution to the local mains. Gas appliances are designed to operate on optimum efficiency at a pressure of 64 mm water gauge and this is obtained by a governor fitted to the inlet side of the gas meter, which also regulates the volume required. As gas contains water vapour which condenses in the mains they must be provided with siphon pots to allow removal of the condensate; for the same reason the service pipe from the main to the meter should fall 0.0085 mm per metre to the main. The size of this pipe for a house could be 25 mm dia. where only radiators are supplied, and 32 mm if cooking, heating and washing are done by gas. The service pipe is commonly in wrought iron or plain mild steel with screwed joints and covered with a bituminous wrapping to prevent corrosion. It should enter the building through a sleeve in the wall, the annular space being filled with a bituminous packing, and the bend to the meter being gradual. One pipe is required per house but a common vertical pipe is used for flats (one pipe per tier of flats with tees to individual meters). The meter is placed as near to the main as possible, positioned so that it is above the main and not less than 760 mm above floor level and fixed on brackets clear of the wall. It should be placed in a ventilated cupboard away from food stores and heating appliances, and not be in a position where dampness exists. The service pipe has a stop valve fitted to it above floor level and the supply is fed through a governor before entering the meter.

† See p. 269 for gas heating.

The two domestic meters rated at 2.8 and 5.6 m^3/hr are 240 mm wide, 300 mm high, 185 mm deep and 310 mm by 390 mm by 230 mm respectively. The former is suitable for a house having two gas fires and other normal domestic appliances; when a warm air unit (see p. 270) is used in addition, the larger meter would be required. If the meters have a coin box for pre-payment they would be 90 mm wider.

The installation pipes from the meter to the appliance can be in mild steel with screwed joints, copper with capillary joints (as for water, see p. 227), and lead; flexible metal pipe can be used for portable appliances. Pipe clips should be spaced not more than 1.5 m apart, the pipes may be in ducts or exposed, in either case they require protection from corrosion by painting. The appliance having the largest consumption in an installation is fed with the biggest pipe and branches are taken off this to the other fittings. Manufacturers give the consumption in m^3/h, and the following may be used as a guide. Clothes dryers, 0.57; radiators, 0.42 to 1.4; instantaneous sink heaters, 2 to 2.3; wash boilers, 1.7 to 2.8; and cookers, 2.8. Table 44 gives the discharges in m^3 for different sizes and lengths of pipe.

TABLE 44 PIPE SIZES FOR GAS INSTALLATIONS

Size of Pipe (internal dia. (mm))	Length of Pipe (m)									
	3	6	9	12	15	18	21	24	27	30
12	33	23	19	–	–	–	–	–	–	–
19	69	49	39	33	30	28	–	–	–	–
25	143	100	82	72	64	58	53	50	47	–
32	283	200	163	141	126	116	107	100	94	90

To allow for friction losses in the pipe, the following fittings are given equivalent lengths in m.

Pipe size	90° bends	Elbows and tees
12 to 25	0.3	0.6
32 to 38	0.3	0.9

There are two kinds of burners for appliances, the bunsen and the neat flame types. In the former, part of the combustion air is admitted to the burner pipe between the switch tap and the flame; in the neat flame type, the burner is not aerated and the whole of the combustion air is drawn from the atmosphere round the flame. The bunsen type is used in cookers, washing machines and gas pokers; the neat flame pattern in radiators, water heaters, air heating units, etc.

Multipoint water heaters, radiators and large appliances of the type shown in Fig. 116 must be provided with a flue delivering to the open air (see p. 269).

CHAPTER TWELVE

THERMAL INSULATION AND HEATING SYSTEMS

Syllabus. ***U*-value, thermal conductivity, surface resistance, cavities and air spaces. Building Regulation thermal insulation requirements and calculations. Roof insulation, vapour barrier, pattern staining.**

Heating systems. Solid fuel appliances, open fire with brick, tiled, faience, and marble fireplace surrounds, convector, stoves, cooker, back to back and combination grates. Oil-fired boiler. Electrical heating including the "off-peak" underfloor system. Space heating by warmed air from gas fired installation.

THERMAL INSULATION

The cost of reducing heat losses in buildings by provision of suitable thermal insulation is always worth while, an adequately thermally insulated building is warmer in winter and cooler in summer. Furthermore, when heat losses are reduced, less heat is required to maintain the air of a room at a given temperature and in consequence a saving in fuel costs is effected. The additional capital cost of providing adequate thermal insulation is recovered by lower heating charges over approximately the first five years of the life of the building; B.S. 8207: C.O.P. Energy Efficiency in Buildings deals with this aspect. The Building Regulations include a part Conservation of Fuel and Power devoted to thermal insulation.

Definitions. (1) The unit of *force* is the newton (N). Force = mass x acceleration = kg x metre/second second. So 1 N = 1 kg x 1 m/s^2. The earth's gravitational acceleration is 9.806 65 m/s^2, therefore the force exerted by gravity on a mass of 1 kg = 1 kg x 9.806 65 = 9.81 N (see p. 129).

(2) The unit of *work*, *energy* (capacity to do work) and *quantity of heat* is the joule (J) = work done when the point of application of a force of 1 N is displaced through a distance of 1 m in the direction of the force. Or, work = force x distance = N x m. From (1) this = kg x m/s^2 x m = kg x m^2/s^2 joule.

(3) The unit of *power* and *heat flow rate* is the watt (W). Power = energy per unit time; heat flow rate = quantity of heat per unit time; both these are therefore measured in joule per second (J/s). From (2) J/s = (kg x m^2/s^2)/s = kg x m^2/s^3 which is given the name watt. So 1 J/s = 1 W. Note that the unit of time is included in the conception of watt.

(4) The unit of *intensity of heat flow rate* is W/m^2 = heat flow rate per unit area, from (7) below it will be noted that this is the same as: *U*-value x temperature difference. If the heat flow rate per unit area is multiplied by the area then the total heat loss from that particular area is found in watts; *i.e.* $(W/m^2)m^2 = W$.

(5) The unit of *thermal conductivity* (denoted by letters *Tc*) is W/m °C. Thermal conductivity, or heat transfer, is the amount of heat passing through 1 m thickness of material of area 1 m^2 in one second if the temperature difference between the two faces of the material is 1°C. *Tc* follows from (4) and can be set out thus:

$$Tc = \frac{\text{heat flow rate x thickness}}{\text{area x temperature difference}} = \frac{\text{watt x metre}}{\text{square metre x degree Celsius}} = \frac{\text{W x m}}{\text{m}^2 \text{ x °C}}$$

= W/m °C.*

Tc can also be expressed as J m/m^2 s °C which is the same as W/m °C.

(6) ***Thermal resistance*** (R) = $\dfrac{\text{thickness}}{Tc} = \text{m} \div \dfrac{\text{W}}{\text{m °C}} = \text{m}^2\ \text{°C/W}$.

(7) The *U-value*** (known also as *coefficient of heat transfer, thermal conductance* and *thermal transmittance*) = $\dfrac{\text{heat flow rate}}{\text{area x temperature difference}}$

$= \dfrac{\text{watt}}{\text{square metre x degree Celsius}} = \text{W/m}^2\ \text{°C}$.

U-value also = $\dfrac{\text{conductivity}\ (Tc)}{\text{thickness}} = \dfrac{\text{W}}{\text{m °C}} \times \dfrac{1}{\text{m}} = \text{W/m}^2\ \text{°C}$. Note that this is the reciprocal of the thermal resistance.

(8) *Specific heat capacity* = the quantity of heat required to raise unit mass of body by unit temperature increment and the unit is J/kg °C.

The use of the above terms will be understood by reference to the examples on p. 254. *U*-value and thermal conductivity are amplified below.

* In this equation, and others below, because temperature *difference* is being considered the symbol °C (degrees Celsius) could be put as °K (degrees Kelvin); because 0°C = 273°K and 100°C = 373°K – a difference of 100° in each case.

** This name derives from the Imperial heat unit of B.T.U.

U-**Value.** Heat losses in buildings occur through windows, external walls, ground floors and roofs, the amount depending primarily upon the nature and the thickness of the materials comprising these structural elements and their respective thermal conductances. Other factors which influence the heat flow through external walls and roofs are the surface resistances and the degree of exposure of the building. Air spaces provide some resistance to the passage of heat and this is taken into account where cavity wall construction occurs, as for example in 275 mm brick walls. In order to assess the heat loss taking place through a given structure the *thermal transmittance coefficient* or *coefficient of heat transfer* must be known. This coefficient, which is termed the *U-value* or the overall air-to-air heat loss coefficient, is the amount of heat (expressed in W/m² °C) which passes through m² of the structure for 1° C temperature difference between the air on one side and the air on the other side. *The lower the U-value, the better the insulation.* The use of double glazing to reduce heat losses is described in Chap. IX.

The following are typical *U*-values in W/m² °C for common types of construction: 215 mm brick wall, plastered internally, 2.96; 275 mm brick cavity wall plastered internally, 1.7; single glazing, 5.7; double glazing, 12 mm air cavity, 2.8; triple glazing, 12 mm air cavity, 2; 100 mm concrete roof with 20 mm asphalt and 12 mm plaster ceiling, 3.65; same roof with suspended 22 mm fibreboard ceiling over which 25 mm glassfibre is draped, 0.56; corrugated fibre-cement roof, 8; corrugated fibre-cement roof with 25 mm glass quiet underlay and flat fibre sheet soffit, 1.08; roof tiles on felt, 2; wood joist floor (ventilated), 1.7.

Thermal Conductivity (*Tc*). Materials vary considerably in their respective resistances to the passage of heat, *i.e.*, the heat flow through the thickness of the material. *Thermal conductivity* expresses the rate of heat flow; and is influenced by the moisture content, porosity, density and temperature of the material.

It will be noted that the thermal conductivity relates to a 1 metre thickness of a material. For materials of other thicknesses the U-value is obtained by dividing the thickness of the material by the Tc-value. When the thickness is reduced, the thermal conductance is increased; conversely, a reduction in the thermal conductance can be effected by increasing the thickness of a material (*e.g.*, the thickness of brickwork in a wall), but such a method would be wasteful of material and would result in unnecessary structural thicknesses where the material concerned was of high thermal conductivity. For example concrete has a *k*-value between 1.08 and 1.8 W/m² °C depending upon the density and nature of the aggregate used. Special concretes such as those made of light-weight aggregate (pumice, foamed slag, vermiculite, expanded shale or clay, etc.), or aerated concrete, have thermal conductivities ranging from about 0.144 to 0.43 W/m² °C. In contrast to these figures, slab cork has a thermal conductivity of 0.043 W/m² °C. The following comparison shows how the thickness of a poor insulating material has to be increased in order to achieve the same thermal insulation provided by a good insulating material:

A 25-mm thickness of cork has a Tc-value of 0.043 W/mK, so R = 0.025 ÷

TABLE 45 THERMAL CONDUCTIVITY AND THERMAL RESISTANCE VALUES

Material & density (kg/m³)	Tc (W/mK)	thickness (t) (m)	-R (m²K/W) for thickness in column 3
1	2	3	4
asphalt 1 700	0.05	0.019	0.04
brickwork 2 000	1.24*	0.013	0.08
	0.92**	0.103	0.11
concrete 2 200	1.6*	0.1	0.06
	1.45**	0.1	0.07
500	0.18*	0.1	0.6
	0.16**	0.15	0.94
chipboard 800	0.15	0.02	0.13
fibreboard 300	0.057	0.013	0.23
fibre-cement insul. bd. 750	0.12	0.01	0.08
fibre-cement sheet 1 600	0.4	0.06	0.01
glass fibre 12	0.04	0.05	1.25
hardboard 900	0.13	0.005	0.04
mineral fibre (rock & slag) 16	0.04	0.08	2
plasterboard	0.16	0.0125	0.08
plaster & skim (2 mm)	0.16	0.015	0.09
plywood 530	0.14	0.0125	0.09
polystyrene (expanded) 15	0.037	0.0127	0.34
screed (cement: sand) 2 100	1.28	0.025	0.02
limestone, 2180	1.5	0.1	0.07
sandstone 2000	1.3	0.1	0.08
timber, softwood	0.13	0.025	0.19
hardwood	0.15	0.025	0.17
woodwool slabs 500	0.1	0.05	0.5

* exposed
** protected

0.043 = 0.58, therefore the U-value is 1 ÷ 0.58 = 1.72 W/m²k. The same thickness of concrete has a Tc-value of 0.51 W/mK, so R = 0.025 ÷ 0.51 = 0.049, therefore the U-value is 1 ÷ 0.049 = 20.4 W/m²K. Therefore to provide the same *U*-value as cork the concrete thickness would need to be increased by 20.4 ÷ 1.72 = 11.9 times; *i.e.* to 25 × 11.8 = 295 mm thickness.

Typical average figures for thermal conductivity (Tc) and thermal resistance (R) are given in Table 45 for the thickness of different materials; R = m ÷ Tc.

When two or more materials having different thermal conductivities are used in a composite structure it becomes necessary to assess their combined value, that is the total thermal conductance of the full structure thickness – see Examples under "Calculation of *U*-values" below.

Surface Resistances. Allowance must be made for the resistance which a material provides at its surface to the emission of heat therefrom, to the air in contact with it. The amount of resistance offered at the surface depends upon a number of factors; for instance, a wind blowing across the surface will hasten the emission of heat by convection and colder surroundings will increase heat lost by radiation. Resistance will also be affected by the degree of exposure of the surface, whether it is sheltered or severe; and will also vary with climatic conditions.

Resistances are normally higher for internal surfaces than for external ones. For external walls, a total resistance of 0.178 m² °C/W is often used in the computation of *U*-values. This resistance is obtained by taking the internal surface resistance as 0.123 m² °C/W and the external surface resistance as 0.055 m² °C/W. A more accurate value can be ontained by reference to the table prepared by the Institution of Heating and Ventilating Engineers, which gives values for walls related to their orientation and relative degree of exposure, the latter being classified under "sheltered", "normal", or "severe".

For the internal surface resistances of floors and ceilings, a difference will occur depending upon whether the heat flow is upwards or downwards, less resistance being offered to upward flow. For flat roofs and pitched roofs a total surface resistance of 0.15 is often used, this being made up of 0.106 and 0.044 m² °C/W for internal and external surface resistances respectively. Some reduction in external resistance will occur with corrugated surfaces for these have a larger exposed area.

Cavities and Air Spaces. An important contribution to the insulation value of walls and other structures is made by inherent cavities and air spaces.* Still air is a good insulator and the high insulation value of cellular materials is due largely to the numerous minute air spaces they contain. Ventilation of cavities, sometimes done in 275 mm brick walling, will set up air movement in the 70 mm space and reduce the insulation efficiency. It has been established that a cavity 20 mm in width has a thermal resistance only very slightly smaller than one 70 mm wide, but when it is less than 20 mm a greater reduction occurs. For an unventilated cavity in a 275 mm brick wall the thermal resistance is approximately 0.18 m² °C/W, this value includes the resistances of the surfaces facing the cavity in addition to the air space itself. In certain forms of roof and other constructions where cavities are formed they may be lined with insulating material, or one or both sides of the enclosed space may be faced with reflective insulation such as aluminium foil which will reduce the heat loss by radiation. In this case the thermal resistance of the cavity is increased considerably.

Building Regulations for Thermal Insulation of Buildings. These stipulate the *minimum* thermal insulation standards for roofs, walls and floors and are given in Table 46 in the form of *maximum* permitted U-values and *maximum* permitted single glazed areas.

* Reference should be made to the value of double glazing described on p. 154 and pp. 218–219.

Note.

In late 1989 it is expected that changes will be made to the Building Regulations to improve thermal insulation standards from those given in the following pages. These are the changes:

***Instead of the 4 types of building** as shown in Table 46, only 2 are proposed: (1) dwellings and (2) other buildings.*

***The new maximum U-values** (W/m² °K) for dwellings to be 0.25 for roofs, 0.45 for walls and 0.45 for ground floors (the latter is a new provision). For other buildings the values for the three elements are all 0.45 W/m² °K. These **values apply if**, in the case of dwellings, the maximum area of the single glazing is 15% of the floor area (not the wall area as before). For other buildings the percentage is that of the area of the surface in which the glazing is placed.*

***By using multiple glazing and provided the same percentage of glazing is used**, then reductions in insulation standards elsewhere is permitted. Thus if the window area remains as 15% of the floor area but half of it is double glazed **then the U-value can stay at 0.6** W/m² °K. Also if the U-value of the ground floor is no worse than 0.35 W/m² °K the U-value of the house roof can remain at the present 0.35 W/m² °K value.*

The following example show how the Regulations can be applied.

Example 1. A small workshop of internal dimensions 15 m by 10 m by 5 m high is to be built using double glazed windows. There are single glazed rooflights. Find the areas of the glazing which will satisfy the Building Regulations.

Wall area (including windows) $= (15 + 15 + 10 + 10) \times 5 = 250\ m^2$

Permissible area of double glazed windows $= 2 \times 15\% \times 250 = 75\ m^2$

Permissible area of single glazed rooflights $= 20\% \times 150 = 30\ m^2$

Hence the permitted window area is 75 m^2 and the permitted roof glazing is 30 m^2, *provided* the wall and roof areas are insulated (as shown in later examples) to give the U-values shown in Table 46.

TABLE 46 MAXIMUM U-VALUES AND MAXIMUM SINGLE GLAZED AREAS

Building type	External walls	Roofs	Exposed floors	maximum single glazed areas	
	max. U-value (W/m² °C)				
1. house & flat	0.6	0.35	0.6	windows and rooflights together 12% of perimeter wall area	
2. other residential, hotels and institutional	0.6	0.6	0.6	25% of exposed wall area	20% of roof area
3. places of assembly, offices & shops*	0.6	0.6	0.6	35% of exposed wall area	20% of roof area
4. industrial & storage	0.7	0.7	0.7	15% of exposed wall area	20% of roof area

Notes.

* Not shop display windows.

Glazing areas may be doubled for double glazing and trebled for triple glazing. The figures at 2, 3 and 4 industrial apply *only* to buildings with a floor area more than 30 m² when: 2 and 3 buildings have a heating system with an output more than 25W per sq. metre of floor area (50W for industrial buildngs).

Areas of walls, floors and roofs are between internal faces and in the case of a roof, in the plane of the insulation. A roof of pitch more than 70 degrees is classed as a wall. Cills, lintels and jambs may be counted as windows. An external door with 2 m² or more glazing is counted as part of the window area.

The following example shows how the thermal insulation can be provided to ensure that the construction meets the Building Regulation requirements.

Example 2. An office building is proposed to be constructed with a 100 mm thick reinforced concrete roof covered with 19 mm asphalt on felt and a 13 mm plaster ceiling. Find the U-value of the roof, there are no rooflights.

From Table 45 the thermal resistances (R) (m^2K/W) are:

asphalt & felt	= 0.04
concrete	= 0.06
plaster	= 0.07
surface resistance	= 0.15
total R	= 0.32

therefore U-value $= \dfrac{1}{0.32} = 3.12\ W/m^2K$

This is well above the permitted value of 0.6 W/m²K; so provide a suspended ceiling of 13 mm fibreboard with vapour barrier above it covered with 50 mm glass fibre which will give the following figures:

R from example above	= 0.32
less plaster ceiling	0.07
	0.25
cavity	= 0.18
glass fibre	= 1.25
fibreboard	= 0.23
revised total R	= 1.91

therefore U-value now $= \dfrac{1}{1.91} = 0.52\ W/m^2K$

As this is below the maximum of 0.6 allowed the **improved construction is** satisfactory.

Example 3.

A house wall is constructed as below. Find the U-value.

(Note from p. 253 that $R = t \div Tc$)

Construction	Thickness (t) (m)	Thermal conductivity (Tc) (W/mK)	Thermal resistance (R) (m²K/W)
external wall surface	–	–	0.06
outer brick leaf (2 000 kg/m³)	0.1025	1.24	0.8
cavity			0.18
block inner leaf (500 kg/m³)	0.15	0.13	1.15
inner lining of plasterboard	0.0125	0.16	0.08
backed with polystyrene	0.019	0.037	0.51
internal wal surface	–	–	0.12
		Total =	2.9

therefore $U = \dfrac{1}{2.9} = 0.34\ W/m^2K$

This is satisfactory and the kind of U-value to which the **Building Regulations** should aspire rather than the present higher 0.6 value. **Note that in the above** calculations R of 0.18 has been taken for the cavity, **it is best excluded because of the** modest ventilation to the outside air. This would reduce R thus: $2.9 - 0.18 = 2.72$. Hence U would become $1 \div 2.72 = 0.37$.

Total Heat Flow Rate. Having found the *U*-value of a piece of construction the heat flow rate and therefore the total heat flow or *beat loss* from it can be found thus:

Example 4. **In Example 2 where the roof has a final improved *U*-value of** 0.52 W/m² °C assume the roof has an area of 20 m² and the outside temperature is −1 °C. The required indoor temperature is 18°C.

Heat flow rate per unit area = *U*-value × temperature different this is 19 as it ranges from −1 to +18. = 0.52 × 19 = 9.88 W/m².

If the roof had an area of 100 m² the total heat flow through it would be 9.88 × 100 = 988W

As well as providing construction to reduce *heat loss* the Building Regulations, for some buildings, allow account to be taken of *heat gains* from the sun, industrial processes and artificial light etc. This does not apply to the following:

(1) A dewelling; (2) heating systems which provide water for industrial processes; (3) systems for a building with a floor area not more than 125 m²; (or for individual appliances with an output rating of 10 kW or less.

When use is made of the clause, adequate controls have to be used: thermostats, thermostatic radiator valves etc. and where hot water heating is employed there must be an external temperature sensing device which regulates the output.

Hot water storage vessels ad pipes must be adequately insulted.

Roof Ventilation

If a roof is pitched at 15° or more th roof sapce should allow for cross ventilation to it by openings equal to a gap 10 mm wide along the length of the eaves. If the roof is pitched at a lesser slope the following provisions apply, they also apply for slopes of 15° or more if the ceiling follows the roof slope: ventilation openings on opposite sides of an area equal to ventialtion along the full length of the eaves 25 mm wide; the gap between the underside of the roof covering and the top of the insulation to be at least 50 mm to permit air circulation.

Roof Insulation. The two methods of reducing heat losses from roofs covered with light-weight sheeting are to place the insulation above or below the purlins. The provision of the air space in the latter method improves the U-value. Roof finishes that are sealed, like bituminous felt bedded on bitumen give a better insulation than sheeted material with open joints, although the latter construction is improved by having a felt lining below the covering. This is largely due to the effects of wind on the roof, a high wind causing losses at the unsealed laps of sheeted material.

When a ceiling is used it is usually best to apply insulation at that level to enable the roof space to be free of condensation, this is a Building Regulation clause, as is the following paragraph.

Roof insulation above a concrete roof as well as reducing heat losses is also useful in preventing the absorption of solar heat which would cause expansion of the slab and cracking of walls and internal finishes. Typical insulation is given on p. 134 **and flat roofs are kept in better condition if covered with white reflective chippings to diminish the build-up of heat, and limit the slab expansion (see p. 134). In any case expansion joints in concrete roofs should be placed at about 30 m intervals.**

Vapour Barrier. Insulating materials that are allowed to become damp lose some of their efficiency. With internal linings, condensation is the principal cause of loss.

Air containing water vapour has a dew-point temperature, and if it comes into contact with a surface which is below this temperature, its moisture will condense. If the surface is impermeable, the condensation will appear on the surface. If the material is permeable, the condensation will occur on the surface or at some point inside the material· if the particular section is below the dew-point temperature.

In the case of an fibre cement sheet roof, condensation will occur when the temperature of the sheeting is below the dew-point temperature of the air in the building. It can be avoided by insulating the roof to raise the temperature of the internal surface above the dew point. If the insulating material is permeable, the vapour will pass through and condense on the sheeting. Hence the need for a *vapour barrier* to prevent this flow of moisture. It also follows that the vapour barrier must be placed on the warm side of the structure so that its temperature is above the dew point. It may consist of any suitable vapour proof material but care must be taken to seal all joints in the insulation and any laps in the barrier. A number of appropriate materials are: High gloss paint, sprayed p.v.c. film, coated bitumen felts, polythene and p.v.c. sheet, pitch or bitumen.

For a concrete roof insulated with fibreboard and having felt waterproofing, the barrier may be applied at the roof soffit (or between the concrete and the insulation, *provided* that the concrete is reasonably impervious and does not retain an excessive quantity of moisture — see p. 134). A metal deck roof incorporating insulating board and felt on its external surface can either be vapour sealed by having a layer of felt bonded to the top of the deck before the insulation is fixed or by a suitable impervious spray finish to the underside of the deck. A ceiling of plasterboard which has a backing of polythene bonded to it forms an inexpensive, easily applied vapour barrier.

If the moisture is given off by the process carried on in the building, ventilation must be considered to reduce the moisture content. Since if the process ejects vapour into the room at high temperature, it will be practically impossible to prevent condensation by insulation alone in cold weather. Condensation does not occur behind windows where double (see B, Fig. 52 and Fig. 95) or triple glazing is used, or where a cavity of dehydrated air is provided between two sheets of glass.

Pattern Staining. This occurs in ceilings which are in contact with beams and structural framing, the lines of beams and members being reproduced as a pattern of light and shade on the visible side of the ceiling. It is caused by dust particles which are attracted to and deposited on cold surfaces, and which move away from hotter surfaces. The colder the surface, the greater is the deposition of dust; the variation in the rate of deposit on the solid and void areas being due to the different rates of heat transference through them. Thus, the cooler the surface, the more readily is the dust deposited, and the more quickly is the area

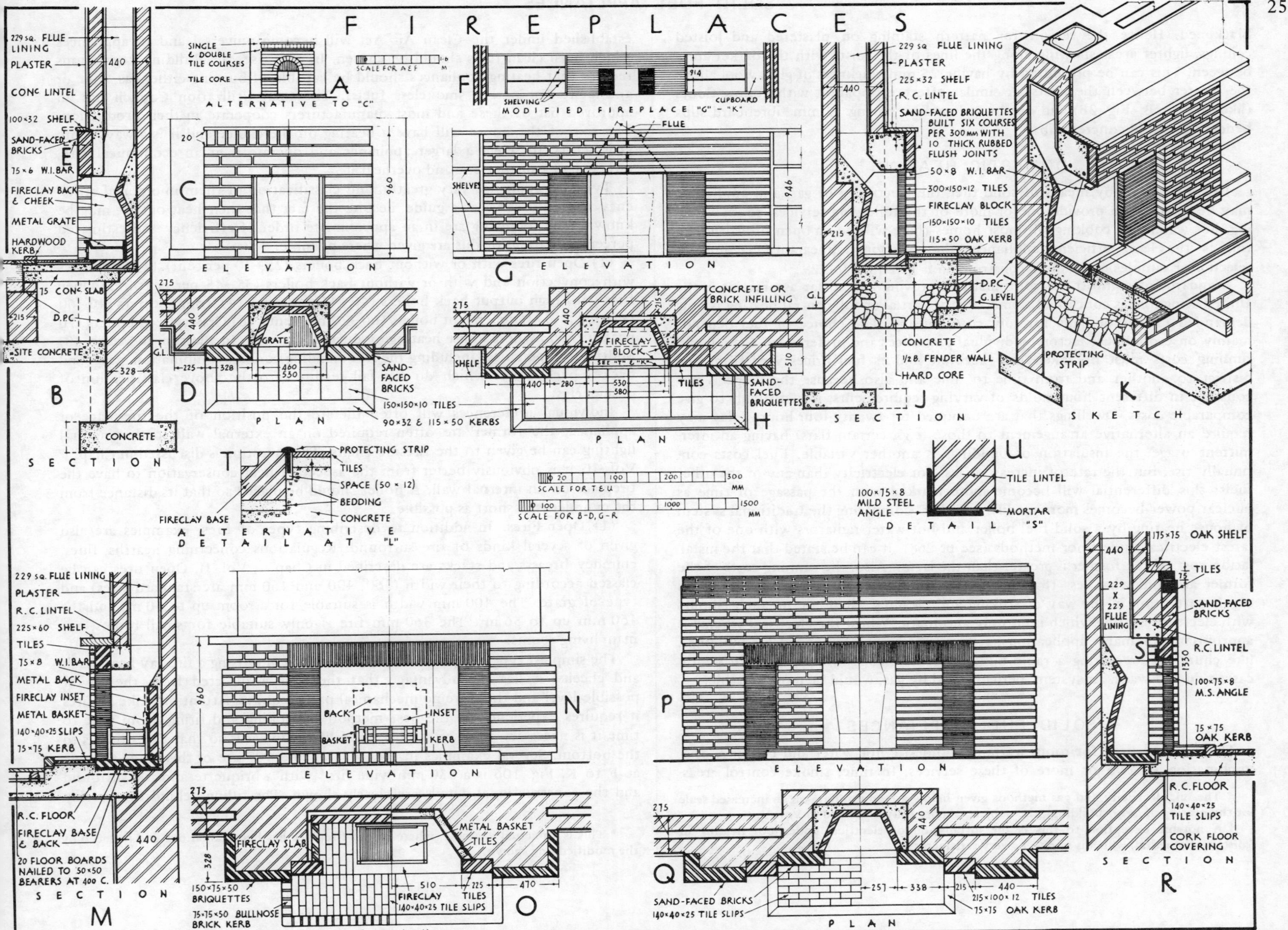

FIREPLACES
229 sq. FLUE LINING
PLASTER
440
CONC LINTEL
100×32 SHELF
SAND-FACED BRICKS
75×6 W.I. BAR
FIRECLAY BACK & CHEEK
METAL GRATE
HARDWOOD KERB
75 CONC SLAB
215
D.P.C.
SITE CONCRETE
328
B
CONCRETE
SECTION
SINGLE & DOUBLE TILE COURSES
TILE CORE
A
ALTERNATIVE TO "C"
SCALE FOR A E F
F
SHELVING
CUPBOARD
914
MODIFIED FIREPLACE "G" "K"
FLUE
20
C
960
SHELVES
G
946
ELEVATION
ELEVATION
275
440
GRATE
G.L.
225
328
460
550
SAND-FACED BRICKS
150×150×10 TILES
90×32 & 115×50 KERBS
D
PLAN
215
CONCRETE OR BRICK INFILLING
FIRECLAY BLOCK
SEE "T" & "K"
SHELF
440
280
530
580
TILES
510
SAND-FACED BRIQUETTES
H
PLAN
229 sq FLUE LINING
PLASTER
225×32 SHELF
R.C. LINTEL
SAND-FACED BRIQUETTES BUILT SIX COURSES PER 300 MM WITH 10 THICK RUBBED FLUSH JOINTS
50×8 W.I. BAR
300×150×12 TILES
FIRECLAY BLOCK
150×150×10 TILES
115×50 OAK KERB
G.L.
CONCRETE
1/2 B FENDER WALL
HARD CORE
J
SECTION
D.P.C.
G. LEVEL
PROTECTING STRIP
K
SKETCH
PROTECTING STRIP
TILES
SPACE (50 ÷ 12)
BEDDING
CONCRETE
FIRECLAY BASE
T
ALTERNATIVE DETAIL AT "L"
SCALE FOR T & U
SCALE FOR B-D, G-R
U
TILE LINTEL
100×75×8 MILD STEEL ANGLE
MORTAR
DETAIL "S"
229 sq. FLUE LINING
PLASTER
R.C. LINTEL
225×60 SHELF
TILES
75×8 W.I. BAR
METAL BACK
FIRECLAY INSET
METAL BASKET
140×40×25 SLIPS
75×75 KERB
R.C. FLOOR
FIRECLAY BASE & BACK
440
20 FLOOR BOARDS NAILED TO 50×50 BEARERS AT 400 C.
SECTION
M
N
960
BACK
INSET
BASKET
KERB
ELEVATION
275
FIRECLAY SLAB
328
METAL BASKET
TILES
510
225
470
150×75×50 BRIQUETTES
75×75×50 BULLNOSE BRICK KERB
FIRECLAY
140×40×25 TILE SLIPS
TILES
O
PLAN
P
ELEVATION
Q
440
257
338
215
440
SAND-FACED BRICKS
140×40×25 TILE SLIPS
215×100×12 TILES
75×75 OAK KERB
PLAN
175×75 OAK SHELF
TILES
229 × 229 FLUE LINING
SAND-FACED BRICKS
R.C. LINTEL
1350
100×75×8 M.S. ANGLE
S
75×75 OAK KERB
R.C. FLOOR
140×40×25 TILE SLIPS
CORK FLOOR COVERING
SECTION
R

FIGURE 106

blackened. Hence the reason for pattern staining on plastered and joisted ceilings, lighter areas showing along the lines of the joists with the darker areas between. This can be prevented by having 25 mm thickness of glass wool above the plaster between the joists. A similar effect is apparent with hollow floors (like that at B, Fig. 28) and can be reduced by having 12 mm fibreboard slips beneath the solid concrete ribs.

DOMESTIC HEATING*

Heating can be by means of solid fuel, oil, electricity or gas, and appliances may be required to provide one or more of the following services: room warming, hot water and cooking. In most homes there will be an open fire; although this is the least efficient appliance, the satisfying appearance favours its selection. Examples of fireplace construction is given in Vol. 2.

Standards of comfort are continually improving and so far as practice in the United Kingdom is concerned, some kind of partial or full central heating is now demanded except perhaps for low cost housing. The choice of fuel depends mainly on economical factors, individual prejudices and preferences. Capital and running costs must be taken into account and as fuel prices vary from one district to another and from time to time and also because the usage is not constant in different households of varying requirements, it is difficult to give comparable costs. Dwellings that are occupied for twenty-four hours a day may require an alternative arrangement to those (*e.g.*, certain flats) having an intermittent usage; the insulation of buildings is another variable. Fuel costs continually rise, but the rate of increase is less for electricity than any of the other fuels; this differential will become more marked with the passage of time as nuclear power becomes more readily available. Comparing the traditional system of house heating by a solid fuel boiler and hot water radiators with one of the latest electrical underfloor methods (see p. 268), it can be stated that the installation cost of the former is greater than the latter. Also, the running costs of the former are somewhat less than the latter. In addition, whereas a boiler needs regular attention in the way of stoking and cleaning, there are no such labours with electrical heating which is entirely automatic. Whilst the electrical scheme is appropriate for many applications, it may not be recommended for buildings, like churches,† requiring a rapid build-up of heat for short periods. In such a case, a ducted warm air system, perhaps fired by gas, would be more suitable.

SOLID FUEL APPLIANCES

These can be used for room warming, domestic hot water and cooking, or a combination of two or more of these services. In time, smoke control areas established under the Clean Air Act will become universal and so appliances which burn clean fuels should be chosen. In any case, the Building Regulations require that heating appliances should be capable of burning either gas, coke or anthracite (or patent smokeless fuels). The Coal Utilization Council has an approved list of these and most manufacturers cooperate in their production. The size of the house will have a bearing on the choice and it is always more satisfactory to select a larger appliance and operate it at an economical rate, rather than a smaller one and overheat it.

Types of appliance vary greatly, and classification of them in order of efficiency can only serve as a guide, despite the fact that their heat output may be known. The following are in an approximate order of efficiency and estimated percentage ratings of this are given where possible.

(1) Open fires with or without back boilers (25–30 per cent). (2) Open fires with convection and with or without back boilers (35–45 per cent). (3) Open fires with high output back boilers (40–45 per cent). (4) Room heaters (40–60 per cent). (5) Independent boilers (60–70 per cent). (6) Gravity feed boilers (70 per cent). (7) Whole house heating by ducted warm air. In addition there are: (8) Multi-duty appliances including the free-standing cooker, combination grate, and back-to-back grate, which do not fall readily into the above classification of efficiencies.

Individual preferences will often dictate the position of the fire-place or appliance, the former are often required on an external wall so that natural lighting can be given to the fireside chairs. This question is discussed in Chap. I, Vol. II; it is obviously better from the aspect of heat conservation to have the fireplace on an internal wall. A boiler should be placed so that its distance from the cylinder is as short as possible.

(1) Open Fires. In addition to describing types of fires, examples are also given of several kinds of fire surround. Regulations concerning hearths, flues, chimney breasts and stacks are described in Chap. I, Vol. II. Open fires can be classed according to their width (360, 400 and 460 mm are standard sizes) and type of grate. The 400 mm width is suitable for a room up to 50 m^3 and the 460 mm up to 56 m^3. The 360 mm fire is only suitable for small rooms, not main living rooms.

The simplest type of open fire is the sunk fire comprising a fireclay base, back and cheeks; it has the advantage that the heat is directed from the lowest possible level and there are no mechanical parts requiring attention. Like all fires it requires experience of the best method of stoking and firing, from time to time it is necessary to insert a poker and lift it upwards so that the ash falls to the bottom. Several examples in Figs. 73, 77 and 107 are of this kind. The one at F to K, Fig. 106 is a 530 mm wide fire* with a briquette and tile surround and the constructional details are clearly shown. The filling behind the fireclay

* The oil, electricity and gas methods given below are appropriate on an increased scale for the heating of *larger* buildings, this subject is more fully described in Vol. V.

† A notable exception to this is the installation of electrical underfloor heating in Salisbury Cathedral, which is said to be very satisfactory.

* This is an actual example, where an old fireplace has been taken out and replaced by the modified one shown.

lining should be of lean concrete and broken brick to allow for the expansion that occurs – dense fillings cause the fireclay to crack. The hearth is tiled, and at T, the joint between the base and the tiles is made by leaving a gap in which a chromium-plated or vitreous enamelled protecting strip is placed. Another surround using the same materials is given at P to R, where the same sized lining is adopted.

Although the sunk fire will burn smokeless fuels perfectly satisfactorily provided the flue is properly constructed as described in Vol. II, it may not be approved by all authorities in smoke control areas, who usually require a fire grate as described below.

The example in Figs. 107 and 108, shows a sunk hearth with a traditional surround of mahogany and marble of a type favoured for restoration work. The wood surround is fabricated in the workshop for fixing as one unit on site. The marble slabs are independently secured by copper cramps against plaster dabs (see Fig. 88) and the opening itself is surrounded by a metal trim overlapping the marble.

The next type of open fire has a grate firebox, this gives the best performance when burning smokeless fuels if the fire bars are spaced 16 mm apart (13 mm for grates with underfloor air supply, see below). An example of a fireplace with a simple fire grate is shown at B, C and D, Fig. 106, with an alternative elevation at A, both having a brick surround; if desired, a wide shelf can be provided by having a brick on edge as at E. The grate is fitted with a pivoted front plate which provides some control over the burning. The one at M, N and O has a larger fire opening with an independent basket grate which can have a metal back with fireclay inset. Two types of fire back are shown at O, fireclay slabs on the left and tiles on the right.

Another example with a grate is given at A to K, Fig. 109, this is also controlled by a hinged air valve. Two kinds of faience (see p. 145) surround are shown, that on the left has large slabs with a pilaster and the one on the right has alternating broad and narrow strips with a hardwood shelf and surround (detail at F). The detail at E is a variant showing 100 mm thick faience blocks instead of slabs. The section at A shows the use of a smoke shelf, which is mistakenly advocated by some as a defence against down draughts of smoke, it is of course a shelf for the collection of soot which is not easy to keep clean; providing the flue and the stack are constructed as described in Chap. I, Vol. II, the sloping finish as noted by the broken line is more satisfactory and smoke will not be blown into the room.

Details L to S, Fig. 109 indicate a grate with an air pipe supplying combustion air direct from the outside. This is known as a grate having an underfloor primary air supply. The air pipe terminates at a control valve (2) and there is another valve (1) in the fire front, this arrangement enables the fire to be boosted rapidly without the need for opening the room door. Suitable adjustment of these controls will govern the rate of combustion; and if the hinged fall plate is lowered, overnight burning at a slow rate can be accomplished. Two types of faience surround are drawn at M and N, these are faience blocks, as before, filled with weak concrete and are jointed by means of metal dowels (see P) or joggles detailed at R and S. The detail at Q shows how the faience surround is held back to the wall by means of metal cramps.

Details A′ to E′, Fig. 109 show two types of precast tile surround fireplaces and the method of manufacture. This is done as shown at D′, where the tiles are laid face down on a slate-topped bench, the edges are formed against slate slabs and a wooden internal shutter is used to contain the 1 : 1 : 2 concrete backing. This is 50 to 75 mm thick, reinforced, and made with rapid-hardening Portland cement so that the formwork can be stripped and re-used twenty-four hours after casting. Two or more ear-plates (see A′ and E′) are cast into the concrete and these are pivoted to provide tolerance for fixing to plugs in the brick joints.

Open fires can be fitted with an adjustable *throat restrictor* similar to that shown in Fig. 110. This device can control the area of the flue at the throat and so reduce the amount of air drawn up the chimney after the fire has begun to burn well. A certain amount of conflict arises between the need to provide sufficient combustion air and the desirability of reducing draughts. Probably the best solution is to have sealed draught-proof windows, leaving the room door unsealed, this will give enough air to prevent the fire from smoking.

An open fire is frequently used in conjunction with a back boiler to give hot water and room heating combined. The boiler is placed at the back of the fire

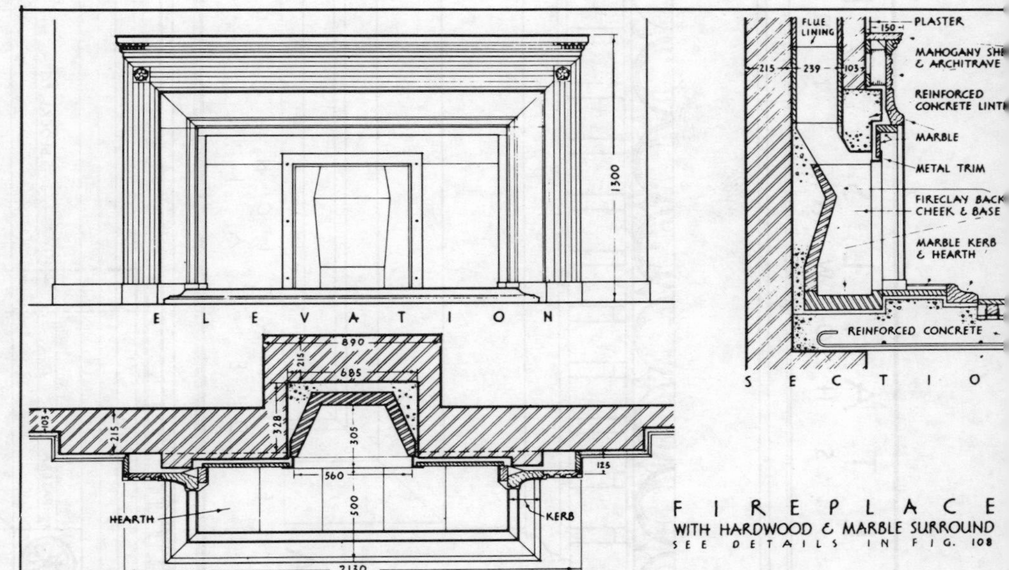

FIGURE 107

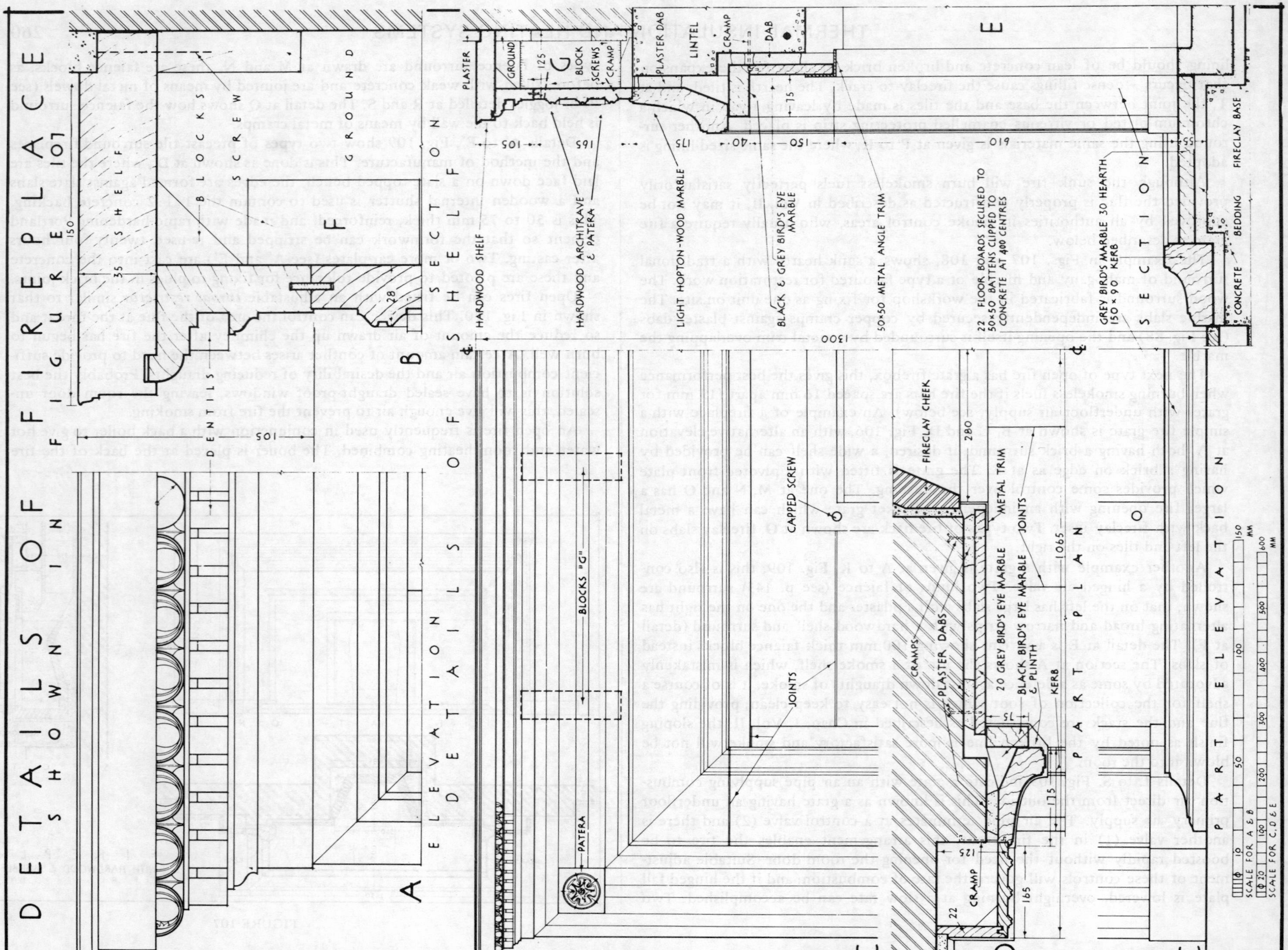

DETAILS OF FIREPLACE
SHOWN IN FIGURE 107

A ELEVATION
B SECTION
ELEVATION
DETAILS OF F
SECTION OF F
G
C PART PLAN
D
E SECTION

SHELF
35
150
BLOCKS
SCREW
GROUND
DENTILS
105
166
HARDWOOD SHELF
28
HARDWOOD ARCHITRAVE & PATERA
BLOCKS "G"
PATERA
PLASTER
GROUND
25
BLOCK
SCREWS
PATERA
CRAMP
PLASTER DAB
LINTEL
CRAMP
DAB
15
LIGHT HOPTON-WOOD MARBLE
BLACK & GREY BIRD'S EYE MARBLE
50×50 METAL ANGLE TRIM
22 FLOOR BOARDS SECURED TO 50×50 BATTENS CLIPPED TO CONCRETE AT 400 CENTRES
GREY BIRD'S MARBLE 30 HEARTH
150×90 KERB
FIRECLAY BASE
BEDDING
CONCRETE
FIRECLAY CHEEK
CAPPED SCREW
280
METAL TRIM
JOINTS
20 GREY BIRD'S EYE MARBLE
BLACK BIRD'S EYE MARBLE & PLINTH
KERB
CRAMPS
PLASTER DABS
JOINTS
165
125
22
CRAMP
SCALE FOR A & B
SCALE FOR C, D & E

FIGURE 108

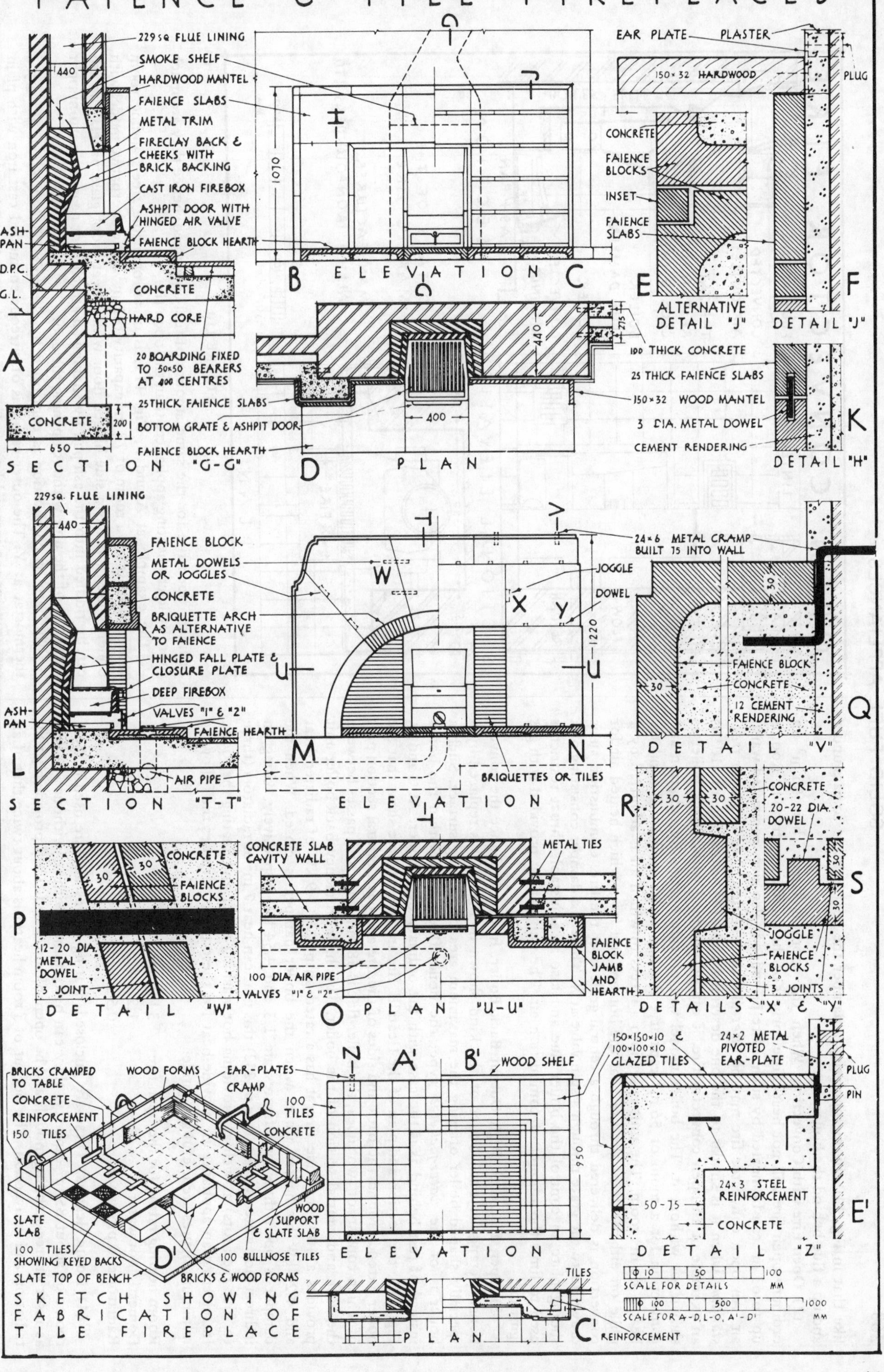
FAIENCE & TILE FIREPLACES
229sq FLUE LINING
440
SMOKE SHELF
HARDWOOD MANTEL
FAIENCE SLABS
METAL TRIM
FIRECLAY BACK & CHEEKS WITH BRICK BACKING
CAST IRON FIREBOX
ASHPIT DOOR WITH HINGED AIR VALVE
ASH-PAN
FAIENCE BLOCK HEARTH
D.P.C.
G.L.
CONCRETE
HARD CORE
A
20 BOARDING FIXED TO 50×50 BEARERS AT 400 CENTRES
25THICK FAIENCE SLABS
CONCRETE
200
BOTTOM GRATE & ASHPIT DOOR
650
FAIENCE BLOCK HEARTH
SECTION "G-G"
1070
B ELEVATION C
440
400
D PLAN
EAR PLATE
PLASTER
150×32 HARDWOOD
PLUG
CONCRETE
FAIENCE BLOCKS
INSET
FAIENCE SLABS
E
ALTERNATIVE DETAIL "J"
F
DETAIL "J"
225
100 THICK CONCRETE
25 THICK FAIENCE SLABS
150×32 WOOD MANTEL
3 DIA. METAL DOWEL
K
CEMENT RENDERING
DETAIL "H"
229sq. FLUE LINING
440
FAIENCE BLOCK
METAL DOWELS OR JOGGLES
CONCRETE
BRIQUETTE ARCH AS ALTERNATIVE TO FAIENCE
HINGED FALL PLATE & CLOSURE PLATE
DEEP FIREBOX
ASH-PAN
VALVES "1" & "2"
FAIENCE HEARTH
AIR PIPE
L
SECTION "T-T"
W
X
Y
JOGGLE
DOWEL
1220
U
M
N
BRIQUETTES OR TILES
ELEVATION
24×6 METAL CRAMP BUILT 75 INTO WALL
30
FAIENCE BLOCK
CONCRETE
12 CEMENT RENDERING
Q
DETAIL "V"
30
CONCRETE
FAIENCE BLOCKS
P
12-20 DIA. METAL DOWEL
3 JOINT
DETAIL "W"
CONCRETE SLAB CAVITY WALL
METAL TIES
FAIENCE BLOCK JAMB AND HEARTH
100 DIA. AIR PIPE
VALVES "1" & "2"
O PLAN "U-U"
R
CONCRETE
20-22 DIA. DOWEL
S
JOGGLE
FAIENCE BLOCKS
3 JOINTS
DETAILS "X" & "Y"
BRICKS CRAMPED TO TABLE
CONCRETE
REINFORCEMENT
150 TILES
WOOD FORMS
EAR-PLATES
CRAMP
100 TILES
CONCRETE
WOOD SUPPORT & SLATE SLAB
SLATE SLAB
100 TILES SHOWING KEYED BACKS
D'
100 BULLNOSE TILES
SLATE TOP OF BENCH
BRICKS & WOOD FORMS
SKETCH SHOWING FABRICATION OF TILE FIREPLACE
A'
B'
WOOD SHELF
950
ELEVATION
TILES
PLAN
C'
REINFORCEMENT
150×150×10 & 100×100×10 GLAZED TILES
24×2 METAL PIVOTED EAR-PLATE
PLUG
PIN
24×3 STEEL REINFORCEMENT
50-75
CONCRETE
E'
DETAIL "Z"
10
50
100
SCALE FOR DETAILS
MM
100
500
1000
SCALE FOR A-D, L-O, A'-D'
MM

FIGURE 109

like that in Fig. 110; by manipulating a damper the heat is made to pass under and up a flue behind the boiler.

(2) Open Fire with Convection. When the room is larger than 56 m^3 an ordinary open fire will not heat those corners of the room away from it. Rooms up to 63 m^3 can be heated by such a fire provided it also gives convected warm air. An open convector fire may be *inset* like the one described below or *free-standing* when it is similar to the one described under (4) below. Figure 110* is an example of an open convector fire, it can be provided with a back boiler as shown, or without it. The boiler model will provide heating by radiation and convection for a room of 56 m^3 capacity; the non-boiler model will similarly heat a 63 m^3 room. The unit is set into a recess to which air is admitted by a grille on either side of the fire near the bottom and from which heated air for convection is delivered through a central grille over the fire. Combustion air is drawn in to the grate through a spin valve at X. There is a damper consisting of a sliding plate to control the boiler flue and also an adjustable throat restrictor used to limit the amount of combustion air. The unit can be provided with gas ignition.

(3) Open Fire with High Output Back Boiler. In this appliance the conventional rectangular back boiler of the kind shown in Fig. 110 is replaced by a specially shaped boiler offering the maximum area of heating surface. Such a boiler is of the *water-jacketed* type; the boiler flue passes within the boiler instead of just behind as is the case with the ordinary back boiler. At C and D, Fig. 111, the section and plan of the Heatall† fire are given. These show that the boiler extends round the back and sides of the fire and has a central section part of which consists of two tubes; the boiler flue is 58 mm wide and passes between the back and central section of the boiler. This high efficiency back boiler unit provides a 400 mm wide fire, it has a rated output of 1.9 kW of radiated heat and 4.25 kW by heated water when the boiler damper is closed. When the damper is open these two figures are 1.3 and 4.54 kW respectively. Using an indirect hot water system (see p. 232) this unit can heat 7 m^2 of radiators (three to four radiators) as well as providing hot washing water and heating the room. In selecting an appliance to provide heat for these three purposes the following minimum figures are useful as a guide:

Room heating rating for the open fire	3 kW/m^3
Domestic hot water	1.2 kW
Radiator and pipework	0.5 kW/m^2

(4) Room Heaters. These are enclosed heating stoves and are used to heat rooms of about 85 m^3 capacity, they can be obtained with or without a boiler, as inset or free-standing models and be openable or closed. They provide heat by radiation and convection. The output of a room heater is about twice that of an ordinary open fire for the same amount of fuel consumed; hence they are much more efficient heating appliances than the open fire.

The example at A and B, Fig. 111, is of an openable free-standing room heater suitable for a room of 78 m^3 capacity (42 m^3 if the alternative model with boiler is used). It has a side hinged door with a heat-proof glass panel. The ash can be riddled into the ash-pan by shaking an attachment near the bottom right hand side of the unit without opening the door.

The rate of combustion is controlled by the spin valve at X and also by a thermostat at Y. The outer casing is of vitreous enamelled cast iron with plain cast iron for the internal lining. The convected air is drawn in at the bottom of each side of the appliance, is heated as it passes between the two casings and emitted through a grille near the top at each side.

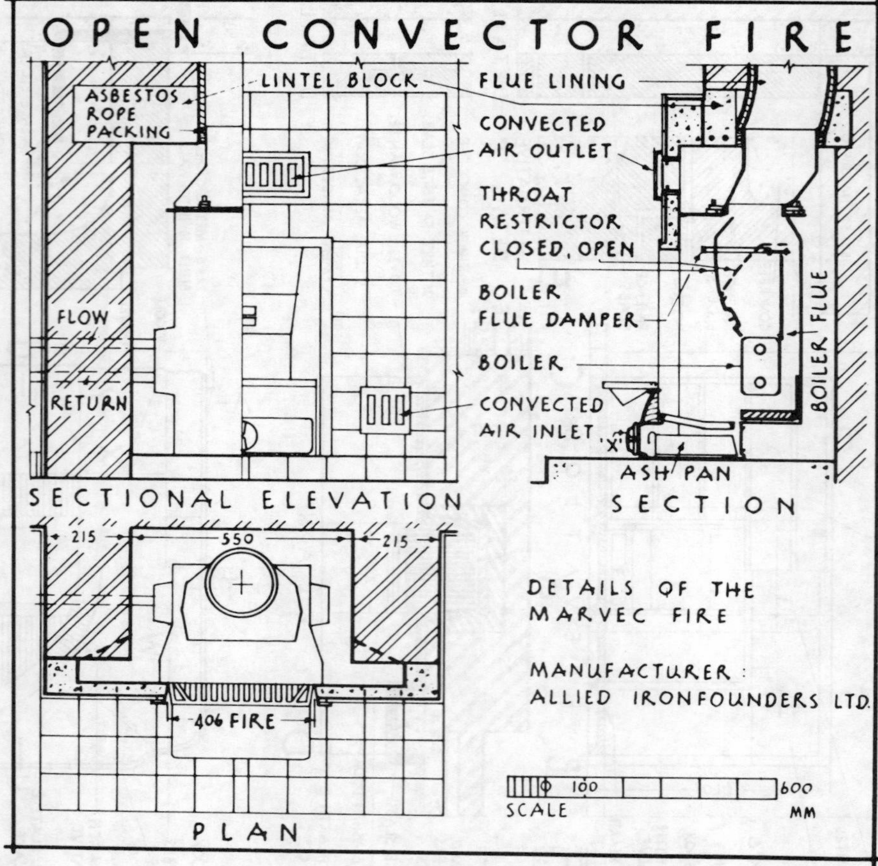

FIGURE 110

* The Marvec fire by Allied Ironfounders Ltd.
† Manufactured by J. Lea (Leyland) Ltd.

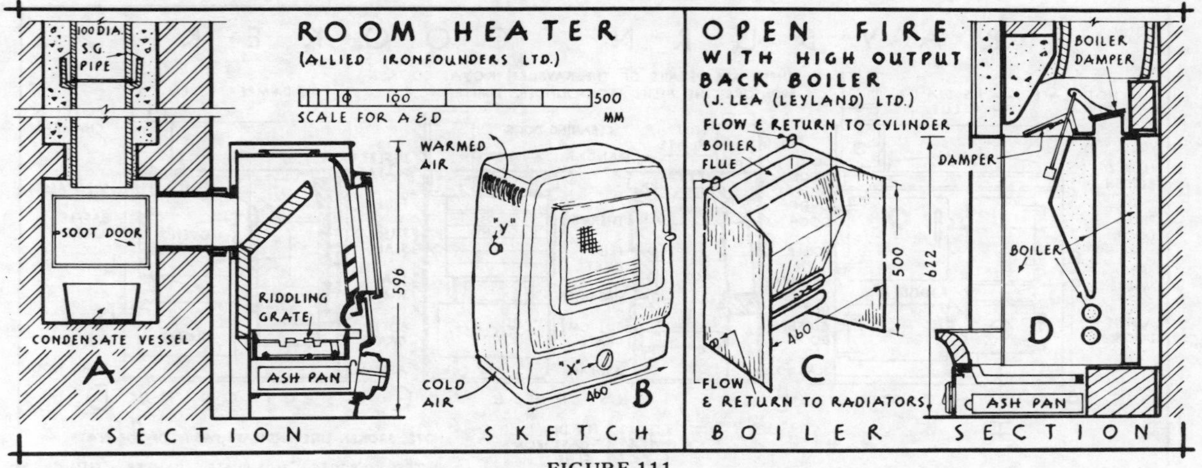

FIGURE 111

Flues. The Building Regulations require that all flues either be lined with socketed clay flue linings or salt-glazed pipes or constructed of concrete flue blocks. This is not to imply that the traditional 225 mm by 225 mm parged flue is not satisfactory for the open fire, in fact such flues have been used satisfactorily for many years. The reason for the Building Regulation requirement is that an open fire may be replaced at some time in the life of the building by a closed heating stove or boiler. It is desirable that such appliances discharge into a flue with an impervious lining to prevent damage to the building from condensation within the chimney.

The products of combustion contain water vapour,* sulphur and tarry compounds and if these condense in the flue than can discolour the walls of rooms. Because a much greater amount of air passes up a chimney from an open fire than from a closed heater condensation seldom occurs in the former. In order to guard against condensation from flue effluents from room heaters and boilers the flue must be lined and enclosed in an insulating concrete made of broken brick. The Building Regulations also stipulate that where the heating appliance does not communicate with a fireplace recess the bottom of the flue must be provided with a chamber fitted with a close fitting access door containing a collecting vessel for the condensate. These provisions are shown in Fig. 111; note that the flue liner projects into the chamber to allow the condensate to drip into the collecting pot.

(5) Independent Boilers. These can be of the open fire or closed fire type and with or without thermostats; they are used to provide domestic washing water and to heat radiators. On a rating basis of providing 19 kW/m^2 of boiler heating surface independent boilers have a rated output varying from 3.2 to 14.6 W. This output range is increased if the boiler is charged with fuel every two hours to provide 31.6 kW/m^2 of boiler heating surface.

(6) Gravity Feed Boiler. This is a very efficient appliance, needing attention perhaps once in every twenty-four hours. It is primarily intended for space heating with radiators. Capacities are up to 44 kW.

* The B.R.E. estimates that 0.4 kg of water vapour is produced from 1 kg of coal; for gas and oil fuels the amount of water vapour is approximately doubled.

(7) Warm Air System. This is an alternative to radiators and frequently used for open plan houses. Warmed air driven by a fan is delivered by ducts to the rooms. The unit is similar in appearance to the gas appliance in Fig. 116 and is operated on the *down draught* principle so that bituminous fuel can be burnt almost smokelessly. A typical house installation has an output of 10.25 kW for space heating, plus 230 litres of hot water per day and an efficiency of between 60 and 80 per cent. In another type the air for warming is blown through a heat exchanger containing hot water instead of solid fuel.

(8) Multi-Duty Appliances. Compact appliances which give the three services of cooking, room warming and water heating are (*a*) freestanding cookers, (*b*) combination grates, and (*c*) back-to-back grates.

(*a*) **Freestanding Cookers.** These appliances are thermally insulated, and the fire is readily kept under control to ensure efficiency and the economical consumption of solid fuel (such as coal, coke, anthracite or smokeless fuel) with the minimum of smoke emission. As the cooker is an independent unit it is unnecessary to provide a recessed chimney breast for its accommodation, although, if needed, the appliance can be fitted in an existing recess and connected to an existing flue.

Figure 112 shows an example of this type of appliance, the Rayburn Cooker.* It consists of a firebox with a boiler behind and an ashpit below, an oven and a hot closet. With two or three exceptions, such as the hot closet, the ashpan and the outer casing to the back and sides (which are of 1.6 mm thick wrought iron) and the copper boiler, the appliance is made of cast iron, being in the main 4 to 5 mm thick. The front casing and doors are vitreous enamelled in various colours, and the top and hot plates are finished with black enamel.

The firebox is lined with fireclay slabs or firebricks (see B, D and G); these

* Sponsors: The Allied Ironfounders Ltd.

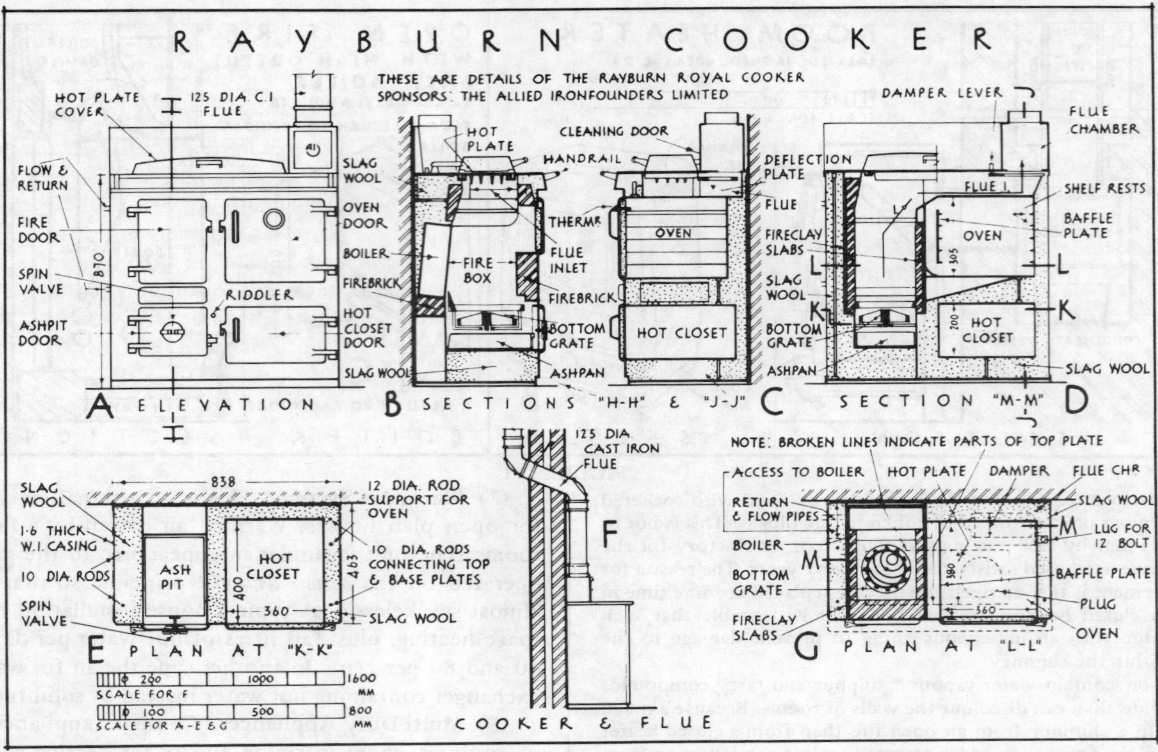

FIGURE 112

are bedded and jointed in fire cement; the width of the fire is approximately 230 mm. The bottom grate is loose fitting and can be readily removed. A removable ashpan is provided below the grate, and the cooker is placed on a hearth of normal fire-resisting construction.

The boiler is seated on a firebrick supported on a cast iron plate; as this brick is bevelled on its top surface, the boiler is given a slight forward tilt.

A vertical baffle plate is fixed in and extends the full depth of the oven to ensure effective circulation of the hot gases. An oven ventilator consisting of a short 12 mm dia. pipe is fixed at the top near the front right-hand corner (see C). A thermometer, which projects into the oven, is fixed to the outside of the door. A horizontal flue is provided above the oven (see B, C and D); the hot gases and smoke, after traversing this flue, escape up the 125 mm dia. cast iron flue (see arrows "1" at D); the latter is shown connected to the top of a flue chamber or box which is screwed to the top plate. To prevent excessive wear by the high temperature gases, protection is afforded by an increased thickness of metal at the inlet to the horizontal flue and by a 14 mm thick deflection plate screwed to the underside of the top plate with an asbestos pad packing between the plates (see C and D).

A hot plate is fitted in the top plate and is provided with a hinged insulated cover. There is a hot closet below the oven.

Accurate fuel combustion control is obtained by the spin valve in the ashpit door which regulates the air supply. The draught and oven temperature are further controlled by a damper which slides over an opening in the top plate at the base of the vertical flue chamber (see C, D and G). Access to the boiler is obtained by the removal of a portion of the top plate which is in two pieces.

A plate rack and vitreous enamelled splash plate (not shown) are usually fixed at the back of the cooker and a handrail at the front.

The cooker is shown connected to a 125 mm dia. cast iron flue which is taken as high as possible before leading it outside. Cleaning doors are provided at the flue chamber above the oven and at the bends (see F) and the flue should be continued to above the ridge of the roof. If, instead of the cast iron flue an ordinary brick flue is preferred, a soot door must be provided in the flue wall at about 600 mm above the flue chamber. This provision is also necessary if the appliance is connected to an existing flue.

The cooker is placed in position on a hearth of normal construction.

When the fire has to be cleaned out, the circular bottom grate, is rotated by an in-and-out movement of the riddler (see A).

Another merit of this type of appliance is the readiness with which the fire can be kept in overnight with little fuel consumption. For overnight burning, the fire is riddled, fuel is added to the level of the bottom of the fire door opening (the normal charge), the ashpit door is closed, the spin valve is closed and then re-opened a quarter of a turn, and an excess of draught is checked by closing the damper. In the morning, the fire is riddled, the spin valve and damper are opened, and, when the fire is burning brightly, the firebox is charged with fuel.

(*b*) Combination Grates. These consist of an open fire with back boiler and one or more ovens for cooking. They were once very popular multi-duty appliances; their use has declined as most housewives prefer to have a room heater with a back boiler plus an electric or gas cooker.

(*c*) Back-to-Back Grates. These serve the same purpose as the combination grates and for the same reason are declining in popularity. The unit is placed in a wall dividing the kitchen from the living room. The open fire part of the unit faces the living room and the cooker is situated in the kitchen.

Manufacture. The following description is typical of cast iron appliances.

The sections of the grate are cast in a metal moulding box of the required shape and size. A box is in two parts, the lower half being called the *drag* and the upper half the *cope*. Specially prepared sand is used which must have the necessary qualities to ensure clean surface castings, clean impressions of the patterns, adequate adhesion and bond to enable the tamped sand to be lifted in the cope without collapsing, etc. Water is added to the sand to increase this bond and improve adhesion. The drag is placed over the metal pattern (a replica of the section to be cast) and filled with well tamped sand. More sand is added to cover the pattern liberally and well consolidated. It is then turned over on to a prepared bed of sand, the cope fitted over the opposite side of the pattern and the same process followed as for the drag. The cope is lifted, the pattern removed, and the cope with sand layer is replaced. This must be done carefully in order not to damage the impressions. There is thus formed a mould of the shape and dimensions of the required casting. The molten cast iron from the furnace is poured into a large receptacle on a bogey which is conveyed near to the moulds, and a ladle full of the metal is taken by a workman who pours it down a hole or *gate* formed at the top of the moulds, to fill the void made by the pattern.

The castings after preparation for enamelling by filing and grinding are annealed (see p. 29) to burn out impurities and discover any latent weakness. They are then thoroughly cleaned by shot-blasting; the iron shot, sprayed by means of compressed air, removes the sand and skin from the castings to form roughened surfaces which are then sprayed with vitreous enamel. After being dried, they are loaded into a furnace where they are subjected to a temperature of 850° C to fuse the enamel to the cast iron; after about 20 min. the castings are removed from the furnace and the vitreous enamelling process is completed.

Bracket shelves, door and damper handles and pedal openers are electroplated; the chromium or nickel coatings provide protection against tarnish and corrosion and impart a pleasing appearance.

The various sections are assembled, the parts being screwed together after being bedded in fire-cement. Any needing true tight-fitting surfaces (such as the rims of the doors), and any requiring the removal of irregularities, are machined smooth.

OIL-FIRED HEATING

Oil burning is a dearer system than solid fuel, it is more easily controlled and there are no labour costs of stoking and ash removal.

Medium and heavy grade oils are used for the larger industrial installations, but for domestic purposes requiring an output of around 15 kW, the most usual fuel is commercial grade paraffin. An economical storage capacity is provided by a 2 700 litre mild steel tank for oil purchased in 2 300 litre lots. The tank should be housed in a separate chamber with 215 mm brick walls and a concrete roof, be in an accessible position for fuel delivery, and must be made oil-proof with cement rendering to a sufficient height to contain the contents of the tank should this become defective. The door of the room should be fire resisting and have a threshold above the oil-proofed level. The tank is fixed on dwarf walls, given a slight fall away from the supply pipe to the boiler, and has a drain cock at the lower end to enable the sludge to be removed. Also, it requires a filling pipe, vent pipe and a fusible link connection to the boiler which will automatically close the supply in the event of a fire breakout. The head of oil required at the boiler should be within the limits of 0.5 and 3 m.

An example of a thermostatically controlled appliance for domestic use is the Redfyre Centramatic "50" Oil-Fired Boiler* shown in Fig. 113. This has a water output of 15 kW continuous rating; it consumes 1.7 litres per hour of commercial grade paraffin through a 10 mm dia. copper feed pipe which must include a cartridge type filter. The maximum radiator surface it can heat is 25 m^2 when used solely for central heating, or when combined with a 180 litre indirect cylinder for washing water it will heat radiators and circulating pipes up to 18 m^2. The boiler can be used with an existing 215 mm square flue or alternatively a 150 mm dia. asbestos-cement or steel pipe flue can be adopted.

The main parts of the boiler are the *oil float valve* which controls the supply, a *burner pot* where oil is lit by an *electric igniter element* and vaporized, and the 18 litre insulated *boiler* which has top and bottom sections connected by tubes in the heating chamber. The boiler has 38 mm dia. tappings for the flow and return pipes to the cylinder on the left-hand side (provision is also made for an extra return tapping on the right-hand side), see E, F, G and H.

A 5 amp socket outlet is required for the electrical connection. When the boiler thermostat (see D) is turned on to the desired temperature reading, the igniter and boiler lamps are switched on and electric current is passed to the oil float control valve, the igniter element and a time delay relay. The latter starts the fan (see H) which supplies combustion air to the burner pot where the oil is lit after a one-minute interval. After a further two to three minutes the temperature in the combustion zone has risen sufficiently to operate a *flue thermostat* (see G) which switches off the igniter and its lamp. As soon as the desired temperature has been reached, the electric supply to the oil float valve and the time delay are cut off and the boiler lamp extinguished.

* Manufactured by Newton Chambers & Co. Ltd., who also make a similar model of 23 kW output.

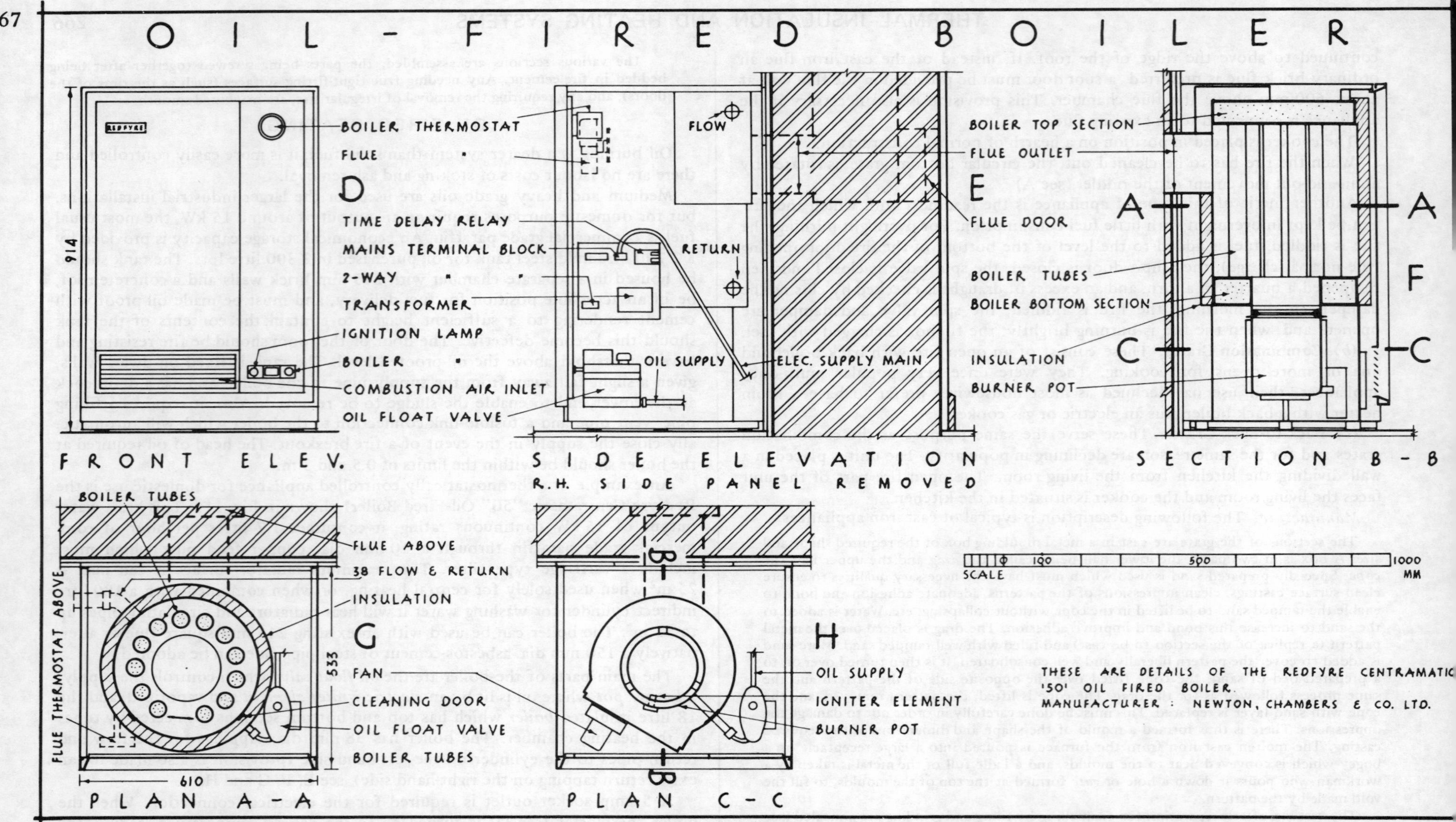
OIL-FIRED BOILER
BOILER THERMOSTAT
FLUE
TIME DELAY RELAY
MAINS TERMINAL BLOCK
2-WAY "
TRANSFORMER
IGNITION LAMP
BOILER "
COMBUSTION AIR INLET
OIL FLOAT VALVE
FLOW
RETURN
OIL SUPPLY
ELEC. SUPPLY MAIN
BOILER TOP SECTION
FLUE OUTLET
FLUE DOOR
BOILER TUBES
BOILER BOTTOM SECTION
INSULATION
BURNER POT
D
E
A
F
C
914
FRONT ELEV.
SIDE ELEVATION
R.H. SIDE PANEL REMOVED
SECTION B-B
BOILER TUBES
FLUE ABOVE
38 FLOW & RETURN
INSULATION
FAN
CLEANING DOOR
OIL FLOAT VALVE
BOILER TUBES
G
H
535
610
FLUE THERMOSTAT ABOVE
OIL SUPPLY
IGNITER ELEMENT
BURNER POT
B
SCALE 0 100 500 1000 MM
THESE ARE DETAILS OF THE REDFYRE CENTRAMATIC 50 OIL FIRED BOILER.
MANUFACTURER: NEWTON, CHAMBERS & CO. LTD.
PLAN A-A
PLAN C-C

FIGURE 113

ELECTRICAL HEATING*

Electric heating appliances supply heat by radiation† (high or low temperature) and convection† or by a combination of both methods. Electric fires are of three types, the fire bar, the reflector and the fan heater. The former has a coil of wire set in grooves of a fireclay panel and emits both types of heat in equal proportion. The reflector type has a fireclay rod wound with wire and fixed in front of a curved metal reflecting plate; it gives approximately twice as much radiated heat as convected and is most suitable for occasional use, the heat being supplied in a concentrated beam. The fan heater has a fan blowing air over a heated element; it provides a quick way of heating. These types are high temperature radiators and are available in sizes up to 2.5 kW.

The low temperature radiant heaters consist of steel or non-metallic panels enclosing the heating elements and backed with insulation, they operate at 38 to 121° C; another form work at 38° C and can be embedded in plaster finishes; there are also oil or water-filled panel heaters.

Of the many types of convection heater, one of the most common is the tubular type of oval or circular cross section; it normally has a loading of 200 W per metre in lengths from 0.6 to 5 m. They are often fixed to the skirting below windows or can be used to prevent down draughts from roof lights. A similar kind is in the form of a skirting moulding. The cabinet convector heater (0.75 to 3 kW) is another popular domestic appliance, being safer than the open type for the element is concealed; cold air enters at the bottom, passes over elements and is discharged at the top. A further type is the oil or water-filled pressed metal or cast iron radiator fitted with a heating element, sizes range from $\frac{1}{2}$ to 3 kW.

Another type is the thermal storage heater operating from an off-peak supply on the same principle as underfloor heating (see below) and consisting of electrical resistance wire coils looped through holes in concrete blocks fitted inside an insulated metal casing. They can be used conveniently for existing premises, but for new buildings, the following method is more appropriate.

Electrical underfloor Heating. Installations of this type, with electric cables in the floor have increased considerably in recent years, it is a commendable system with easy automatic control; the capital cost is less than any of the other forms of central heating although the running cost is higher (however price increases are lower for off-peak – see p. 259), and there are no maintenance or labour charges for re-fuelling and supervision. On balance therefore, the economics cannot be faulted and the convenience, cleanness, provision of heat *low down* in the room and *evenly* over the whole area, coupled with thermostatic control are formidable advantages unpossessed by any other central heating arrangement.‡ Heat transmission is approximately equally divided between radiation and convection. The Electricity Boards encourage it because the operation is at off-peak periods enabling generating plant to be used more economically. Special tariffs are available, the cheapest applies when current† is taken only between 10 p.m. on any day and 9 a.m. on the following day. A fractionally dearer tariff operates if, in addition to the above times, current is consumed between 10 a.m. and 5 p.m.; the extra cost of this "mid-day boost" is worthwhile for most domestic circuits.

The system is a thermal storage one where the concrete floor of the building is heated, so that its surface temperature is 24° C, by special wires built into it to form panels – one or more per room. Two types are used, the withdrawable method where the heating wires are housed in special conduit (see V, Fig. 92) or in ducts made with inflatable tubing. In the other type, the p.v.c.-covered cables are embedded directly in the concrete; this is the most common, being approximately 50 per cent cheaper to install than the other; faults are unlikely to occur and even if they do they can be traced by a special detector.

The embedded system is shown in Fig. 114; ground floor construction consists of hardcore with a 32 to 50 mm thick blinding layer of sand covered with d.p.c.; over this, a sub-floor of 100 mm minimum concrete (1 : 2 : 4) is laid and the cables are placed on it from 100 to 230 mm apart to give a loading of approximately 160 W/m². They are laid in a continuous length with the ends connected to a thermostat set at the required room temperature, placed 1.7 m above floor level and fed from the distribution board. There would normally be one panel of cables in each room and after it has been tested, a 50 to 65 mm thick layer of screed‡ (1 : 1 : 2) is laid over it and levelled; this makes a satisfactory floor finish if covered with thermoplastic tiles or felt and carpet. An alternative floor construction would be to have a 100 mm layer of waterproofed concrete (instead of the blinding); after this has dried it can be painted with two coats of waterproofing compound, the 100 mm concrete floor and screed would then be laid as before. The following floor finishes are also suitable: mosaic, marble, terrazzo, wood blocks, linoleum and tiles of the following materials: cork, p.v.c., and quarries; rubber-backed carpet should not be used.

It is particularly important to prevent heat losses at the edges of the slab and this can be done by having vertical insulation (25 mm thick foamed polystyrene, for example) at the edge of the sub-floor and screed and for a 600 mm§ wide strip all round the underside against external walls as shown in Fig. 114. In the case of upper floors, the edges cannot always be insulated, but the screed usually can; the whole of the soffit of the floor should be insulated in any case.

* See Chap. XI for electrical installations.

† Radiant heat passes from a warm body to a colder one without heating the air between. Heat by convection is distributed by air having passed over a warm surface.

‡ There is a corresponding system of small-bore water tubes embedded in the floor, water in pipes is much more difficult to control than electricity in wires and there appears to be little to recommend the water installation.

† Having provided an off-peak circuit, the water cylinder immersion heater can be coupled to it for giving domestic hot water. The cylinder should be lagged and it will be found that if the tariff incorporating a mid-day boost is used, a 180 litre cylinder will be sufficient for a household of five.

‡ Where possible and in order to give a good key, the screed should be laid not more than two hours after the 100 mm thick concrete; this means that the electrical contractor will have to work carefully in positioning the cables on concrete that has not hardened. Alternatively, the base concrete should be left rough and the unreinforced screed laid at a later date in areas not exceeding 9 m² for a 65 mm thickness, to allow for expansion. This area can be increased by not more than 50 per cent where light reinforcement is included in the screed. In any case, expansion joints made with a dovetailed timber strip should be placed between the edges of adjacent panels in the different rooms.

§ If the floor is to be carpeted the insulation must extend over the whole area.

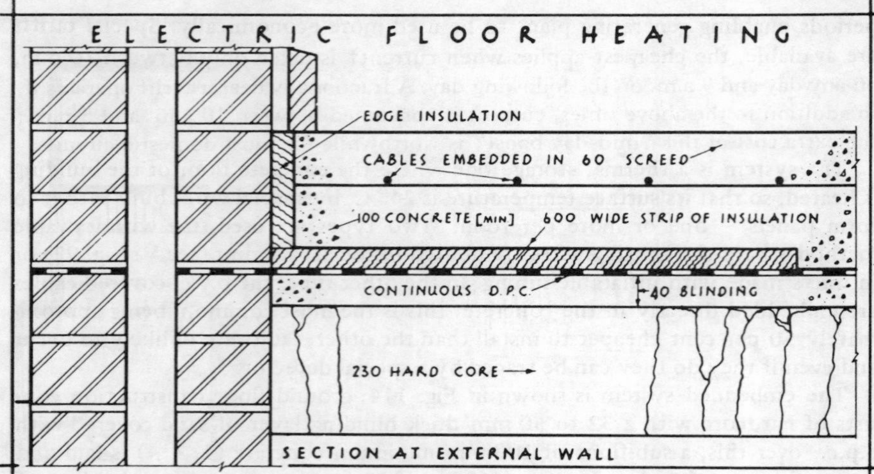

FIGURE 114

Apart from the room thermostats for each panel, the main regulating equipment comprises a separate meter recording the off-peak consumption, a time switch, main switch and fuse board for the individual panel circuits; in larger schemes, a contactor is also needed. Whilst it is not essential, an external anticipatory control thermostat can also be included to further regulate the supply.

GAS HEATING†

The use of gas radiators needs little comment, they are efficient means of providing a rapid build-up of heat in a room by radiation. They comprise a series of fireclay radiants (up which the flame passes) mounted in front of a fireclay backing; neat flame burners are used (see p. 250), the consumption of gas being of the order of 0.09 to 0.12 m^3/hr. All gas radiators require a flue; for many types of instantaneous water heaters which are fixed on an external wall, a simple asbestos terminal flue block can be built in so that it discharges behind the heater directly to the open air. A gas radiator can be provided with a flue* of the type shown in Fig. 115. These are blocks having a flue-way of 305 mm by 60 mm and made of dense refractory concrete with a keyed joint as shown at P; a 1:1 cement and sand mortar bedding is used to bed the blocks. Corbels and other specials are obtainable as shown, the building-in blocks at V are placed behind the radiator and double blocks given at R can also be used for back-to-back radiators. In some areas, the Gas Board will permit the use of branch flues for flats, this reduces installation costs and comprises a 200 mm square main flue from ground floor to roof, each radiator has its own 200 mm by 150 mm

† See Chap. XI for gas installations.
* Complying with B.S. 1289 Flue Blocks and Masonry Terminals for Gas Appliances.

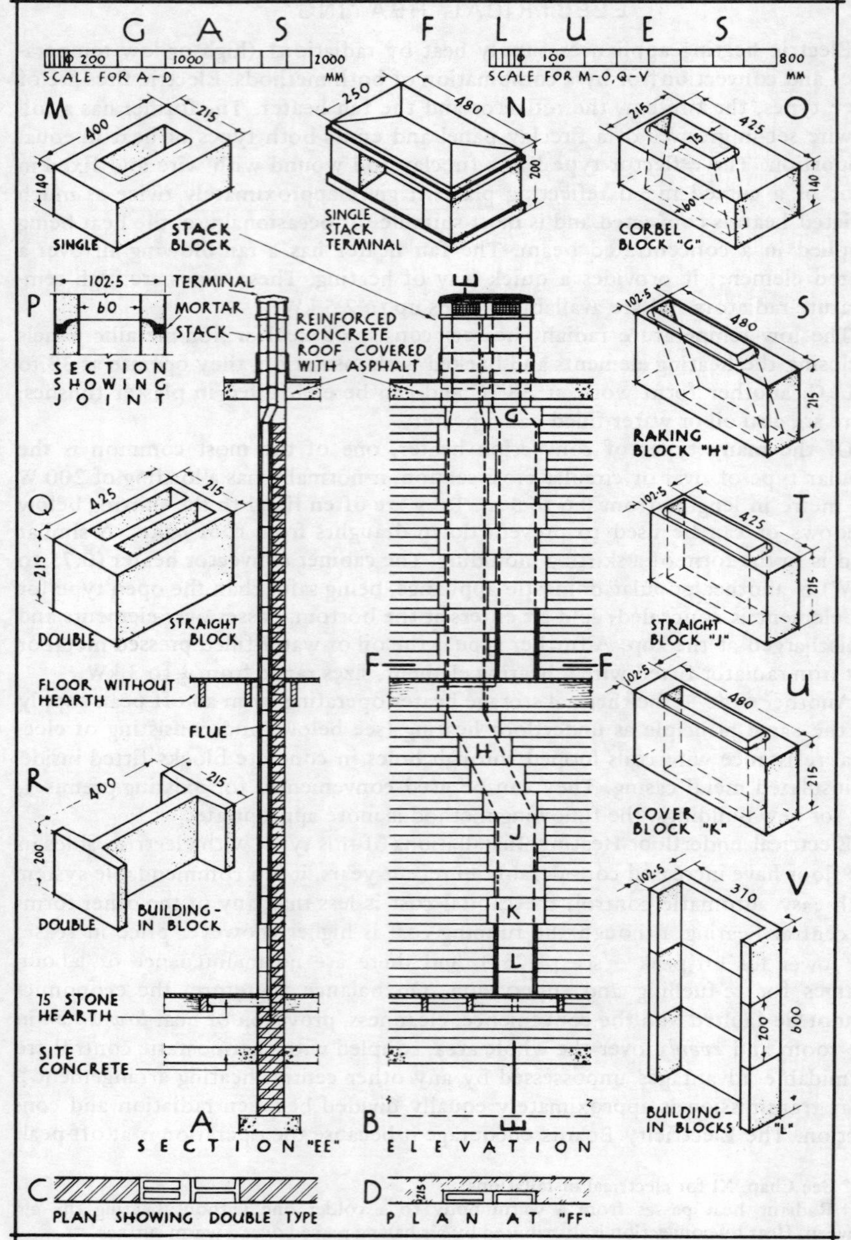

FIGURE 115

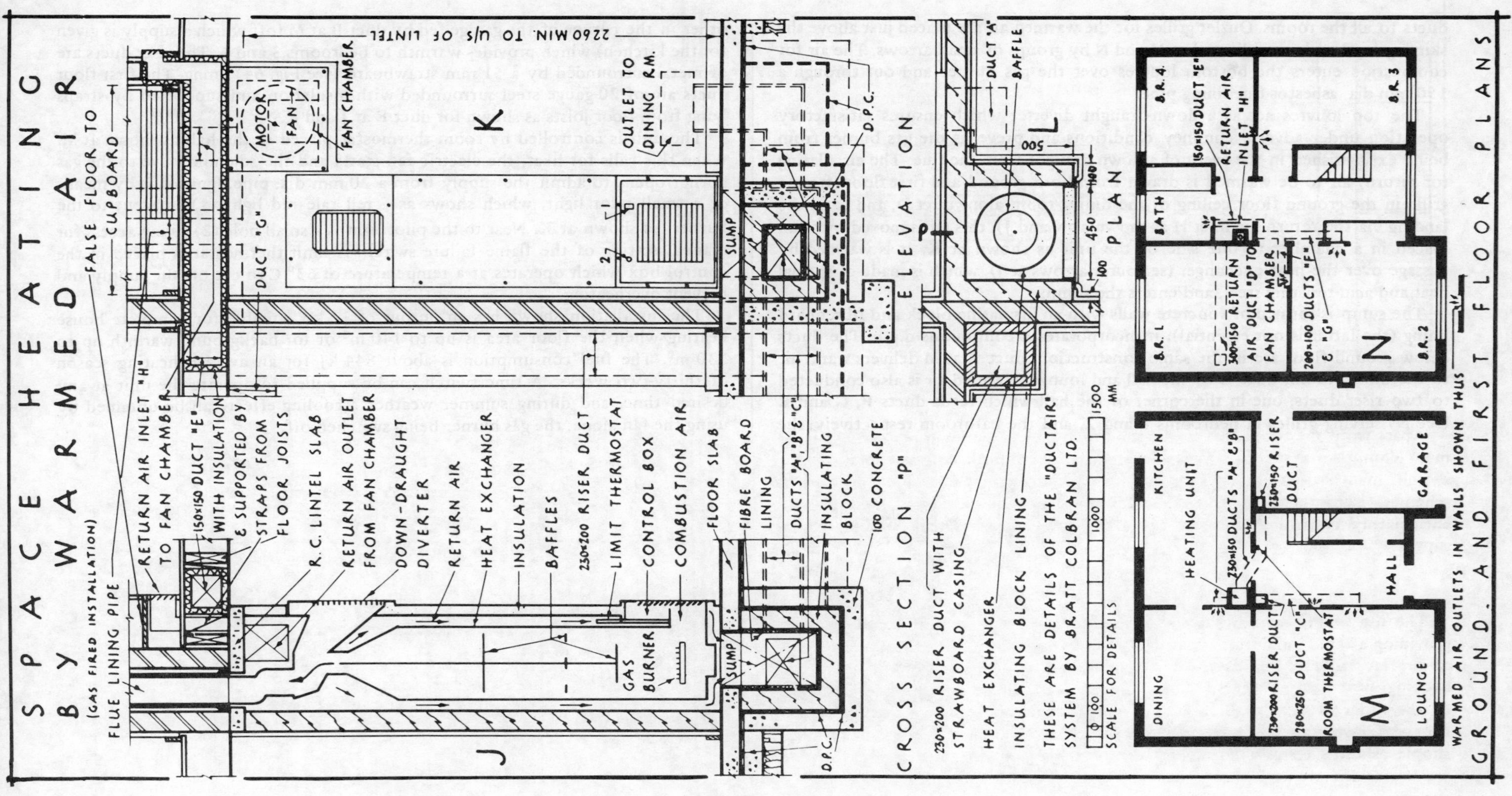

FIGURE 116

flue rising 3 m and then joined to the main flue. In another arrangement, the appliances are connected direct to a large flue (560 mm by 380 mm) extending from ground floor to roof, this is joined by a tee junction at the bottom to a horizontal duct. The latter is below ground floor level and passes across the building and is open at both ends to short vertical ducts rising 1.2 m above the outside level and being open to the air via a grille.

Gas-fired boilers to similar rating to oil-fired boilers are available.

Space Heating by a Gas-fired Appliance. Figure 116 shows an example of the warm air ducted heating system with a gas burning heat exchanger unit which is placed in a central position in the house to provide warmed air. It is housed in a 450 mm by 500 mm chamber with an insulating block lining as shown in the plans at L and M.

The internal construction is given at J and shows the unit sited over a sump, this is a collecting point and a distribution centre for warmed air at 63° C via ducts to all the rooms. Outlet grilles for the warmed air are placed just above the skirting level and are indicated at M and N by groups of small arrows. The air for combustion enters the bottom louvres over the gas burner and out through a 150 mm dia. asbestos flue lining pipe.

The top louvres act as a down-draught diverter which ensures satisfactory operation under adverse chimney conditions and prevents the gas burner from being extinguished in the event of a down draught from the flue. The circulating (or return) air to be warmed is drawn from both ground and first floor (from a grille in the ground floor ceiling of the dining-room along duct D, and from the landing via the return air inlet H as shown at N and J); this air is moved by a fan placed in a chamber to one side of the unit as shown at K. It is warmed by passage over the heat exchanger (see outer arrows at J), which is made of special heat and acid-resisting steel, and enters the sump.

The sump is formed of concrete walls with an insulating block and fibreboard lining (the latter is not essential); it incorporates a continuous d.p.c. The ducts below ground floor are in the same construction, duct A at M delivers warm air to the dining-room, duct C to the hall and lounge. Warmed air is also conducted to two riser ducts, one in the corner of the hall which feeds ducts F, G and E (see N) serving grilles in bedrooms 1 and 2, and the bathroom respectively; the other in the corner of the garage fed by duct B at M (off which a supply is given for the kitchen) which provides warmth to bedrooms 3 and 4. The riser ducts are of metal surrounded by a 51 mm strawboard (see Fig. 64) lining. The first floor ducts are of 20-gauge steel surrounded with insulation and supported by straps hung from floor joists as shown for duct E at J and K.

The unit is controlled by room thermostat placed in the hall as shown at M. When this calls for heat, the electric fan starts and the solenoid valve to the gas burner opens to admit the supply from a 20 mm dia. pipe. Ignition is by means of a small pilot light, which shows as a tell tale red light (1) adjacent to the burner, as shown at K. Near to the pilot light is a small hole (2) giving access for manual setting of the flame failure switch. A limit thermostat is placed in the control box which operates at a temperature of 63° C to cut off the supply and prevent overheating.

The installation shown has an output of 12 kW suitable for complete house heating when the floor area is up to 140 m^2 or for background warmth up to 230 m^2. The fuel consumption is about 844 kJ for an average heating season of thirty-two weeks. A time switch can be supplied to operate the unit at any desired time, and during summer weather a cooling effect can be obtained by using the fan alone, the gas burner being switched off.

INDEX